Contents in Brief

Focal Points and Connections

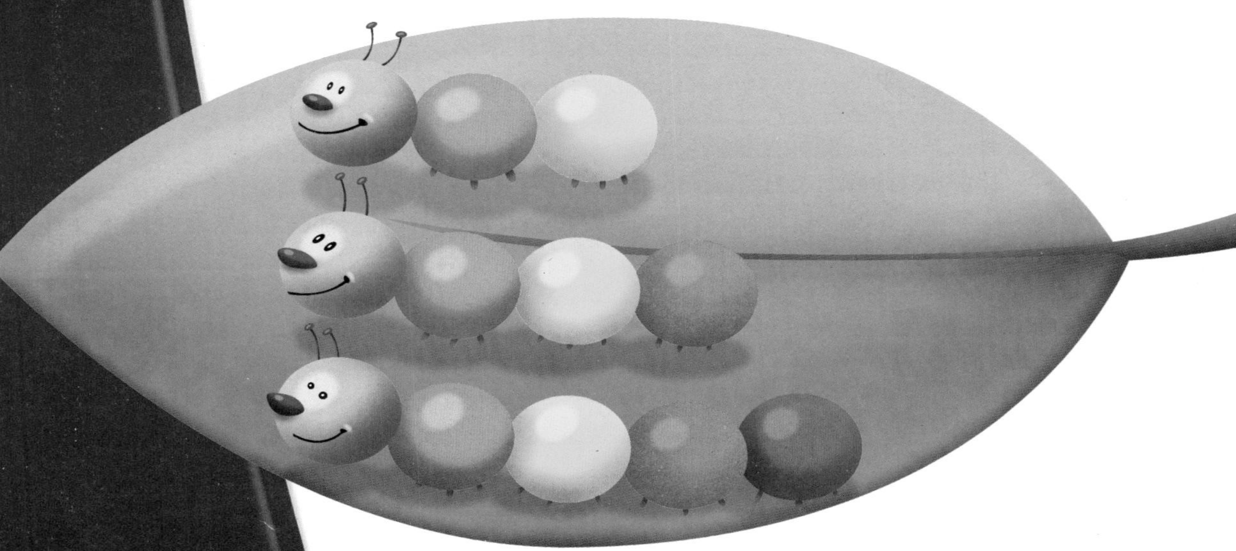

About the Cover

Shapes, position, and patterns are featured topics in Kindergarten. Have students identify all of the shapes on the cover. Ask students to use words such as near/far to describe the position of the crab or the trees. Then have students describe the patterns they see on the cover.

Three Horizontally Aligned Programs

- Common vocabulary
- Common manipulatives
- Common technology
- Common Professional Development
- Aligned to NCTM Focal Points

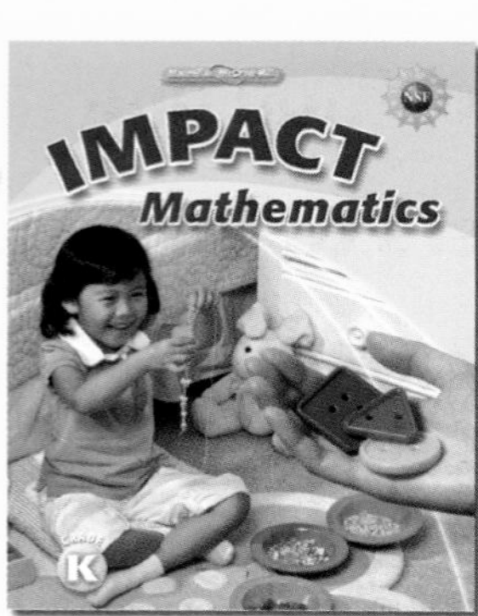

Grade K

NSF-funded, integrated performance assessment aligned with investigative instruction

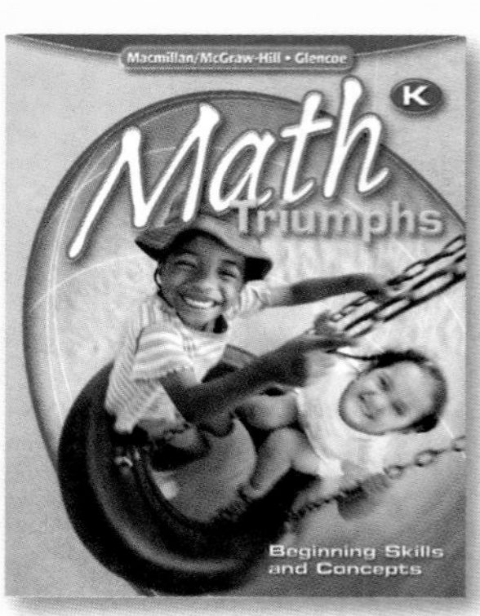

Grade K

Intensive Intervention for students two or more years below grade level (Tier 3 RTI)

The McGraw-Hill Companies

Macmillan/McGraw-Hill

Send all inquiries to:
Macmillan/McGraw-Hill
8787 Orion Place
Columbus, OH 43240-4027

Volume 1
ISBN: 978-0-02-105735-1 *(Teacher Edition)*
MHID: 0-02-105735-4 *(Teacher Edition)*
ISBN: 978-0-02-105723-8 *(Student Edition)*
MHID: 0-02-105723-0 *(Student Edition)*

Printed in the United States of America.
5 6 7 8 9 10 RJE/LEH 16 15 14 13 12 11 10

Benefits of Student Edition Organization

Math Connects, kindergarten Student Edition, has a 3-part organization.

1. **Start Smart** gets students ready for kindergarten with a review of key math standards that are prerequisites for kindergarten.
2. **Chapters 1–12** Each chapter has coherent groups of lessons focused on related kindergarten math standards and the NCTM Focal Points.
3. **Looking Ahead** prepares students for success with lessons on several key math standards.

The organization and pacing of ***Math Connects*** helps ensure in-depth coverage of all kindergarten standards and a good start for grade 1.

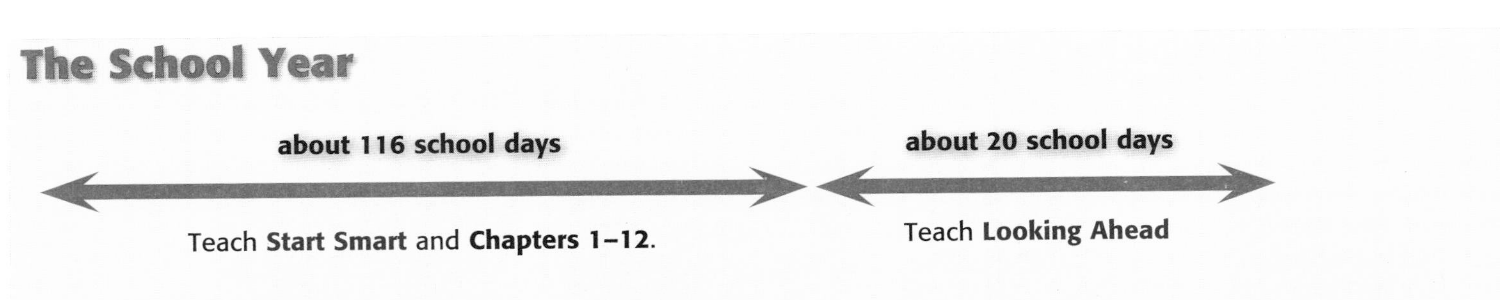

Pacing Guide
Each chapter includes days for review and assessment.

Start Smart	12 days
Chapter 1	9 days
Chapter 2	10 days
Chapter 3	8 days
Chapter 4	10 days
Chapter 5	7 days
Chapter 6	9 days
Chapter 7	8 days
Chapter 8	8 days
Chapter 9	9 days
Chapter 10	10 days
Chapter 11	8 days
Chapter 12	8 days
Total	116 days
Looking Ahead	20 days

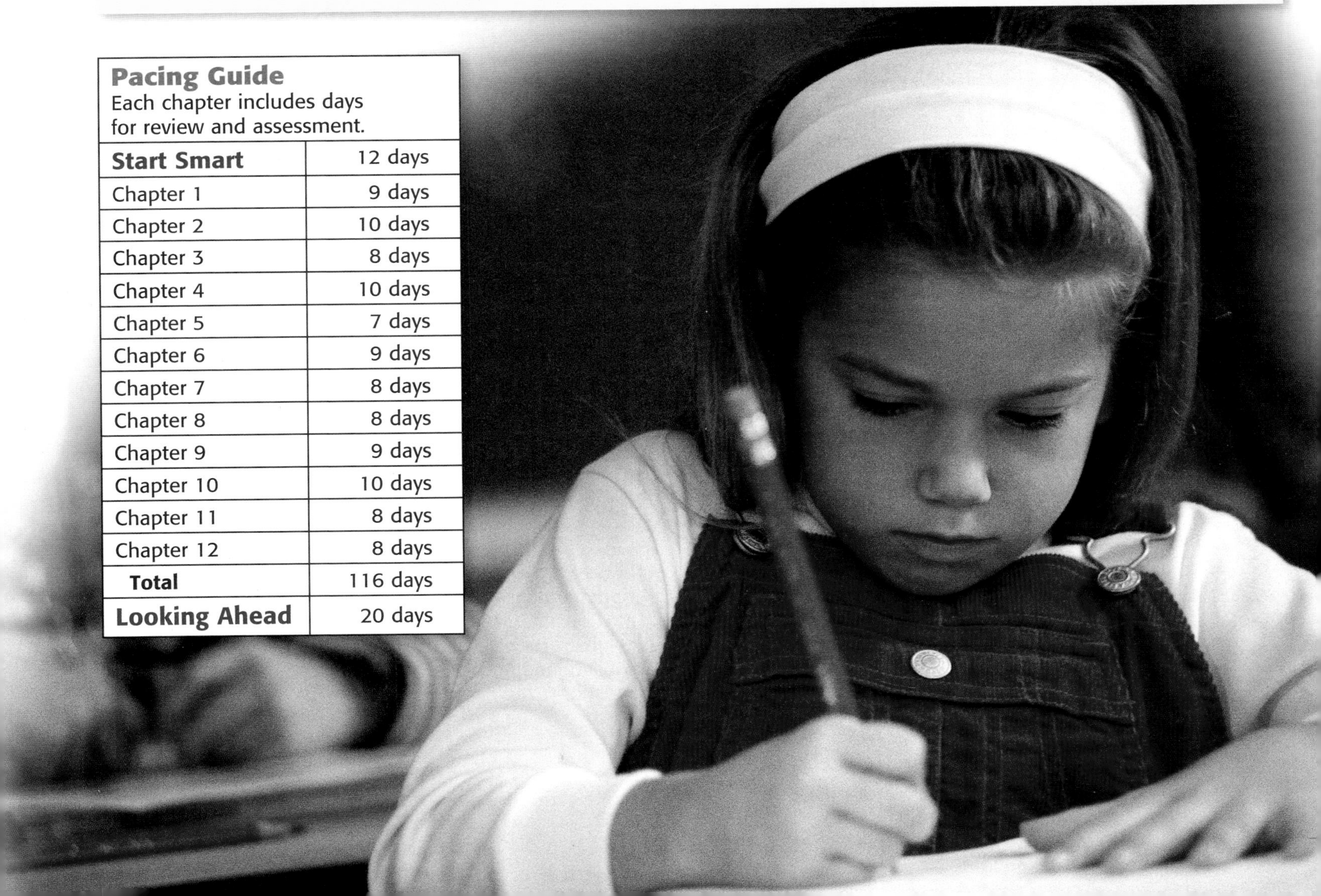

Authors

Mary Behr Altieri
Putnam/Northern Westchester BOCES
Yorktown Heights, New York

Don S. Balka
Professor Emeritus
Saint Mary's College
Notre Dame, Indiana

Roger Day, Ph.D.
Mathematics Department Chair
Pontiac Township High School
Pontiac, Illinois

Philip D. Gonsalves
Mathematics Coordinator
Alameda County Office of Education and California State University East Bay
Hayward, California

Ellen C. Grace
Mathematics Consultant
Albuquerque, New Mexico

Stephen Krulik
Professor Emeritus Mathematics Education
Temple University
Cherry Hill, New Jersey

Carol E. Malloy, Ph.D
Associate Professor of Mathematics Education
University of North Carolina at Chapel Hill
Chapel Hill, North Carolina

Rhonda J. Molix-Bailey
Mathematics Consultant
Mathematics by Design
Desoto, Texas

Lois Gordon Moseley
Staff Developer
NUMBERS: Mathematics Professional Development
Houston, Texas

Brian Mowry
Independent Math Educational Consultant/Part-Time Pre-K Instructional Specialist
Austin Independent School District
Austin, Texas

Christina L. Myren
Consultant Teacher
Conejo Valley Unified School District
Thousand Oaks, California

Jack Price
Professor Emeritus
California State Polytechnic University
Pomona, California

Mary Esther Reynosa
Instructional Specialist for Elementary Mathematics
Northside Independent School District
San Antonio, Texas

Rafaela M. Santa Cruz
SDSU/CGU Doctoral Program in Education
San Diego State University
San Diego, California

Robyn Silbey
Math Content Coach
Montgomery County Public Schools
Gaithersburg, Maryland

Kathleen Vielhaber
Mathematics Consultant
St. Louis, Missouri

Contributing Authors

Donna J. Long
Mathematics Consultant
Indianapolis, Indiana

FOLDABLES™ **Dinah Zike**
Educational Consultant
Dinah-Might Activities, Inc.
San Antonio, Texas

Consultants

Macmillan/McGraw-Hill wishes to thank the following professionals for their feedback. They were instrumental in providing valuable input toward the development of this program in these specific areas.

Mathematical Content

Viken Hovsepian
Professor of Mathematics
Rio Hondo College
Whittier, California

Grant A. Fraser, Ph.D.
Professor of Mathematics
California State University, Los Angeles
Los Angeles, California

Arthur K. Wayman, Ph.D.
Professor of Mathematics Emeritus
California State University, Long Beach
Long Beach, California

Assessment

Jane D. Gawronski, Ph.D.
Director of Assessment and Outreach
San Diego State University
San Diego, California

Cognitive Guided Instruction

Susan B. Empson, Ph.D.
Associate Professor of Mathematics and Science Education
University of Texas at Austin
Austin, Texas

English Learners

Cheryl Avalos
Mathematics Consultant
Los Angeles County Office of Education, Retired
Hacienda Heights, California

Kathryn Heinze
Graduate School of Education
Hamline University
St. Paul, Minnesota

Family Involvement

Paul Giganti, Jr.
Mathematics Education Consultant
Albany, California

Literature

David M. Schwartz
Children's Author, Speaker, Storyteller
Oakland, California

Vertical Alignment

Berchie Holliday
National Educational Consultant
Silver Spring, Maryland

Deborah A. Hutchens, Ed.D.
Principal
Norfolk Highlands Elementary
Chesapeake, Virginia

Reviewers

Each reviewer reviewed at least two chapters of the Student Edition, giving feedback and suggestions for improving the effectiveness of the mathematics instruction.

Ernestine D. Austin
Facilitating Teacher/Basic Skills Teacher
LORE School
Ewing, NJ

Susie Bellah
Kindergarten Teacher
Lakeland Elementary
Humble, TX

Megan Bennett
Elementary Math Coordinator
Hartford Public Schools
Hartford, CT

Susan T. Blankenship
5th Grade Teacher – Math
Stanford Elementary School
Stanford, KY

Wendy Buchanan
3rd Grade Teacher
The Classical Center at Vial
Garland, TX

Sandra Signorelli Coelho
Associate Director for Mathematics
PIMMS at Wesleyan University
Middletown, CT

Joanne DeMizio
Asst. Supt., Math and Science Curriculum
Archdiocese of New York
New York, NY

Anthony Dentino
Supervisor of Mathematics
Brick Township Schools
Brick, NJ

Lorrie L. Drennon
Math Teacher
Collins Middle School
Corsicana, TX

Ethel A. Edwards
Director of Curriculum and Instruction
Topeka Public Schools
Topeka, KS

Carolyn Elender
District Elementary Math Instructional Specialist
Pasadena ISD
Pasadena, TX

Monica Engel
Educator Second Grade
Pioneer Elementary School
Bolingbrook, IL

Anna Dahinden Flynn
Math Teacher
Coulson Tough K-6 Elementary
The Woodlands, TX

Brenda M. Foxx
Principal
University Park Elementary
University Park, MD

Katherine A. Frontier
Elementary Teacher
Laidlaw
Western Springs, IL

Susan J. Furphy
5th Grade Teacher
Nisley Elementary
Grand Jct., CO

Peter Gatz
Student Services Coordinator
Brooks Elementary
Aurora, IL

Amber Gregersen
Teacher – 2nd Grade
Nisley Elementary
Grand Junction, Colorado

Roberta Grindle
Math and Language Arts Academic Intervention Service Provider
Cumberland Head Elementary School
Plattsburgh, NY

Sr. Helen Lucille Habig, RSM
Assistant Superintendent/Mathematics
Archdiocese of Cincinnati
Cincinnati, Ohio

Holly L. Hepp
Math Facilitator
Barringer Academic Center
Charlotte, NC

Martha J. Hickman
2nd Grade Teacher
Dr. James Craik Elementary School
Pomfret, MD

Margie Hill
District Coordinating Teacher for Mathematics, K-12
Blue Valley USD 229
Overland Park, KS

Carol H. Joyce
5th Grade Teacher
Nathanael Greene Elementary
Liberty, NC

Stella K. Kostante
Curriculum Coach
Roosevelt Elementary
Pittsburgh, PA

Pamela Fleming Lowe
Fourth Grade eMINTS Teacher
O'Neal Elementary
Poplar Bluff, MO

Lauren May, NBCT
4th Grade Teacher
May Watts Elementary School
Naperville, IL

Lorraine Moore
Grade 3 Math Teacher
Cowpens Elementary School
Cowpens, SC

Shannon L. Moorehead
4th Grade Teacher
Centervile Elementary
Anderson, SC

Gina M. Musselman, M.Ed
Kindergarten Teacher
Padeo Verde Elementary
Peoria, AZ

Jen Neufeld
3rd Grade Teacher
Kendall
Naperville, IL

Cathie Osiecki
K-5 Mathematics Coordinator
Middletown Public Schools
Middletown, CT

Phyllis L. Pacilli
Elementary Education Teacher
Fullerton Elementary
Addison, IL

Cindy Pearson
4th/5th Grade Teacher
John D. Spicer Elementary
Haltom City, TX 76137

Herminio M. Planas
Mathematics Curriculum Specialist
Administrative Offices-Bridgeport Public Schools
Bridgeport, CT

Jo J. Puree
Educator
Lackamas Elementary
Yelm, WA

Teresa M. Reynolds
Third Grade Teacher
Forrest View Elementary
Everett, WA

Dr. John A. Rhodes
Director of Mathematics
Indian Prairie SD #204
Aurora, IL

Amy Romm
First Grade Teacher
Starline Elementary
Lake Havasu, AZ

Delores M. Rushing
Numeracy Coach
Dept. of Academic Services-Mathematics Department
Washington, DC

Daniel L. Scudder
Mathematics/Technology Specialist
Boone Elementary
Houston, TX

Laura Seymour
Resource Teacher Leader –Elementary Math & Science, Retired
Dearborn Public Schools
Dearborn, MI

Petra Siprian
Teacher
Army Trail Elementary School
Addison, IL

Sandra Stein
K-5 Mathematics Consultant
St. Clair County Regional Educational Service Agency
Marysville, MI

Barb Stoflet
Curriculum Specialist
Roseville Area Schools
Roseville, MN

Kim Summers
Principal
Dynard Elementary
Chaptico, MD

Ann C. Teater
4th Grade Teacher
Lancaster Elementary
Lancaster, KY

Anne E. Tunney
Teacher
City of Erie School District
Erie, PA

Joylien Weathers
1st Grade Teacher
Mesa View Elementary
Grand Junction, CO

Christine F. Weiss
Third Grade Teacher
Robert C. Hill Elementary School
Romeoville, IL

Mathematics Teacher Handbook

Table of Contents

PreK–12 Mathematics: Focus on Kindergarten

Welcome to Math Connects

Concepts • Skills • Problem Solving

The only true vertically aligned PreK–12 Mathematics Curriculum

Math Connects offers three dimensions of vertical alignment.

❶ Content Design

Vertical content alignment is a process that ensures you and your students experience an articulated, coherent sequence of content from grade level to grade level. This provides you with the assurance that content is introduced, reinforced, and assessed at appropriate times in the series, eliminating gaps and unnecessary duplication. You are able to target your instruction to student needs because you are not teaching content intended to be covered later or that students have previously mastered.

❷ Instructional Design

Our strong vertical alignment in instructional approach from PreKindergarten through Algebra 2 provides a smooth transition for students from elementary to middle school to high school. Our common vocabulary, technology, manipulatives, lesson planning, and Data-Driven Decision Making reduces the confusion students often encounter when transitioning between grade levels without this built-in articulation.

❸ Visual Design

The student pages of ***Math Connects*** have a consistent visual design from grade to grade. This aids students' transition from elementary school to middle school and from middle school to Algebra 1. Students are more likely to succeed when they are already familiar with how to navigate student pages.

PreK-2 | 3–5

5 Keys to Success

❶ Backmapping

According to College Board research, about 80% of students who successfully complete Algebra 1 and Geometry by 10th grade attend and succeed in college. (Changing the Odds: Factors Increasing Access to College, 1990) ***Math Connects*** was conceived and developed by backmapping with the final result in mind–student success in Algebra 1 and beyond.

❷ Balanced, In-Depth Content

Math Connects was developed to specifically target the skills and topics that give students the most difficulty, such as Problem Solving, in each grade span.

Grades K–2	Grades 3–5
1. Problem Solving 2. Money 3. Time 4. Measurement 5. Fractions 6. Computation	1. Problem Solving 2. Fractions 3. Measurement 4. Decimals 5. Time 6. Algebra
Grades 6–8	**Grades 9–12**
1. Fractions 2. Problem Solving 3. Measurement 4. Algebra 5. Computation	1. Problem Solving 2. Fractions 3. Algebra 4. Geometry 5. Computation 6. Probability

– *K–12 Math Market Analysis Survey,* Open Book Publishing, 2006

❸ Ongoing Assessment

Math Connects includes diagnostic, formative, and summative assessment; data-driven instruction; intervention options; and performance tracking, as well as remediation, acceleration, and enrichment tools throughout the program.

❹ Intervention and Differentiated Instruction

A three-tiered Response To Intervention (RTI) is provided.

TIER 1 **Daily Intervention** Reteach masters and Alternative Strategy suggestions address concepts from a different modality or learning style.

TIER 2 **Strategic Intervention** Teachers can use the myriad of intervention tips and ancillary materials, such as the Strategic Intervention Guide (1–5) and Study Guide and Intervention (6–8).

TIER 3 **Intensive Intervention** For students who are two or more years below grade level, ***Math Triumphs*** provides step-by-step instruction, vocabulary support, and data-driven decision making to help students succeed.

❺ Professional Development

Math Connects includes many opportunities for teacher professional development. Additional learning opportunities in various formats–video, online, and on-site instruction–are fully aligned and articulated from Kindergarten through Algebra 2.

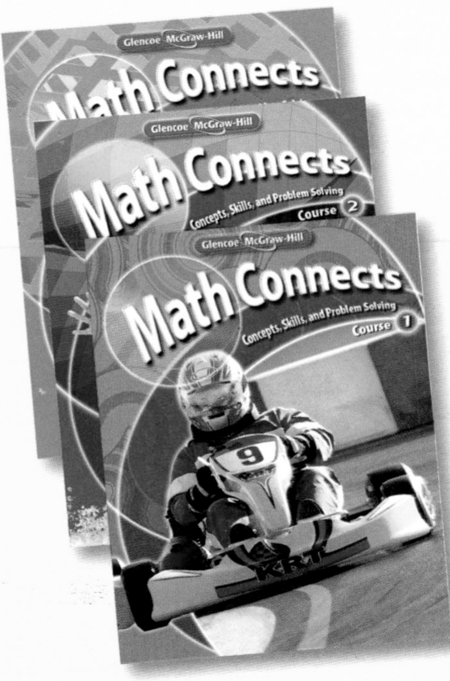

6–8

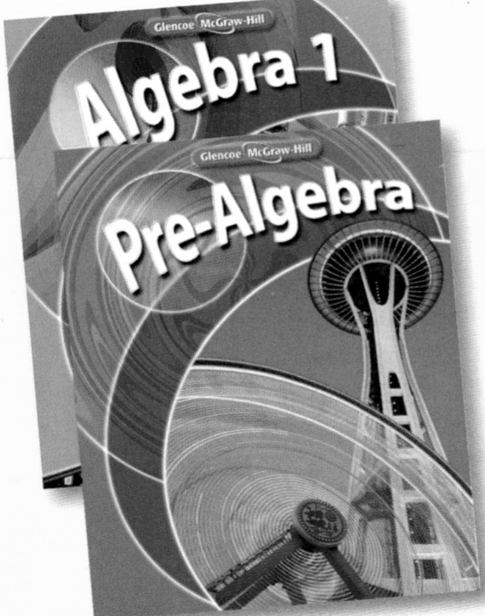

Pre-Algebra and Algebra 1

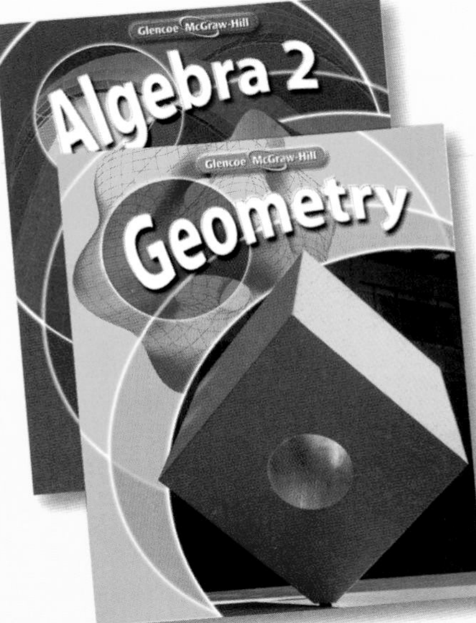

Geometry and Algebra 2

The Research Base

Continuous research with teachers, students, academician, and leading experts helps to build a solid foundation for ***Math Connects.***

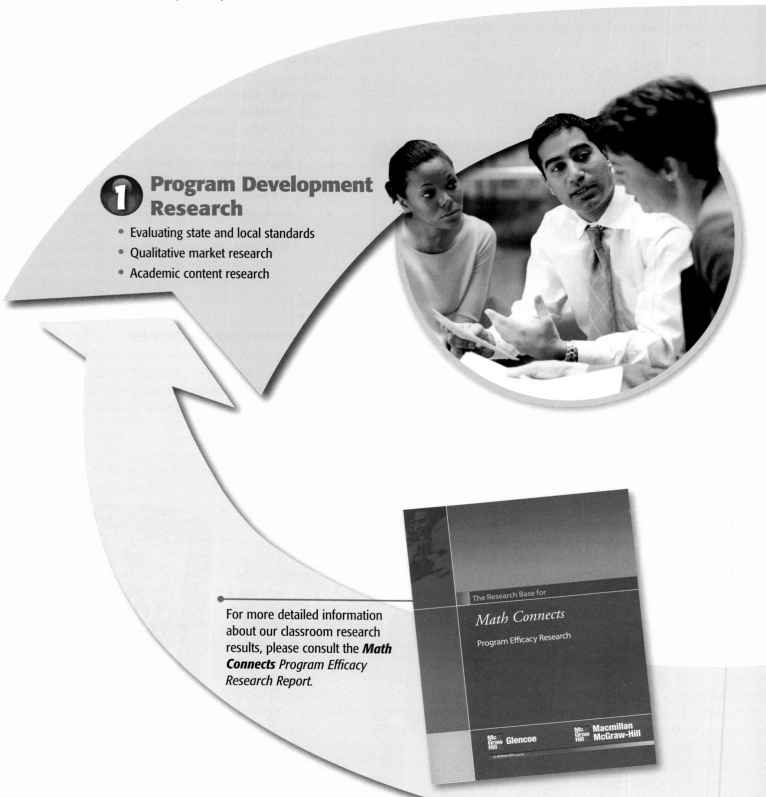

1 Program Development Research

- Evaluating state and local standards
- Qualitative market research
- Academic content research

For more detailed information about our classroom research results, please consult the ***Math Connects*** *Program Efficacy Research Report.*

for *Math Connects*

2 Formative Research

- Pedagogical research base
- Classroom field tests
- Teacher advisory boards
- Academic consultants and reviewers

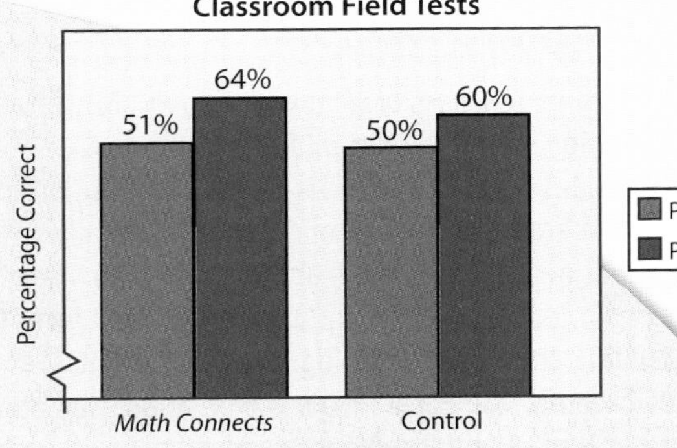

Students using a field test of the ***Math Connects*** program **(experimental group)** had ***higher*** pre-test to post-test gains than students using other textbook programs **(control group).**

3 Summative Research

- Evidence of increased test scores
- Quasi-experimental program efficacy research
- Longitudinal studies
- Qualitative program evaluations

Access all ***Math Connects*** research at macmillanmh.com.

NCTM Focal Points

The NCTM Focal Points

In 2006, the National Council of Teachers of Mathematics (NCTM) released the Curriculum Focal Points for Pre-Kindergarten through Grade 8 Mathematics. These Curriculum Focal Points focus on the most important mathematical topics for each grade level. The concepts are vertically-aligned and expect a level of depth, complexity, and rigor at each level. They comprise related ideas, concepts, skills, and procedures that form the foundation for understanding and lasting learning. The Focal Points emphasize depth versus breadth. The Focal Points will be addressed and highlighted throughout our PreK-8 and Pre-Algebra series.

NCTM Focal Points for Grade K	Supporting Chapters in *Math Connects*
Number and Operations	Chapters 1, 2, 4, 6, 8, 11, 12
Geometry	Chapter 10
Measurement	Chapters 7, 9
Connections to the Focal Points	
Data Analysis	Chapters 1, 5
Geometry	Chapter 10
Algebra	Chapter 3

What is the benefit to you in your classroom?

These Focal Points identify content for each grade level that should be mastered in order for your students to have true mathematical understanding–being able to not only calculate the answer, but to explain the answer and how to apply the calculation. The NCTM Focal Points were used as the basis in the development of ***Math Connects.*** The authors have incorporated the Focal Points into the content to assist you in building depth of understanding.

The Curriculum Focal Points identify key mathematical ideas for this grade. They are not discrete topics or a checklist to be mastered; rather, they provide a framework for the majority of instruction at a particular grade level and the foundation for future mathematics study. The complete document may be viewed at www.nctm.org/focalpoints.

KEY

GK-FP1 Grade K Focal Point 1	**GK-FP5C** Grade K Focal Point 5 Connection
GK-FP2 Grade K Focal Point 2	**GK-FP6C** Grade K Focal Point 6 Connection
GK-FP3 Grade K Focal Point 3	
GK-FP4C Grade K Focal Point 4 Connection	

GK-FP1 *Number and Operations:* **Representing, comparing, and ordering whole numbers and joining and separating sets**

Children use numbers, including written numerals, to represent quantities and to solve quantitative problems, such as counting objects in a set, creating a set with a given number of objects, comparing and ordering sets or numerals by using both cardinal and ordinal meanings, and modeling simple joining and separating situations with objects. They choose, combine, and apply effective strategies for answering quantitative questions, including quickly recognizing the number in a small set, counting and producing sets of given sizes, counting the number in combined sets, and counting backward.

GK-FP2 *Geometry:* **Describing shapes and space**

Children interpret the physical world with geometric ideas (e.g., shape, orientation, spatial relations) and describe it with corresponding vocabulary. They identify, name, and describe a variety of shapes, such as squares, triangles, circles, rectangles, (regular) hexagons, and (isosceles) trapezoids presented in a variety of ways (e.g., with different sizes or orientations), as well as such three-dimensional shapes as spheres, cubes, and cylinders. They use basic shapes and spatial reasoning to model objects in their environment and to construct more complex shapes.

GK-FP3 *Measurement:* **Ordering objects by measurable attributes**

Children use measurable attributes, such as length or weight, to solve problems by comparing and ordering objects. They compare the lengths of two objects both directly (by comparing them with each other) and indirectly (by comparing both with a third object), and they order several objects according to length.

Connections to the Focal Points

GK-FP4C *Data Analysis:* Children sort objects and use one or more attributes to solve problems. For example, they might sort solids that roll easily from those that do not. Or they might collect data and use counting to answer such questions as, "What is our favorite snack?" They re-sort objects by using new attributes (e.g., after sorting solids according to which ones roll, they might re-sort the solids according to which ones stack easily).

GK-FP5C *Geometry:* Children integrate their understandings of geometry, measurement, and number. For example, they understand, discuss, and create simple navigational directions (e.g., "Walk forward 10 steps, turn right, and walk forward 5 steps").

GK-FP6C *Algebra:* Children identify, duplicate, and extend simple number patterns and sequential and growing patterns (e.g., patterns made with shapes) as preparation for creating rules that describe relationships.

Program Philosophy

Balanced Instruction, Vertically-Aligned from Grades PreK through Algebra 1

The vertical alignment of ***Math Connects*** PreK-8 and ***Algebra 1*** incorporates a balance of instruction throughout. These programs provide students a balanced approach to mathematics by:

- investigating concepts and building conceptual understanding.
- developing, reinforcing, and mastering computational and procedural skills.
- applying mathematics to problem-solving situations.

This sequence of Student Edition pages illustrates the vertically-aligned development of the conceptual understanding and corresponding computational and procedural skills for an important algebra topic.

Primary Students use two-color counters to model addition sentences. This activity forms a basis for future understanding of and success in solving algebraic equations.

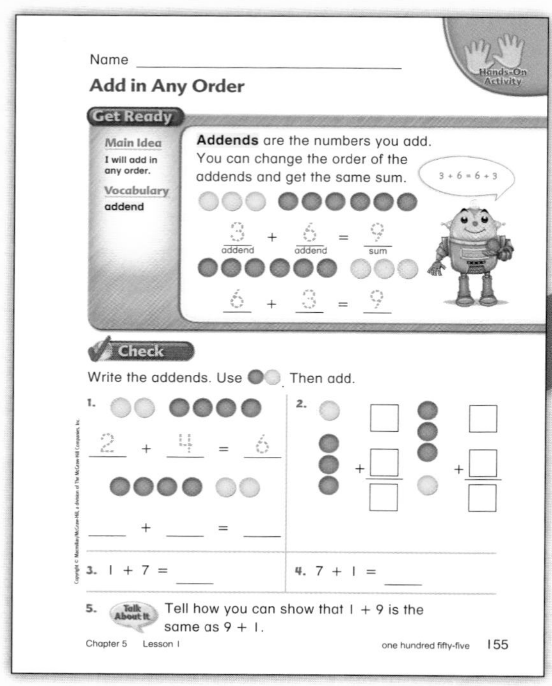

Name ______________________

Add in Any Order

Hands-On Activity

Get Ready

Main Idea
I will add in any order.

Vocabulary
addend

Addends are the numbers you add. You can change the order of the addends and get the same sum.

3 + 6 = 6 + 3

3 + 6 = 9
addend addend sum

6 + 3 = 9

Check

Write the addends. Use counters. Then add.

1. 2 + 4 = 6
   ___ + ___ = ___

2. □ + □ = □ ; □ + □ = □

3. 1 + 7 = ___

4. 7 + 1 = ___

5. Talk About It Tell how you can show that 1 + 9 is the same as 9 + 1.

Copyright © Macmillan/McGraw-Hill, a division of The McGraw-Hill Companies, Inc.

Chapter 5 Lesson 1 one hundred fifty-five 155

Math Connects, Grade 1, Student Edition, page 155

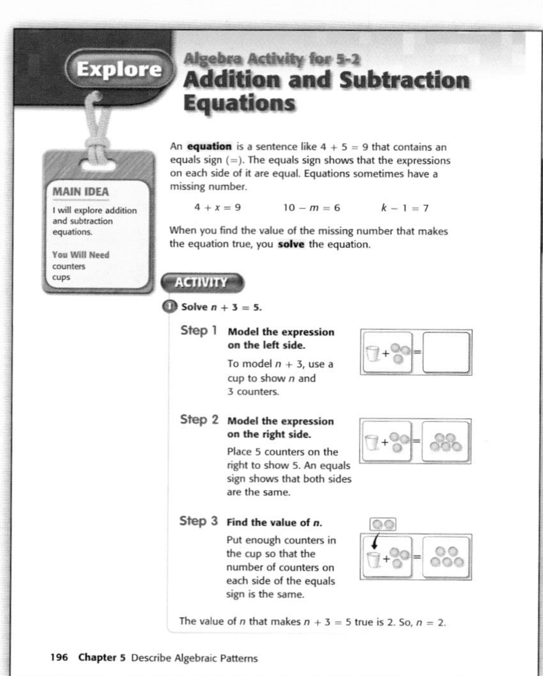

Explore Algebra Activity for 5-2

Addition and Subtraction Equations

MAIN IDEA
I will explore addition and subtraction equations.

You Will Need
counters
cups

An **equation** is a sentence like $4 + 5 = 9$ that contains an equals sign (=). The equals sign shows that the expressions on each side of it are equal. Equations sometimes have a missing number.

$4 + x = 9$ $10 - m = 6$ $k - 1 = 7$

When you find the value of the missing number that makes the equation true, you **solve** the equation.

ACTIVITY

1. **Solve $n + 3 = 5$.**

Step 1 **Model the expression on the left side.** To model $n + 3$, use a cup to show n and 3 counters.

Step 2 **Model the expression on the right side.** Place 5 counters on the right to show 5. An equals sign shows that both sides are the same.

Step 3 **Find the value of n.** Put enough counters in the cup so that the number of counters on each side of the equals sign is the same.

The value of n that makes $n + 3 = 5$ true is 2. So, $n = 2$.

196 **Chapter 5** Describe Algebraic Patterns

Math Connects, Grade 4, Student Edition, page 196

Intermediate Students build on their experience with counters to using cups and counters to model and solve addition and subtraction equations. The exercises are designed to help students bridge the gap from using cups and counters to solving equations symbolically.

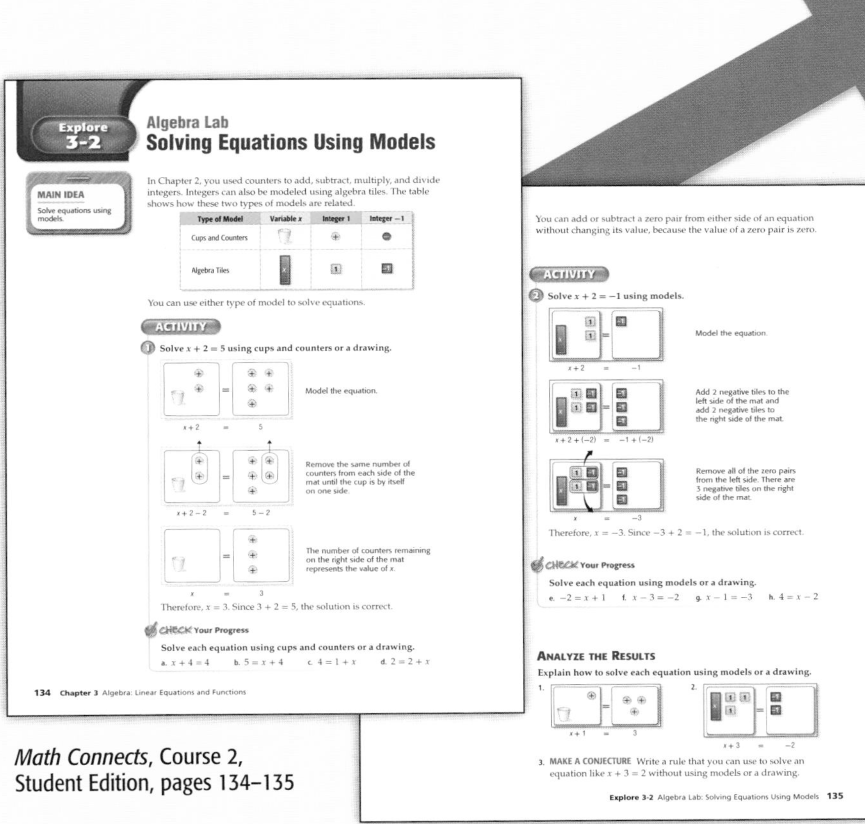

Explore 3-2

Algebra Lab

Solving Equations Using Models

MAIN IDEA

Solve equations using models.

In Chapter 2, you used counters to add, subtract, multiply, and divide integers. Integers can also be modeled using algebra tiles. The table shows how these two types of models are related.

Type of Model	Variable x	Integer 1	Integer −1
Cups and Counters			
Algebra Tiles			

You can use either type of model to solve equations.

ACTIVITY

1 **Solve $x + 2 = 5$ using cups and counters or a drawing.**

$x + 2 = 5$ — Model the equation.

$x + 2 - 2 = 5 - 2$ — Remove the same number of counters from each side of the mat until the cup is by itself on one side.

$x = 3$ — The number of counters remaining on the right side of the mat represents the value of x.

Therefore, $x = 3$. Since $3 + 2 = 5$, the solution is correct.

CHECK Your Progress

Solve each equation using cups and counters or a drawing.

a. $x + 4 = 4$ b. $5 = x + 4$ c. $4 = 1 + x$ d. $2 = 2 + x$

134 **Chapter 3** Algebra: Linear Equations and Functions

You can add or subtract a zero pair from either side of an equation without changing its value, because the value of a zero pair is zero.

ACTIVITY

2 **Solve $x + 2 = -1$ using models.**

$x + 2 = -1$ — Model the equation.

$x + 2 + (-2) = -1 + (-2)$ — Add 2 negative tiles to the left side of the mat and add 2 negative tiles to the right side of the mat.

$x = -3$ — Remove all of the zero pairs from the left side. There are 3 negative tiles on the right side of the mat.

Therefore, $x = -3$. Since $-3 + 2 = -1$, the solution is correct.

CHECK Your Progress

Solve each equation using models or a drawing.

e. $-2 = x + 1$ f. $x - 3 = -2$ g. $x - 1 = -3$ h. $4 = x - 2$

ANALYZE THE RESULTS

Explain how to solve each equation using models or a drawing.

1. $x + 1 = 3$
2. $x + 3 = -2$
3. **MAKE A CONJECTURE** Write a rule that you can use to solve an equation like $x + 3 = 2$ without using models or a drawing.

Explore 3-2 Algebra Lab: Solving Equations Using Models 135

Math Connects, Course 2,
Student Edition, pages 134–135

Middle School Students represent the variable *x* as a cup, as a counter, or as a written *x*. In this Algebra Lab, students make the transition from cups and counters to the more abstract algebra tiles. In the next lesson, students solve simple equations symbolically.

EXPLORE 2-4

Algebra Lab

Solving Multi-Step Equations

You can use an equation model to solve multi-step equations.

ACTIVITY

Concepts in Motion
Animation algebra1.com

Solve $3x + 5 = -7$.

Step 1 Model the equation.

$3x + 5 = -7$

Place 3 x-tiles and 5 positive 1-tiles on one side of the mat. Place 7 negative 1-tiles on the other side of the mat.

Step 2 Isolate the x-term.

$3x + 5 - 5 = -7 - 5$

Since there are 5 positive 1-tiles with the x-tiles, add 5 negative 1-tiles to each side to form zero pairs.

Step 3 Remove zero pairs.

$3x = -12$

Group the tiles to form zero pairs and remove the zero pairs.

Step 4 Group the tiles.

$\frac{3x}{3} = \frac{-12}{3}$

Separate the tiles into 3 equal groups to match the 3 x-tiles. Each x tile is paired with 4 negative 1 tiles. Thus, $x = -4$.

MODEL **Use algebra tiles to solve each equation.**

1. $2x - 3 = -9$
2. $3x + 5 = 14$
3. $3x - 2 = 10$
4. $-8 = 2x + 4$
5. $3 + 4x = 11$
6. $2x + 7 = 1$
7. $9 = 4x - 7$
8. $7 + 3x = -8$
9. $3x - 1 = -10$
10. **MAKE A CONJECTURE** What steps would you use to solve $7x - 12 = -61$?

Explore 2-4 Algebra Lab: Solving Multi-Step Equations **91**

Glencoe Algebra 1,
Student Edition, page 91

Algebra 1 Students continue the use of algebra tiles to investigate solving multi-step equations. In the next lesson, students apply the procedure developed in the Algebra Lab to a symbolic approach.

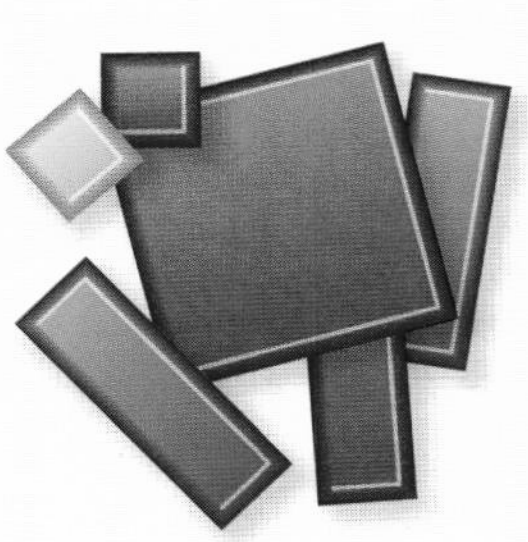

Continuity of Instruction The instructional sequence described demonstrates the power of backward mapping from the desired result, success in Algebra 1. This process of development avoids gaps and overlaps between grade levels and ensures that at each grade level the concepts and skills are built on the strong foundation developed in previous grades. The same approach was used across all strands throughout the entire PreK-12 series.

TEACHER
HANDBOOK

Program Philosophy Balance of Instruction

Relevant Problem Solving

Math Connects provides students with the appropriate development of problem-solving strategies, skills, and applications from PreK through grade 5. In grades 6–8, students continue to learn and apply problem-solving skills and strategies. Students are provided with ongoing opportunities to apply their math skills and solve problems using visual thinking, logical reasoning, number sense, and algebra.

Problem-Solving Strategies and Skills

Problem-Solving Strategy or **Skill** lessons introduce students to multiples methods for solving problems all using the *four-step* plan.

- Understand
- Plan
- Solve
- Check

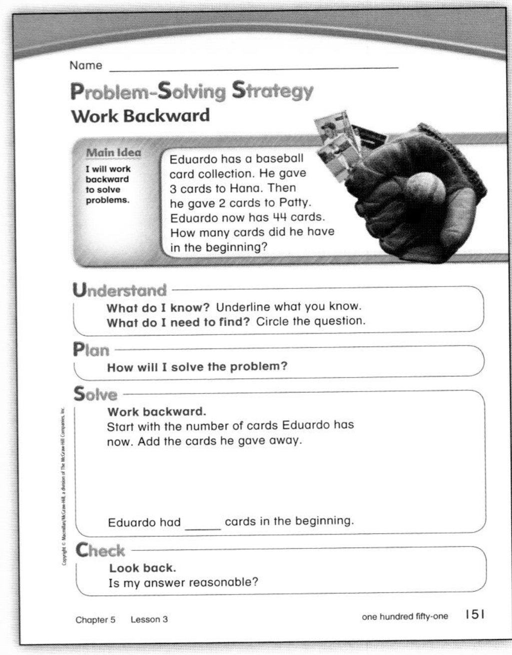
Name
Problem-Solving Strategy
Work Backward
Main Idea
I will work backward to solve problems.
Eduardo has a baseball card collection. He gave 3 cards to Hana. Then he gave 2 cards to Patty. Eduardo now has 44 cards. How many cards did he have in the beginning?
Understand
What do I know? Underline what you know.
What do I need to find? Circle the question.
Plan
How will I solve the problem?
Solve
Work backward.
Start with the number of cards Eduardo has now. Add the cards he gave away.
Eduardo had _____ cards in the beginning.
Check
Look back.
Is my answer reasonable?
Chapter 5 Lesson 3 one hundred fifty-one 151

Math Connects, Grade 2
Student Edition, page 151

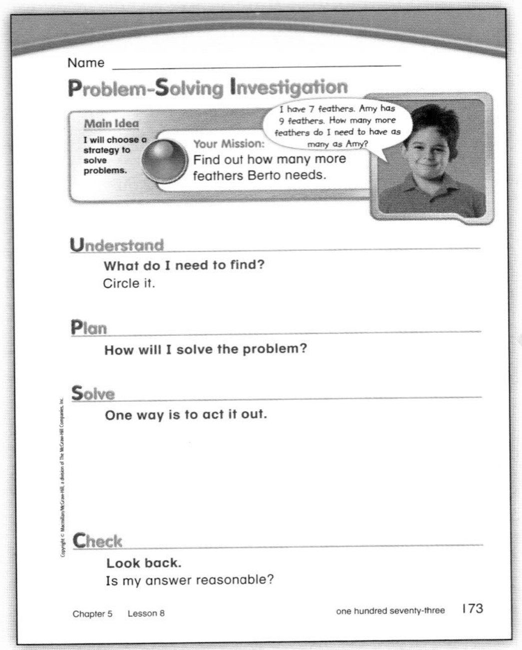
Name
Problem-Solving Investigation
Main Idea
I will choose a strategy to solve problems.
I have 7 feathers. Amy has 9 feathers. How many more feathers do I need to have as many as Amy?
Your Mission:
Find out how many more feathers Berto needs.
Understand
What do I need to find?
Circle it.
Plan
How will I solve the problem?
Solve
One way is to act it out.
Check
Look back.
Is my answer reasonable?
Chapter 5 Lesson 8 one hundred seventy-three 173

Math Connects, Grade 1
Student Edition, page 173

Problem-Solving Investigations

Problem-Solving Investigation lessons help students learn to choose appropriate strategies and apply them in problem-solving situations.

Real-World Problem Solving

Each chapter has a Problem Solving lesson that makes a tie to another discipline. These lessons encourage students to see problem solving in real-world applications.

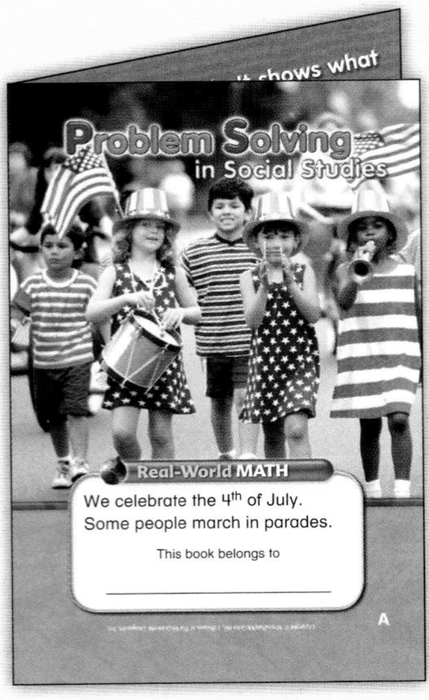
...t shows what
Problem Solving in Social Studies
Real-World MATH
We celebrate the 4th of July.
Some people march in parades.
This book belongs to
A

Math Connects, Kindergarten
Student Edition, pages 143–144

Real-World Problem Solving Readers

Fiction and nonfiction leveled readers extend problem-solving skills and strategies and make real-world applications. The books are provided for On Level, Sheltered English, and Spanish readers.

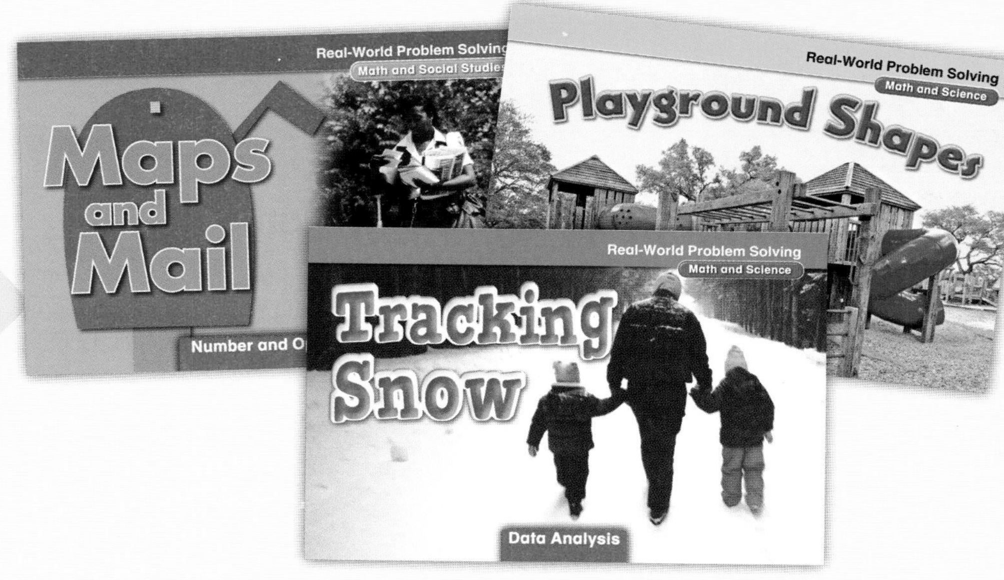

Data File Problems

The Data File features present math in real-world settings. Students are asked to use data to solve problems.

H.O.T. Problems

H.O.T. Problems require students to use **Higher Order Thinking** skills to solve problems.

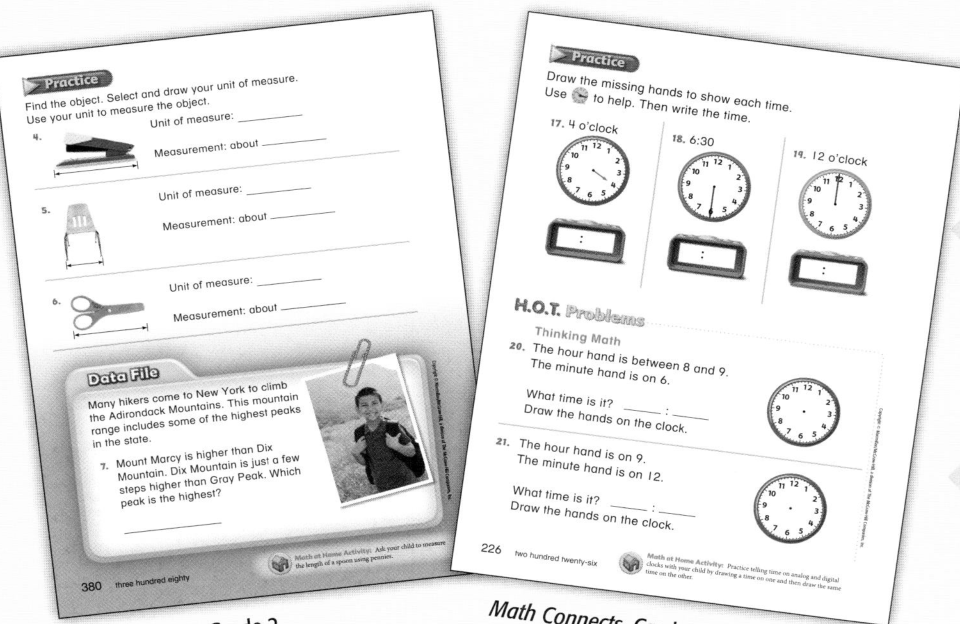
Practice

Find the object. Select and draw your unit of measure. Use your unit to measure the object.

4. Unit of measure: ______ Measurement: about ______

5. Unit of measure: ______ Measurement: about ______

6. Unit of measure: ______ Measurement: about ______

Data File

Many hikers come to New York to climb the Adirondack Mountains. This mountain range includes some of the highest peaks in the state.

7. Mount Marcy is higher than Dix Mountain. Dix Mountain is just a few steps higher than Gray Peak. Which peak is the highest?

______

380 three hundred eighty

Practice

Draw the missing hands to show each time. Use 🕒 to help. Then write the time.

17. 4 o'clock

18. 6:30

19. 12 o'clock

H.O.T. Problems

Thinking Math

20. The hour hand is between 8 and 9. The minute hand is on 6.

What time is it? ____ : ____

Draw the hands on the clock.

21. The hour hand is on 9. The minute hand is on 12.

What time is it? ____ : ____

Draw the hands on the clock.

226 two hundred twenty-six

Math Connects, Grade 2
Student Edition, page 380

Math Connects, Grade 1
Student Edition, page 226

Looking Ahead

Looking Ahead lessons introduce important concepts and skills that students can use.

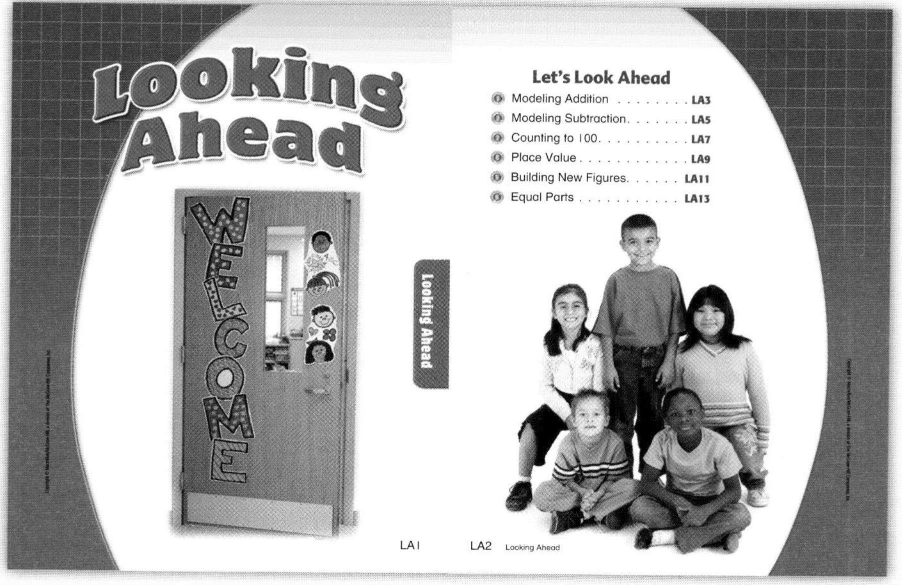
Looking Ahead

Let's Look Ahead

Looking Ahead

LA1 LA2 Looking Ahead

Math Connects, Kindergarten
Student Edition, pages LA1–LA2

Comprehensive Assessment System

Data-Driven Decision Making

Math Connects offers frequent and meaningful assessment of student progress within the curriculum structure and printed teacher support materials. See pages T22 and T23 for digital assessment solutions.

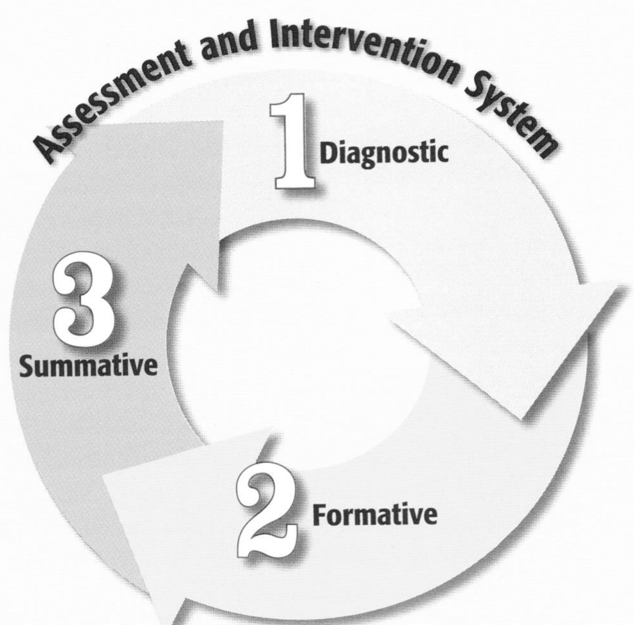

1 Diagnostic

Initial Assessment Assess students' knowledge **at the beginning of the year** with the *Diagnostic and Placement Tests*. This booklet will help you determine whether your students need additional materials and resources to meet grade-level standards.

Entry-Level Assessment Assess students' prior knowledge **at the beginning of a chapter or lesson** with one of the following options.

Student Edition

- Are You Ready?

Teacher Edition

- Intervention Options
- 5-Minute Check

Additional Resources

- Chapter Resource Masters, Chapter Diagnostic Test

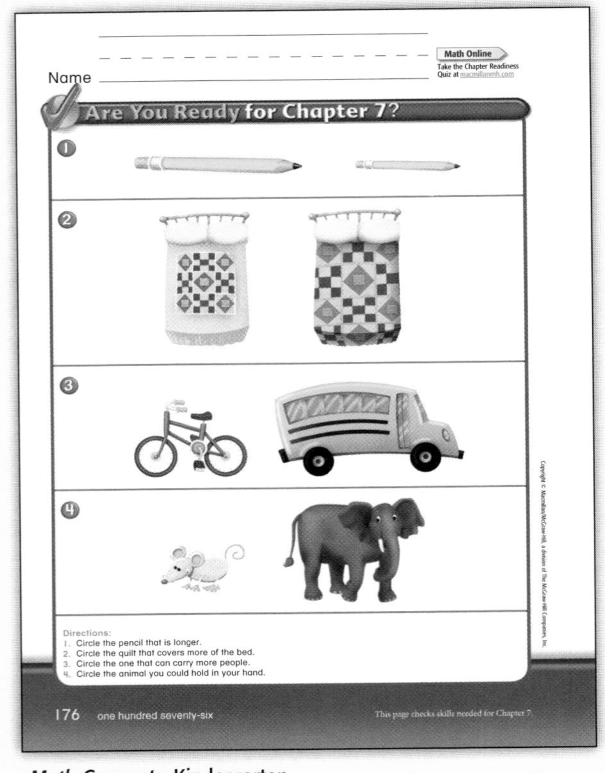

Math Online
Take the Chapter Readiness Quiz at macmillanmh.com

Name

Are You Ready for Chapter 7?

1
2
3
4

Directions:
1. Circle the pencil that is longer.
2. Circle the quilt that covers more of the bed.
3. Circle the one that can carry more people.
4. Circle the animal you could hold in your hand.

Copyright © Macmillan/McGraw-Hill, a division of The McGraw-Hill Companies, Inc.

176 one hundred seventy-six

This page checks skills needed for Chapter 7.

Math Connects, Kindergarten
Student Edition, page 176

Formative

Progress Monitoring Determine if students are progressing adequately as you teach each lesson. Use the assessments to differentiate lesson instruction and practice.

Student Edition
- Mid-Chapter Check
- Find the Error
- Check What You Know
- Talk About It
- Writing in Math
- Study Guide and Review
- Foldables™

Teacher Edition
- Alternate Teaching Strategy
- Step 4 (Assess) of the Teaching Plan
- Quick Check
- Data-Driven Decision Making

Additional Resources
Chapter Resource Masters
- Mid-Chapter Test
- 3 Quizzes

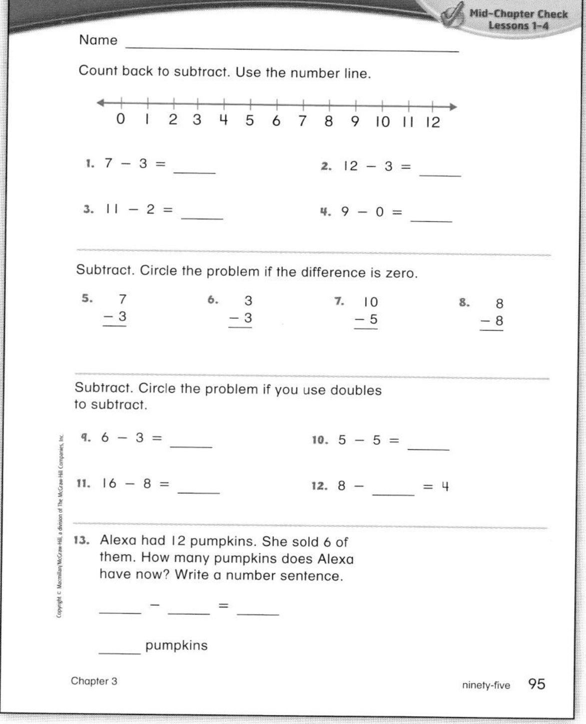

Mid-Chapter Check Lessons 1–4

Name ______

Count back to subtract. Use the number line.

0 1 2 3 4 5 6 7 8 9 10 11 12

1. 7 − 3 = ____ 2. 12 − 3 = ____

3. 11 − 2 = ____ 4. 9 − 0 = ____

Subtract. Circle the problem if the difference is zero.

5. 7 − 3 6. 3 − 3 7. 10 − 5 8. 8 − 8

Subtract. Circle the problem if you use doubles to subtract.

9. 6 − 3 = ____ 10. 5 − 5 = ____

11. 16 − 8 = ____ 12. 8 − ____ = 4

13. Alexa had 12 pumpkins. She sold 6 of them. How many pumpkins does Alexa have now? Write a number sentence.

____ − ____ = ____

____ pumpkins

Chapter 3 ninety-five 95

Math Connects, Grade 2
Student Edition, page 95

Summative

Summative Evaluation Assess student success in learning the concepts in each chapter.

Student Edition
- Chapter Test
- Test Practice
- Foldables™

Teacher Edition
- Data-Driven Decision Making

Additional Resources
Chapter Resource Masters
- Oral Assessment
- Listening Assessment
- 4 Leveled Chapter Tests
- Cumulative Test

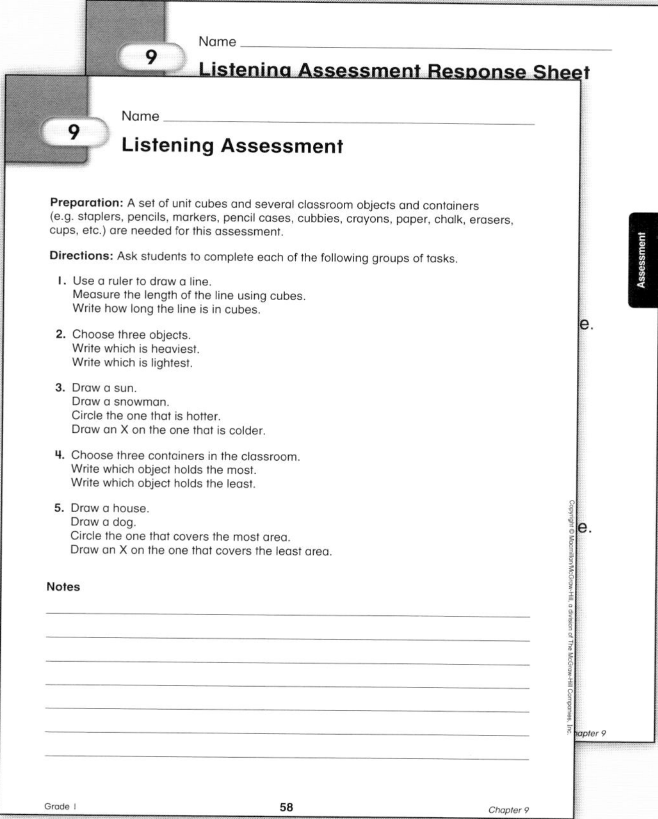

9 Name ______

Listening Assessment Response Sheet

9 Name ______

Listening Assessment

Preparation: A set of unit cubes and several classroom objects and containers (e.g. staplers, pencils, markers, pencil cases, cubbies, crayons, paper, chalk, erasers, cups, etc.) are needed for this assessment.

Directions: Ask students to complete each of the following groups of tasks.

1. Use a ruler to draw a line.
   Measure the length of the line using cubes.
   Write how long the line is in cubes.
2. Choose three objects.
   Write which is heaviest.
   Write which is lightest.
3. Draw a sun.
   Draw a snowman.
   Circle the one that is hotter.
   Draw an X on the one that is colder.
4. Choose three containers in the classroom.
   Write which object holds the most.
   Write which object holds the least.
5. Draw a house.
   Draw a dog.
   Circle the one that covers the most area.
   Draw an X on the one that covers the least area.

Notes

Grade 1 58 Chapter 9

Math Connects, Grade 1
Chapter 9 Resource Masters, pages 58–59

Comprehensive Assessment System

Data-Driven Decision Making

Math Connects provides digital assessment options to create, customize, administer, and instantly score a variety of assessments. These digital solutions offer the same quality assessments and reporting as the print resources in easy-to-use technology tools.

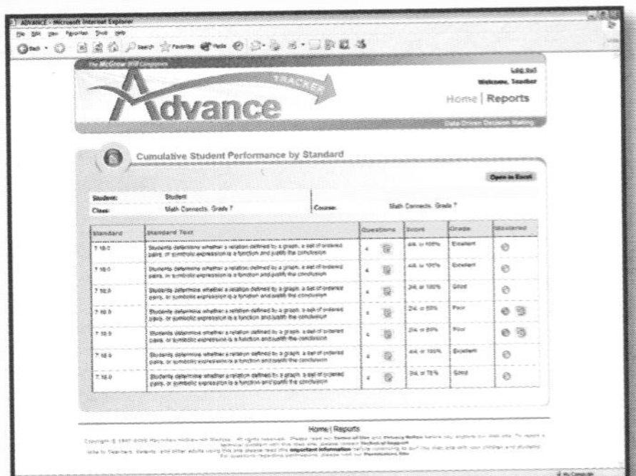

Math Connects, Grade 4

Advance Tracker helps teachers administer online tests, diagnose student achievement, and create prescriptive reports for a student or class.

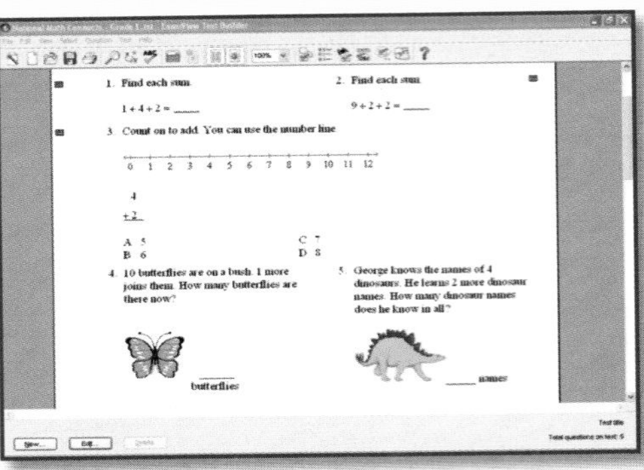

Math Connects, Grade 1

ExamView Assessment Suite allows teachers to create and customize their own assessment and assignments. Print in one or two columns to match state test.

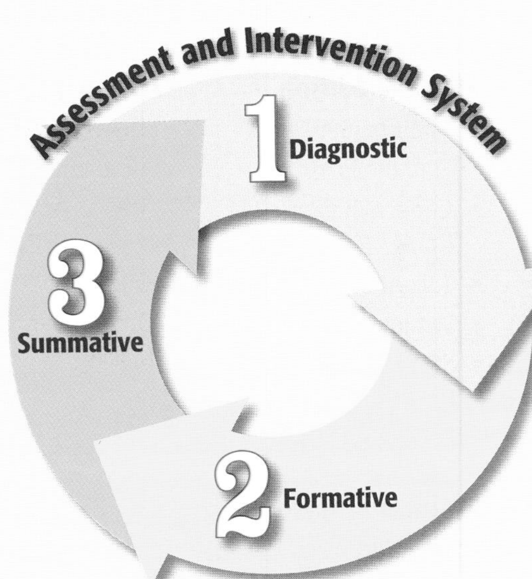

1 Diagnostic

Initial Assessment Assess students' knowledge **at the beginning of the year** with the *Diagnostic and Placement Tests.* These assessments will help you determine whether your students need additional materials and resources to meet grade-level standards.

- Diagnostic and Placement Tests

- Diagnostic and Placement Tests

Entry–Level Assessment Assess students' prior knowledge **at the beginning of a chapter or lesson.**

Math Online macmillanmh.com Students can complete online tests and the results are emailed to the teacher.

- Chapter Readiness

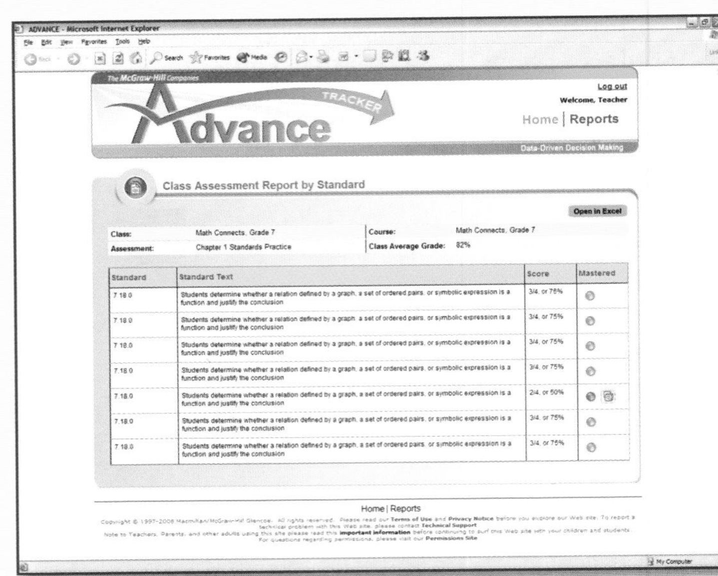

Math Connects Grade 2 Advance Tracker

Formative

Progress Monitoring Determine if students are progressing adequately as you teach each lesson. Use the assessments to differentiate lesson instruction and practice.

- Mid-Chapter Test
- Study Guide and Review

Math Online macmillanmh.com

- Self-Check Quizzes

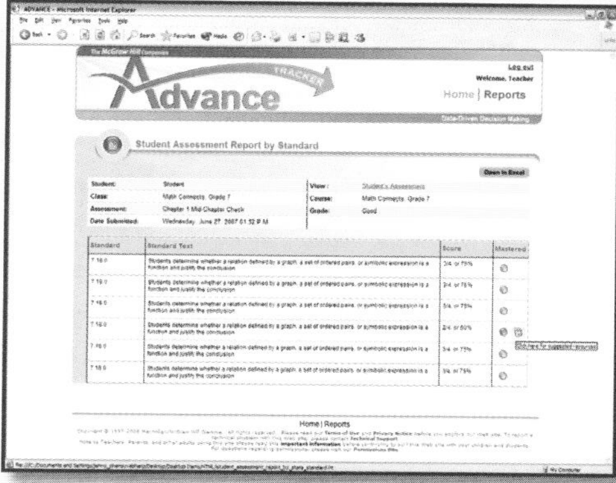

Math Connects, Kindergarten, Advance Tracker

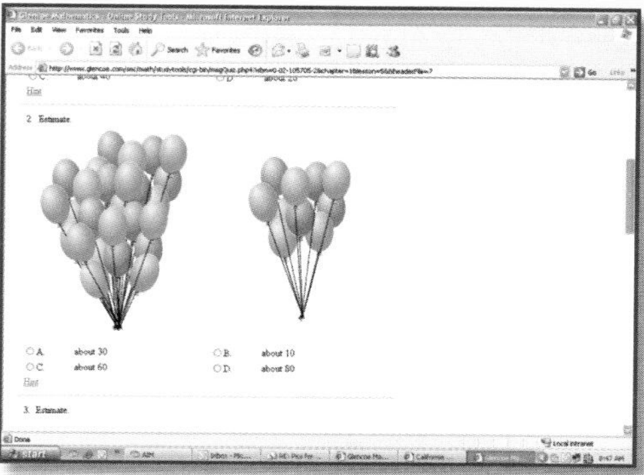

Math Connects, Grade 1, Self-Check Quiz

Summative

Summative Evaluation Assess students' success in learning the concepts in each chapter.

- Chapter Tests
- Cumulative Standardized Test Practice

- Chapter Tests
- Cumulative Standardized Test Practice

Math Online macmillanmh.com

- Chapter Tests

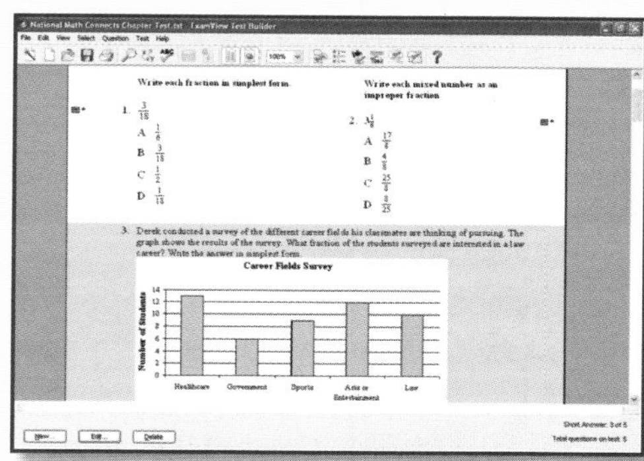

Math Connects, Grade 2, ExamView Assessment Suite

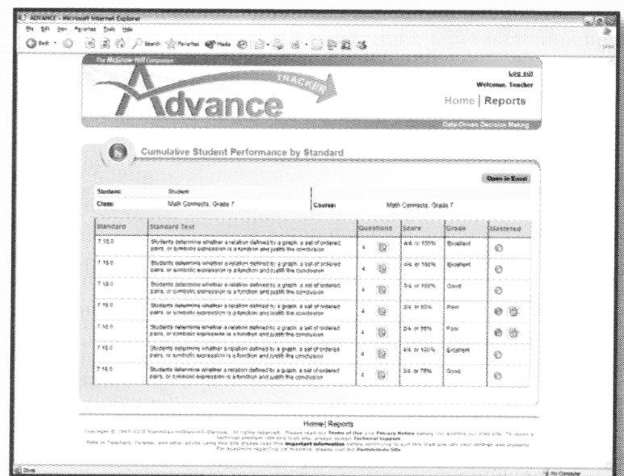

Math Connects, Grade 1, Advance Tracker

Differentiated Instruction

Reaching All Learners

Math Connects, provides extensive support for reaching all learners.

Every chapter and lesson includes suggestions for identifying and meeting your students' needs. Strategies include differentiation in pacing and student grouping, alternate approaches, ways to enhance instruction with manipulatives, questions to promote higher-order thinking, and language hints.

Personalize instruction for:

- BL Students who are below or approaching grade level
- ELL English language learners
- AL Students who are above or beyond grade level

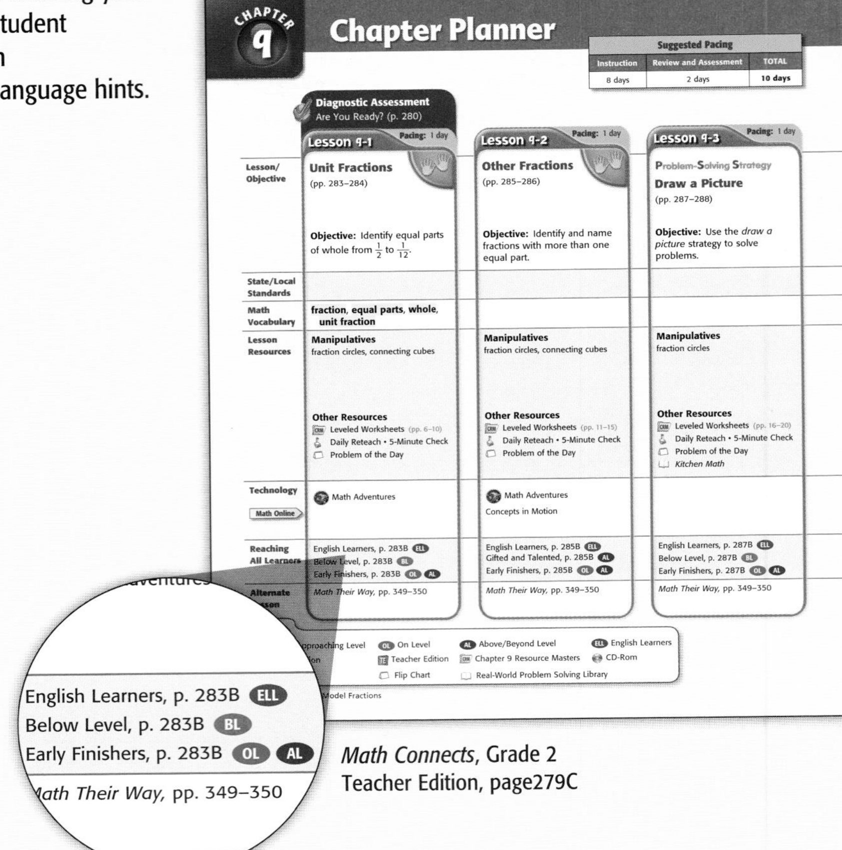

CHAPTER 9 Chapter Planner

Suggested Pacing		
Instruction	Review and Assessment	TOTAL
8 days	2 days	10 days

Diagnostic Assessment
Are You Ready? (p. 280)

	Lesson 9-1 (Pacing: 1 day)	Lesson 9-2 (Pacing: 1 day)	Lesson 9-3 (Pacing: 1 day)
Lesson/Objective	Unit Fractions (pp. 283–284) Objective: Identify equal parts of whole from $\frac{1}{2}$ to $\frac{1}{12}$.	Other Fractions (pp. 285–286) Objective: Identify and name fractions with more than one equal part.	Problem-Solving Strategy Draw a Picture (pp. 287–288) Objective: Use the *draw a picture* strategy to solve problems.
State/Local Standards			
Math Vocabulary	fraction, equal parts, whole, unit fraction		
Lesson Resources	Manipulatives: fraction circles, connecting cubes. Other Resources: Leveled Worksheets (pp. 6–10); Daily Reteach • 5-Minute Check; Problem of the Day	Manipulatives: fraction circles, connecting cubes. Other Resources: Leveled Worksheets (pp. 11–15); Daily Reteach • 5-Minute Check; Problem of the Day	Manipulatives: fraction circles. Other Resources: Leveled Worksheets (pp. 16–20); Daily Reteach • 5-Minute Check; Problem of the Day; *Kitchen Math*
Technology (Math Online)	Math Adventures	Math Adventures; Concepts in Motion	
Reaching All Learners	English Learners, p. 283B ELL; Below Level, p. 283B BL; Early Finishers, p. 283B OL AL	English Learners, p. 285B ELL; Gifted and Talented, p. 285B AL; Early Finishers, p. 285B OL AL	English Learners, p. 287B ELL; Below Level, p. 287B BL; Early Finishers, p. 287B OL AL
Alternate Lesson	*Math Their Way*, pp. 349–350	*Math Their Way*, pp. 349–350	*Math Their Way*, pp. 349–350

Key: Approaching Level; OL On Level; AL Above/Beyond Level; ELL English Learners; Teacher Edition; Chapter 9 Resource Masters; CD-Rom; Flip Chart; Real-World Problem Solving Library

English Learners, p. 283B ELL
Below Level, p. 283B BL
Early Finishers, p. 283B OL AL
Math Their Way, pp. 349–350

Math Connects, Grade 2
Teacher Edition, page279C

Leveled Exercise Sets

The assignments for each lesson are leveled for students.

- BL Below or Approaching Grade Level
- OL On Grade Level
- AL Above or Beyond Grade Level

Leveled Resources

All of the blackline masters and transparencies that accompany the program, as well as all of the Teacher Edition pages, are available on the **TeacherWorks Plus™ CD-ROM.** Resources and assignments are leveled for students who are:

- BL Below or Approaching Grade Level
- OL On Grade Level
- AL Above or Beyond Grade Level
- ELL English Language Learners

Learning Stations

Cross-curricular learning centers offer students guided opportunities to explore chapter concepts as individuals or in small groups. Content areas include:

- Science
- Social Studies
- Reading
- Art
- Health
- Writing
- Music

Learning Station cards are English on one side and Spanish on the other.

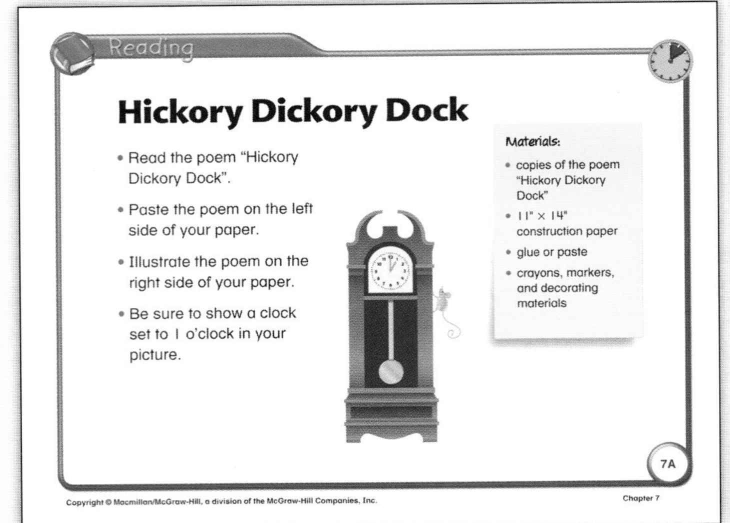

Math Connects, Grade 1
Learning Station Card 7A

ɅAdvanced Learners

ʌcceleration and Enrichment Resources and assignments for tudents who are above level may be used with advanced earners. In particular, the **Enrich Masters** provide students with aluable opportunities for extending your lessons.

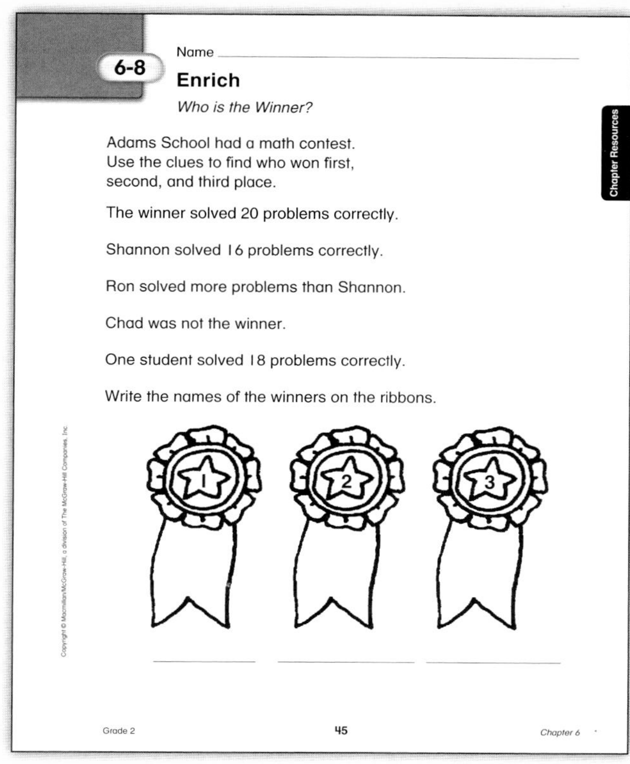

6-8

Name

Enrich

Who is the Winner?

Adams School had a math contest.
Use the clues to find who won first, second, and third place.

The winner solved 20 problems correctly.

Shannon solved 16 problems correctly.

Ron solved more problems than Shannon.

Chad was not the winner.

One student solved 18 problems correctly.

Write the names of the winners on the ribbons.

1 2 3

Copyright © Macmillan/McGraw-Hill, a division of The McGraw-Hill Companies, Inc.

Chapter Resources

Grade 2 45 Chapter 6

Math Connects, Grade 2,
Chapter 6 Resource Masters, page 45

ELL English Language Learners

ʖur authors have identified seven keys for effective instruction vith English language learner students and used them ıroughout the program.

1. Simplify language, not concepts.
2. Activate background knowledge.
3. Teach in multiple modalities.
4. Use core vocabulary and common use verbs.
5. Express mathematical understanding in different ways.
6. Incorporate higher-level problem-solving skills.
7. Provide a mathematics-rich classroom environment.

he English Language Learners Guide provides additional ɹpport for English language learner students that can be used lone or with core instruction in the Student Edition and eacher Edition.

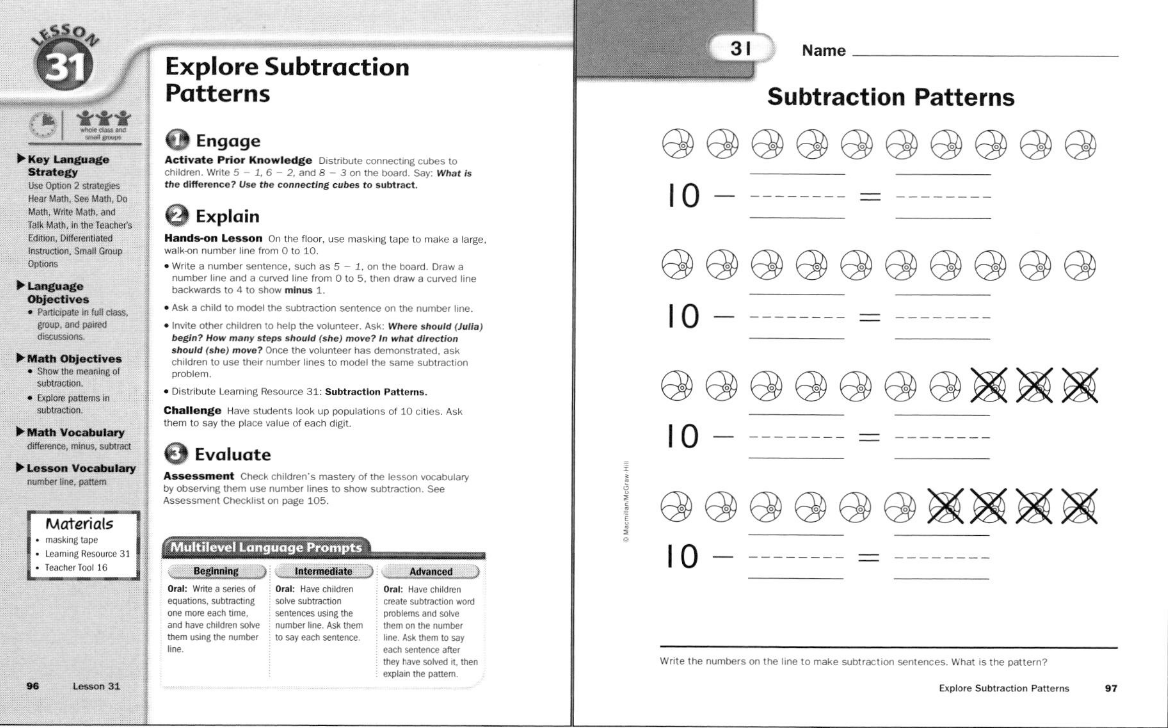

LESSON 31

whole class and small groups

▶ Key Language Strategy
Use Option 2 strategies Hear Math, See Math, Do Math, Write Math, and Talk Math, in the Teacher's Edition, Differentiated Instruction, Small Group Options

▶ Language Objectives
- Participate in full class, group, and paired discussions.

▶ Math Objectives
- Show the meaning of subtraction.
- Explore patterns in subtraction.

▶ Math Vocabulary
difference, minus, subtract

▶ Lesson Vocabulary
number line, pattern

Materials
- masking tape
- Learning Resource 31
- Teacher Tool 16

Explore Subtraction Patterns

1 Engage

Activate Prior Knowledge Distribute connecting cubes to children. Write 5 − 1, 6 − 2, and 8 − 3 on the board. Say: ***What is the difference? Use the connecting cubes to subtract.***

2 Explain

Hands-on Lesson On the floor, use masking tape to make a large, walk-on number line from 0 to 10.
- Write a number sentence, such as 5 − 1, on the board. Draw a number line and a curved line from 0 to 5, then draw a curved line backwards to 4 to show **minus** 1.
- Ask a child to model the subtraction sentence on the number line.
- Invite other children to help the volunteer. Ask: ***Where should (Julia) begin? How many steps should (she) move? In what direction should (she) move?*** Once the volunteer has demonstrated, ask children to use their number lines to model the same subtraction problem.
- Distribute Learning Resource 31: **Subtraction Patterns.**

Challenge Have students look up populations of 10 cities. Ask them to say the place value of each digit.

3 Evaluate

Assessment Check children's mastery of the lesson vocabulary by observing them use number lines to show subtraction. See Assessment Checklist on page 105.

Multilevel Language Prompts

Beginning	Intermediate	Advanced
Oral: Write a series of equations, subtracting one more each time, and have children solve them using the number line.	**Oral:** Have children solve subtraction sentences using the number line. Ask them to say each sentence.	**Oral:** Have children create subtraction word problems and solve them on the number line. Ask them to say each sentence after they have solved it, then explain the pattern.

96 Lesson 31

31 Name

Subtraction Patterns

10 − ______ = ______

10 − ______ = ______

10 − ______ = ______

10 − ______ = ______

© Macmillan/McGraw-Hill

Write the numbers on the line to make subtraction sentences. What is the pattern?

Explore Subtraction Patterns 97

ath Connects, Kindergarten
.L Guide, pages 96–97

Blending Your Instruction

Basal – NSF-Funded – Tier 3 Intervention

Math Connects, IMPACT Mathematics, and ***Math Triumphs*** provide a three-pronged approach to mathematics instruction. This unique combination provides built-in strategies to easily tip the balance of instruction to a more conceptual approach or to a more skills-based approach, depending on the needs of your students.

These programs are horizontally aligned in the following ways.

- Common vocabulary
- Common manipulatives
- Common teacher planning guides
- Common technology
- Common authors
- Common professional development

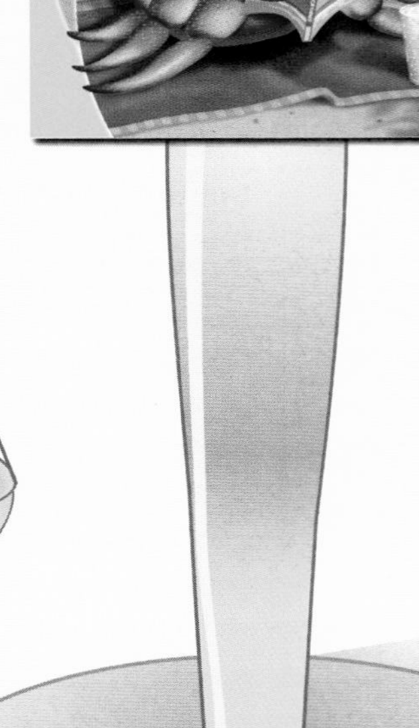

RTI (Response to Intervention)

In the ***Math Connects*** Teacher Editions, the Data-Driven Decision Making chart provides a comprehensive RTI (Response to Intervention) beginning with diagnostic review and continuing with prescriptions at all three RTI tiers.

- **Tier 1** – Leveled exercise sets and leveled resources
- **Tier 2** – Strategic Intervention Guide (1–5), Study Guide and Intervention (6–8)
- **Tier 3** – Intensive Intervention, ***Math Triumphs***

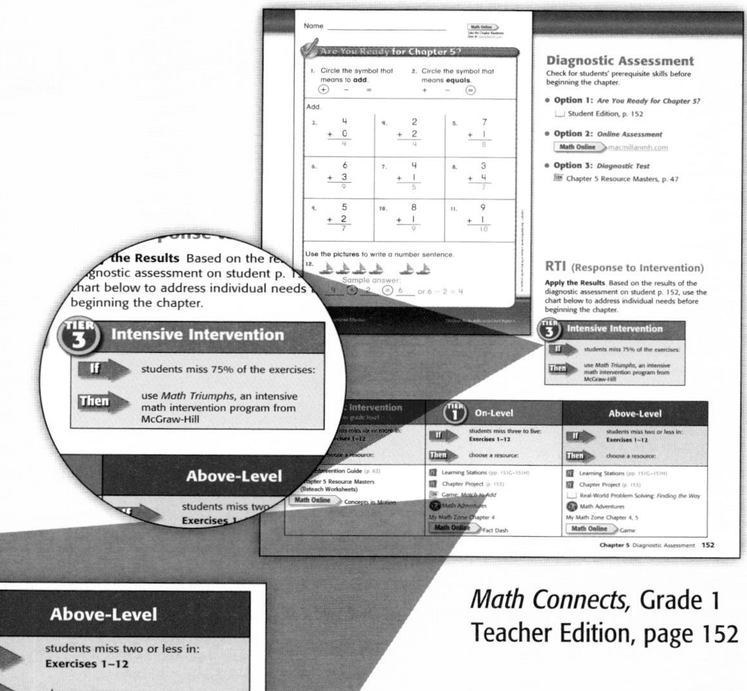

TIER 2 Strategic Intervention below grade level	TIER 1 On-Level	Above-Level
If students miss six or more in: **Exercises 1–12**	**If** students miss three to five: **Exercises 1–12**	**If** students miss two or less in: **Exercises 1–12**
Then choose a resource:	**Then** choose a resource:	**Then** choose a resource:
Strategic Intervention Guide (p. 62) CRM Chapter 5 Resource Masters (Reteach Worksheets) Math Online Concepts in Motion	TE Learning Stations (pp. 151G–151H) TE Chapter Project (p. 153) CRM Game: *Match to Add* Math Adventures My Math Zone Chapter 4 Math Online Fact Dash	TE Learning Stations (pp. 151G–151H) TE Chapter Project (p. 153) Real-World Problem Solving: *Finding the Way* Math Adventures My Math Zone Chapter 4, 5 Math Online Game

Math Connects, Grade 1
Teacher Edition, page 152

The Chapter Planner, also in the Teacher Edition of ***Math Connects,*** references alternative lessons found in ***IMPACT Mathematics.*** These lessons provide opportunities for investigative instruction with hands-on explorations.

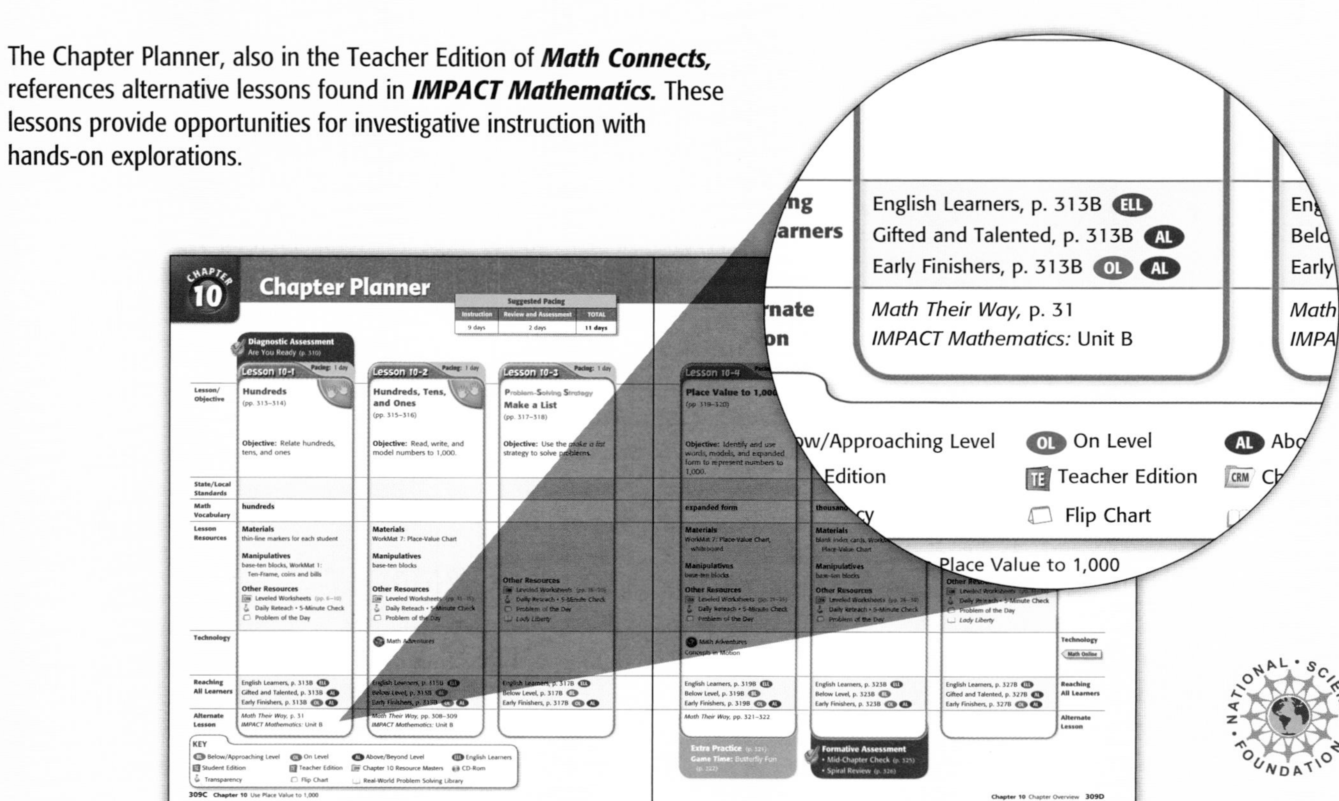

Math Connects, Grade 2
Teacher Edition, pages 309C–309D

Planning for Success

Ease of Use

Math Connects has a strong instructional model that includes differentiated instructional options, reteaching, reinforcement, and extension options, Teacher Tips to help address various learners, Pre-AP/Advanced items, and assessment linked with instruction.

Convenient Lesson Planning at Your Fingertips

The **Chapter Overview** helps you plan your instruction by showing the objectives to be covered, suggested pacing, and coverage of Focal Points.

TeacherWorks™ Plus

This electronic lesson planner contains multi-purpose management software including the Teacher Edition pages, program blackline masters, and daily calendars that make planning a snap.

CHAPTER 4

Chapter Overview

Chapter-at-a-Glance

Lesson	Math Objective	State/Local Standards
4-1 **Numbers 6 and 7** (pp. 101–102)	Name, recognize, and count the numerals 6 and 7 using concrete objects and illustrations.	
4-2 **Number 8** (pp. 103–104)	Name, recognize, and count the numeral 8 using concrete objects and illustrations.	
4-3 **Read and Write 6, 7, and 8** (pp. 105–106)	Recognize and write the numerals 6, 7, and 8.	
4-4 **Numbers 9 and 10** (pp. 109–110)	Name, recognize, and count the numerals 9 and 10 using concrete objects and illustrations.	
4-5 **Read and Write 9 and 10** (pp. 111–112)	Recognize and write the numerals 9 and 10.	
4-6 **Problem-Solving Strategy: Draw a Picture** (pp. 113–114)	Count, recognize, represent, and name numerals 6 through 10 using concrete objects and illustrations.	
4-7 **Compare Numbers to 10** (pp. 115–116)	Use one-to-one correspondence and counting to compare sets and determine which has more than, less than, or whether the sets are the same/equal.	
4-8 **Order Numbers to 10** (pp. 117–118)	Order numbers from 1 to 10 in sequence using illustrations.	
4-9 **Ordinal Numbers** (pp. 119–120)	Use ordinal numbers to describe the position of an object in a row.	

Use Numbers to 10

BIG Idea Understanding numbers to 10 and their relative values and magnitudes is of critical importance. The numbers to 10 serve as the first layer of the foundation for numeration, place value, and whole number operations.

- Numbers from six to 10 are represented concretely, pictorially, and symbolically.
- Students' understanding of each number and its value is applied as they compose, compare and order numbers.

Algebra Students prepare for algebra by relating quantities and sets to written numbers. (Lesson 4-3)

Geometry Students are introduced to basic shapes. (Lesson 4-1)

Focal Points and Connections
See page iv for key.

GK-FP1 *Number and Operations:* **Representing, comparing, and ordering whole numbers and joining and separating sets**

Children use numbers, including written numerals, to represent quantities and to solve quantitative problems, such as counting objects in a set, creating a set with a given number of objects, comparing and ordering sets or numerals by using both cardinal and ordinal meanings, and modeling simple joining and separating with objects. They choose, combine, strategies for answering quantitat quickly recognizing the numb and producing sets of giver combined sets, and cour

97A **Chapter 4** Use Numbers to 10

Math Connects, Kindergarten
Teacher Edition, page 97A

Use Numbers to 10

Skills Trace
Vertical Alignment

Pre-Kindergarten
In Pre-K, students learned to:
- Count by ones to 10
- Arrange sets of concrete objects in one-to-one correspondence.
- Name "how many" are in a set of up to three (or more) objects without counting (e.g., recognizing two or three crayons in a box).

Kindergarten
During this chapter, students learn to:
- Name, recognize, and count the quantities 9 and 10.
- Represent and order a number of objects.

After this chapter, students will learn to:
- Collect information about objects in their environment.
- Name, recognize, and count a number of objects up to 30.

First Grade
In first grade, students will learn to:
- Model addition.
- Represent equivalent forms of the same number.
- Show the meaning of addition and subtraction.
- Count, read, and write whole numbers to 100.

Back-Mapping and Vertical Alignment McGraw-Hill's *Math Connects* program was conceived and developed with the final results in mind: student success in Algebra 1 and beyond. The authors, using the **NCTM Focal Points and Focal Connections** as their guide, developed this brand new series by back-mapping from Algebra 1 concepts, and vertically aligning the topics so that they build upon prior skills and concepts and serve as a foundation for future topics.

Math Vocabulary

The following math vocabulary words for Chapter 4 are listed in the glossary of the ***Student Edition***. You can find interactive definitions in 13 languages in the ***eGlossary*** at macmillanmh.com

eight (p. 103) 8

ordinal numbers (p. 119)

nine (p. 109) 9

seven (p. 101) 7

six (p. 101) 6

ten (p. 109) 10

Chapter 4 Chapter Overview **97B**

Math Connects, Kindergarten
Teacher Edition, page 97B

Vertical Alignment Skills Trace

Topics are presented to build upon prior grade level skills and concepts and to serve as a foundation for future topics.

What the Research Says

Citations from research help to validate ***Math Connects*** program. An additional Research Bibliography can be found in the **Teacher Reference Handbook.**

Professional Development

Targeted professional development has been articulated throughout the program. Actual classroom video clips are especially helpful when planning lessons and differentiating instruction. See page T32 for more information.

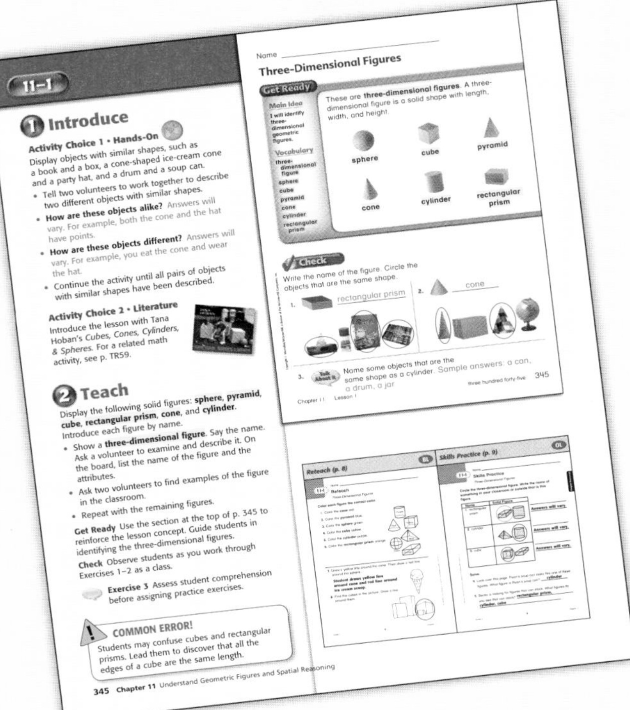

11-1

1 Introduce

Activity Choice 1 • Hands-On
Display objects with similar shapes, such as a book and a box, a cone-shaped ice-cream cone and a party hat, and a drum and a soup can.

- Tell two volunteers to work together to describe two different objects with similar shapes.
- **How are these objects alike?** Answers will vary. For example, both the cone and the hat have points.
- **How are these objects different?** Answers will vary. For example, you eat the cone and wear the hat.
- Continue the activity until all pairs of objects with similar shapes have been described.

Activity Choice 2 • Literature
Introduce the lesson with Tana Hoban's *Cubes, Cones, Cylinders, & Spheres*. For a related math activity, see p. TR59.

2 Teach
Display the following solid figures: **sphere, pyramid, cube, rectangular prism, cone,** and **cylinder**. Introduce each figure by name.

- Show a **three-dimensional figure**. Say the name. Ask a volunteer to examine and describe it. On the board, list the name of the figure and the attributes.
- Ask two volunteers to find examples of the figure in the classroom.
- Repeat with the remaining figures.

Get Ready Use the section at the top of p. 345 to reinforce the lesson concept. Guide students in identifying the three-dimensional figures.

Check Observe students as you work through Exercises 1–2 as a class.

Exercise 3 Assess student comprehension before assigning practice exercises.

COMMON ERROR!
Students may confuse cubes and rectangular prisms. Lead them to discover that all the edges of a cube are the same length.

345 Chapter 11 Understand Geometric Figures and Spatial Reasoning

Name

Three-Dimensional Figures

Get Ready

Main Idea
I will identify three-dimensional geometric figures.

Vocabulary
three-dimensional figure, sphere, cube, pyramid, cone, cylinder, rectangular prism

These are **three-dimensional figures**. A three-dimensional figure is a solid shape with length, width, and height.

sphere, cube, pyramid, cone, cylinder, rectangular prism

Check
Write the name of the figure. Circle the objects that are the same shape.

1. rectangular prism
2. cone
3. Name some objects that are the same shape as a cylinder. Sample answers: a can, a drum, a jar

Chapter 11 Lesson 1 three hundred forty-five 345

Reteach (p. 8)

Skills Practice (p. 9)

Math Connects, Grade 2
Teacher Edition, page 345

Four-Step Teaching Plan

Organizes your instruction as you **Focus** and **Teach** and help your students **Practice** and **Assess** what they've learned.

Scaffolding Questions

Each lesson contains **Scaffolding Questions** for you to use to help students investigate and understand the main ideas of the lesson.

Vertical Alignment

Vertical Alignment at the beginning of each chapter shows the objectives that lead into and follow the current lesson's content for a coherent PreK–12 scope and sequence.

Differentiated Practice

Because most classrooms include students at a wide range of ability levels, **Differentiated Practice** allows you to customize your assignments.

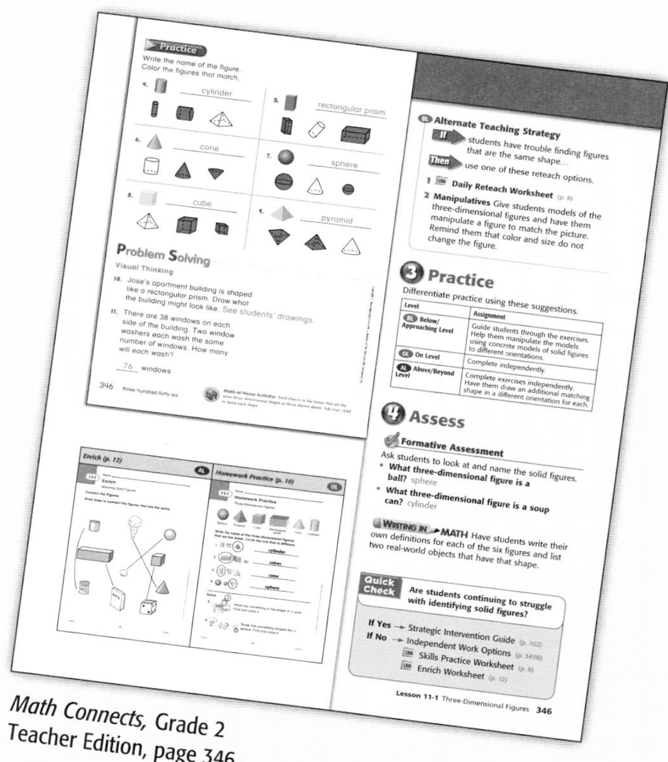

Practice
Write the name of the figure. Color the figures that match.

4. cylinder
5. rectangular prism
6. cone
7. sphere
8. cube
9. pyramid

Problem Solving
Visual Thinking

10. Jose's apartment building is shaped like a rectangular prism. Draw what the building might look like. See students' drawings.
11. There are 38 windows on each side of the building. Two window washers each wash the same number of windows. How many will each wash? 76 windows

346 three hundred forty-six

Alternate Teaching Strategy
If students have trouble finding figures that are the same shape...
Then use one of these reteach options.
1 Daily Reteach Worksheet (p. 8)
2 **Manipulatives** Give students models of the three-dimensional figures and have them manipulate a figure to match the picture. Remind them that color and size do not change the figure.

3 Practice
Differentiate practice using these suggestions.

Level	Assignment
BL Below/Approaching Level	Guide students through the exercises. Help them manipulate the models using concrete models of solid figures to different orientations.
OL On Level	Complete independently.
AL Above/Beyond Level	Complete exercises independently. Have them draw an additional matching shape in a different orientation for each.

4 Assess

Formative Assessment
Ask students to look at and name the solid figures.
- **What three-dimensional figure is a ball?** sphere
- **What three-dimensional figure is a soup can?** cylinder

WRITING IN MATH Have students write their own definitions for each of the six figures and list two real-world objects that have that shape.

Quick Check Are students continuing to struggle with identifying solid figures?
If Yes → Strategic Intervention Guide (p. 102)
If No → Independent Work Options (p. 345B)
Skills Practice Worksheet (p. 9)
Enrich Worksheet (p. 12)

Lesson 11-1 Three-Dimensional Figures 346

Enrich (p. 12)

Homework Practice (p. 10)

Math Connects, Grade 2
Teacher Edition, page 346

Planning for Success
State-of-the-Art Technology

Math Connects provides fully integrated technology resources for teachers, students, and parents.

For Teachers

 **TeacherWorks™ Plus** is your all-in-one planner and resource center.

- entire Teacher Edition
- all print ancillaries
- electronic lesson planner

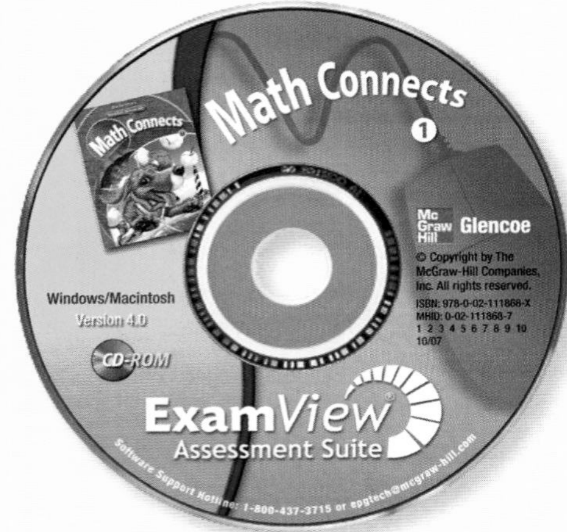

 **ExamView® Assessment Suite** allows teachers to create and customize their own assessment and assignments.

New features:

- correlated to state standards
- online content update
- one- or two-column formatting

Advance TRACKER Learner Management System helps you track progress and differentiate your instruction.

- formative assessments aligned to standards
- links to intervention help

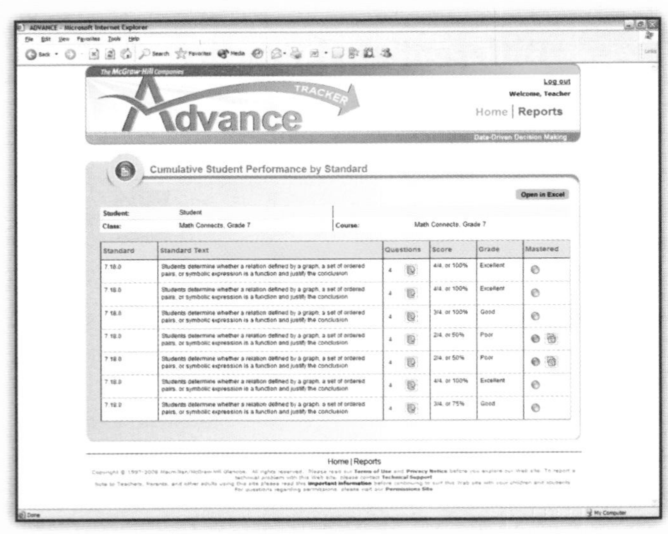

Other Technology: My Math Zone (CD-ROM)
Math Songs (English and Spanish, CD-ROM)

For Students

 **StudentWorks™ Plus** is your students' backpack solution.

- entire Student Edition
- all student worksheets
- links to **Math Online**

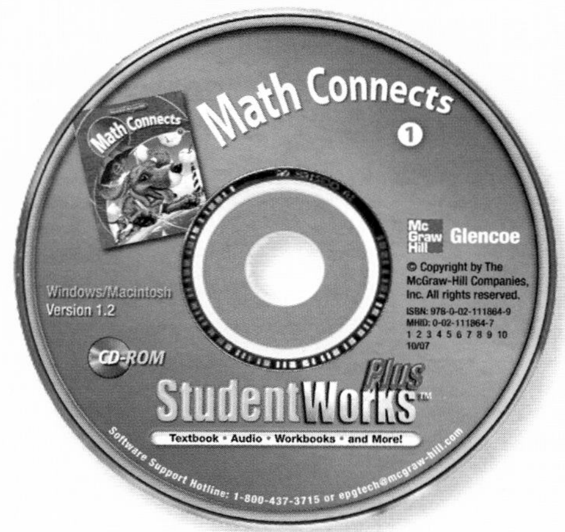

Math Online provides a wealth of resources – convenient for students and parents!

- Self-Check Quizzes
- Personal Tutor
- Concepts in Motion
- Math Adventures with Dot and Ray
- eGlossary (14 languages)
- Math Tool Chest
- And much, much more!

Math Online *Math Connect's* **eBook** is easy to use, easy to read, and packed with features.

- links to online study tools and resources right from the page
- includes audio

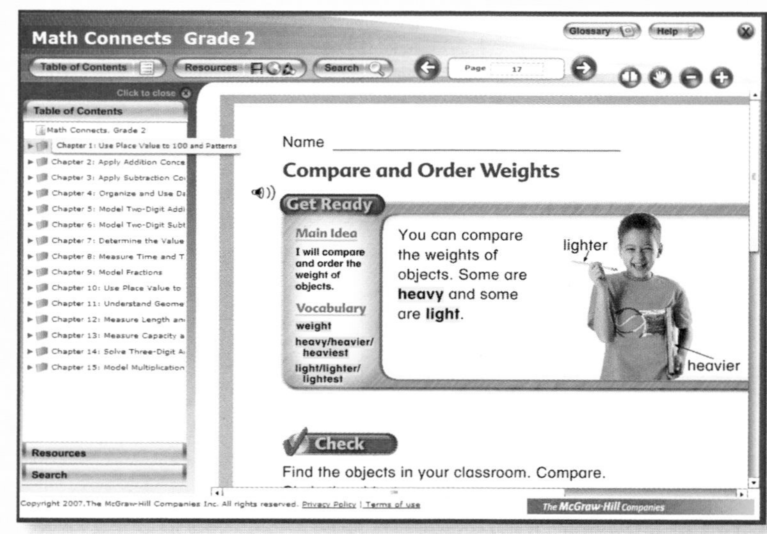

Other Technology: Math Adventures with Dot and Ray (CD-ROM)
Math Tool Chest (CD-ROM)

PreK-12 Data-Driven Professional Development

McGraw-Hill Professional Development (MHPD) provides a comprehensive plan for mathematics that is fully aligned and articulated with ***Math Connects K–8*** and the ***Glencoe Mathematics*** high school series.

Professional Development Needs	Online Courses	DVD Workshops	Video Library	Teach-Use-Succeed	Ready-Access Math
Has immediate classroom application	✓	✓	✓	✓	✓
Builds content knowledge	✓	✓			✓
Promotes best teaching practices		✓	✓		
Supports new and experienced teachers	✓	✓	✓	✓	✓
Allows customization of courses	✓	✓			✓
Can be self-paced	✓	✓		✓	✓
Adaptable for various timeframes	✓	✓	✓	✓	✓
Is grade-level specific			✓	✓	✓
Promotes a learning community	✓	✓			✓
Provides vertically-aligned content	✓	✓	✓		✓
Helps with RTI (Response to Intervention), Tiers 1–3	✓	✓	✓		✓

Use students' mathematics achievement data to help develop a targeted Professional Development Plan.

Accredited Online Courses

(available for purchase)

- Watch video clips of math classrooms Complete interactive exercises Develop electronic portfolios.
- Complete each 3- to 5-hour online module one segment at a time.
- University credit (additional tuition charge)

DVD Workshops

- Watch video clips of classroom mathematics lessons and commentaries by leading educators.
- Complete lessons and activities.

MHPD Online

- Access this online Professional Development resource for K–12 educators.
- Link to relevant Web sites.
- Download grade-level student resources.

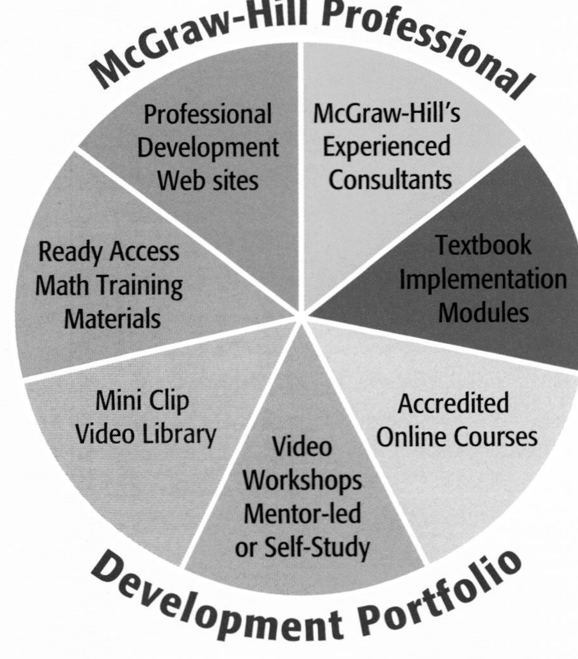

Video Library — Math Online

- Access hundreds of K–12 video clips.
- See clips that illustrate mathematics content and instructional strategies.
- Watch demonstrations or commentaries by math specialists

Teach-Use-Succeed Textbook Implementation Modules

- Watch an experienced teacher demonstrate the *Math Connects* K–8 Student Editions, Teacher Editions, and program ancillaries
- Online or DVD

Ready-Access Math, Personalized Professional Development

- Access training materials for nearly 300 mathematics professional development lessons.
- Create a customized sequence of professional development sessions.
- Deliver 45–60 minute after-school professional development sessions.

Teacher Edition

Macmillan McGraw-Hill

Math Connects

K

Lemonade 5¢

BEACH VACATIONS

Table of Contents

Volume 1

Authors

Altieri • Balka • Day • Gonsalves • Grace • Krulik
Malloy • Molix-Bailey • Moseley • Mowry • Myren
Price • Reynosa • Santa Cruz • Silbey • Vielhaber

Macmillan/McGraw-Hill

Contents

Start Smart

Focal Points and Connections

GK-FP4C

Compare and Sort Objects

Contents

GK-FP1

Chapter 2 Use Numbers 0 to 5

Contents

Focal Points and Connections

GK-FP6C

Describe Position and Patterns

Contents

GK-FP1

Chapter 4 Use Numbers to 10

Contents

Focal Points and Connections

GK-FP4C

Chapter 5 Construct and Use Graphs

Contents

GK-FP1

Chapter 6 Use Numbers to 20

Focal Points and Connections

GK-FP3

Compare Measurements

Contents

GK-FP1

Chapter 8 Use Numbers Beyond 20

GK-FP3

Chapter 9 Use Time

Contents

GK-FP2

Chapter 10 Describe Geometric Figures

Contents

Focal Points and Connections

GK-FP1

Chapter 11 Model Addition

Contents

Focal Points and Connections
GK-FP1

Chapter 12 Model Subtraction

Looking Ahead

Problem-Solving Projects

Contents

Student Handbook

Lesson Planner

Objective

Analyze and solve problems using pictures.

Review Vocabulary

above, below, next to

Materials: pattern blocks

Begin the year with the lessons found in the **Start Smart** section. These lessons help students get ready for the coming year by reviewing and reinforcing skills and concepts they learned in prekindergarten. The Start Smart lessons also prepare students for skills and concepts they will need for success in kindergarten.

Initial Assessment

Inventory/Placement Test At the beginning of the year, administer the Inventory/Placement Test found in the Chapter 1 Resource Masters to identify what concepts to review before beginning Chapter 1.

CRM **Chapter 1 Resource Masters**
Inventory/Placement Test (p. 35)

End-of-Year Assessment

At the end of the year, use the End-of-Year Test to assess student comprehension of the skills and concepts presented in kindergarten.

CRM **Chapter 12 Resource Masters**
End-of-Year Test (p. 64)

Activate Prior Knowledge

Discuss the photograph and read *Did You Know?* on Student Edition page 2.

- Lead a discussion about the Spotted Salamander in the photograph.
- **How many colors are on the Spotted Salamander?** two colors **What are the colors?** yellow and brown
- **Describe the salamander's skin.** Sample answer: a smooth body
- **Have you ever seen a Spotted Salamander? If so, where?** Sample answer: Yes, on a tree.

Using student page 2.

- Identify the plants and animals in the picture: Spotted salamander, palmetto tree, Carolina Wren, and an Eastern Tiger Swallowtail.
- Have students use the picture to locate each object.
- Review the terms **above**, **below**, and **next to**. Have students take turns demonstrating each word.
- Ask students to circle the animal that is above the palmetto tree.
- Have students underline the animal that is next to the palmetto tree.
- Tell students to put an X on the animal that is below the palmetto tree.

Start Smart
Start Smart
Let's Review!

Children Celebrating Their Country
Copyright © Macmillan/McGraw-Hill, a division of The McGraw-Hill Companies, Inc.

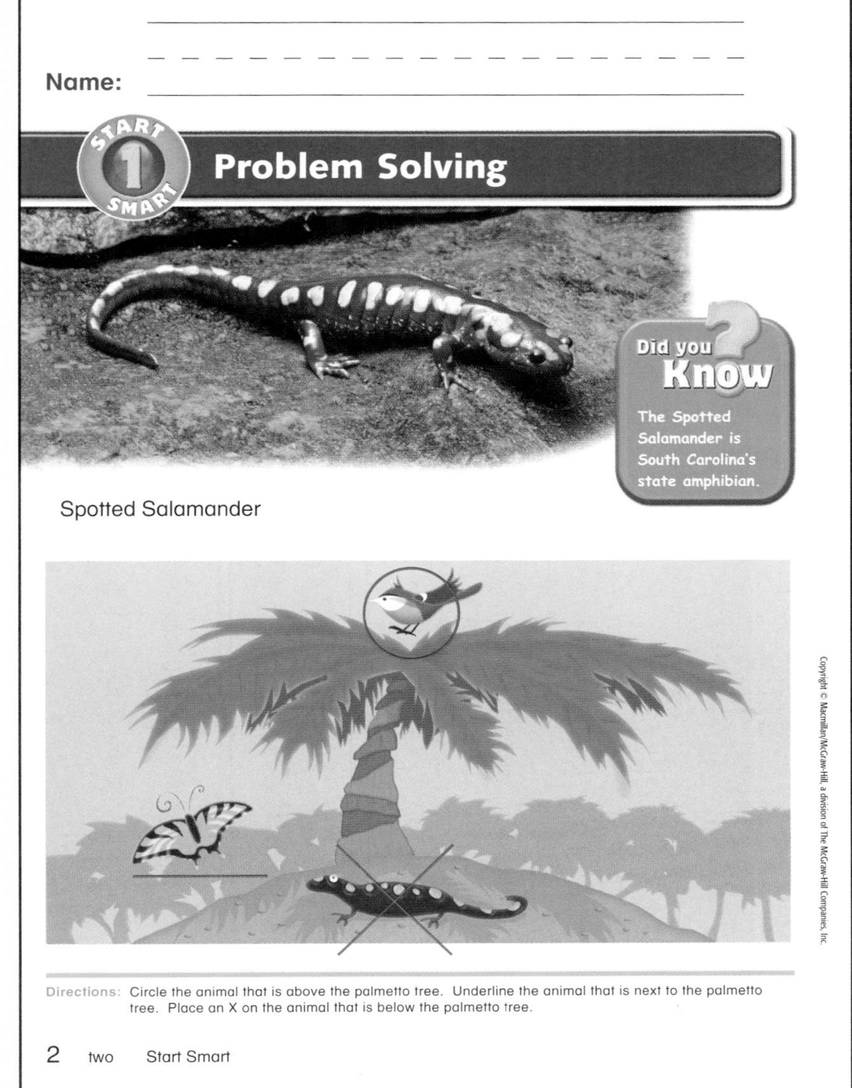
Name:
START 1 SMART
Problem Solving
Did you Know
The Spotted Salamander is South Carolina's state amphibian.
Spotted Salamander
Directions: Circle the animal that is above the palmetto tree. Underline the animal that is next to the palmetto tree. Place an X on the animal that is below the palmetto tree.
2 two Start Smart
Copyright © Macmillan/McGraw-Hill, a division of The McGraw-Hill Companies, Inc.

Assess and Close

Use Pattern Blocks Divide students into small groups and give them a handful of blocks.

- Have students work together to follow your directions using position words to make a 3 × 3 grid of pattern blocks.

More *FUN* Facts

- Spotted Salamanders do not develop spots until they mature into adulthood.
- The palmetto is South Carolina's state tree. It also appears on the South Carolina state seal and state flag.
- A Carolina wren is South Carolina's state bird. A male wren reportedly sings around 3,000 times in one day.
- The Eastern Tiger Swallowtail is South Carolina's state butterfly. It has an organ behind its head that omits a foul-smelling odor which protects it from predators.

Lesson Planner

Objectives

Match sets of objects using one-to-one correspondence.

Review Vocabulary

more than, less than, same number

Materials: string, construction paper, crayons, baskets

Manipulatives: connecting cubes, pattern blocks, attribute buttons

Activate Prior Knowledge

Discuss the photograph and read *Did You Know?* on Student Edition page 3.

- Lead a class discussion about the monarch butterfly.
- **What do you notice about the butterfly?** Sample answer: Each side of the butterfly is the same.
- **What other objects have sides that are the same?** people, windows, figures (triangle, square)

Using student page 3.

- Show students two baskets with three attribute buttons in each basket. Count the buttons in the first and second baskets as a class.
- **Is there the same number of buttons in each basket?** yes
- Place the buttons from each basket side by side to show the same or equal number of buttons. String a piece of yarn between buttons in each group to show a one-to-one correspondence. There will be a match for every button.
- **If I put one more button in one of the baskets, would there be the same number of buttons in each basket?** no
- Line the buttons up again and show a one-to-one correspondence with string. One group of buttons will have **more than** the other group. The group with more buttons will not have a match for every button.
- **If I take a button out of the basket, will there be the same number of buttons in each basket?** no **Which basket of buttons has less than the other basket?** the basket from which a button was taken
- Line the buttons up again and show a one-to-one correspondence with string. The group with more buttons will not have a match for every button.
- Direct students to p. 3. Guide students in drawing a line to match each butterfly to a flower. Have students count each butterfly. Then count each flower.
- **Is there the same number of butterflies and flowers?** no

Using student page 4.

- Review with students the concept of matching the same or equal groups of items.
- Show students three connecting cubes. Invite a volunteer to match the number of connecting cubes with the same number of pattern blocks.
- Continue until students are able to match groups.
- Ask students to count each group of insects. Have students draw a line from each group of insects to the corresponding number of flowers.

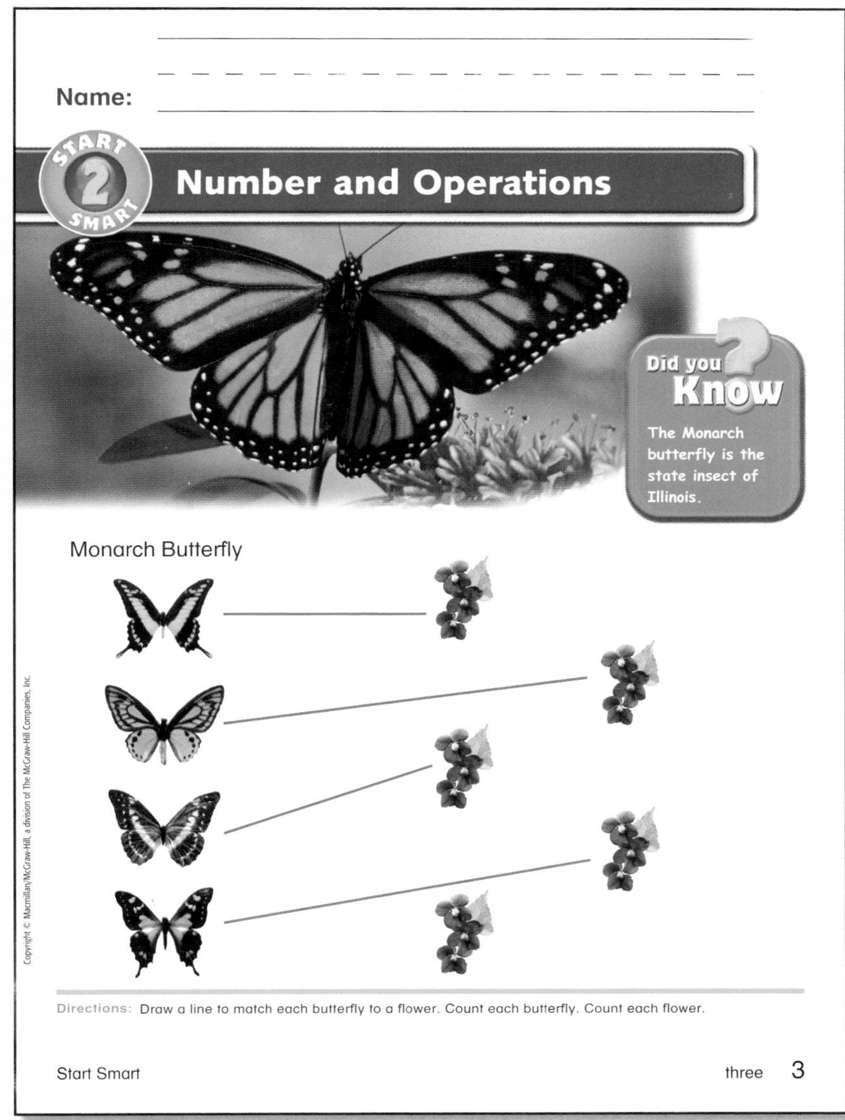

Name:
Number and Operations
Did you Know
The Monarch butterfly is the state insect of Illinois.
Monarch Butterfly
Directions: Draw a line to match each butterfly to a flower. Count each butterfly. Count each flower.
Start Smart
three 3

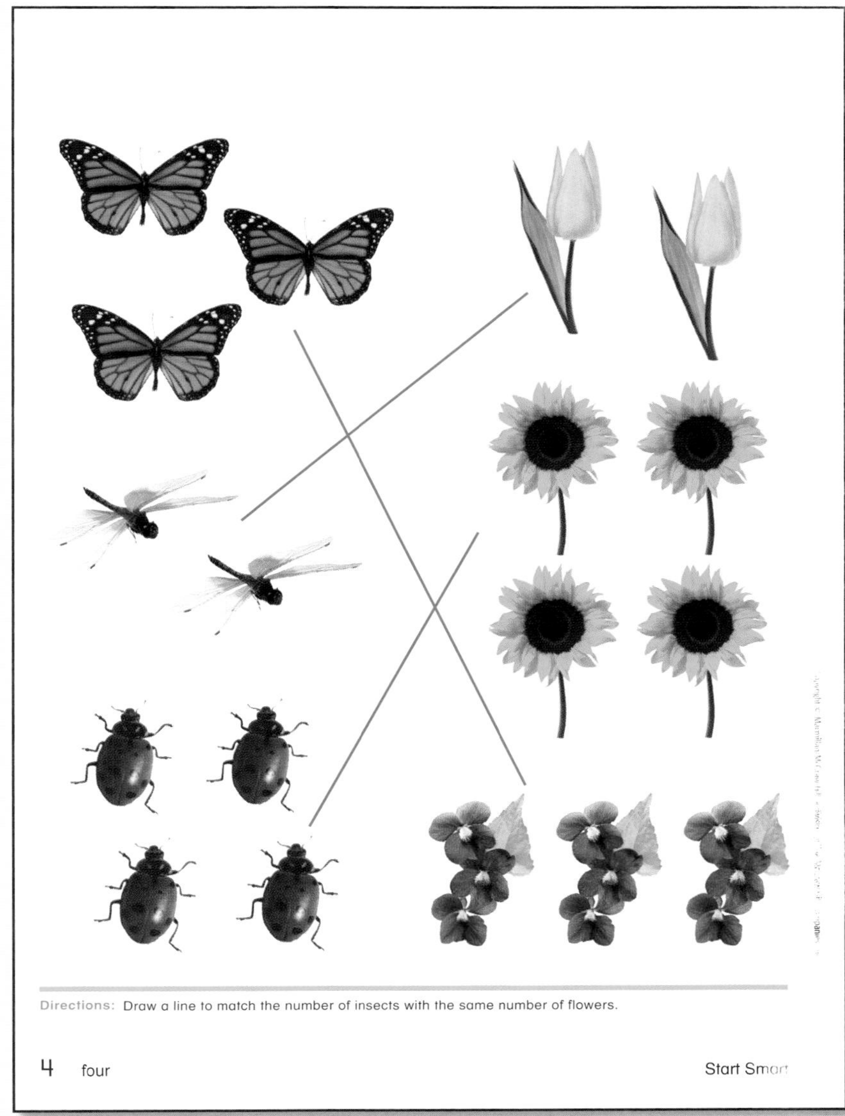

Directions: Draw a line to match the number of insects with the same number of flowers.
4 four
Start Smart

Assess and Close

Make Equal Groups Have students practice matching groups of connecting cubes.

- Give each student a handful of connecting cubes.
- Put together a stack of three connecting cubes.
- Ask students to make a stack of cubes to match yours.
- Continue this activity several times, assessing students' understanding of the concept.
- If time permits, have students fold a piece of construction paper in half and draw and color two matching groups of his or her favorite animal.

More *FUN* Facts

- The monarch butterfly became the Illinois state insect in 1975 after a third grade class had suggested it in 1974.
- Monarch butterflies are different than other butterflies. They do not hibernate, or sleep during the winter. Monarch butterflies fly to a different place when the seasons change.
- The life cycle of a monarch includes these four stages: egg, caterpillar (yellow, black, and white striped), chrysalis, and butterfly.
- The transformation takes about a month to complete.

Lesson Planner

Objective

Identify various patterns.

Review Vocabulary

pattern

Materials: crayons
Manipulatives: two-colored counters, connecting cubes

Activate Prior Knowledge

Discuss the photograph and read *Did You Know?* on Student Edition page 5.

- Ask students if anyone has played miniature golf. If so, have them tell about their experiences.
- If no one has played miniature golf, explain what miniature golf is.
- **What types of objects do you use to play miniature golf?** putter, golf balls
- **Do you play miniature golf inside, outside, or both?** Sample answer: both

Using student page 5.

- Explain to students that they will be identifying a pattern.
- Review with students the meaning of a pattern.
- **What is the pattern in problem 1?** Sample answer: an AB pattern using pink, green, pink, green.
- Have students copy the pattern underneath using crayons.

Using student page 6.

- Review different clapping, word, and pattern block patterns with students until they are able to identify various patterns.
- Have students identify the patterns in problems 3-5.
- Have students copy each pattern underneath using crayons.

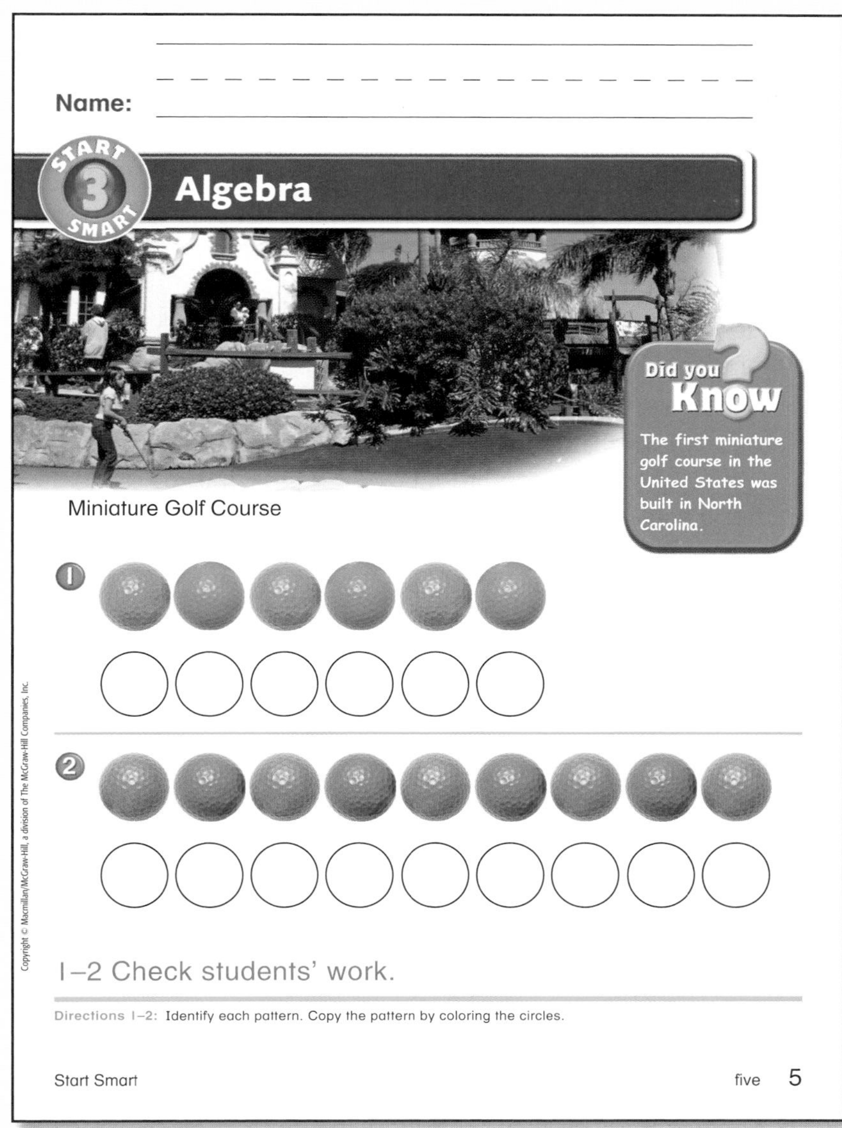

Name:
START 3 SMART
Algebra
Did you Know
The first miniature golf course in the United States was built in North Carolina.
Miniature Golf Course
1
2
1–2 Check students' work.
Directions 1–2: Identify each pattern. Copy the pattern by coloring the circles.
Start Smart
five 5

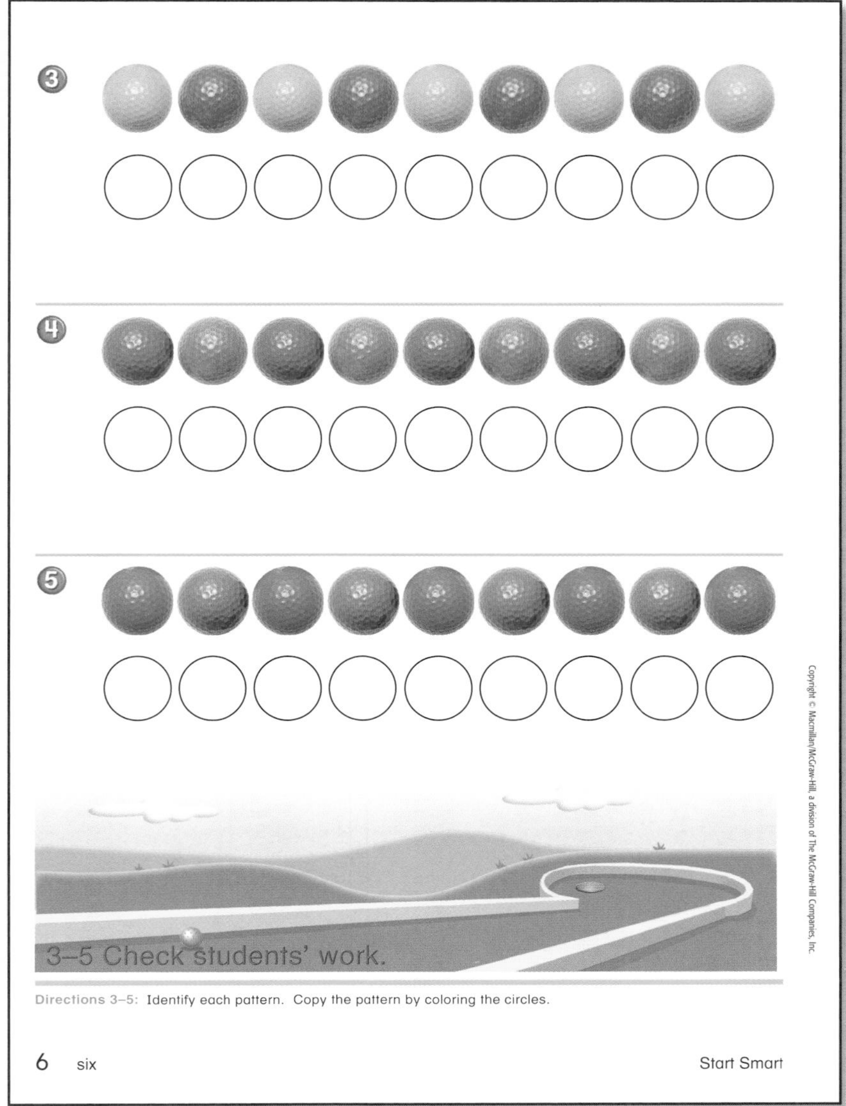

3
4
5
3–5 Check students' work.
Directions 3–5: Identify each pattern. Copy the pattern by coloring the circles.
6 six
Start Smart

Assess and Close

Connecting Cube Patterns Divide students into pairs.

- Give each pair a bag of connecting cubes.
- Have one student create a pattern using the connecting cubes. Make sure the pattern is repeated at least three times.
- Have the partner identify the pattern unit and copy the pattern on a piece of paper using crayons.
- Then have each pair of students switch roles and repeat the activity.

More *FUN* Facts

- In 1916, James Barber built the first miniature golf course in the United States in a garden at his residence in Pinehurst, North Carolina.
- The first golf ball was made out of wood.
- The average golf ball has 336 dimples.
- The first miniature golf course in the world was built in Scotland in 1867.

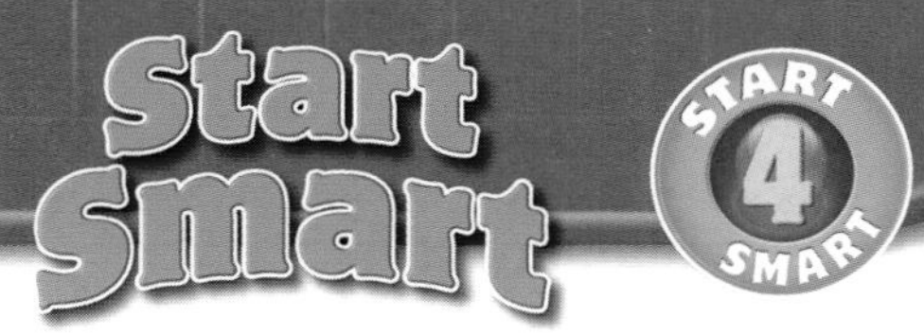

Lesson Planner

Objectives

Compare objects according to size; compare two objects according to length.

Review Vocabulary

longer, shorter

Materials: classroom objects, modeling clay

Activate Prior Knowledge

Discuss the introduction and read *Did You Know?* on Student Edition page 7.

- Lead a discussion about a tug-of-war match.
- Ask students if they have ever participated in a tug-of-war match. If there are no students who have participated, explain the specifics of a tug-of-war match.
- Discuss with students tips on how to safely participate in a tug-of-war match. Such as let students know that it is not safe to wrap the rope around their hands. Inform students that if a student falls down then they need to stop the match immediately.
- Ask students if they have ever played tug-of-war with their cat or dog.
- Have students look at the photo at the top of the page. **Which group do you think will win the tug-of-war match? Why?** Sample answer: the left side because they look older
- Have students point to the group of students that are on the left side of the rope and the group on the right side of the rope. Ask if the number of students on the left side of the rope have more, less, or the same number of students as the right side. Sample answer: the same number of students
- Have students look around the room and fill in these sentence frames with different objects: A ___ is larger than a ___. A ___ is smaller than a ___. Sample answers: book, eraser; paper clip, ruler

Using student page 7.

- Ask students to look at the length of each rope. Have students point to the rope that is longer in Exercise 1.
- Have students circle the longer rope.
- Repeat for Exercise 2.

Using student page 8.

- Review with the students the terms *longer and shorter,* using objects in the room.
- **Name an object that is longer than a crayon?** Sample answer: a pencil
- **Name an object that is shorter than a book?** Sample answer: an eraser
- **Can you find two objects in the classroom that are the same size?** Sample answer: two crayons
- Have students compare pairs of objects in the picture. Have students circle the object that is longer, and place an X by the object that is shorter.

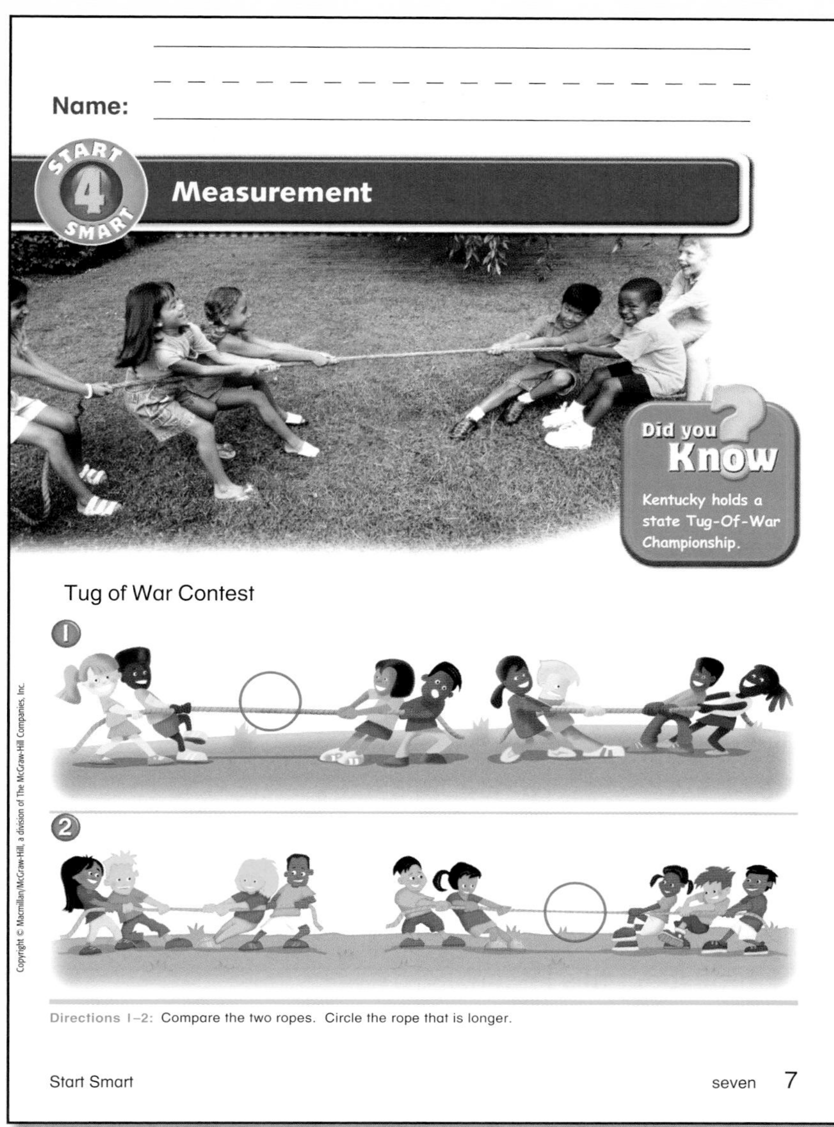

Name:
START 4 SMART
Measurement
Did you Know
Kentucky holds a state Tug-Of-War Championship.
Tug of War Contest
1
2
Directions 1–2: Compare the two ropes. Circle the rope that is longer.
Start Smart
seven 7
Copyright © Macmillan/McGraw-Hill, a division of The McGraw-Hill Companies, Inc.

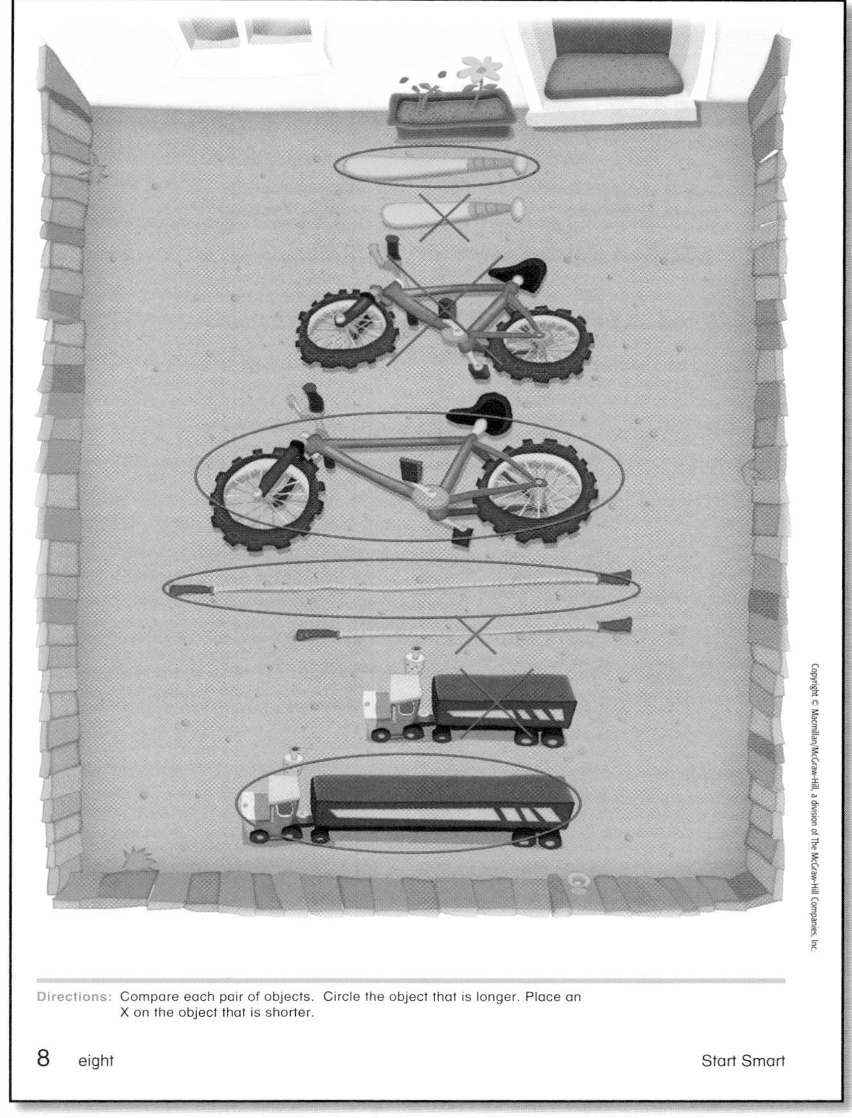

Directions: Compare each pair of objects. Circle the object that is longer. Place an X on the object that is shorter.
8 eight
Start Smart
Copyright © Macmillan/McGraw-Hill, a division of The McGraw-Hill Companies, Inc.

Assess and Close

Model Size Have students work with a partner. Give each pair modeling clay.

- Ask each student to make a clay snake.
- Have partners work together to decide which is longer and which is shorter.
- Walk around the room to be sure each student is using the correct vocabulary to describe the clay snakes.

More *FUN* Facts

- Kentucky's State Tug-of-War Championship is held every July in Fordsville, Kentucky.
- Each team is made up of eight members and teams are placed in weight classes to compete.
- In 1900, tug of war was a part of the Olympic Games.
- Many countries have tug-of-war clubs where men and women participate.

Lesson Planner

Objectives

Identify a circle, a square, and a triangle.

Review Vocabulary

circle, triangle, square

Materials: crayons; the book *The Shape of Things* by Dayle Ann Dodds, or another book about figures
Manipulatives: pattern blocks

Activate Prior Knowledge

Discuss the photograph and read *Did You Know?* on Student Edition page 9.

- Lead a class discussion about the kite contest.
- **What figures are the kites?** Sample answer: triangular
- **Have you flown a kite? What did your kite look like?** Sample answers: Yes; my kite was shaped like a box and had square-shaped sides.
- **Where would you fly a kite?** Sample answer: at a park

Using student page 9.

- **Why is the beach a good place to fly a kite?** It is windy, there are no trees, there is room to run with your kite. **How many sides does a triangle have?** three
- **What do you notice about the sides of a square?** They are all the same size.
- **Does a circle have any sides?** No
- Review the names of colors and figures with students to assess their ability to identify them.
- Some students may need to refer to the board or posters showing examples of the different colors and figures throughout this lesson.
- Have students trace and finish coloring each figure.
- Have students color each kite the same color as the figure it matches.

Using student page 10.

- Have students use green, blue, and purple crayons to color the figures that make up the kite. Have students color each circle green, each square blue, and each triangle purple.
- Ask students to draw their own kite below the kite on the page using circles, triangles, and squares. Have students share their drawings with the class.

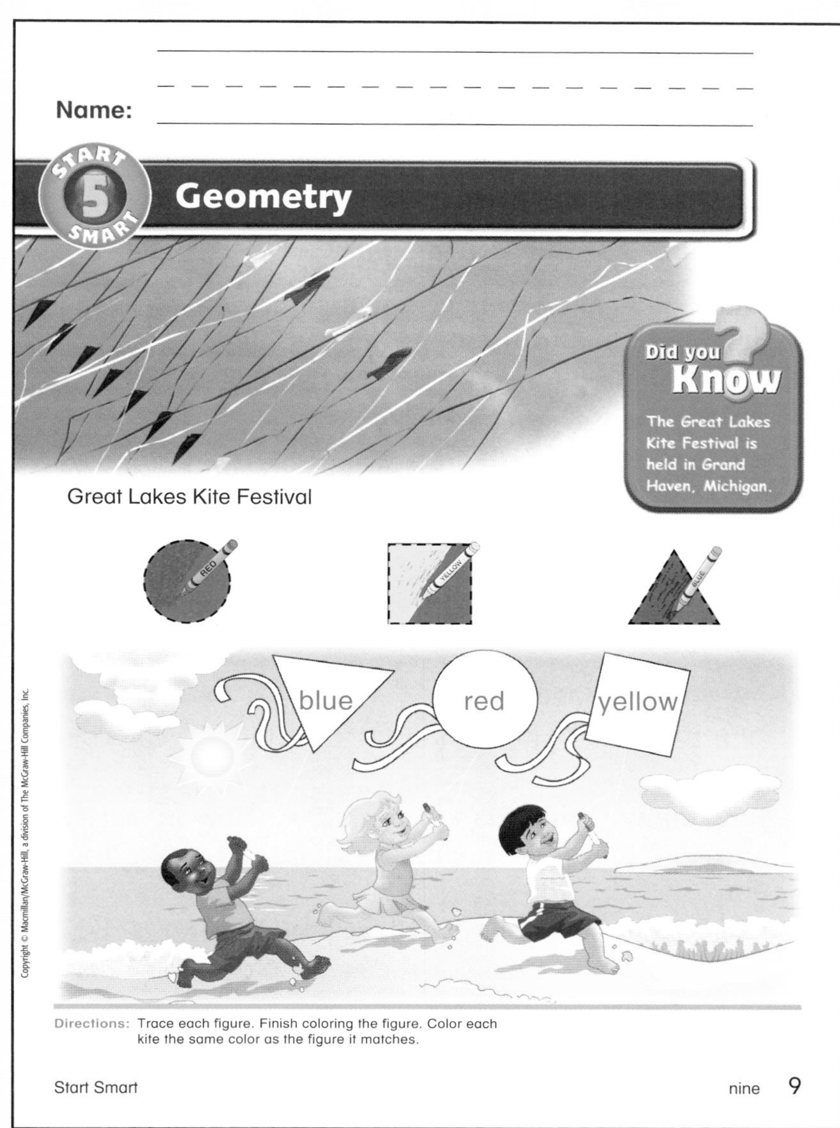

Name:
Start Smart 5
Geometry
Did you Know
The Great Lakes Kite Festival is held in Grand Haven, Michigan.
Great Lakes Kite Festival
blue
red
yellow
Directions: Trace each figure. Finish coloring the figure. Color each kite the same color as the figure it matches.
Start Smart
nine 9

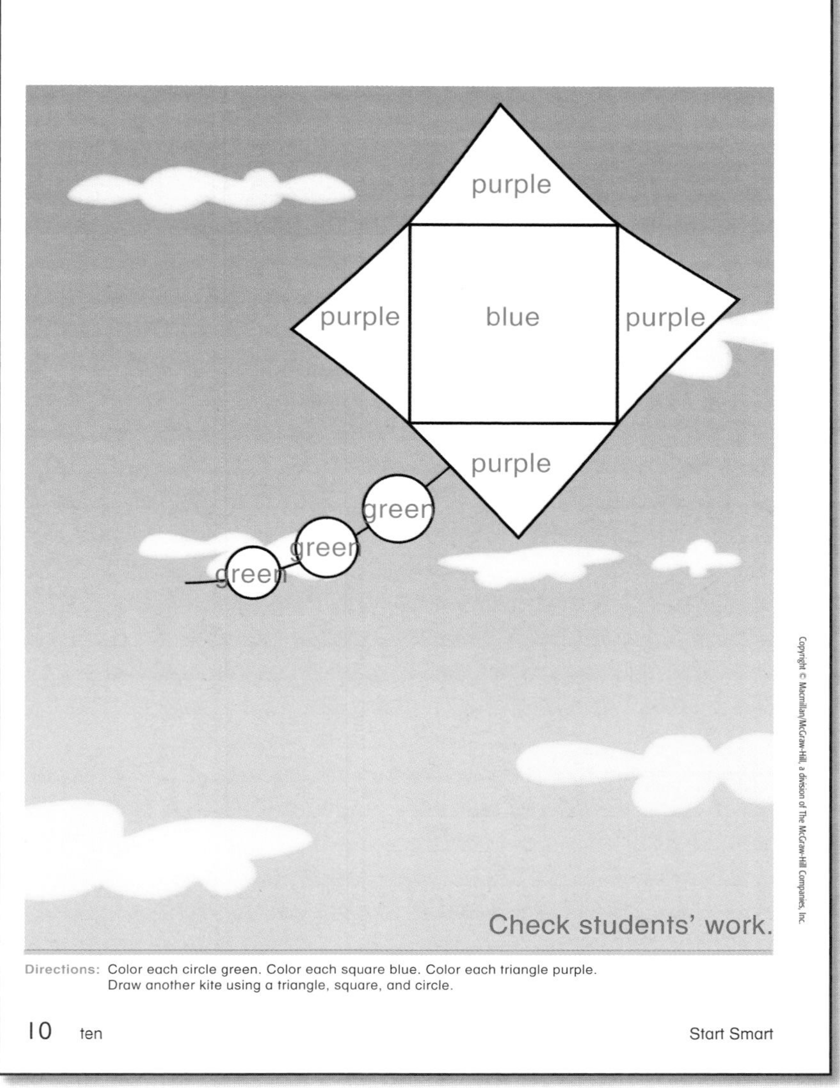

Assess and Close

Read About Figures Give each student a shape of pattern block. Read the book *The Shape of Things* by Dayle Ann Dodds, or another book about figures aloud to the class.

- As you read, have students hold up the correct figure or figures you are reading about or the figure or figures they see on the page.
- When you have finished reading, discuss with students which figures were used in the illustrations, and the different items that were made with circles, squares, and triangles.

More FUN Facts

- April is National Kite Month.
- The Great Lakes Kite Festival features a Fighter Kite Competition, which looks like a game of tag in the air.
- At night, illuminated kites light up the sky.
- Some kites at the festival are over 90 feet long.

Lesson Planner

Objectives

Create and use graphs to answer questions.

Materials: crayons, glue, different colored construction paper squares, chart paper
Manipulatives: color tiles

Activate Prior Knowledge

Discuss the photograph and read *Did You Know?* on Student Edition page 11.

- Lead a class discussion about birds.
- **What kinds of birds have you seen in your neighborhood, on TV, or at the zoo?** Sample answers: mockingbirds, parrots, bluebirds
- Write responses on the chalkboard.
- Ask students to vote for their favorite bird by raising their hands. Remind them that they may vote only once. Point to each bird, then count and write the number of responses.
- **What bird got the most votes?** Answers will depend upon data collected.

Using student page 11.

- Direct students' attention to the tree. Identify each bird by color.
- **How many blue birds are there?** two **How many gray birds are there?** three **How many red birds are there?** one
- Have students place a color tile on the graph for each bird and then color a square on the graph to determine how many of each type of bird is in the tree.

Using student page 12.

- Have students look at the shelves in the pet store.
- **How many birdcages are there?** five Have students place five color tiles on the graph next to the birdcage.
- **How many birdseed bells are there?** four Have students place four color tiles on the graph next to the bell.
- Have students color squares on the graph to show how many bird cages and bird seed bells are at the store.
- **Does the pet store have more birdcages or birdseed bells?** birdcages Have students circle the group that has more objects.

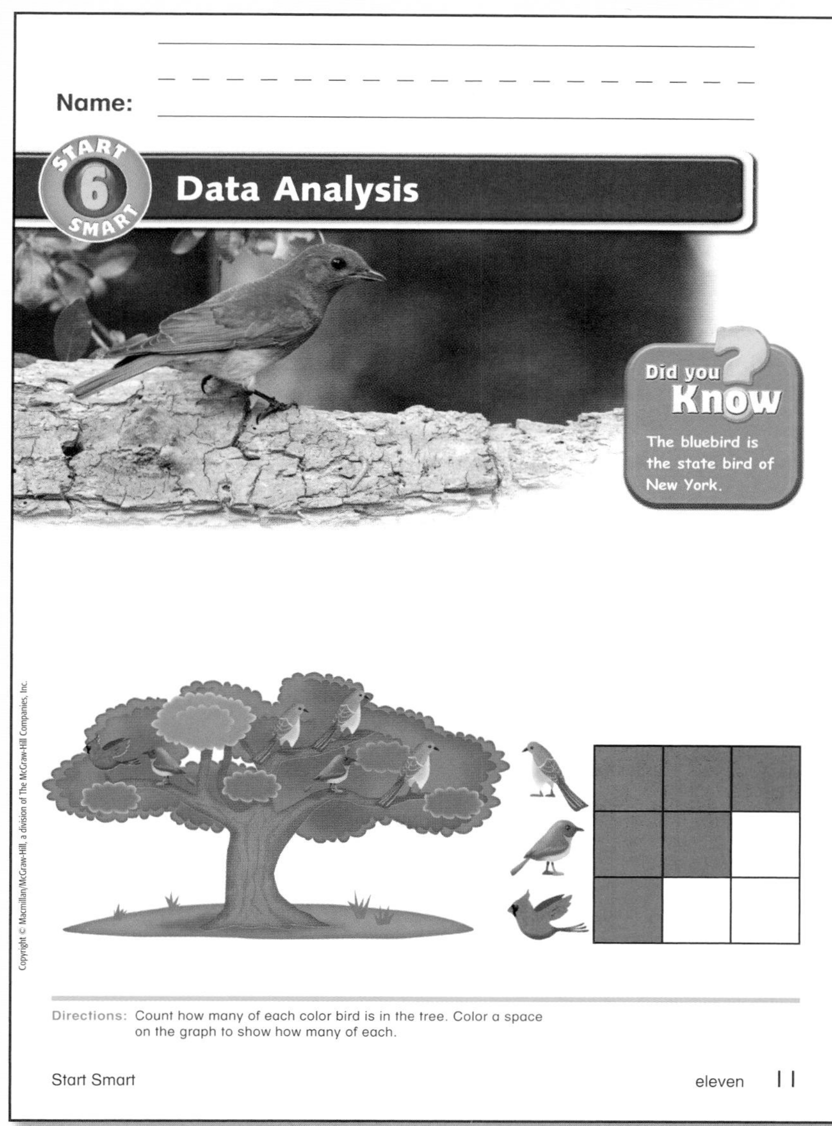

Name:
START 6 SMART
Data Analysis
Did you Know
The bluebird is the state bird of New York.
Directions: Count how many of each color bird is in the tree. Color a space on the graph to show how many of each.
Start Smart
eleven 11

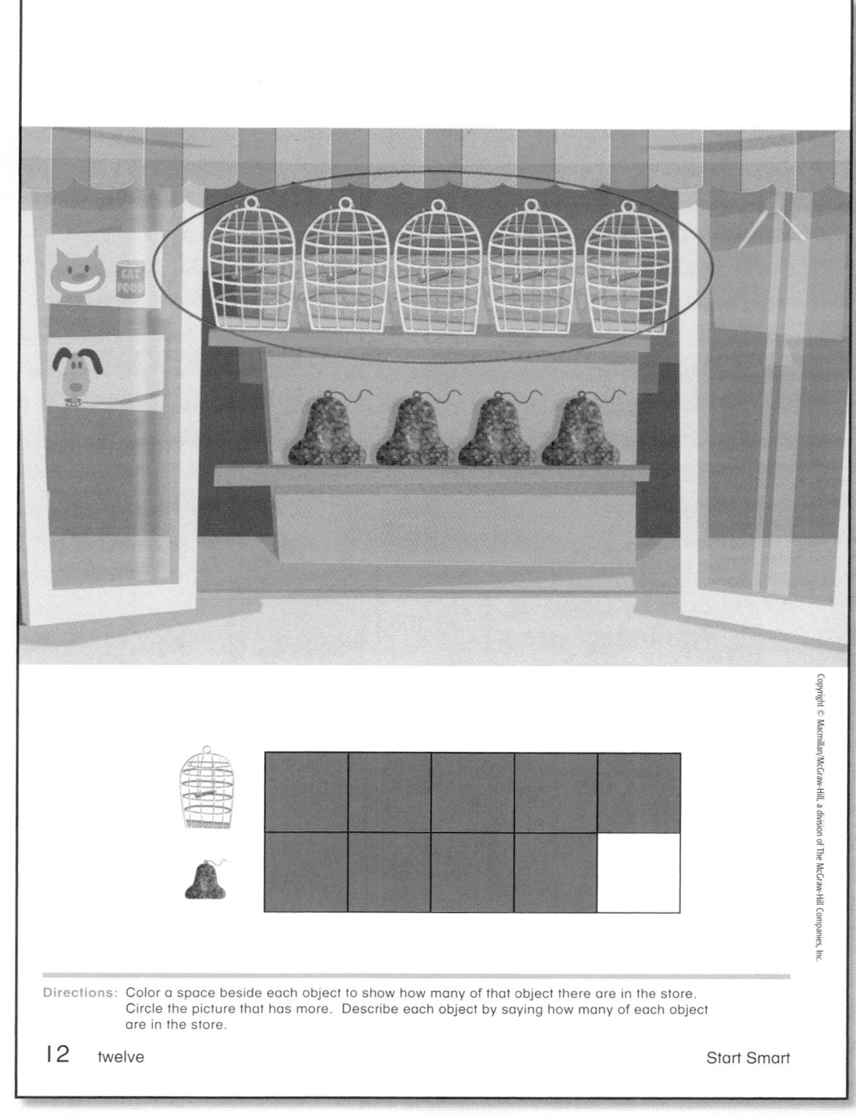

Directions: Color a space beside each object to show how many of that object there are in the store. Circle the picture that has more. Describe each object by saying how many of each object are in the store.
12 twelve
Start Smart

Assess and Close

Graph Favorite Colors Work as a class to make a graph of students' favorite colors.

- Create a graph on chart paper by gluing a different colored construction paper square to the first column of each row in the graph.
- Explain to students that they will get to vote one time with a construction paper square of their favorite color.
- Ask students to glue their colored square to the graph in the row that matches their favorite color.
- Discuss the class color graph with students. **What color do students like the most? What color do students like the least?** Answers will vary depending on student choices.

More *FUN* Facts

- Female bluebirds build the nests.
- Males bring nesting material for the female to use.
- Putting out a small dish of mealworms can attract bluebirds.
- Bluebirds are the state bird in: New York, Missouri, Idaho, and Nevada.
- On average it takes two to five days for a bluebird to build a nest.
- A bluebird can actually be red, white, or blue.

Chapter Overview

Chapter-at-a-Glance

In Chapter 1, the emphasis is on sorting objects by observing one or more attributes as well as classifying them through the use of logical reasoning.

Lesson		Math Objective	State/Local Standards
1-1	**Alike and Different** (pp. 17–18)	Identify objects that are alike and different.	
1-2	**Sort by One Attribute** (pp. 19–20)	Sort objects using one attribute.	
1-3	**Problem Solving Strategy: Act It Out** (pp. 21–22)	Sort objects to determine whether or not they belong in a group.	
1-4	**Sort by More Than One Attribute** (pp. 23–24)	Sort objects using more than one attribute.	
1-5	**Same Number** (pp. 27–28)	Use one-to-one correspondence to show equal groups.	
1-6	**More Than** (pp. 29–30)	Use one-to-one correspondence to identify a group with more.	
1-7	**Less Than** (pp. 31–32)	Use one-to-one correspondence to identify a group with less.	

Compare and Sort Objects

BIG Idea Understanding the relationship between numbers and quantities begins with comparing sets. To develop number sense, students need to sort and classify objects in sets to understand and make comparison.

Algebra Students prepare for algebraic equations through comparing sets of the same or equal number, more, or less value.
Lessons 1-5, 1-6, 1-7

Geometry Students prepare for geometry through comparing the attributes of objects. Lessons 1-1, 1-2, 1-4

Measurement Students prepare for measurement through the comparison of sets. Lessons 1-5, 1-6, 1-7

GK-FP1 *Number and Operations:* **Representing, comparing, and ordering whole numbers and joining and separating sets**

Children use numbers, including written numerals, to represent quantities and to solve quantitative problems, such as counting objects in a set, creating a set with a given number of objects, comparing and ordering sets or numerals by using both cardinal and ordinal meanings, and modeling simple joining and separating situations with objects. They choose, combine, and apply effective strategies for answering quantitative questions, including quickly recognizing the number in a small set, counting and producing sets of given sizes, counting the number in combined sets, and counting backward.

Skills Trace
Vertical Alignment

PreKindergarten

In PreK, students learned to:

- Compare the numbers of concrete objects using language (e.g., "same" or "equal," "one more," "more than," "less than").
- Sort objects into groups by an attribute and begin to explain how the grouping was done.

Kindergarten

During this chapter, students learn to:

- Identify, sort, and compare objects by one attribute and identify objects that do not belong to a particular group.
- Communicate mathemathical ideas and justify their reasoning.
- Compare two or more sets of objects and identify which set is the same number as, more than, or less than the other.

After this chapter, students will learn to:

- Understand the relationship between numbers and quantities.

First Grade

In first grade, students will learn to:

- Identify patterns in addition facts (sums to 18) and the corresponding subtraction facts.

Backmapping and Vertical Alignment **McGraw-Hill's *Math Connects*** program was conceived and developed with the final results in mind: student success in Algebra 1 and beyond. The authors, using the **NCTM Focal Points and Focal Connections** as their guide, developed this brand new series by backmapping from Algebra 1 concepts, and vertically aligning the topics so that they build upon prior skills and concepts and serve as a foundation for future topics.

Math Vocabulary

The following math vocabulary words for Chapter 1 are listed in the glossary of the ***Student Edition***. You can find interactive definitions in 13 languages in the ***eGlossary*** at macmillanmh.com.

alike, **different** (p. 17)

less than (p. 31)

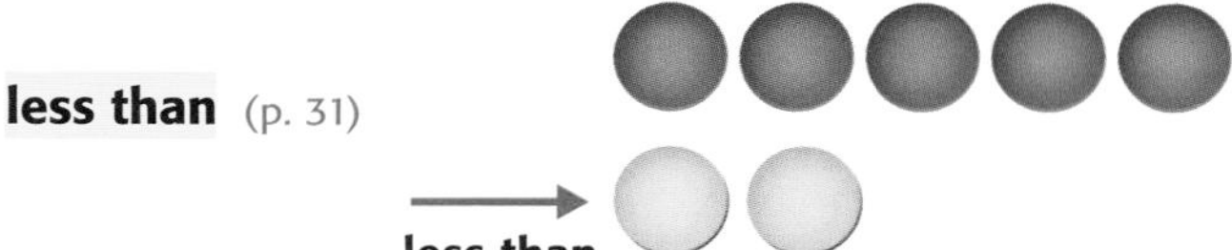

more than (p. 29)

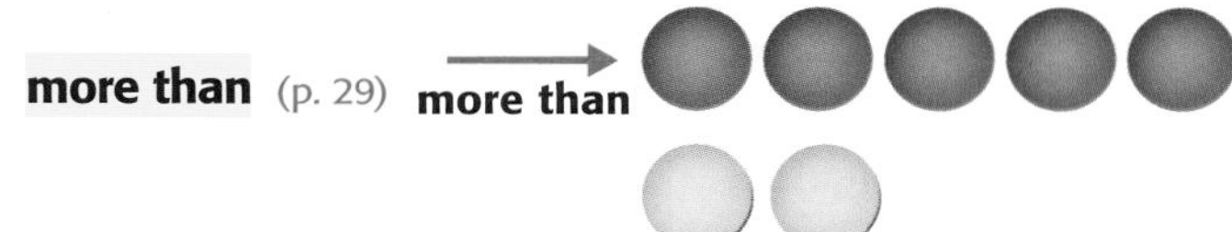

same number (p. 17)

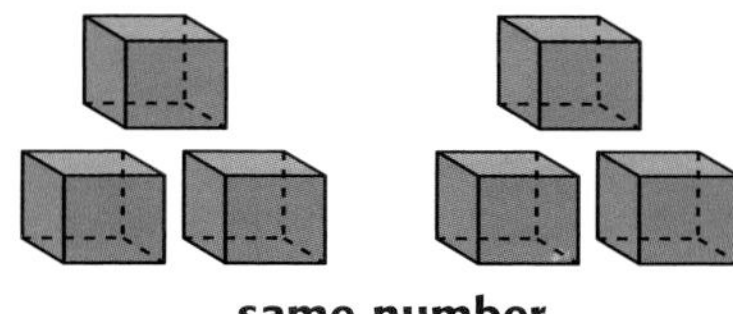

sort (p. 19)

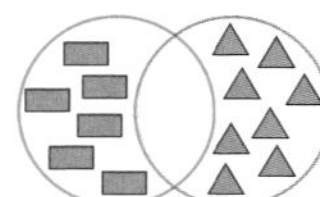

sorted or grouped by figure

Visual Vocabulary Cards Use Visual Vocabulary Cards 20, 25, and 39 to introduce the vocabulary in this chapter. (The Define/Example/Ask routine is printed on the back of each card.)

Chapter Planner

Suggested Pacing		
Instruction	Review and Assessment	TOTAL
7 days	2 days	**9 days**

Diagnostic Assessment
Are You Ready? (p. 14)

	Lesson 1-1 Pacing: 1 day	Lesson 1-2 Pacing: 1 day	Lesson 1-3 Pacing: 1 day
Lesson/ Objective	**Alike and Different** (pp. 17–18) **Objective:** Identify objects that are alike and different.	**Sort by One Attribute** (pp. 19–20) **Objective:** Sort objects using one attribute.	**Problem-Solving Strategy** **Act It Out** (pp. 21–22) **Objective:** Sort objects to determine whether or not they belong in a group.
State/Local Standards			
Math Vocabulary	**alike**, **different**	**sort**	
Lesson Resources	**Materials** crayons, bag, triangle/drum, markers **Manipulatives** attribute buttons, connecting cubes **Other Resources** CRM Leveled Worksheets (pp. 6–9) Daily Reteach Problem of the Day	**Materials** chart paper, orange and blue items, tray, big and small items, yarn, string **Manipulatives** attribute buttons **Other Resources** CRM Leveled Worksheets (pp. 10–13) Daily Reteach Problem of the Day	**Materials** cat-related objects, fish-related objects, glue, letter and number shapes, coins, bags, scissors **Manipulatives** connecting cubes, attribute buttons **Other Resources** CRM Leveled Worksheets (pp. 14–18) Daily Reteach Problem of the Day *Inside My Classroom*
Technology Math Online	Math Adventures	Math Song Track 2 Math Adventures	
Reaching All Learners	Gifted and Talented, p. 17B AL English Learners, p. 17B ELL Early Finishers, p. 17B OL AL	Gifted and Talented, p. 19B AL English Learners, p. 19B ELL Early Finishers, p. 19B OL AL	Below Level, p. 21 BL English Learners, p. 21B ELL Early Finishers, p. 21B OL AL
Alternate Lesson	*Math Their Way,* pp. 59–60 *IMPACT Mathematics:* Unit I	*Math Their Way,* pp. 76–77 *IMPACT Mathematics:* Unit I	

KEY

BL Below/Approaching Level · OL On Level · AL Above/Beyond Level · ELL English Learners
SE Student Edition · TE Teacher Edition · CRM Chapter 1 Resource Masters · CD-Rom
Transparency · Flip Chart · Real-World Problem Solving Library

	Lesson 1-4 (Pacing: 1 day)	Lesson 1-5 (Pacing: 1 day)	Lesson 1-6 (Pacing: 1 day)
Lesson/ Objective	**Sort by More Than One Attribute** (pp. 23–24) **Objective:** Sort objects using more than one attribute.	**Same Number** (pp. 27–28) **Objective:** Use one-to-one correspondence to show equal groups.	**More Than** (pp. 29–30) **Objective:** Use one-to-one correspondence to identify a group with more.
State/Local Standards			
Math Vocabulary		**same number**	**more than**
Lesson Resources	**Materials** shape cards **Manipulatives** attribute buttons **Other Resources** CRM Leveled Worksheets (pp. 19–22) Daily Reteach Problem of the Day	**Materials** yarn, books **Manipulatives** connecting cubes, counters, color tiles **Other Resources** CRM Leveled Worksheets (pp. 23–26) Daily Reteach Problem of the Day	**Materials** magnetic board, chalkboard, eraser, magnetic letters, cups, beans **Manipulatives** counters, attribute buttons, color tiles **Other Resources** CRM Leveled Worksheets (pp. 27–30) Daily Reteach Problem of the Day
Technology Math Online	Math Song Track 2 Math Adventures Concepts in Motion	Math Adventures	Math Adventures Concepts in Motion
Reaching All Learners	Below Level, p. 23 BL English Learners, p. 23B ELL Early Finishers, p. 23B OL AL	Below Level, p. 27 BL English Learners, p. 27B ELL Early Finishers, p. 27B OL AL	Below Level, p. 29 BL English Learners, p. 29B ELL Early Finishers, p. 29B OL AL
Alternate Lesson	*Math Their Way,* p. 80 *IMPACT Mathematics:* Unit I	*Math Their Way,* pp. 126–127 *IMPACT Mathematics:* Unit A	*IMPACT Mathematics:* Unit A

Formative Assessment
Mid-Chapter Check (p. 25)

Game Time: Button Up! (p. 26)

Chapter Planner

The one-stop **Assessment Options** planner organizes the resources available for diagnostic, formative, and summative assessment in this chapter.

Lesson 1-7

Pacing: 1 day

Lesson/ Objective	**Less Than** (pp. 31–32) **Objective:** Use one-to-one correspondence to identify a group with less.
State/Local Standards	
Math Vocabulary	**less than**
Lesson Resources	**Materials:** chart paper, balls **Manipulatives** connecting cubes, attribute buttons, color tiles, counters **Other Resources** CRM Leveled Worksheets (pp. 31–34) Daily Reteach Problem of the Day
Technology Math Online	Math Adventures
Reaching All Learners	Below Level, p. 31 BL English Learners, p. 31B ELL Early Finishers, p. 31B OL AL
Alternate Lesson	*Math Their Way,* pp. 125–126 *IMPACT Mathematics:* Unit A

Problem Solving in Science (p. 33)

Summative Assessment
- Chapter Review/Test (p. 35)
- Test Practice (p. 37)

Assessment Options

Diagnostic Assessment

- SE *Option 1:* Are You Ready? (p. 14)
- *Option 2:* Online Quiz (macmillanmh.com)
- CRM *Option 3:* Diagnostic Test (p. 38)

Formative Assessment

- TE Alternate Teaching Strategies (every lesson)
- TE Writing in Math (every lesson)
- TE Line Up (every lesson)
- SE Mid-Chapter Check (p. 25)
- CRM Mid-Chapter Test (p. 39)

Summative Assessment

- SE Chapter Review/Test (p. 35)
- SE Test Practice (p. 37)
- CRM Leveled Chapter Tests (pp. 44–51)
- CRM Cumulative Test Practice (p. 52)
- CRM Listening Assessment (p. 42)
- CRM Oral Assessment (p. 40)
- Exam*View*® Assessment Suite
- Advance Tracker

McGraw-Hill Professional Development

Targeted professional development has been articulated throughout **McGraw-Hill's *Math Connects*** program. The **McGraw-Hill Professional Development Video Library** provides short videos that support the **NCTM Focal Points and Focal Connections**. For more information, visit macmillanmh.com.

Model Lessons

Instructional Strategies

Assessment Tips

Sorting is an integral part of the mathematics that kindergarten children will be learning.

- It is important to observe each student on several different occasions because one observation at one given moment is not a good sample.
- Observe each student at least twice in each lesson as they are completing sorting activities.
- The more times a student is observed, the better chance you will have to ascertain whether he/she has a deep understanding of the concept.
- Keep accurate records of each observation.

Teacher Notes

Learning Stations

Cross-Curricular Links

Cross-curricular **Learning Stations** give students self-guided opportunities to explore chapter concepts.

Reading

 pair LOGICAL 

Bean Sort

- Listen to the story.
- Scoop the beans.
- Sort the beans by color.

Teacher Note: You may want to read these stories on tape so students can work independently: Twins Two by Two *by Catherine Arnholt,* Fruits: A Caribbean Counting Poem *by Valerie Bloom, or* Ten Seeds *by Ruth Brown. Have students use a scoop to get some mixed beans out of the jar (or box). Students should pour the beans out of the scoop onto their desk (or table) before sorting.*

Materials:

- jar or box for beans
- mixed dried beans
- cup, measuring cup, or small cup for scooping beans

Art

  SPATIAL 

Bean Art

- Draw a picture on a plate.
- Glue the beans to the picture.
- Trade with a partner.
- How many beans are on each plate?
- Are there more, less or the same/equal?

Teacher Note: Help students think of ideas for simple pictures to draw on their plates, such as a flower with a stem, a baseball bat, or a smile face. Have students glue an amount of beans less than 10 on their plate. Let dry. Have students place plates side by side and use yarn strips for 1:1 correspondence to compare bean to bean from plate to plate.

Materials:

- crayons
- paper plates
- mixed dried beans
- glue
- strips of yarn

Science

  LOGICAL 

Bean Sprouting

- Fold a paper towel.
- Spray the paper towel with water.
- Put a lima bean and corn seed inside the paper towel.
- Put the paper towel into a bag.
- Wait a few days, then look inside the bag. Alike or different?

Teacher Note: Students should fold the paper towel in quarters by folding it in half twice. Tell students to use the spray bottle to mist the paper towel. Have students write their names on their bags to distinguish them from the others. Make sure the bags are clear plastic. You can use any sprouting beans such as green, wax, soy, or mung beans. Light is not needed for beans to sprout. It will take a few days for sprouts to appear.

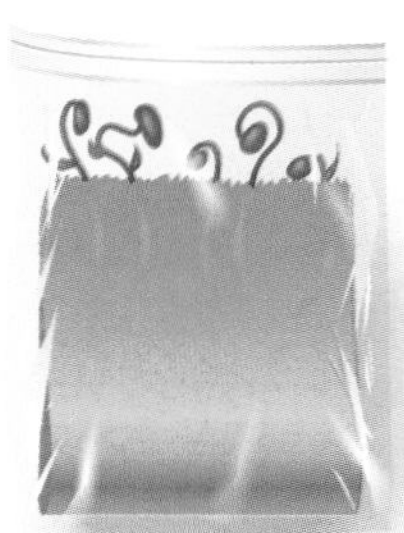

Materials:

- paper towels
- spray bottle full of water
- self-sealing plastic bag
- lima beans and corn
- labels
- crayons

Music

whole class | KINESTHETIC

"Hokey Pokey"

- Stand in a circle.
- Sing "Hokey Pokey."
- Put a body part "in." Compare.
- Sort into groups by the part they put "in."

Teacher Note: Encourage students to choose another favorite part to put "in" and have students sort themselves into groups that chose the same favorite body part. Identify different choices.

Materials:

- none

Social Studies

individual | LOGICAL

Animals in South Africa

- Listen to the story.
- Look at South Africa on a map.
- Scoop some animals out of the container.
- Sort the animals.

Teacher Note: Read One Child, One Seed *aloud. Help students find South Africa on a map or globe. Show students where South Africa is in relation to the United States. Make sure the scoop (or cup) is large enough to hold several animals. Tell students to pour the animals out of the scoop (or cup) onto their desk (or table) before sorting.*

Materials:

- *One Child, One Seed* by Katherine Cave
- world map
- box or container for plastic animals
- plastic wild animals
- measuring cup, or small cup for scooping plastic animals

Calendar Time

Sun, Clouds, or Rain

- Say the days of the week aloud. Ask students to look outside.
- Have students draw a yellow circle on a card if the day is sunny. Have them draw a cloud on a card if the day is cloudy. Have them draw a raindrop on a card if the day is rainy. Explain to students that they will do this for ten days.
- Have students sort their cards into groups.
- Ask which group has more than, less than, or if one group has the same number as the other group.
- Each day, ask if the weather is alike or different from yesterday.

Teacher Note: Have students use different colors for each image: yellow for sun, black or gray for cloud, and blue for raindrop.

Introduce the Chapter

 Real World: Sort Objects

Share with students that they sort objects every day like laundry and food from a grocery store.

- **Why do we sort things?** Sample answer: to put like things together for organization
- **What would happen if things were not sorted?** Sample answer: We could not find what we need.
- Divide students into pairs. Give each pair a handful of pasta (elbow macaroni, spiral, penne, bowtie, etc.).
- Ask students to sort the pasta into piles by style.
- **Can you find another way to sort the pasta?** Sample answers: broken, not broken

Use the Student Page

Have students turn to p. 13. Guide students to discuss the image on the page and answer the Explore questions.

Key Vocabulary

Introduce the key vocabulary in the chapter using the routine below.

Define: When you sort, you group together items that have something in common.
Example: When you group buttons by color, you are sorting.
Ask: Besides sorting by color, what is another way to sort objects?

Diagnostic Assessment

Check for students' prerequisite skills before beginning the chapter.

- **Option 1:** ***Are You Ready for Chapter 1?***
  SE Student Edition, p. 14
- **Option 2:** ***Online Assessment Quiz***

  Math Online macmillanmh.com
- **Option 3:** ***Diagnostic Test***
  CRM Chapter 1 Resource Masters, p. 38

Each chapter provides three options for **Diagnostic Assessment**. Based on the results, **Intervention Options** include suggestions for intensive and strategic students, as well as on-level and above-level students.

RTI (Response to Intervention)

Apply the Results Based on the results of the diagnostic assessment on p. 14, use the chart on the next page to address individual needs before and during the chapter.

TIER 3	Intensive Intervention
If	students miss three or four of the exercises:
Then	use Chapters 2, 8, and 9 of *Math Triumphs*, an intensive math intervention program from McGraw-Hill

Dinah Zike's Foldables

Guide students to create a Display Case Foldable graphic organizer for sorting and classifying.

 Make a four-door book out of a shutter fold.

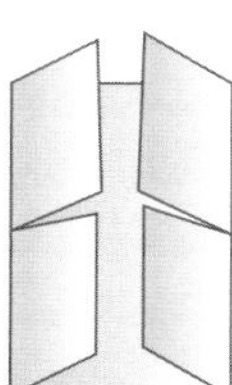

2. Fold the two inside corners back to the outer edges (mountains) of the shutter fold. This will result in two tacos that will make the four-door book look like it has a shirt collar. Do the same thing to the bottom of the four-door book.

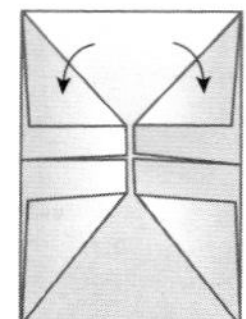

3. Form a 90-degree angle and overlap the folder triangles to make a display case that does not use staples or glue. Or, as illustrated, cut off all four triangles, and staple or glue the sides.

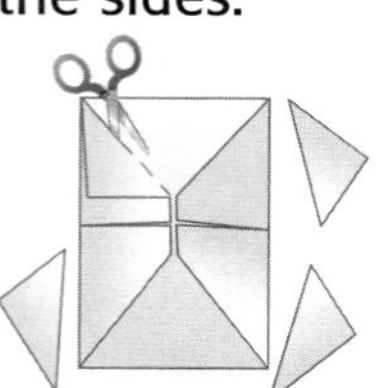

 Place two of the same object in one display case and two different objects in the second display case.

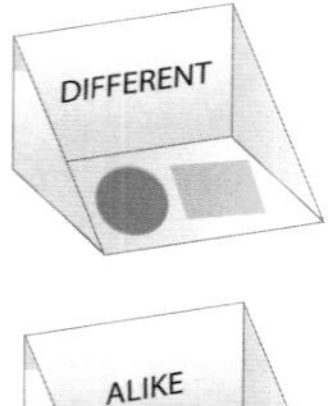

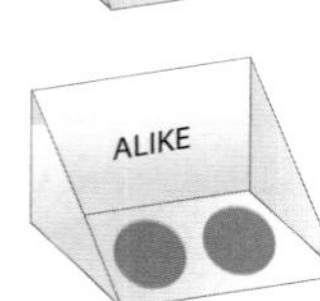

When to Use It *Lessons 1-1, 1-2, 1-3, 1-4, and 1-6 (Additional instructions for using the Foldable with these lessons are found on pp. 25 and 35.)*

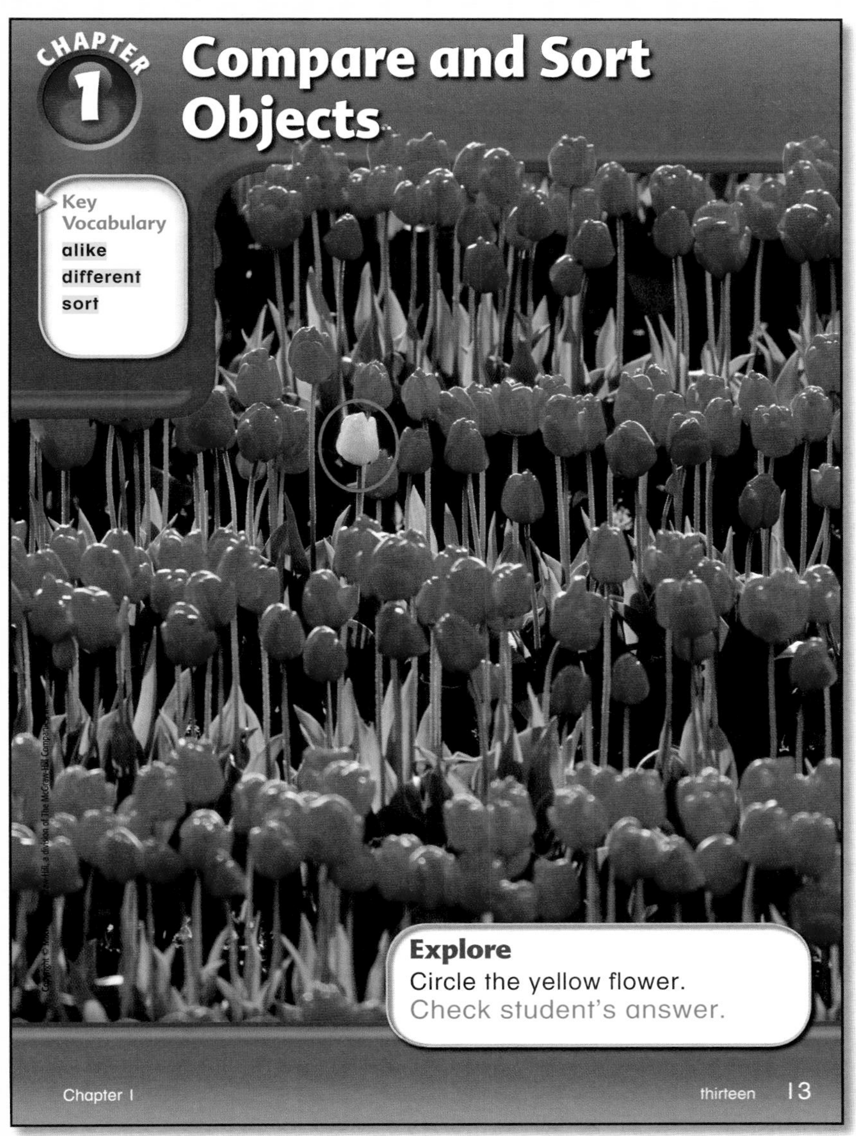

CHAPTER 1
Compare and Sort Objects
Key Vocabulary
alike
different
sort
Explore
Circle the yellow flower.
Check student's answer.
Chapter 1
thirteen 13

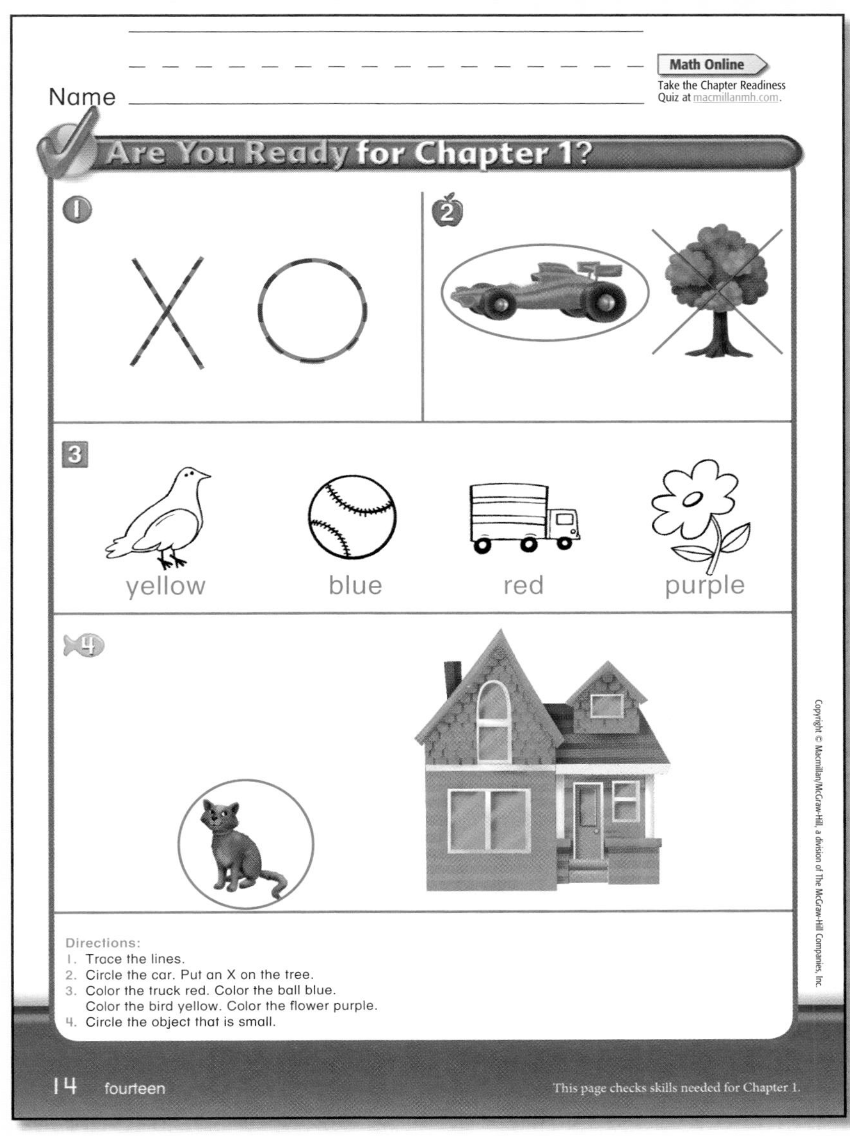

Name
Math Online
Take the Chapter Readiness Quiz at macmillanmh.com.
Are You Ready for Chapter 1?
yellow
blue
red
purple
Directions:
1. Trace the lines.
2. Circle the car. Put an X on the tree.
3. Color the truck red. Color the ball blue.
Color the bird yellow. Color the flower purple.
4. Circle the object that is small.
14 fourteen
This page checks skills needed for Chapter 1.

RTI (Response to Intervention)

TIER 2 Strategic Intervention below/approaching grade level	TIER 1 On-Level	Above/Beyond Level
If students miss two in: **Exercises 1–4** **Then** Choose a resource:	**If** students miss one in: **Exercises 1–4** **Then** Choose a resource:	**If** students miss none in: **Exercises 1–4** **Then** Choose a resource:
TE Start Smart 1: Problem Solving (p. 1) Math Online Concepts in Motion	TE Learning Stations (pp. 13G–13H) TE Chapter Project (p. 15) CRM Game: Grocery Bag Sort Math Adventures	TE Learning Stations (pp. 13G–13H) TE Chapter Project (p. 15) Real-World Problem Solving: *Inside My Classroom* Math Online Game

WRITING IN ➤ MATH

Starting the Chapter
Ask students to draw two pictures in their Math Journal.

- Have students draw three red dots and two blue dots. Ask students to use the picture to explain the terms *more than* and *less than*.
- Have students draw four green dots and four red dots. Ask them to use this picture to explain the term *same number*.

Chapter 1 Project

Sort Classroom Objects

- Have students practice sorting in the classroom.
- Construction paper, manipulatives, crayons, and other items can be mixed together.
- Students can choose a characteristic to use for sorting these items. For example, if there is a big basket of crayons, have students sort them according to color.

Chapter Projects apply chapter concepts and skills through extended activities and provide additional assessment opportunities.

Chapter 1 Literature List

Lesson	Book Title	Author
1-1	**The Button Box**	Margarette S. Reid
1-2	**Shapes, Shapes, Shapes**	Tana Hoban
1-3	**26 Letters and 99 Cents**	Tana Hoban
1-4	**The Button Box**	Margarette S. Reid
1-5	**More or Less**	Stuart J. Murphy
1-6	**Big Fat Hen**	Keith Baker
1-7	**Bat Jamboree**	Kathi Appett
Any	**Is Your Mama a Llama?**	Steven Kellogg

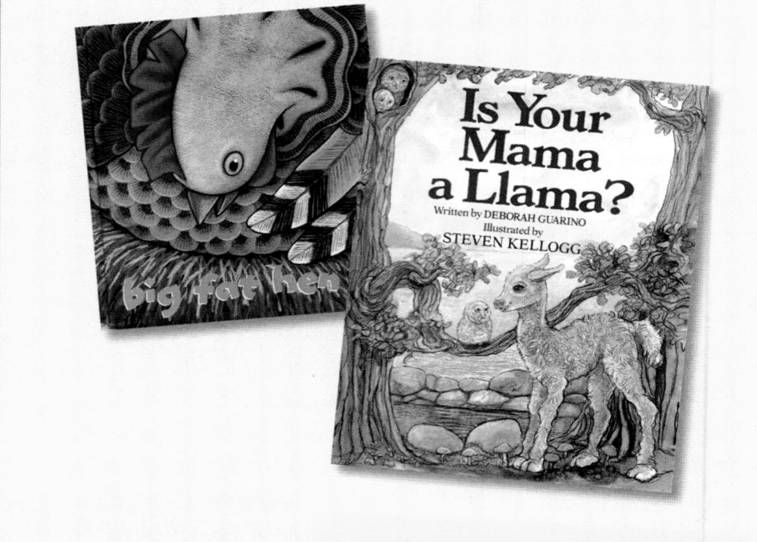

The **Literature List** presents all of the literature referenced in the chapter.

ELL National ESL Standards Alignment for Chapter 1

Lesson, Page	ESL Standard	Modality	Level
1-1, p. 17B	Goal 1, Standard 3, c	Visual, Auditory	Beginning
1-2, p. 19B	Goal 1, Standard 3, k	Visual	Beginning
1-3, p. 21B	Goal 3, Standard 2, b	Social, Auditory	Beginning
1-4, p. 23B	Goal 2, Standard 1, d	Visual/Spatial, Linguistic	Beginning
1-5, p. 27B	Goal 1, Standard 2, c	Visual/Spatial	Beginning
1-6, p. 29B	Goal 2, Standard 2, a	Linguistic, Social	Beginning
1-7, p. 31B	Goal 1, Standard 3, c	Social, Auditory, Kinesthetic	Intermediate
1-1, p. 17B	Goal 1, Standard 3, c	Visual, Auditory	Beginning
1-2, p. 19B	Goal 1, Standard 3, k	Visual	Beginning

The National ESL Standards can be found in the Teacher Reference Handbook.

English

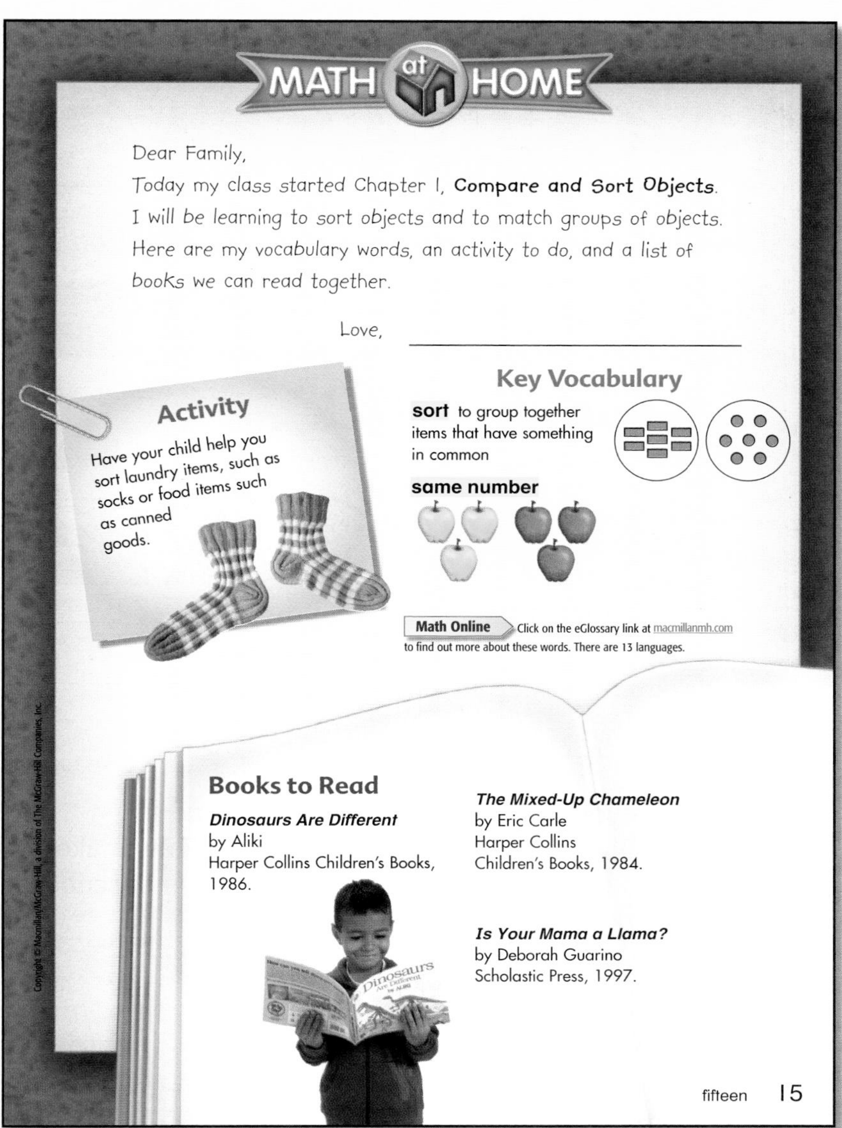

MATH at HOME

Dear Family,

Today my class started Chapter 1, **Compare and Sort Objects**. I will be learning to sort objects and to match groups of objects. Here are my vocabulary words, an activity to do, and a list of books we can read together.

Love, ______________

Activity

Have your child help you sort laundry items, such as socks or food items such as canned goods.

Key Vocabulary

sort to group together items that have something in common

same number

Math Online Click on the eGlossary link at macmillanmh.com to find out more about these words. There are 13 languages.

Books to Read

Dinosaurs Are Different
by Aliki
Harper Collins Children's Books, 1986.

The Mixed-Up Chameleon
by Eric Carle
Harper Collins
Children's Books, 1984.

Is Your Mama a Llama?
by Deborah Guarino
Scholastic Press, 1997.

fifteen 15

Español

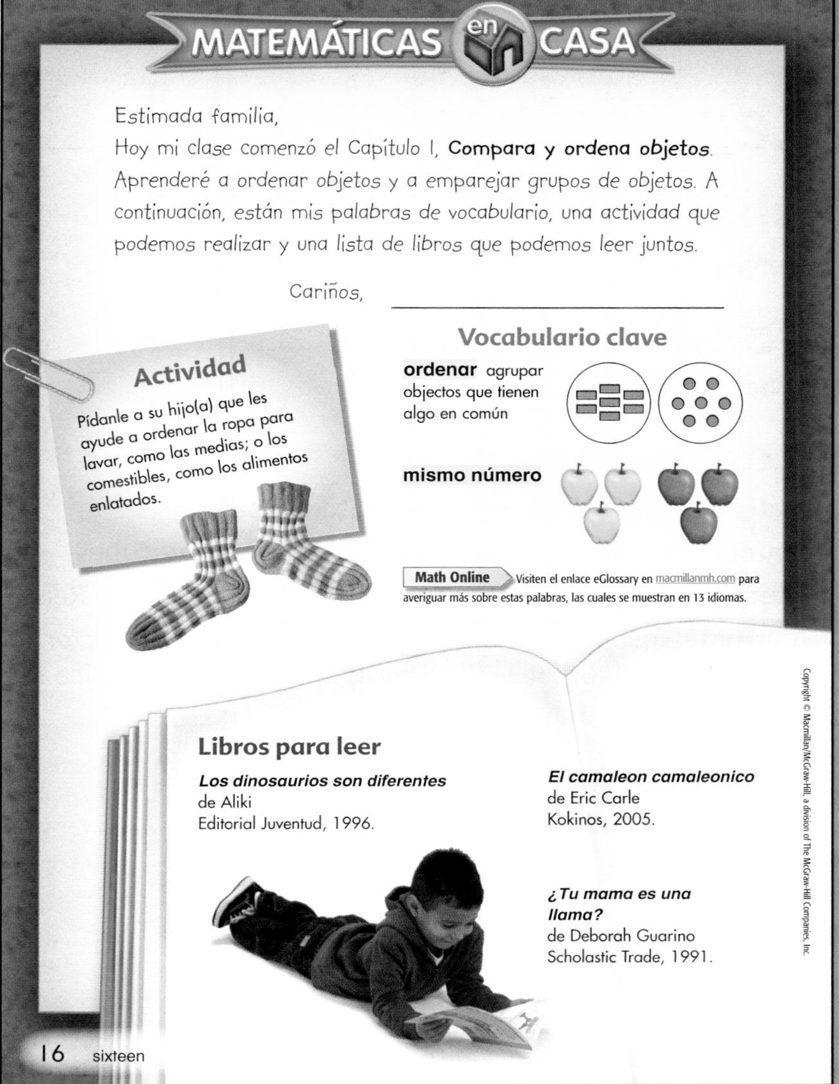

MATEMÁTICAS en CASA

Estimada familia,

Hoy mi clase comenzó el Capítulo 1, **Compara y ordena objetos**. Aprenderé a ordenar objetos y a emparejar grupos de objetos. A continuación, están mis palabras de vocabulario, una actividad que podemos realizar y una lista de libros que podemos leer juntos.

Cariños, ______________

Actividad

Pídanle a su hijo(a) que les ayude a ordenar la ropa para lavar, como las medias; o los comestibles, como los alimentos enlatados.

Vocabulario clave

ordenar agrupar objectos que tienen algo en común

mismo número

Math Online Visiten el enlace eGlossary en macmillanmh.com para averiguar más sobre estas palabras, las cuales se muestran en 13 idiomas.

Libros para leer

Los dinosaurios son diferentes
de Aliki
Editorial Juventud, 1996.

El camaleon camaleonico
de Eric Carle
Kokinos, 2005.

¿Tu mama es una llama?
de Deborah Guarino
Scholastic Trade, 1991.

16 sixteen

- Read the Math at Home letter on p. 15 with the class and have each child sign it.
- Send home copies of the Math at Home letter with each student.
- Use the Spanish letter on p. 16 for students with Spanish-speaking parents or guardians.

Read-Aloud Anthology

For an optional reading activity to introduce this chapter's math concepts, see the Read-Aloud Anthology on p. TR24.

LESSON 1-1

Alike and Different

Lesson Planner

Objective

Identify objects that are alike and different.

Vocabulary

alike, **different**

Resources

Materials: crayons, triangle/drum, markers, bag

Manipulatives: attribute buttons and connecting cubes

Literature Connection: *The Button Box* by Margarette S. Reid

Alternate Lesson: Use *Sorting on the Overhead Projector* on pages 59–60 of *Math Their Way* to provide practice in noticing similarities and differences.
Use *IMPACT Mathematics*: Unit I to provide practice determining whether objects are alike or different.

Teacher Technology
TeacherWorks

Focus on Math Background

Sorting by likenesses and differences is sorting by a single attribute. Since children and adults both wear items of clothing that are alike—shoes, socks, mittens and gloves—these are easy items to point out.

Most early sorting is done by size and color likenesses and differences. Shape as a sorting attribute follows.

Sorting and classifying are foundational skills for both math and science. In mathematics initial classifying activities prepare students for seeing patterns, differences in numbers such as odd and even numbers, and in geometry recognition of both two-dimensional and three-dimensional shapes.

Daily Routine

Use these suggestions before beginning the lesson on p. 17.

5-Minute Check

(Reviews Start Smart 4)

1. How are the pictures alike? How are they different? They are all figures. They are different colors. They have different numbers of sides.

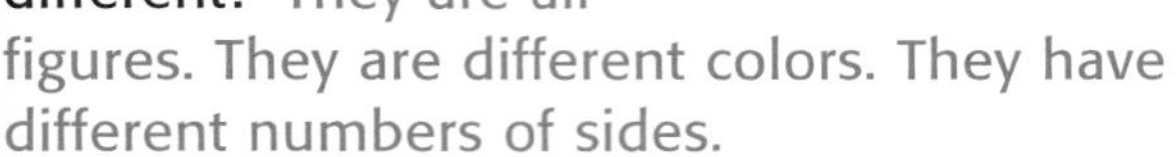

Problem of the Day

Give students a handful of color tiles and a handful of connecting cubes. Have students make groups of cubes and tiles. Ask students to describe the groups of tiles and cubes.

LINE UP Have students wearing jeans line up. Ask volunteers how these students are the same. Have students not wearing jeans to line up. Ask volunteers how these students are different from the first group.

Building Math Vocabulary

Write the vocabulary words **alike** and **different** on each side of a piece of chart paper. Point to the words as you do the following activity.

- Show students a green interlocking cube. Have them find a cube that looks just like it.
- Show two green cubes. Tell students that these cubes are the same.
- Have students find a cube that is different than the green cube.
- **How is the cube you found different?** Sample answer: It is not green; it is a different color.

Building Math Vocabulary and **Reviewing Math Vocabulary** activities introduce and reinforce mathematics vocabulary

Each lesson includes suggestions for **differentiating instruction.** These strategies are keyed for English Language Learners, students above grade level, struggling students, and students with special needs.

Differentiated Instruction

Small Group Options

Option 1 Gifted and Talented AL

KINESTHETIC

Materials: chart paper, crayons, attribute buttons

- Give pairs of students a piece of chart paper with three large circles on it. Draw a different shape above each circle: square, circle, and triangle.
- Give each pair of students 20 or more attribute buttons, using only the shapes square, circle, and triangle.
- Ask students to describe, compare and sort the buttons in the sorting rings.

Option 2 English Language Learners ELL

VISUAL, AUDITORY

Materials: chairs
Core Vocabulary: it, alike, different
Common Use Verb: is

Hear Math This strategy teaches descriptive vocabulary and phonemically similar words.

- Point and say: "**It *is*** a chair." Show an identical chair. Say: "**It *is*** the **same.**" Stress beginning and ending sounds for "**it,**" "***is,***" and "**alike.**"
- Repeat using the word "**different**" with other items.

Independent Work Options

Option 1 Early Finishers OL AL

LOGICAL-MATHEMATICAL

Materials: baskets, attribute blocks

- Give each student a basket of attribute blocks.
- Have students compare and sort the blocks by color.
- Invite students to guess which color has the most.
- If students are ready, have students count and see if they are correct.

Option 2 Student Technology

Math Online macmillanmh.com

 Math Adventures

Option 3 Learning Station: Science (p. 13G)

Direct students to the Science Learning Station for opportunities to explore and extend the lesson concept.

Reteach, Skills Practice, Enrich,* and *Homework Practice Masters are shown for each lesson in the Teacher Edition. These masters can be found in the ***Chapter Resource Masters.***

Leveled Lesson Resources

Additional support for English Language Learners can be found in the ELL Guide (p. 29). ELL

Reteach (p. 6) BL

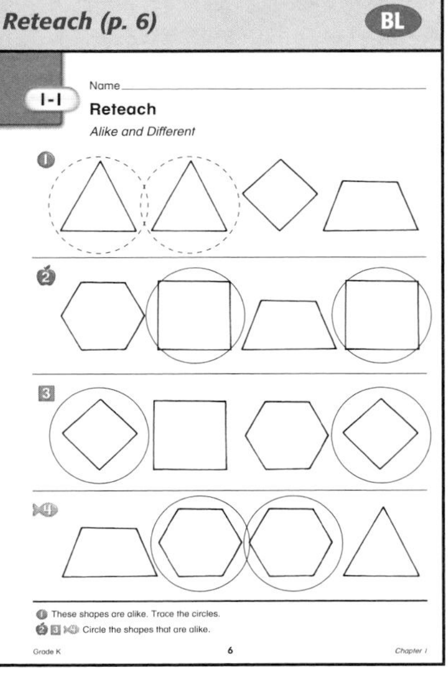
1-1 Name
Reteach
Alike and Different
1 These shapes are alike. Trace the circles.
2 3 4 Circle the shapes that are alike.
Grade K 6 Chapter 1

Skills Practice (p. 7) OL

1-1 Name
Skills Practice
Alike and Different
Possible answer:
1 Find one group of animals that are alike. Color the animals brown.
2 Find another group of animals that are alike. Color the animals yellow.
Grade K 7 Chapter 1

Enrich (p. 9) AL

1-1 Name
Enrich
All Kinds of Animals
The 3 giraffes are colored.
Color the animals that are alike. Put an X on the animals that are different.
Grade K 9 Chapter 1

Homework Practice (p. 8) OL

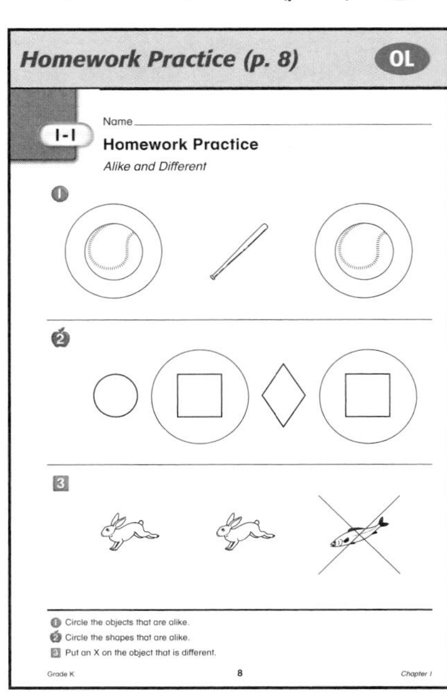
1-1 Name
Homework Practice
Alike and Different
1 Circle the objects that are alike.
2 Circle the shapes that are alike.
3 Put an X on the object that is different.
Grade K 8 Chapter 1

The **Four-Step Teaching Plan** shows you how to **Introduce, Teach, Practice,** and **Assess** each lesson. Each lesson ends with a creative strategy for closing the lesson.

1 Introduce

Circle Time

Activity Choice 1 • Literature

The Button Box
by Margarette S. Reid
Read the book and identify buttons that are alike and different.

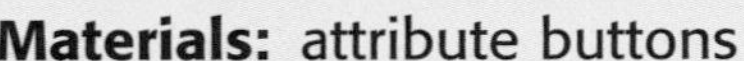

Materials: attribute buttons

- Give students a container of buttons.
- Define ***alike*** and ***different***. Select a button and ask students to find a button that is the alike or different.
- Have students work with a partner to compare and sort buttons from their container that are alike and different.
- Have students share their sorting by identifying and describing each group of buttons.

Activity Choice 2 • Hands-On

Materials: connecting cubes, crayons, bag

- Have students choose one object from a bag filled with connecting cubes and crayons.
- Ask them to look at their object and stand beside someone who has an object that looks like theirs.
- Observe students as they compare and gather together.
- **Why did you choose to stand by (student's name)? How is your object like his/her object?** Sample answers: Our objects look alike. We both have crayons.
- Say the two objects are alike. Explain how the objects are alike using observations such as color, size, function, and shape.
- Repeat, but have students find someone whose object is not like theirs.
- **Why did you choose to stand by (student's name)? How is your object not like his or her object?** Sample answer: Our objects look different; one is a crayon and one is a cube.
- Explain that this is called different. Explain how the objects are different using observations such as color, size, function, and shape.

Each lesson begins with two **Activity Choices**: a **Hands-On** activity and a **Literature Connection.**

2 Teach

Direct students to p. 17.

- Emphasize words *alike* and *different.* Instruct students to compare all the hats on p. 17.
- **How are the hats alike?** same size, color, and shape
- **How are the hats different?** different sizes, colors, shapes and are used at different times (function of the hat)

BL Alternate Teaching Strategy

If students have trouble understanding how to sort by color . . .

Then use one of these reteach options.

1 CRM **Daily Reteach Worksheet** (p. 6)

2 **Sort the Sounds** Have students listen to a strike on a drum and a strike to a musical triangle.

- Have students compare the sounds and explain if the sounds are alike or if they are different.
- Repeat by striking the drum two times. Have students explain if the sounds are alike or if they are different.
- Have students use the drum and/or triangle to show alike and different sounds.

The **Alternate Teaching Strategy** provides two suggestions for remediation for students who did not grasp the concept.

COMMON ERROR!

Students may not sort items correctly because they use too many attributes at the same time. Remind students to sort by one attribute at a time.

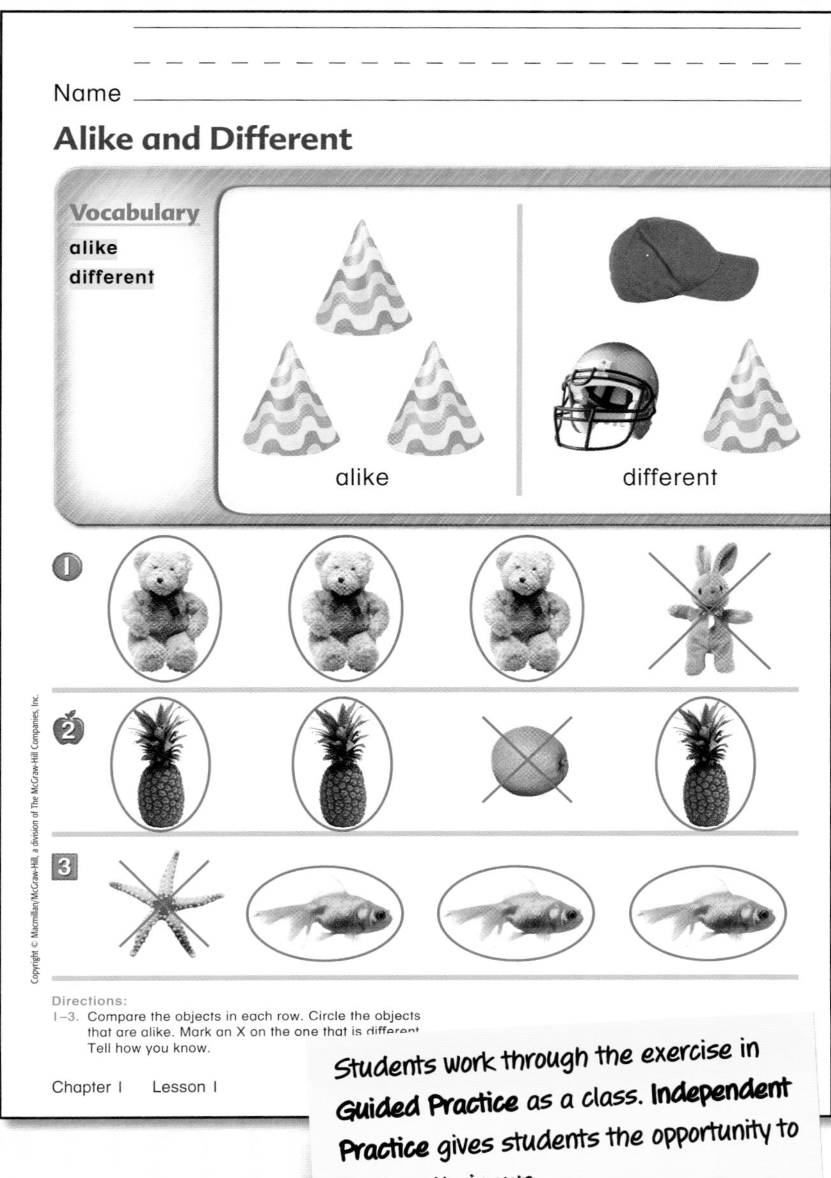

Name
Alike and Different
Vocabulary
alike
different
alike
different
Directions:
1–3. Compare the objects in each row. Circle the objects that are alike. Mark an X on the one that is different. Tell how you know.
Chapter 1 Lesson 1

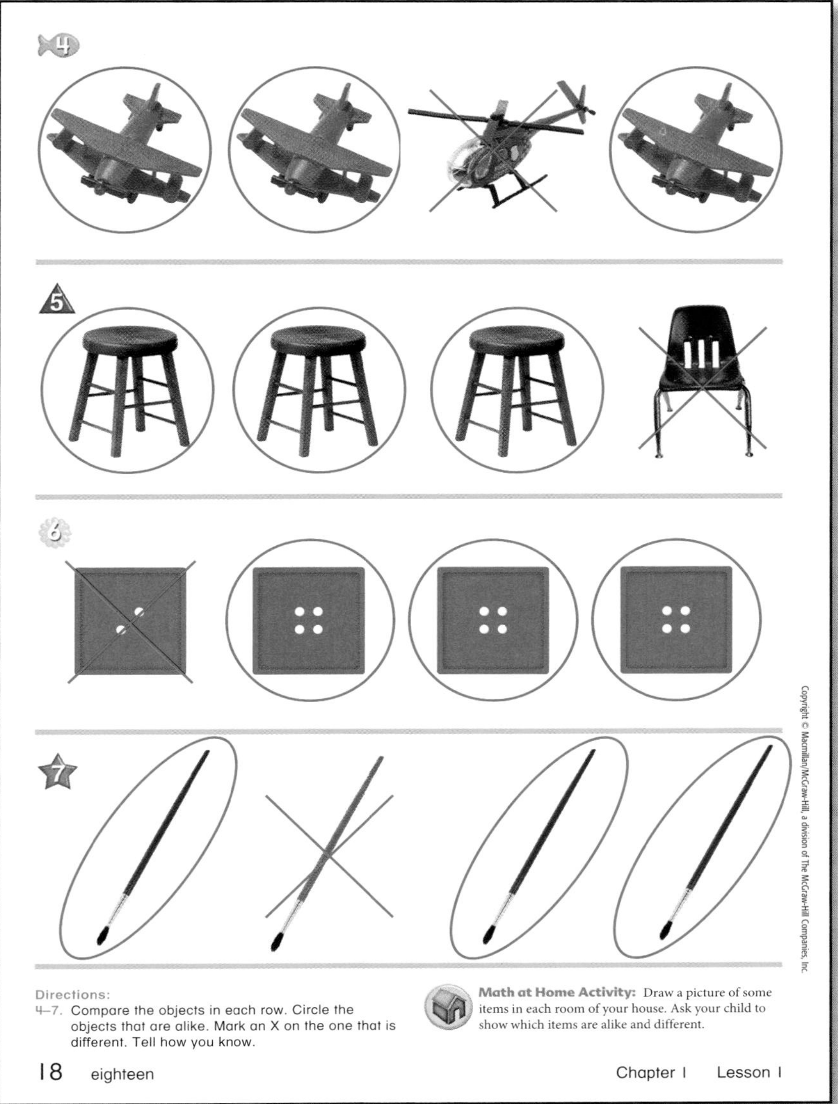

Directions:
4–7. Compare the objects in each row. Circle the objects that are alike. Mark an X on the one that is different. Tell how you know.
Math at Home Activity: Draw a picture of some items in each room of your house. Ask your child to show which items are alike and different.
18 eighteen
Chapter 1 Lesson 1

Students work through the exercise in **Guided Practice** as a class. **Independent Practice** gives students the opportunity to try it on their own.

3 Practice

Guided Practice

- Direct students to Exercise 1 on p. 17. Have them identify each object.
- Talk about how the stuffed animals are alike. Talk about how they are different.
- Ask which item does not belong in the group. Direct students to mark an X on the one that is different. Direct students to circle the objects that are alike. Have students tell you how they know.
- Repeat for Exercises 2 and 3 as a class.

Independent Practice

Have students turn to p. 18. Explain the directions. Have students work independently on the exercises.

4 Assess

Formative Assessment

Have students talk about alike and different.
Write the following numbers on the chalkboard: 2, 8, 2, 2.

- **Which numbers are alike?** 2
- Show crayons and markers. **How are crayons and markers alike? Different?** Sample answer: They are alike in color, but different sizes and shapes.

Quick Check **Are students still struggling with alike and different?**

If Yes → Small Group Options (p. 17B)
If No → Independent Work Options (p. 17B)
CRM Skills Practice Worksheet (p. 7)
CRM Enrich Worksheet (p. 9)

LESSON 1-2

Sort by One Attribute

Lesson Planner

Objective

Sort objects using one attribute.

Vocabulary

sort

Resources

Materials: orange and blue items, big and small items, chart paper, tray, yarn, string

Manipulatives: attribute buttons

Literature Connection: *Shapes, Shapes, Shapes* by Tana Hoban

Alternate Lesson: Adapt *Tiptoe: A Sorting Game* on pages 76–77 of *Math Their Way* for practice in sorting objects by one attribute.
Use *IMPACT Mathematics*: Unit I to provide practice with sorting objects by one attribute.

Teacher Technology
TeacherWorks • Math Songs Track 2 Lesson Plan

Focus on Math Background

Sorting by attributes in the primary grades includes sorting by: color, size, shape, texture, or by a feature such as 'loud and soft' or 'sink or float.' Some sorting can be done by likes and dislikes, which would prepare students for preference surveys and graphs.

Most early sorting is facilitated by providing students with sorting mats for placing "like" objects in a group.

Sorting/classifying by an attribute is a foundational skill for both math and science. When sorting by size, students are preparing for the concepts of greater than and less than.

Daily Routine

Use these suggestions before beginning the lesson on p. 19.

5-Minute Check

(Reviews Lesson 1-1)

1. Draw a blue circle. Ask students to draw a circle that is the same color and a circle that is a different color.
2. Show five different triangle attribute buttons. How are the buttons alike? Different? shape; number of holes, color, size

Problem of the Day

Draw on the chalkboard three flowers with two leaves on the stem and one flower with one leaf on the stem.

- Ask students to look at the flowers and identify which flower is different.
- Ask students to think of a way to make a flower that is different from those on the chalkboard.

LINE UP Have students with shoes that have velcro line up. Have students with shoes that tie line up. Have students with shoes that slip on line up.

Building Math Vocabulary

Write the vocabulary word ***sort*** on the chalkboard. Point to the word as you do the following activity.

- Have students watch as you sort some unit of blocks. Tell students that you are sorting, or putting the blocks into groups.
- Show a block. Ask students to find a block that is like your block and explain why it would be sorted into the same group as the block you showed.
- Ask students to find a block that is different and explain why it would be sorted into a different group.

Small Group and Independent Work Options offer classroom flexibility for students who need additional help or self-directed activity suggestions after completing their work.

Differentiated Instruction

Small Group Options

Option 1 Gifted and Talented AL

INTERPERSONAL

Materials: chart paper, crayons, cups, circular attribute buttons

- Give each pair of students a piece of chart paper with two large sorting rings on it. Have students draw a small circle above one ring and a large circle above the second ring.
- Give each pair of students a cup containing 20 or more attribute buttons. Ask students to describe, identify and sort the attribute buttons in two ways, by color and size.

Option 2 English Language Learners ELL

VISUAL

Materials: cards with simple red or blue shapes, blank cards, crayons

Core Vocabulary: color, red, blue

Common Use Verb: color

See Math This strategy teaches vocabulary.

- Identify and sort by colors.
- Allow students to pick a card and copy the same figure and color on a blank card.
- Repeat with other items as time permits.

Independent Work Options

Option 1 Early Finishers OL AL

LOGICAL

Materials: various manipulatives

- Select a group of geometric figures and ask students to sort them by color.
- Have students describe and identify which objects belong and which do not belong in the group.
- Then have students sort them by size.
- Encourage students to think of other ways to sort the manipulatives.

Option 2 Student Technology

Math Online macmillanmh.com

- Math Songs, "Sort the Veggies" Track 2
- Math Adventures

This program is supported by a wealth of **technology options** on CD-ROM, on DVD, and online.

Option 3 Learning Station: Science (p. 13G)

Direct students to the Science Learning Station for opportunities to explore and extend the lesson concept.

Leveled Lesson Resources

Additional support for English Language Learners can be found in the ELL Guide (p. 27). ELL

Reteach (p. 10) BL

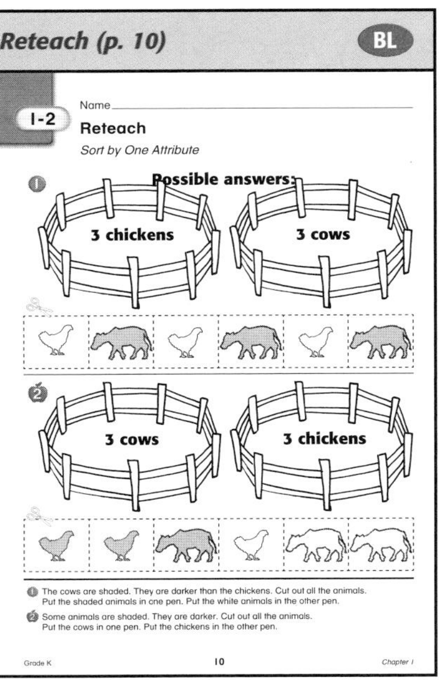

1-2
Name
Reteach
Sort by One Attribute
Possible answers:
3 chickens
3 cows
3 cows
3 chickens
The cows are shaded. They are darker than the chickens. Cut out all the animals. Put the shaded animals in one pen. Put the white animals in the other pen.
Some animals are shaded. They are darker. Cut out all the animals. Put the cows in one pen. Put the chickens in the other pen.
Grade K
10
Chapter 1

Skills Practice (p. 11) OL

1-2
Name
Skills Practice
Sort by One Attribute
Sort the toy animals. Draw a line from each animal to the correct toy box.
Grade K
11
Chapter 1

Enrich (p. 13) AL

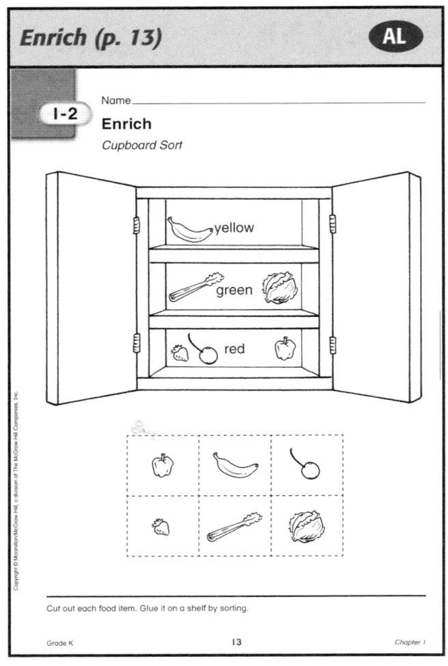

1-2
Name
Enrich
Cupboard Sort
yellow
green
red
Cut out each food item. Glue it on a shelf by sorting.
Grade K
13
Chapter 1

Homework Practice (p. 12) OL

1-2
Name
Homework Practice
Sort by One Attribute
Sort the animals. Draw a line from each animal to the place where it belongs.
Grade K
12
Chapter 1

1 Introduce

Circle Time

Activity Choice 1 • Literature

Shapes, Shapes, Shapes
by Tana Hoban

- Read the book and focus on the attributes of colors and sizes.
- Have students identify and describe, using informal language, items in the classroom that are the same color as items in the book.
- Have students identify and describe, using informal language, items in the classroom that are the same size as items in the book.
- Create a class chart with column headings *Large* and *Small*. Label each row with the names of various colors.
- List the items found in the classroom in the appropriate space on the chart.

Activity Choice 2 • Hands-On 

Materials: orange and blue items, tray, big and small items, yarn

- Make two circles side by side on the floor with yarn.
- Pick up one orange item from the tray. Place it in one circle. Pick up a blue item and place it in the other circle. Repeat.
- Explain that when we make a group of items that are alike in at least one way, we are **sorting**.
- Tell the students they sorted by color. Ask for volunteers to help sort the rest of the objects.
- Share with students that there is another way to sort items. Show the tray of big and small items. Make two new circles with the yarn on the floor side by side.
- Pick a large item from the tray and place it in one circle. Pick a small item from the other tray and place it in the other circle. Repeat.
- **How am I sorting objects?** by size

2 Teach

- Direct students to p. 19. Emphasize vocabulary word *sort*.
- **What is one way we could sort the brushes?** Sample answer: by color
- Have students look at color brushes and name the colors.
- **What is one way we could sort the cups?** Sample answer: by size
- Have students look at the cups and identify, describe, and compare the size of the cups.

BL

Alternate Teaching Strategy

If students have trouble sorting by one attribute . . .

Then use one of these reteach options.

1. CRM **Daily Reteach Worksheet** (p. 10)
2. **Sort Buttons** Have students create necklaces of attribute buttons that are alike.
   - Ask students to describe how the buttons are alike.
   - Explain that they just sorted by that attribute.
   - Repeat using a different attribute.

COMMON ERROR!

Students may key into color first (most of the time). Direct them to other attributes once color is grasped.

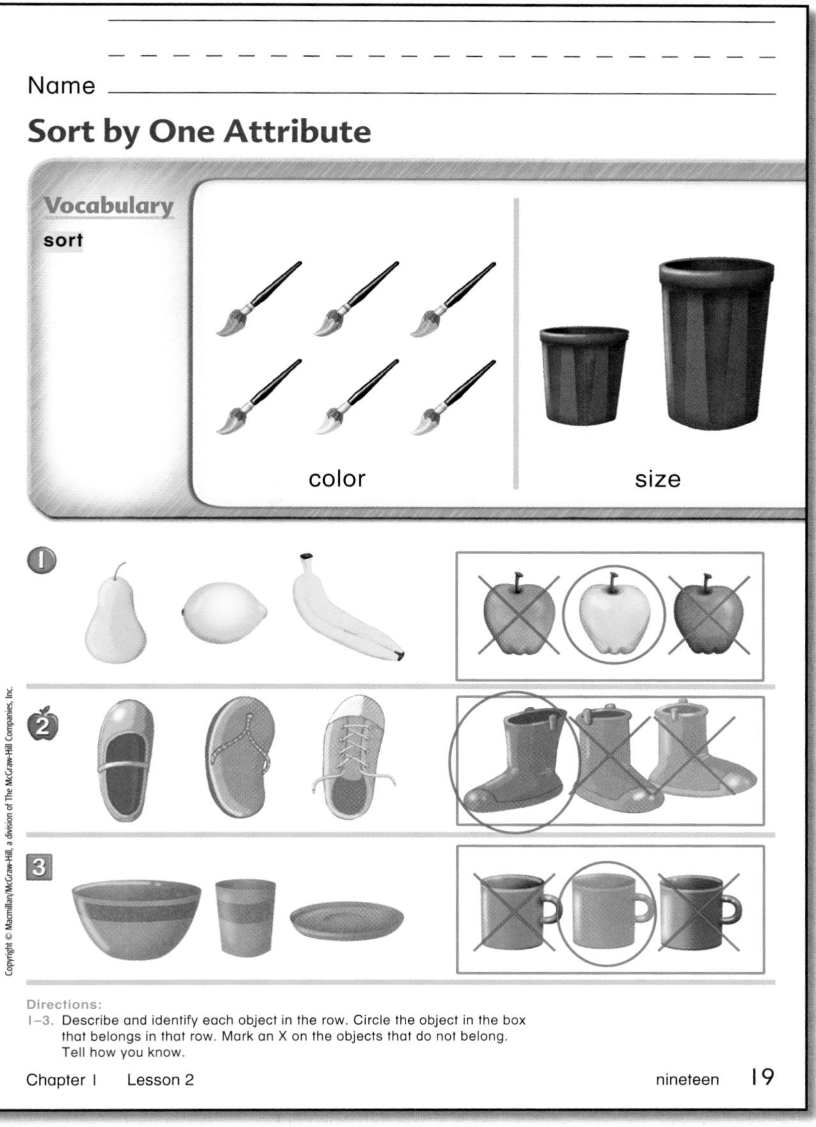

Name
Sort by One Attribute
Vocabulary
sort
color
size
Directions:
1–3. Describe and identify each object in the row. Circle the object in the box that belongs in that row. Mark an X on the objects that do not belong. Tell how you know.
Chapter 1 Lesson 2
nineteen 19

Directions: Sort the picnic items by size. Draw a line from each picnic item to the correct basket.
Math at Home Activity: Help your child sort toys by placing all the same color toys together. Then sort another way.
20 twenty
Chapter 1 Lesson 2

3 Practice

Guided Practice

- Direct students to Exercise 1 on p. 19. Ask students to identify the color of each fruit.
- Ask which apple belongs in the row of fruit. Have students circle the object in the box that belongs in the row.
- Ask why the others do not belong. Have students mark an X on the objects that do not belong.
- Repeat for Exercise 2–3.

Independent Practice

Have students turn to p. 20. Explain the directions. Have students work independently on the exercise.

Quick Check provides reteaching suggestions for students who continue to struggle.

4 Assess

Formative Assessment

Have students discuss alike and different.

- **What can we look at to see if objects are alike or different?** size, color
- Provide large and small attribute buttons. Have students sort by size.
- Provide same size and shape attribute buttons of two colors. Have students sort by color.

Quick Check **Are students still struggling to count and write numbers 1, 2, and 3?**

If Yes → Small Group Options (p. 19B)

If No → Independent Work Options (p. 19B)

CRM Skills Practice Worksheet (p. 11)

CRM Enrich Worksheet (p. 13)

Lesson Planner

Objective

Sort objects to determine whether or not they belong in a group.

Resources

Materials: cat-related objects, fish-related objects, scissors, glue, red bags, blue bags, coins, letter and number shapes

Manipulatives: attribute buttons, connecting cubes

Literature Connection: *26 Letters and 99 Cents* by Tana Hoban

Teacher Technology

TeacherWorks

Real-World Problem Solving Library

Math and Social Studies: *Inside My Classroom*

Use these leveled readers to reinforce and extend problem-solving skills and strategies.

Leveled for:

- OL On Level
- ELL Sheltered English
- SP Spanish

For additional support, see the Real-World Problem Solving Teacher Guide.

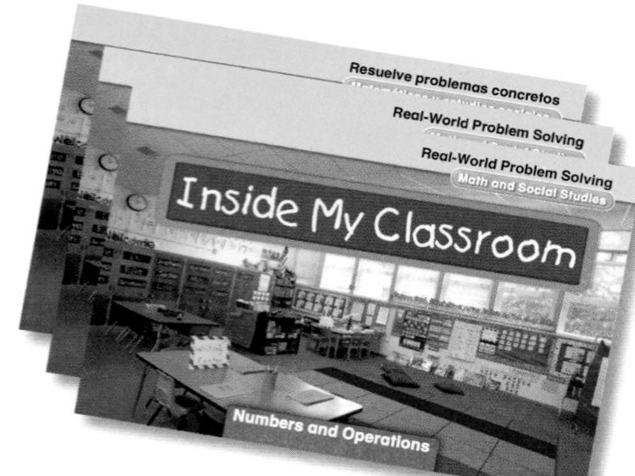

On-level title is available in classroom Big Book.

The **Real-World Problem Solving Readers**, which include fiction and non-fiction leveled readers, extend problem-solving skills and strategies and make real-world connections.

Daily Routine

Use these suggestions before beginning the lesson on p. 21.

5-Minute Check

(Reviews Lesson 1-2)

Tell students to circle the object that belongs in the row.

Problem of the Day

Collect the following pattern blocks:

Tell students to put figures that are alike together and put figures that are different together. Then have them draw a picture of each group by tracing the blocks.

LINE UP Ask a student to line up. Have students with similar shirts line up and say how their shirts are the same. Have remaining students form a separate line and explain how their shirts are different.

Differentiated Instruction

Small Group Options

Option 1 Gifted and Talented AL

KINESTHETIC, LOGICAL

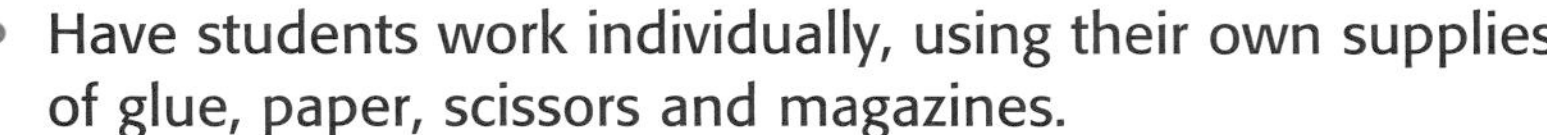

Materials: paper, glue, scissors, magazines

- Have students work individually, using their own supplies of glue, paper, scissors and magazines.
- Have students make 4 groups of pictures on their paper, sorted only by color. The students need to cut out 2 pictures for each of the 4 color groups they have chosen.
- After students have decided on their 4 colors and have cut out 2 pictures of each color, the pictures should be glued onto their papers in the 4 color sorted groups.

Option 2 English Language Learners ELL

SOCIAL AND AUDITORY

Materials: large picture of: places and things they found in them (zoo/animals)
Core Vocabulary: what, belong, thumbs up/down
Common Use Verb: does/doesn't

Hear Math This strategy introduces negative verb forms.

- Show pictures of toy room and some objects.
- Say: **"What doesn't belong?"** Move a toy to pictures and model **thumbs up** and **thumbs down** using **belong/ doesn't belong** vocabulary.
- Discuss results.

Option 1 Early Finishers AL OL

KINESTHETIC

Materials: pictures related to dogs, boxes, pictures related to fish, bags

- Give each student some pictures related to dogs, a box, pictures related to fish, and a bag.
- Have each student put all the dog-related pictures in the box.
- Have each student put all the fish-related pictures in the bag.

Option 2 Student Technology

Math Online macmillanmh.com

Option 3 Learning Station: Music (p. 13H)

Direct students to the Music Learning Station for opportunities to explore and extend the lesson concept.

Leveled Lesson Resources

Reteach (pp. 14–15) BL

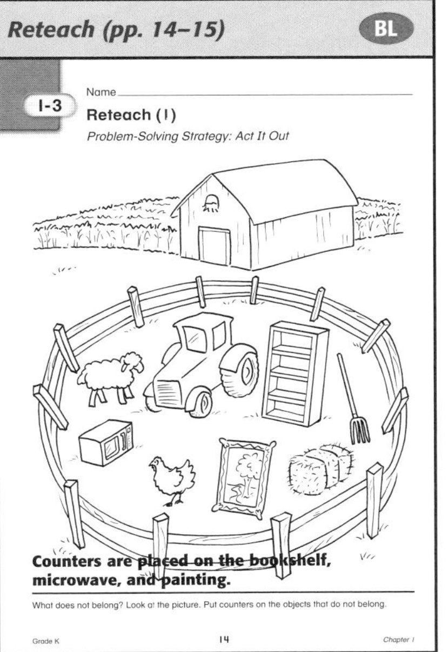

Skills Practice (p. 16) OL

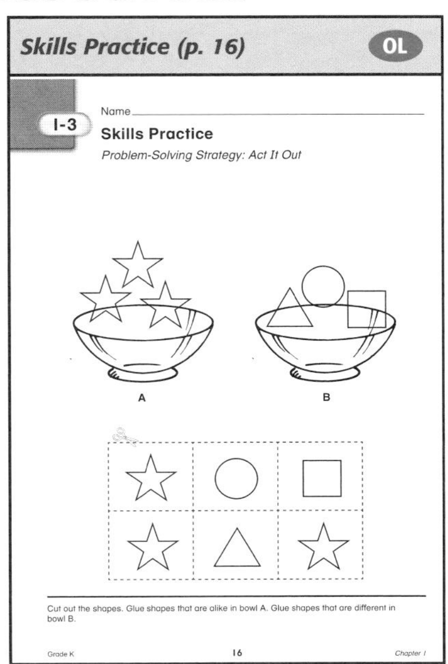

Enrich (p. 18) AL

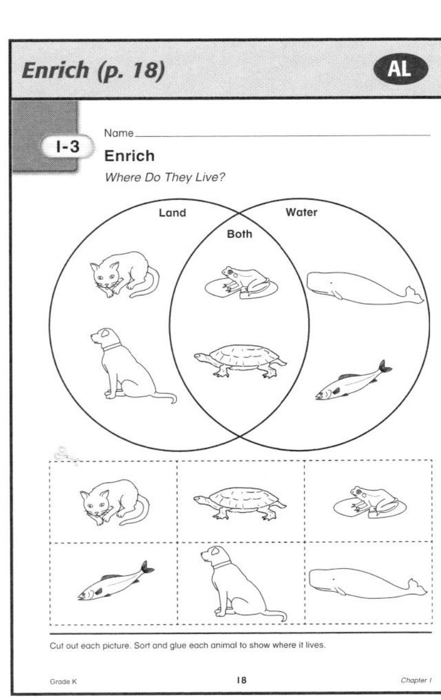

Homework Practice (p. 17) OL

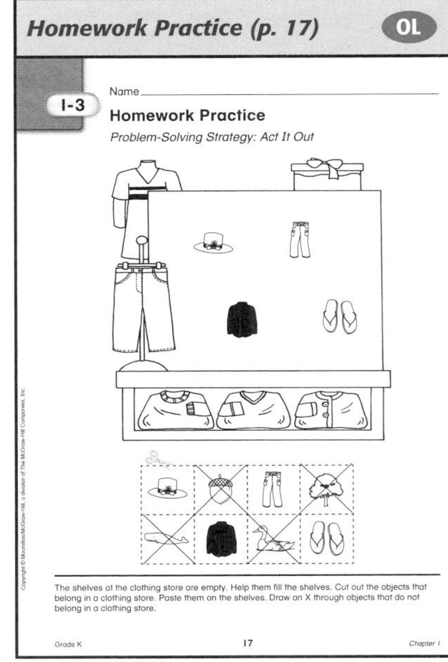

1-3
Name
Homework Practice
Problem-Solving Strategy: Act It Out
The shelves of the clothing store are empty. Help them fill the shelves. Cut out the objects that belong in a clothing store. Paste them on the shelves. Draw an X through objects that do not belong in a clothing store.
Grade K
17
Chapter 1

1 Introduce

Circle Time

Activity Choice 1 • Literature

26 Letters and 99 Cents
by Tana Hoban
Materials: letter and number shapes, coins

- Read the book aloud, referring to the characteristics of the letters, numbers, and coins. Flip the book and continue.
- Put students in groups, giving each group an assortment of letter and number shapes (or cards) and coins. Ask them to sort the items and decide on a name for each group. Students then explain why they sorted and named as they did, including how items are alike and different.
- Ask students to sort items another way and give the groups new names.

Activity Choice 2 • Hands-On

Manipulatives: attribute buttons

- Give each student a green or yellow attribute button.
- Tell students to sort themselves into a green group and a yellow group.
- Discuss with students how they acted it out to sort themselves into groups.

2 Teach

Direct students to the top of p. 21.

Understand Review what students know and what they need to find for each problem.

Plan Have students discuss their strategy for solving the problems.

Solve Guide students to act it out in order to solve the problem. Discuss with students what it means for objects to be alike or different. Have students decide which objects are alike and different and glue them onto the appropriate place on the page.

Check Have students look back at the problem to be sure that the answers fit what they already know about the problem. Discuss with students that mathematical statements can be true or false. Students need to check to make sure their answers are true statements

BL Alternate Teaching Strategy

If students have trouble with solving problems with the *act it out* strategy . . .

Then use one of these reteach options.

1 CRM **Daily Reteach Worksheet** (p. 14)

2 **Use Objects** Have a collection of items related to a fish or a cat.
- Have students put the fish objects and the cat objects in separate piles.

Problem-Solving Strategy lessons help students learn different problem-solving skills and strategies for solving word problems.

COMMON ERROR!

Students may have difficulty solving a sorting problem with objects that are alike and different. Tell them to first gather and group all the objects that are alike. Explain that the objects left will be the different objects.

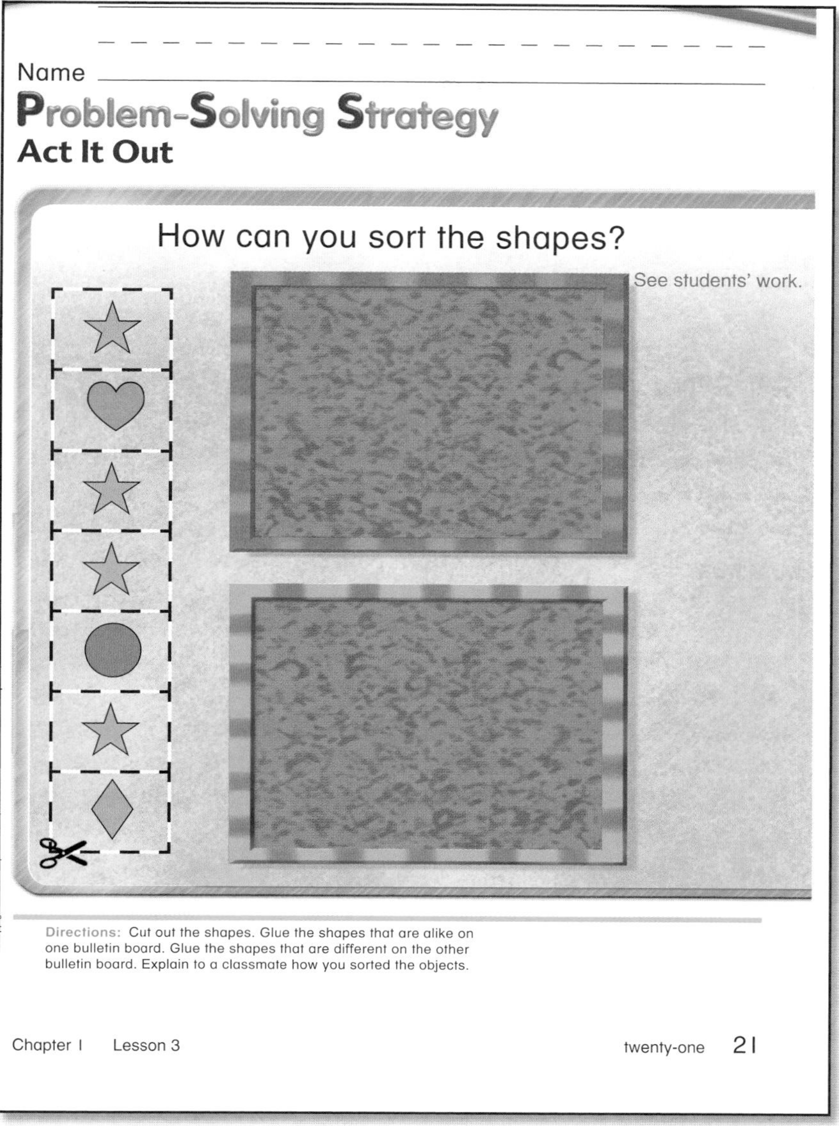

Name
Problem-Solving Strategy
Act It Out
How can you sort the shapes?
See students' work.
Directions: Cut out the shapes. Glue the shapes that are alike on one bulletin board. Glue the shapes that are different on the other bulletin board. Explain to a classmate how you sorted the objects.
Chapter 1 Lesson 3
twenty-one 21

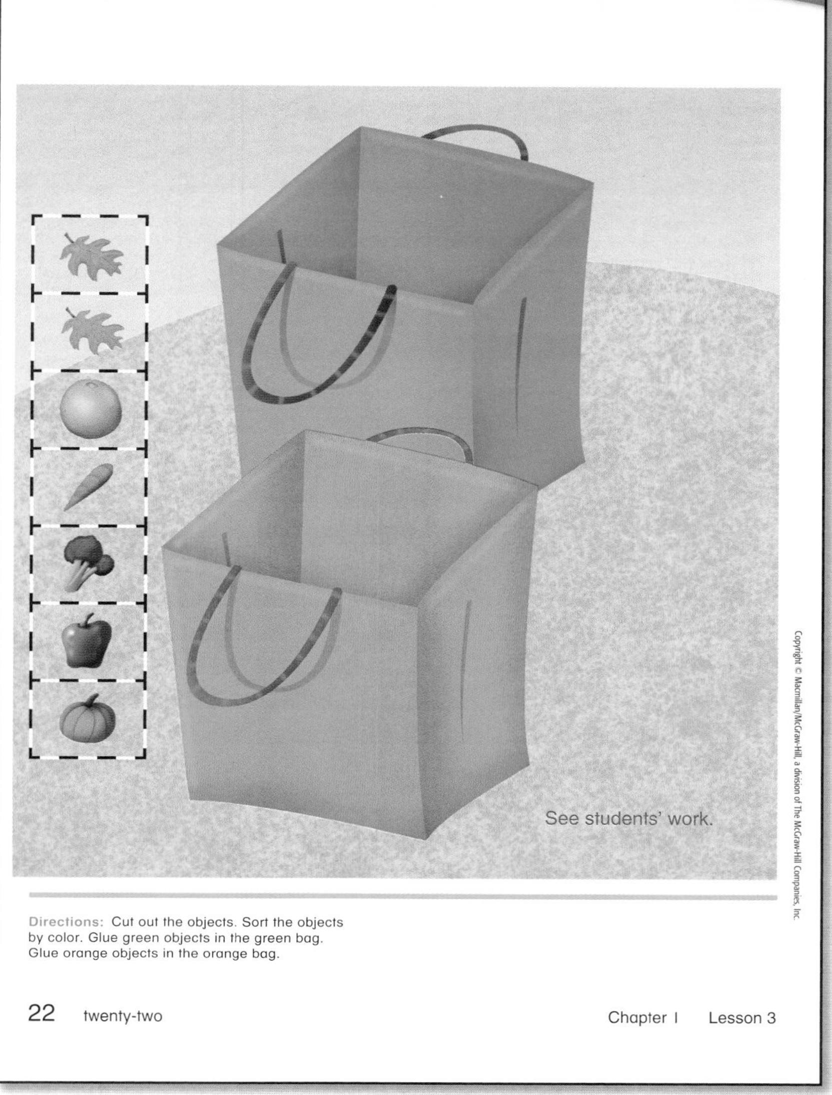

See students' work.
Directions: Cut out the objects. Sort the objects by color. Glue green objects in the green bag. Glue orange objects in the orange bag.
22 twenty-two
Chapter 1 Lesson 3
Copyright © Macmillan/McGraw-Hill, a division of The McGraw-Hill Companies, Inc.

3 Practice

Guided Practice

- Direct students to p. 21.
- Ask students to name the shapes at the side of the page.
- Have students cut out the shapes.
- Tell them to glue the shapes that are alike in one bulletin board.
- Tell them to glue the shapes that are different in the other bulletin board.
- Have students tell a classmate how they sorted the shapes.

Independent Practice

Have students turn to p. 22 and work independently on the exercises.

4 Assess

Formative Assessment

- Give students some red and blue connecting cubes.
- Tell them to put the red cubes in a bag and the blue cubes in another bag.

Quick Check **Are students still struggling to use the problem-solving strategy *act it out?***

If Yes → Small Group Options (p. 21B)

If No → Independent Work Options (p. 21B)

 Skills Practice Worksheet (p. 16)

 Enrich Worksheet (p. 18)

LESSON 1-4

Sort by More Than One Attribute

Lesson Planner

Objective

Sort objects using more than one attribute.

Review Vocabulary

sort

Resources

Materials: cards with simple drawings of shapes colored in red or blue, shape cards, drawing paper, crayons
Manipulatives: attribute buttons
Literature Connection: *The Button Box* by Margarette S. Reid
Alternate Lesson: Adapt *Geoboard Sorting Game* on page 80 of *Math Their Way* for practice in sorting by more than one attribute.
Use *IMPACT Mathematics*: Unit I to provide practice sorting objects by more than one attribute.
Teacher Technology
TeacherWorks • Concepts in Motion • Math Songs Track 2 Lesson Plan

Focus on Math Background

Sorting and classifying by more than one attribute helps students see likenesses and differences and make comparisons. Sorting and classifying are foundational skills for both math and science. When creating and extending patterns, students frequently use more than one attribute in selecting the next object in the pattern.

In more advanced mathematics, students will be asked to discriminate between odd and even numbers, prime and composite numbers, and single and multi-digit numbers. In algebra, one of the underlying concepts is recognizing conditions in the problem situation.

Daily Routine

Use these suggestions before beginning the lesson on p. 23.

5-Minute Check

(Reviews Lesson 1-3)
Show students pictures of a desk, a pencil, a tiger, a crayon, and a book. Which item does not belong in a school? How do you know? Sample answers: Tiger; I use all other objects in school. Tigers belong in a jungle or a zoo.

Problem of the Day

What ways are there to sort dogs? Sample answers: breed, length of fur, color, size, shape of face, tail length

The **5-Minute Check** provides a quick review and assessment of a previous lesson. Use the **Problem of the Day** to challenge students with additional review and higher-order questions.

Have students who packed their lunch line up. Now have students who are buying their lunch line up.

Review Math Vocabulary

Write the word **sort** on the chalkboard. Point to the word as you do the following activity.

- **What does it means to sort?** Sample answer: to group things together that are alike or the same
- **What words are used for sorting?** Sample answers: alike, different, color, shape, size
- Write the words on the chalkboard.
- **What are some things that can be sorted?** Sample answers: toys, crayons, stuffed animals, books, blocks
- Write the words on the chalkboard.

Differentiated Instruction

Small Group Options

Option 1 LOGICAL

Below/Approaching Level (BL)

Materials: attribute buttons

- From a group of attribute buttons, begin to make a group of red figures. **How am I sorting?** By color
- Return the red buttons to the original group and begin to make a group of triangles. **How am I sorting?** By figure
- Use attribute buttons to make a group of blue triangles. **What two ways am I sorting?** By figure and by color

Option 2 VISUAL/SPATIAL, LINGUISTIC

English Language Learners (ELL)

Materials: red, yellow, and blue attribute blocks
Core Vocabulary: sort, yellow, not
Common Use Verb: is/isn't

See Math This strategy introduces color vocabulary and negative contractions.

- Sort for the color yellow. Say: "Is it yellow?"
- Restate "It is not yellow" or "It is yellow" as you sort.
- Repeat using contractions is/isn't as time permits.

Independent Work Options

Option 1 LOGICAL

Early Finishers (OL) (AL)

Materials: attribute buttons

- Have students work in pairs.
- Have one student in the pair sort the buttons into groups with two attributes that are the same.
- Have the partner identify and describe the two common attributes.
- Then have the partner sort by two attributes.

Option 2

Student Technology

Math Online macmillanmh.com

- Math Songs, "Sort the Veggies" Track 2
- Math Adventures

Option 3

Learning Station: Social Studies (p. 13H)

Direct students to the Social Studies Learning Station for opportunities to explore and extend the lesson concept.

Leveled Lesson Resources

Additional support for English Language Learners can be found in the ELL Guide (p. 25). (ELL)

Reteach (p. 19) (BL)

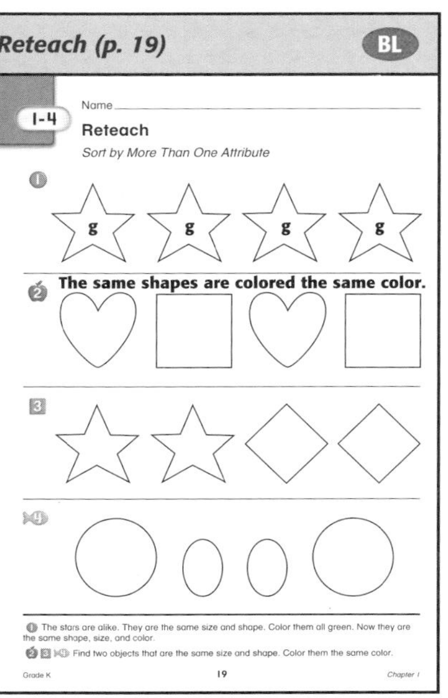

Name
1-4 Reteach
Sort by More Than One Attribute

1. The stars are alike. They are the same size and shape. Color them all green. Now they are the same shape, size, and color.

2. 3. 4. Find two objects that are the same size and shape. Color them the same color.

Grade K 19 Chapter 1

Skills Practice (p. 20) (OL)

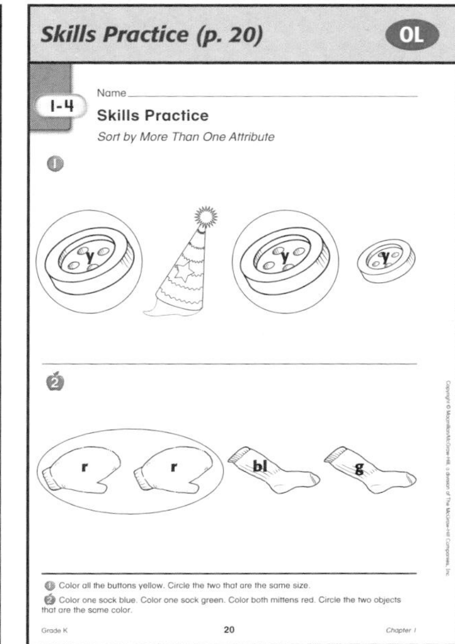

Name
1-4 Skills Practice
Sort by More Than One Attribute

1. Color all the buttons yellow. Circle the two that are the same size.

2. Color one sock blue. Color one sock green. Color both mittens red. Circle the two objects that are the same color.

Grade K 20 Chapter 1

Enrich (p. 22) (AL)

Name
1-4 Enrich
Sort the Laundry

1. Circle the objects that are worn on your feet.

2. Check the objects that you wear on the top part of your body.

3. Put an X on the objects that you put on your legs.

Grade K 22 Chapter 1

Homework Practice (p. 21) (OL)

Name
1-4 Homework Practice
Sort by More Than One Attribute

Color the large balloons red. Color the small flowers yellow.

Grade K 21 Chapter 1

1 Introduce

Circle Time

Activity Choice 1 • Literature

The Button Box
by Margarette S. Reid

- Re-read the book, focusing on the attributes of the buttons, such as size, color, and shape.
- Give students a container of buttons. Have the students identify a button that matches a given attribute.
- Have students work with a partner to **sort** buttons by two attributes, such as find all buttons that are small and blue.
- Have students share their sorting.

Activity Choice 2 • Hands-On

Materials: attribute buttons

- Put the following attribute buttons in the center of a circle: red triangle with 2 holes, green triangle with 2 holes, yellow triangle with two holes, blue triangle with 4 holes.
- As you name the buttons invite students to point to them.
- Demonstrate how to sort by sorting the buttons by shape. Make a group of triangles.
- Have students sort the triangles by looking at another attribute, such as size or color. Show students a large and a small triangle so they know how to identify large and small.
- Combine two attributes such as shape and size, color and size, or color and shape to demonstrate sorting by two attributes.
- Show students how to check for each of the two attributes to determine the group that the button belongs in.
- Have students choose two different attributes, sort the buttons accordingly, and explain their work.

2 Teach

- Direct students to the top of p. 23.
- Have students look at the buttons. Tell students that they are going to practice sorting objects in more than one way.
- **What are some possible ways to sort the buttons?** size, shape, or color
- Discuss each attribute as shown at the top of the page.
- **What two ways could we sort the buttons?** size and shape, shape and color, color and size
- Have students draw a picture of one of the matching buttons on the page.
- Ask students to create a button with two of the same attributes as the one on the page.
- Have students explain the two similar attributes to a classmate.

BL Alternate Teaching Strategy

If students have trouble sorting by more than one attribute . . .

Then use one of these reteach options.

1 CRM **Daily Reteach Worksheet** (p. 19)

2 **Alike and Different** Review the attributes by asking questions and having them touch the holes in each button.

- Have students run their fingers around the edges of the buttons.
- Have them describe each button. Ask students to explain what is alike about the buttons and what is different.

COMMON ERROR!

Students may forget to look at the size, shape, or color of the buttons. Remind students to look carefully at the objects to find more than one attribute.

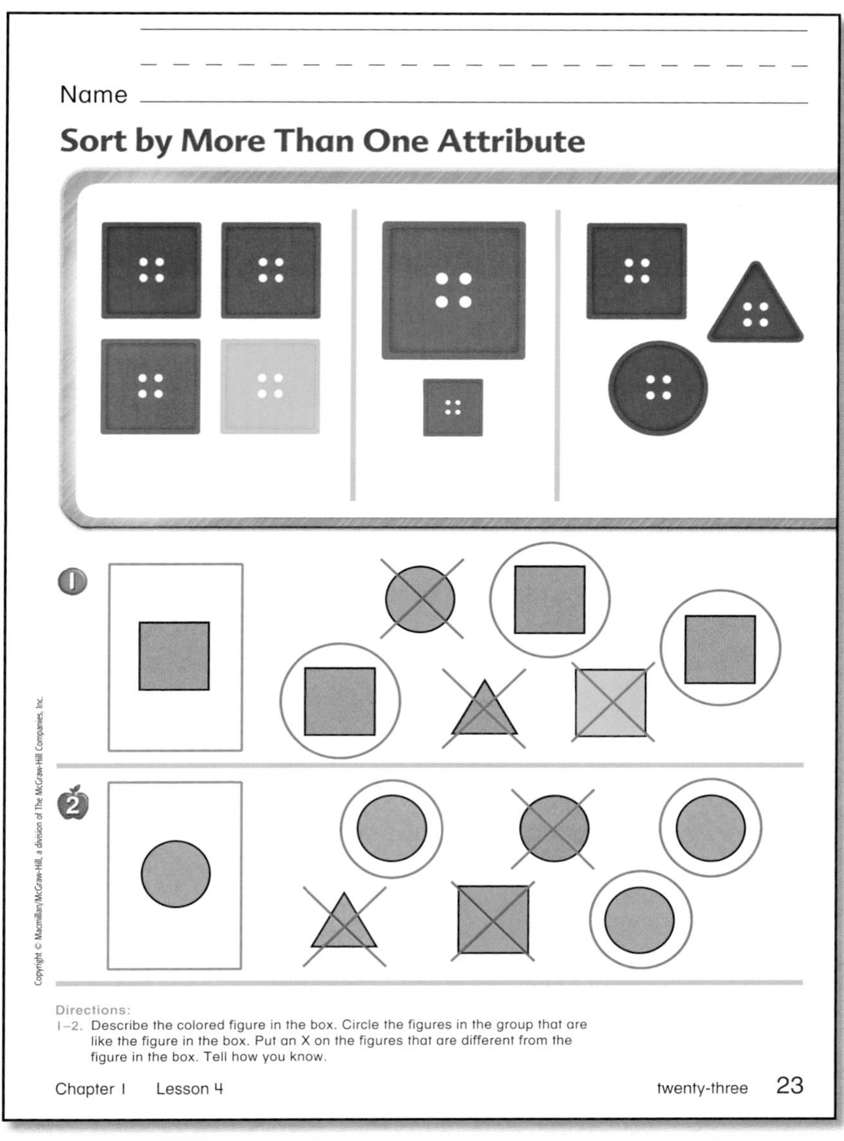

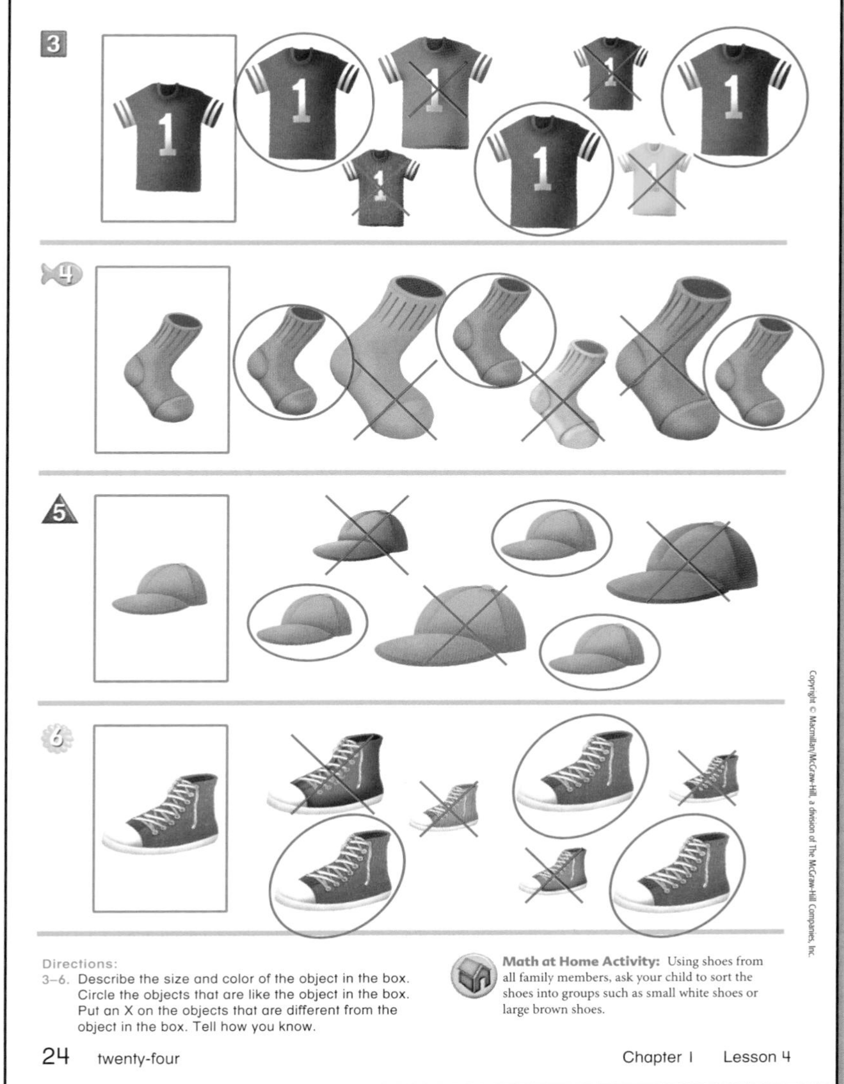

Directions:
3–6. Describe the size and color of the object in the box. Circle the objects that are like the object in the box. Put an X on the objects that are different from the object in the box. Tell how you know.
Math at Home Activity: Using shoes from all family members, ask your child to sort the shoes into groups such as small white shoes or large brown shoes.
24 twenty-four Chapter 1 Lesson 4

3 Practice

Guided Practice

- Direct students to Exercise 1 on p. 23.
- Ask students to describe the object in the box. This is what they will be sorting.
- Guide them in determining which shapes in the group are the same or like the figure and which shapes are not the same (or different) by identifying attributes of color and shape.
- Follow the same procedure for Exercise 2.

Independent Practice

Have students turn to p. 24. Explain the directions. Have students work independently on the exercises.

4 Assess

Formative Assessment

Using various colors of construction paper, cut out large and small figures. Divide students into groups of three, and give each group an assortment of figures.

- For each group, have one student sort the figures by shape and size. Have another student sort by shape and color. Have the third student sort by size and color.

Quick Check **Are students still struggling to sort by more than one attribute?**

If Yes → Small Group Options (p. 23B)

If No → Independent Work Options (p. 23B)

CRM Skills Practice Worksheet (p. 20)

CRM Enrich Worksheet (p. 22)

Mid-Chapter Check

Lessons 1-1 to 1-4

Formative Assessment

Use the Mid-Chapter Check to assess students' progress in the first half of the chapter.

ExamView Assessment Suite Customize and create multiple versions of your Mid-Chapter Check and the test answer keys.

FOLDABLES® Dinah Zike's Foldables

Use these lesson suggestions for incorporating the Foldables during the chapter.

Lesson 1-1 Place two of the same object in one display case and two different objects in the second display case. Make word cards for the terms *alike* and *different*. Encourage students to sort and classify objects as alike or different by placing them in the display cases and labeling them with a word card.

Lesson 1-2 Use the display cases to sort objects by one attribute. For example, students might sort objects by color, size, or shape.

Lesson 1-4 Use the display cases to sort objects by more than one attribute. For example, students might place yellow balls in one case and blue balls in the other.

Lesson 1-5 Students might place one object in each case noting that there are the same number of objects in each case. Add another object to each case to illustrate one-to-one correspondence.

Name

1

2

3

4

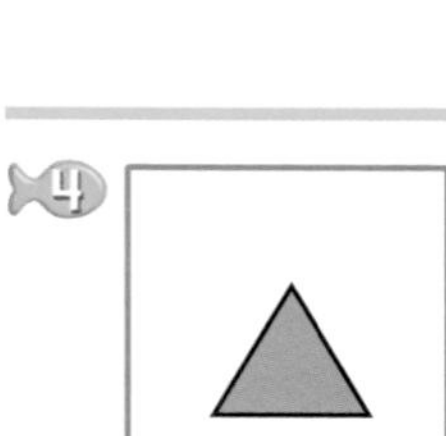
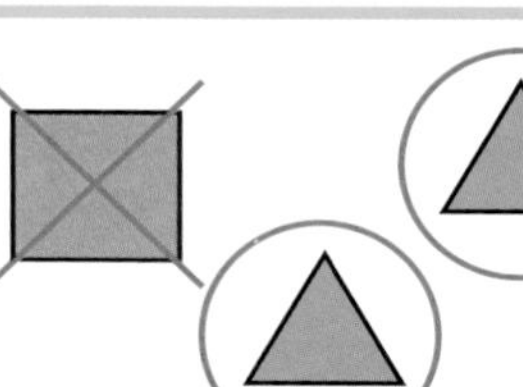
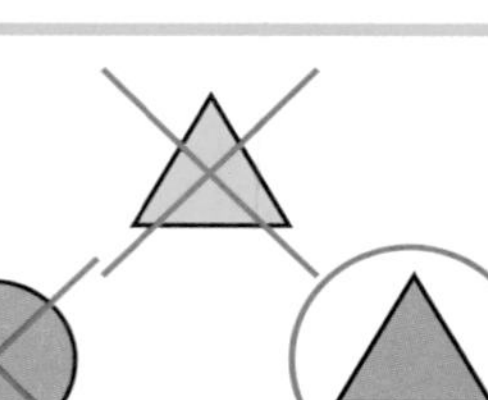

Directions:
1–2. Circle the objects that are alike. Mark an X on the object that is different.
3. Sort the color tiles by drawing a line from each color tile to the same color bag.
4. Describe the colored figure in the box. Circle the figures in the group that are like the object in the box. Put an X on the figures that are different from the object in the box.

The **Mid-Chapter Check** reviews skills and concepts presented in previous lessons. Students' results can be used for **Data-Driven Decision Making.**

Data Driven Decision Making

Based on the results of the Mid-Chapter Check, use the following resources to review concepts that continue to give students problems.

Exercises	State/Local Standards	What's the Math?	Error Analysis	Resources for Review
1–2 **Lesson 1-1**		Sort and classify objects by comparing an attribute. Identify objects that do not belong to a particular group.	Does not circle correct objects. Does not put an X on what is different.	CRM Chapter 1 Resource Masters (Reteach Worksheets) Math Online Concepts in Motion Math Adventures
3 **Lesson 1-2**		Sort and classify objects.	Does not sort correctly. Draws lines to the wrong places.	
4 **Lesson 1-4**		Sort and classify objects by more than one attribute. Identify objects that do not belong to a particular group.	Does not circle correct objects. Does not put an X on what is different.	

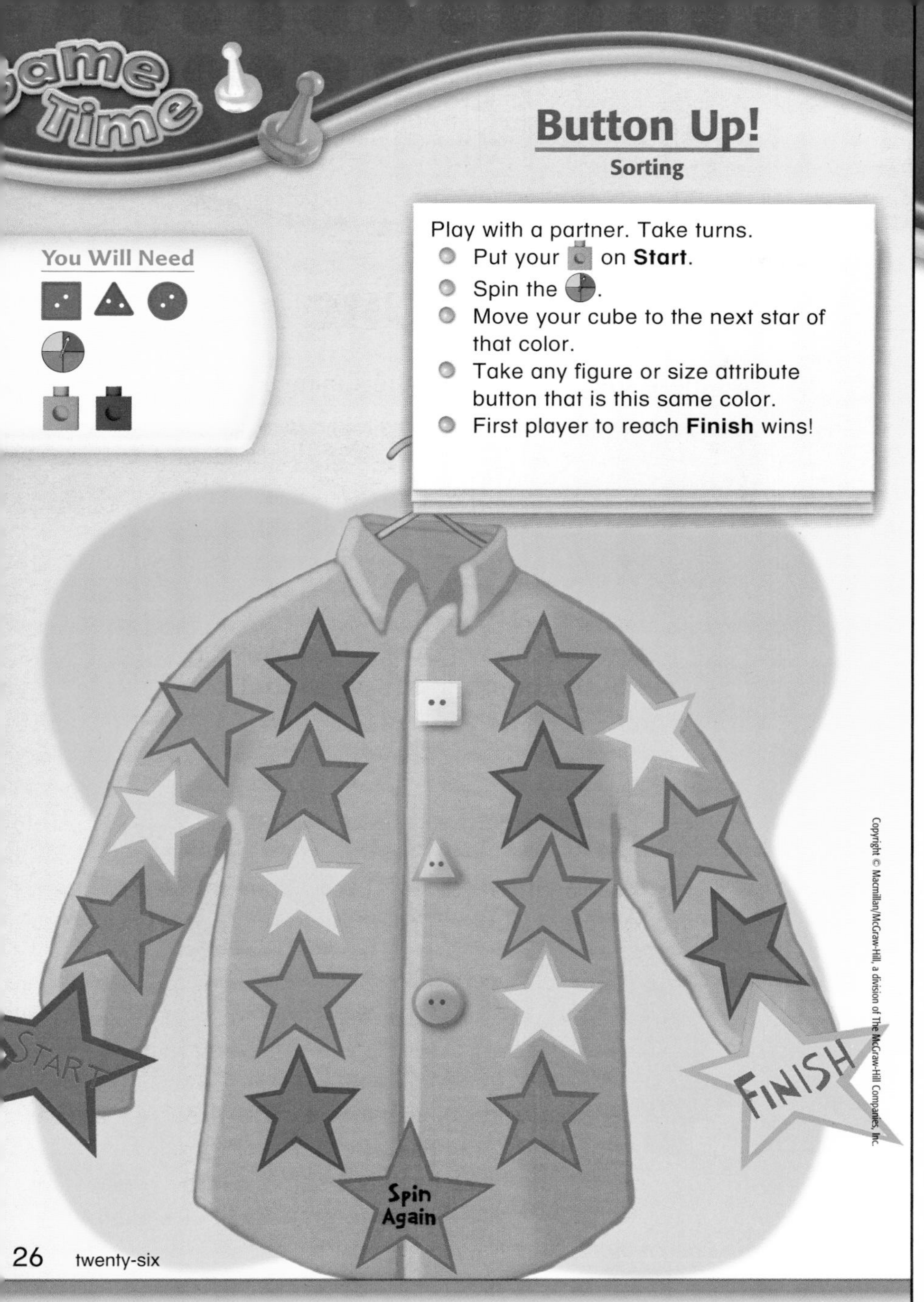
Game Time

Button Up!

Sorting

You Will Need

Play with a partner. Take turns.

- Put your [cube] on **Start**.
- Spin the [spinner].
- Move your cube to the next star of that color.
- Take any figure or size attribute button that is this same color.
- First player to reach **Finish** wins!

START

Spin Again

FINISH

Button Up!

Math Concept: Sorting

Manipulatives: color spinner, orange and purple connecting cubes, attribute buttons

Introduce the game on p. 26 to your students to play as a class, in small groups, or at a learning workstation to review concepts introduced in this chapter.

Instructions

- Assign each student a connecting cube to use as a game piece.
- Have players take turns spinning the spinner and moving their game piece to the next star that is the same color they landed on.
- Players choose any attribute button that is the same color they landed on.
- The first player to reach the finish wins!
- Ask students to work with a partner to sort the attribute buttons they collected.

Extend the Game

Have students sort the buttons using two or more attributes.

Differentiated Practice

Use these leveling suggestions to differentiate the game for all learners.

Level	Assignment
BL Below/Approaching Level	Have students sort the buttons by color.
OL On Level	Have students play the game with the rules as written.
AL Above/Beyond Level	Students must pick up two different buttons after each move and tell how they are alike and different.

Game Time activities reinforce chapter concepts and skills. The Teacher Edition offers suggestions for differentiation and extension.

LESSON 1-5

Same Number

Lesson Planner

Objective

Use one-to-one correspondence to show groups with the same number.

Vocabulary

same number

Resources

Materials: yarn, books
Manipulatives: connecting cubes, counters, color tiles
Literature Connection: *More or Less* by Stuart J. Murphy
Alternate Lesson: Use *Stack, Tell, Spin, and Win* on pages 126–127 of *Math Their Way* for practice in one-to-one correspondence to determine more than or less than. Use *IMPACT Mathematics*: Unit A to provide practice with having groups with the same number of objects.
Teacher Technology
TeacherWorks

Focus on Math Background

Comparing quantities using one-to-one correspondence to determine the group that has a greater quantity is preparation for comparing numbers with symbols for *more than* (>) and *less than* (<).

One–to-one correspondence reinforces the concept of groups having or not having the same number. Using quantity as a comparison is related to sorting and classifying by size.

When working with one-to-one correspondence, students are able to build a foundation for the concept of sharing equally, the foundation for both division and fractions of a whole.

Using a pan scale to show two objects that do not balance is an especially visual and kinesthetic way for young children to see the concept of more than and less than as well as inequality.

Daily Routine

Use these suggestions before beginning the lesson on p. 27.

5-Minute Check

(Reviews Lesson 1-4)
Gather a selection of books. How can we sort some of the books in the classroom? Sample answers: by size, shape, color, subject, number of pages

Problem of the Day

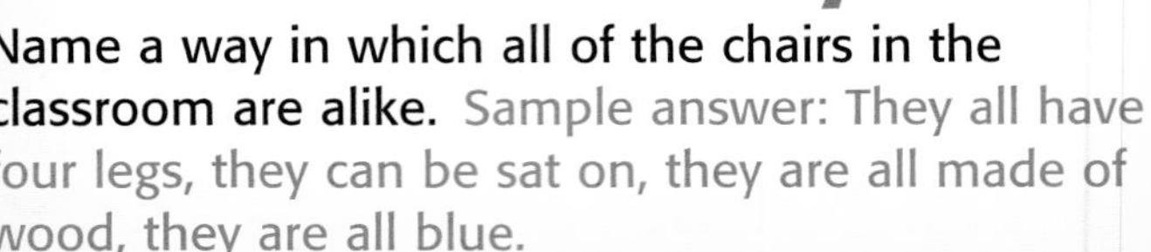

Name a way in which all of the chairs in the classroom are alike. Sample answer: They all have four legs, they can be sat on, they are all made of wood, they are all blue.

LINE UP Ask volunteers to make a line of 3 boys and a line of 3 girls. Ask another boy to get into the line of boys. **Do the lines have the same number?** no **How do we make them have the same number?** Put a girl into the line of girls or take away a boy.

Building Math Vocabulary

Make a train of five connecting cubes. Make another train of three connecting cubes.

- **Are these trains the same? How do you know?** No; one train has more cubes.
- Add two cubes to the train with 3 cubes.
- **Are these trains the same? How do you know?** Yes; both trains have 5 cubes.
- Tell students that the trains represent the **same number**, and that *equal* is another word that means same.

Differentiated Instruction

Small Group Options

Option 1 Below/Approaching Level (BL)

LOGICAL

Materials: attribute buttons, two baskets, pieces of yarn

- Put a group of red buttons into one basket and the same number of green buttons in another basket.
- Have students remove the buttons one at a time from each basket and put the sets of buttons next to each other.
- Use yarn to match a red button to a green button.
- When each red matches up with a green, have students say, "The groups contain the same number."

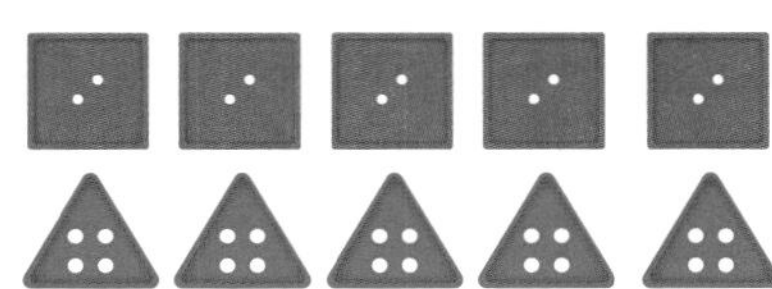

Option 2 English Language Learners (ELL)

VISUAL/SPATIAL

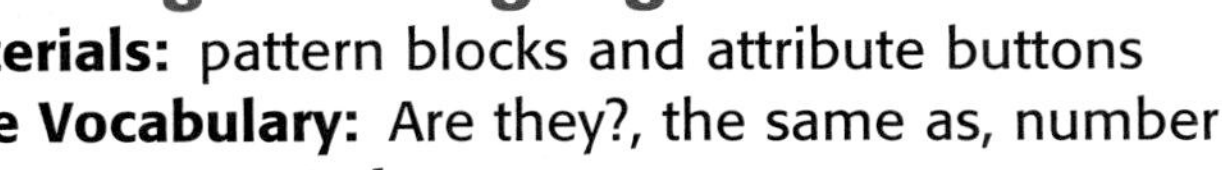

Materials: pattern blocks and attribute buttons
Core Vocabulary: Are they?, the same as, number
Common Use Verb: are

Do Math This strategy teaches sorting vocabulary.

- Show a 2 block and a 2 button group. Say: "They are the **same number.**"
- Repeat with new groups, modeling thumbs up/down while students repeat. Use "Are they the same number?" to prompt students as necessary.

Independent Work Options

Option 1 Early Finishers (OL) (AL)

LOGICAL

Materials: pencils, paper

- Have students make groups containing the same number of pencils and pieces of paper.
- Have students check to see if their sets are equal by matching one pencil with each piece of paper.
- Have students repeat the activity by creating different size sets.

Option 2 Student Technology

Math Online macmillanmh.com

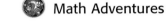

Math Adventures

Option 3 Learning Station: Reading (p. 13G)

Direct students to the Reading Learning Station for opportunities to explore and extend the lesson concept.

Leveled Lesson Resources

Additional support for English Language Learners can be found in the ELL Guide (p. 15). (ELL)

Reteach (p. 23) (BL)

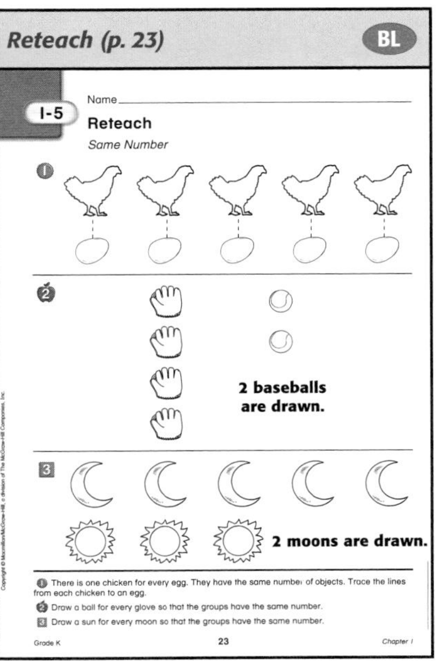

1-5 Name

Reteach

Same Number

2 baseballs are drawn.

2 moons are drawn.

1 There is one chicken for every egg. They have the same number of objects. Trace the lines from each chicken to an egg.

2 Draw a ball for every glove so that the groups have the same number.

3 Draw a sun for every moon so that the groups have the same number.

Grade K 23 Chapter 1

Skills Practice (p. 24) (OL)

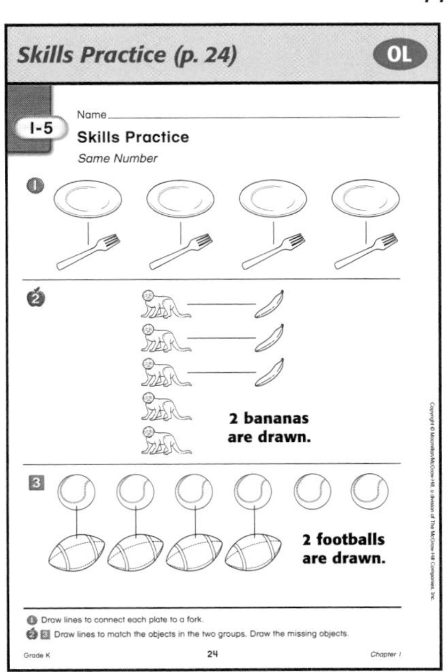

1-5 Name

Skills Practice

Same Number

2 bananas are drawn.

2 footballs are drawn.

1 Draw lines to connect each plate to a fork.

2 3 Draw lines to match the objects in the two groups. Draw the missing objects.

Grade K 24 Chapter 1

Enrich (p. 26) (AL)

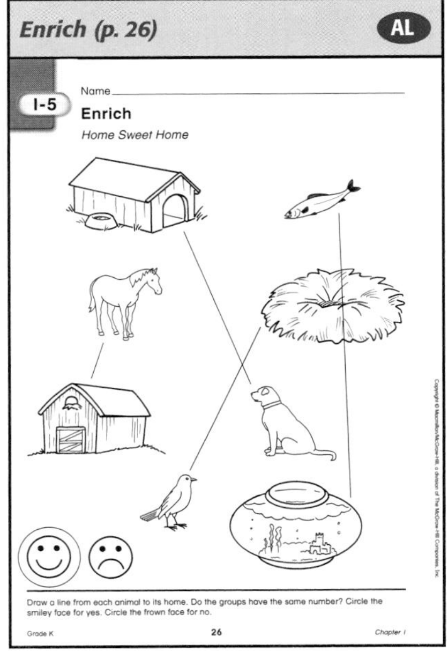

1-5 Name

Enrich

Home Sweet Home

Draw a line from each animal to its home. Do the groups have the same number? Circle the smiley face for yes. Circle the frown face for no.

Grade K 26 Chapter 1

Homework Practice (p. 25) (OL)

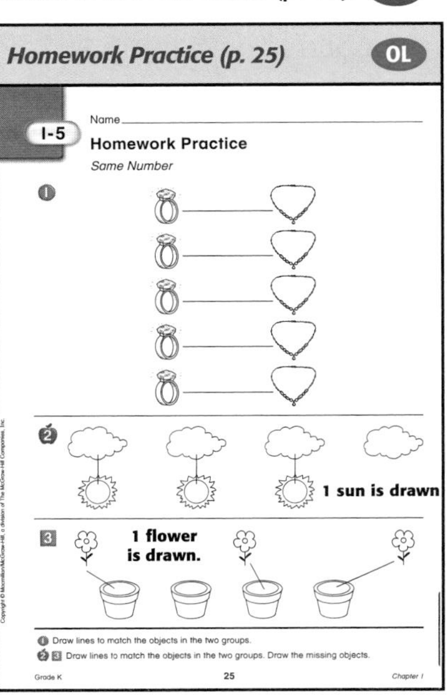

1-5 Name

Homework Practice

Same Number

1 sun is drawn

1 flower is drawn.

1 Draw lines to match the objects in the two groups.

2 3 Draw lines to match the objects in the two groups. Draw the missing objects.

Grade K 25 Chapter 1

1 Introduce

Circle Time

Activity Choice 1 • Literature

More or Less
by Stuart J. Murphy

- Read and discuss the book, focusing on the math vocabulary *more than, less than,* and *same number.*
- Give students manipulatives to use as counters. Using the same manipulatives as the student, represent a number. Have the students represent the same number as your number.
- Have the students continue the activity with a partner.

Activity Choice 2 • Hands-On

Materials: books, color tiles, counters

- Invite four students to line up in a row across the front of the room. Tell the students they are a group.
- Lay four books on the floor in front of the students. Tell the students that this is a group of books.
- One at a time, ask each student to pick up a book and hold it out in front of them.
- Tell students that the number of students and the number of books is the same number. There is the same amount in each group.
- Show a row of six color tiles. Give students counters and have them show how many counters they need to make a group with the same number as the group of color tiles.
- Have students work in pairs using counters and color tiles to show groups with the same number.

2 Teach

- Direct students to p. 27.
- Have students lay one counter on each drum.
- Using the same counters, have students move one on to each drumstick.
- **How many extra counters do you have?** none
- **What can we tell about the amount of counters on the drums and on the drum sticks?** The number of counters are same. This tells us that the groups contain the same number of objects.
- Ask students to trace the lines on the page to match each drum to each drum stick.

BL Alternate Teaching Strategy

If students have trouble identifying groups that contain the same number as each other . . .

Then use one of these reteach options.

1 CRM **Daily Reteach Worksheet** (p. 23)

2 **Find Groups that Contain the Same Number As Each Other** Divide students into two groups. Give each member of one group a piece of yarn.

- Have students pair up with a member from the other group. The partner should hold the other end of the string.
- Ask if the groups contain the same number as each other.

COMMON ERROR!

Students may struggle with groups that have the same number. Have them move the manipulatives to pair up objects, one from each group, to see if they are the same number.

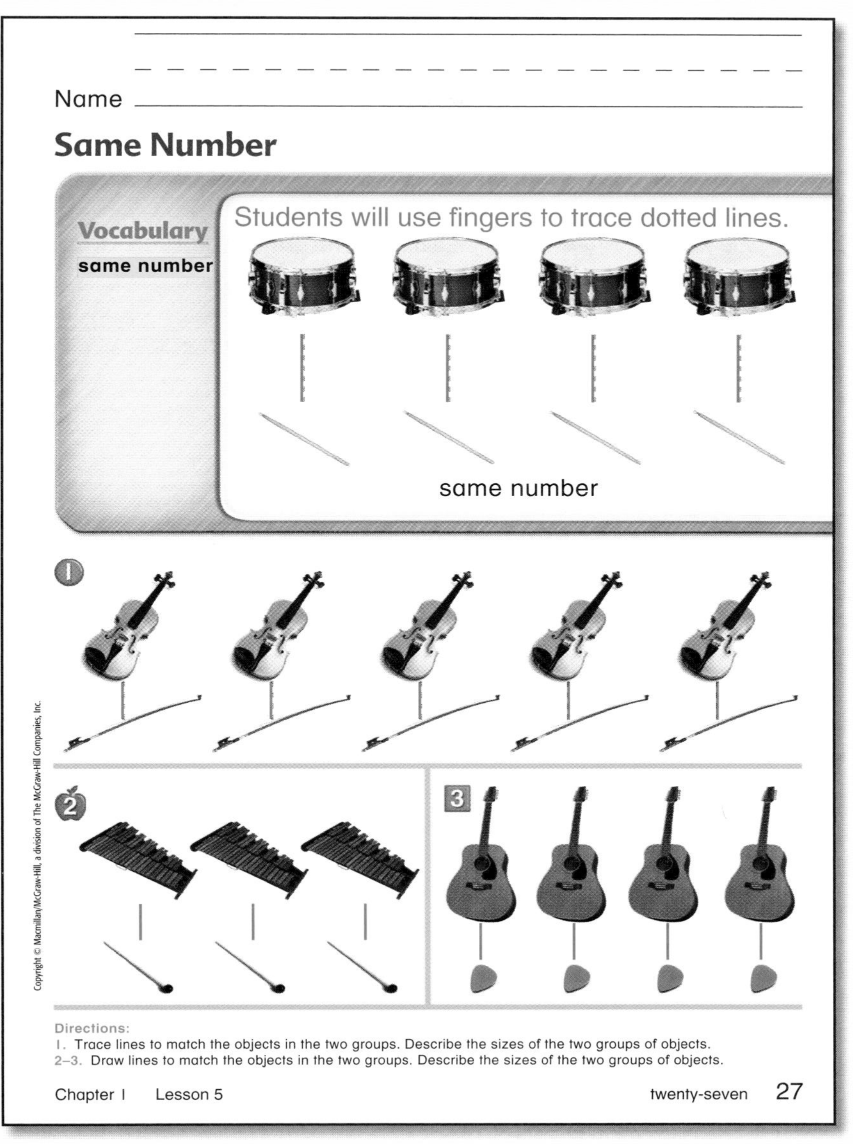

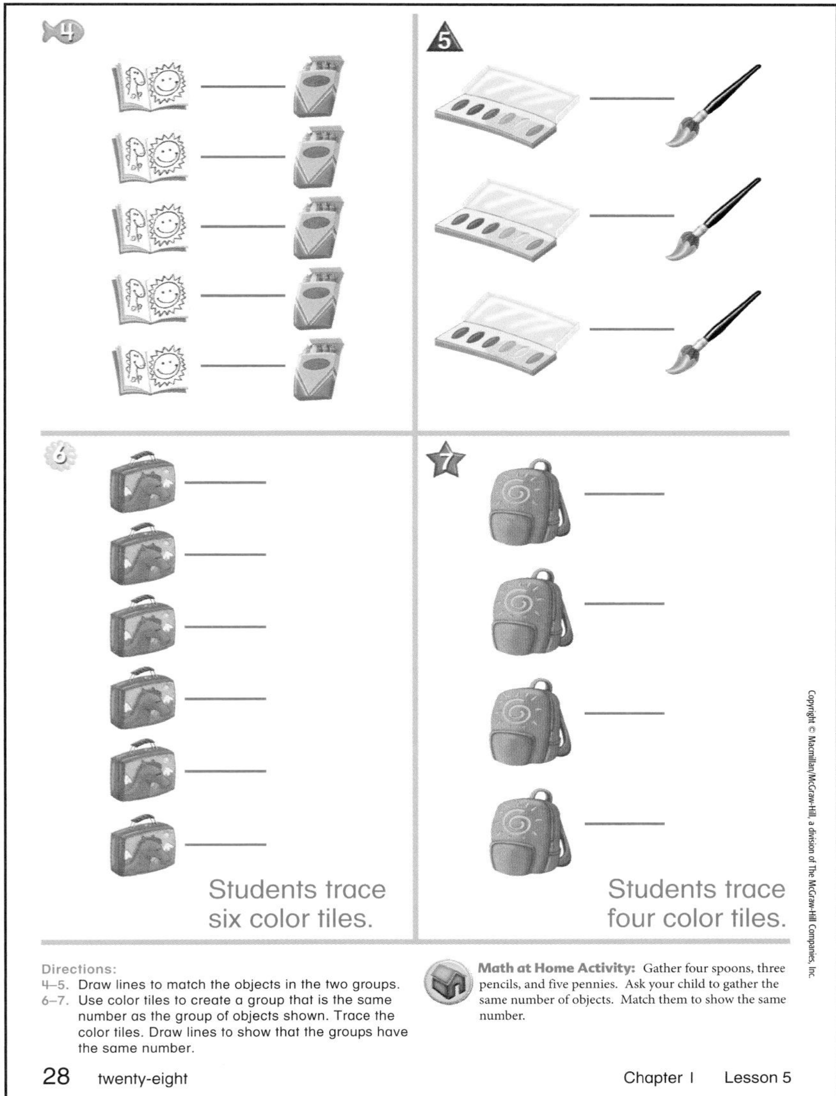

3 Practice

Guided Practice

- Direct students to Exercise 1 on p. 27. Discuss the instrument (violin) and how it is played (with a bow).
- Ask students to identify the groups of objects.
- Tell the students to trace the lines from the violin to a bow.
- Discuss the size of the two groups of objects.
- Work through Exercises 2 and 3 as a class following the same procedure. Discuss the xylophone (struck with a mallet) and guitar (strum with a pick).

Independent Practice

Have students turn to p. 28. Explain the directions. Have students work independently on the exercises.

4 Assess

Formative Assessment

Have students discuss what they know about groups with the same number.

- **How do we know if groups have the same number?** Match each object in one group with an object in the other and see if there are any left.
- Show students a group of five connecting cubes. Have them make a group with the same number using crayons.

Quick Check **Are students still struggling to identify equal groups?**

If Yes → Small Group Options (p. 27B)

If No → Independent Work Options (p. 27B)

CRM Skills Practice Worksheet (p. 24)

CRM Enrich Worksheet (p. 26)

More Than

Lesson Planner

Objective

Use one-to-one correspondence to identify a group with more.

Vocabulary

more than

Resources

Materials: magnetic board, chalkboard, eraser, magnetic letters, cups, beans
Manipulatives: counters, color tiles, attribute buttons
Literature Connection: *Big Fat Hen* by Keith Baker
Alternate Lesson: Use *Handfuls* on pages 125–126 of *Math Their Way* to provide practice in identifying equal to, less than, and more than.
Use *IMPACT Mathematics*: Unit A to provide practice with identifying groups that have more.
Teacher Technology
TeacherWorks • Concepts in Motion

Focus on Math Background

Comparing quantities using one-to-one correspondence to determine the group that has less is preparation for comparing numbers with symbols for *more than* (>) and *less than* (<).

One–to-one correspondence reinforces the concepts of *same* and *equal* when the groups are of the same number. It also introduces the concept of inequality for more and less. Teaching separate lessons on *more than* and *less than* will give students more time to internalize each concept and their relationship.

Using quantity as a comparison is related to sorting and classifying by size, size of group, and capacity or volume. Using a pan scale to show the unbalance of objects is an especially visual and kinesthetic way for young children to see the concept of *more than* and *less than* as well as inequality.

Daily Routine

Use these suggestions before beginning the lesson on p. 29.

5-Minute Check

(Reviews Lesson 1-5)
Show equal amounts of connecting cubes.

1. Do these groups of cubes contain the same number as each other? yes Add another cube to one group. Do the groups contain the same number as each other? no
2. If one train has more cubes than the other, do the trains have the same number? no

Problem of the Day

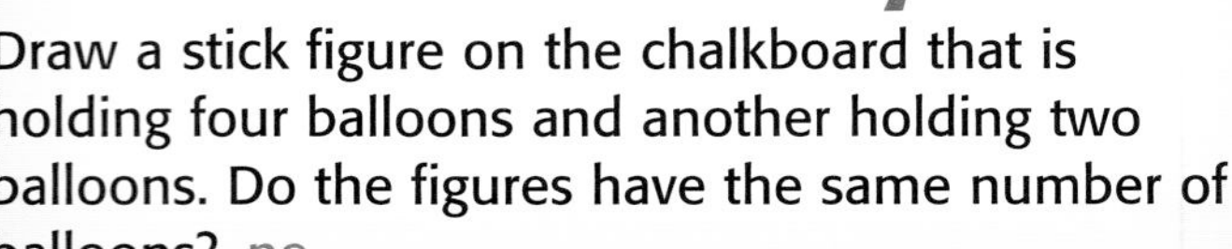

Draw a stick figure on the chalkboard that is holding four balloons and another holding two balloons. Do the figures have the same number of balloons? no

LINE UP Ask all the boys to get in one line. Ask all the girls to get into another line. **Which line has more?** Sample answer: The boys line has more.

Building Math Vocabulary

Make a group of five connecting cubes and another group with six connecting cubes.

- **Do the groups have the same number of cubes? How do you know?** No; the groups have different numbers of cubes.
- Have students match the cubes in each group.
- Tell students that one group of cubes has **more than** the other group.

Visual Vocabulary Cards

Use Visual Vocabulary Card 25 to reinforce the vocabulary introduced in this lesson. (The Define/Example/Ask routine is printed on the back of each card.)

Differentiated Instruction

Small Group Options

Option 1 Below/Approaching Level BL

VISUAL

Materials: two different color counters

- Put two groups of counters on the table. Each should have a different color.
- Students should pair up counters from each group to see which has more than the other.
- Repeat with different size groups. Include groups with the same number.

Option 2 English Language Learners ELL

LINGUISTIC, SOCIAL

Materials: colored paper shapes
Core Vocabulary: more, I, he/she
Common Use Verb: have/has

Talk Math This strategy uses sorting to activate language.

- Give pairs of paper shapes to sort. When students finish, model pairing papers. Say: "**He/She *has* more.**"
- Have students repeat, Saying: "**I *have* more**" or "**He/She *has* more.**" Restate as necessary.

Independent Work Options

Option 1 Early Finishers OL AL

LINGUISTIC

Materials: connecting cubes

- Have early finishers work with a partner.
- Give each student 10 connecting cubes.
- Have each student choose any amount of connecting cubes and hold them in a closed fist.
- Ask each student to take turns predicting who has more or less connecting cubes in their fist.
- Ask them to compare the number of cubes in each group. Then identify which person has more.
- If a student guessed correctly they can choose one of their partners connecting cubes.
- Repeat, having the other student getting a turn to guess.

Option 2 Student Technology

Math Online macmillanmh.com

Math Adventures

Option 3 Learning Station: Art (p. 13G)

Direct students to the Art Learning Station for opportunities to explore and extend the lesson concept.

Leveled Lesson Resources

Reteach (p. 27) BL

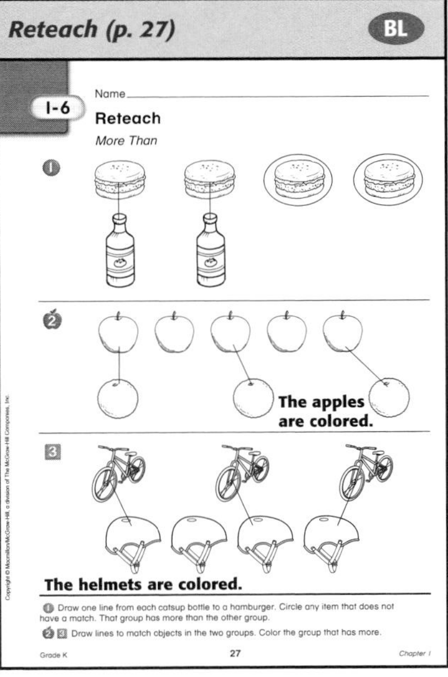

1-6 Name

Reteach

More Than

The apples are colored.

The helmets are colored.

1 Draw one line from each catsup bottle to a hamburger. Circle any item that does not have a match. That group has more than the other group.

2 3 Draw lines to match objects in the two groups. Color the group that has more.

Grade K 27 Chapter 1

Skills Practice (p. 28) OL

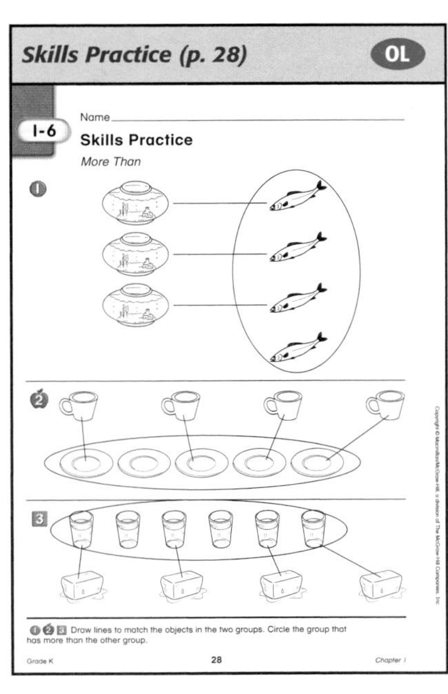

1-6 Name

Skills Practice

More Than

1 2 3 Draw lines to match the objects in the two groups. Circle the group that has more than the other group.

Grade K 28 Chapter 1

Enrich (p. 30) AL

1-6 Name

Enrich

Apple Trees

This tree is colored.

Look at the apples in the trees. Color the tree that has more apples than the other trees.

Grade K 30 Chapter 1

Homework Practice (p. 29) OL

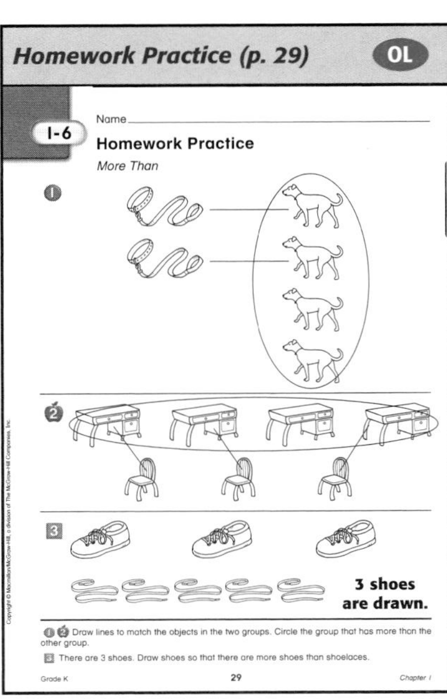

1-6 Name

Homework Practice

More Than

3 shoes are drawn.

1 2 Draw lines to match the objects in the two groups. Circle the group that has more than the other group.

3 There are 3 shoes. Draw shoes so that there are more shoes than shoelaces.

Grade K 29 Chapter 1

1 Introduce

Circle Time

Activity Choice 1 • Literature

Big Fat Hen by Keith Baker
Materials: counters

- On pp. 3–4, model matching one counter with one shoe, and two counters with two chicks. Demonstrate that two counters are **more than** one counter, by pairing the counters.
- As you read the story, ask students to line up counters for comparison.
- Give students cards with pairs of numbers. Students model each number, match the counters, and use "more than" to describe the comparison.

Activity Choice 2 • Hands-On 

Materials: magnetic board or chalkboard, eraser, magnetic letters, attribute buttons

- Draw one large circle on the left side of the board and one large circle on the right.
- Have one student come to the board and place three magnetic objects in one circle. Ask another child to put three magnetic objects in the other circle. Help them line up the objects in a column within each circle for easy matching.
- Define each large circle as a group. Review the concept of groups with the same number.
- Choose another student to add two more magnetic objects to one group on the board.
- Guide students in drawing lines from the objects in one group to the objects in another group to show that there are more objects in one group. Tell the students that this group has more than the other group.
- Give students opportunities to use attribute buttons to make groups with the same number and make groups in which one group of the attribute buttons has more than the other group. Students should check their work by matching objects in each group.

2 Teach

- Direct students to p. 29.
- Give each student three counters. Ask them to lay one counter on each wedge of cheese.
- **Did you have enough counters for each cheese wedge?** yes
- Use these same counters and lay one counter on each mouse.
- **Did you have enough counters for each mouse?** yes
- **Which group has more?** cheese
- Tell students that extra objects in a group tell us that group has more than the other group.
- Direct students to draw a line from the mouse to the cheese to see that there is extra cheese.
- Tell them to circle the group that has more than the other group.

BL Alternate Teaching Strategy

 **If** students have trouble understanding more than . . .

Then use one of these reteach options.

1 CRM **Daily Reteach Worksheet** (p. 27)

2 **Pair to Find More** Have two cups of beans filled with different amounts. Each cup should have a different type of bean. Each cup should have less than 10 beans.
- Ask students to compare the beans in the cups to see which cup has more. They should pair up one bean from each cup. The cup with some left has more than the other cup.
- Repeat activity with groups of different sizes. Include cups holding the same number of beans.

COMMON ERROR!
When showing one-to-one correspondence, students may draw lines matching members from one set to the same member in another set.

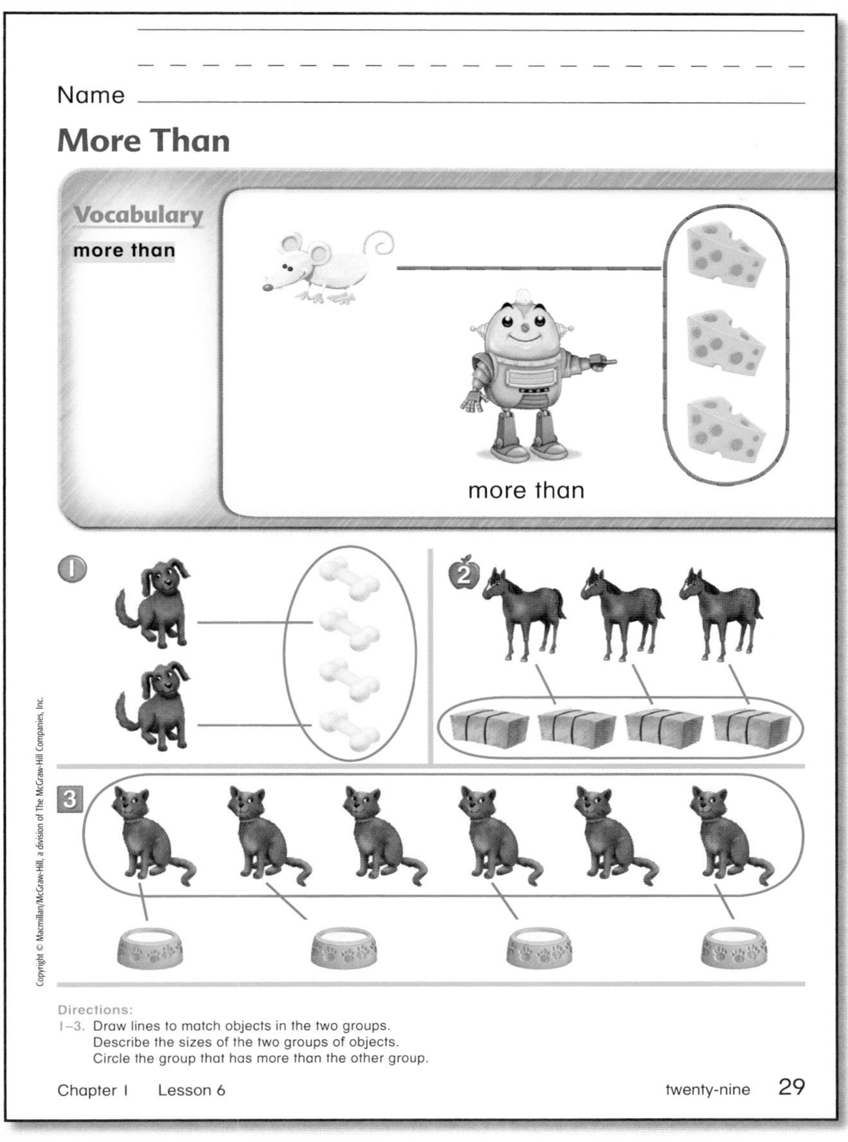

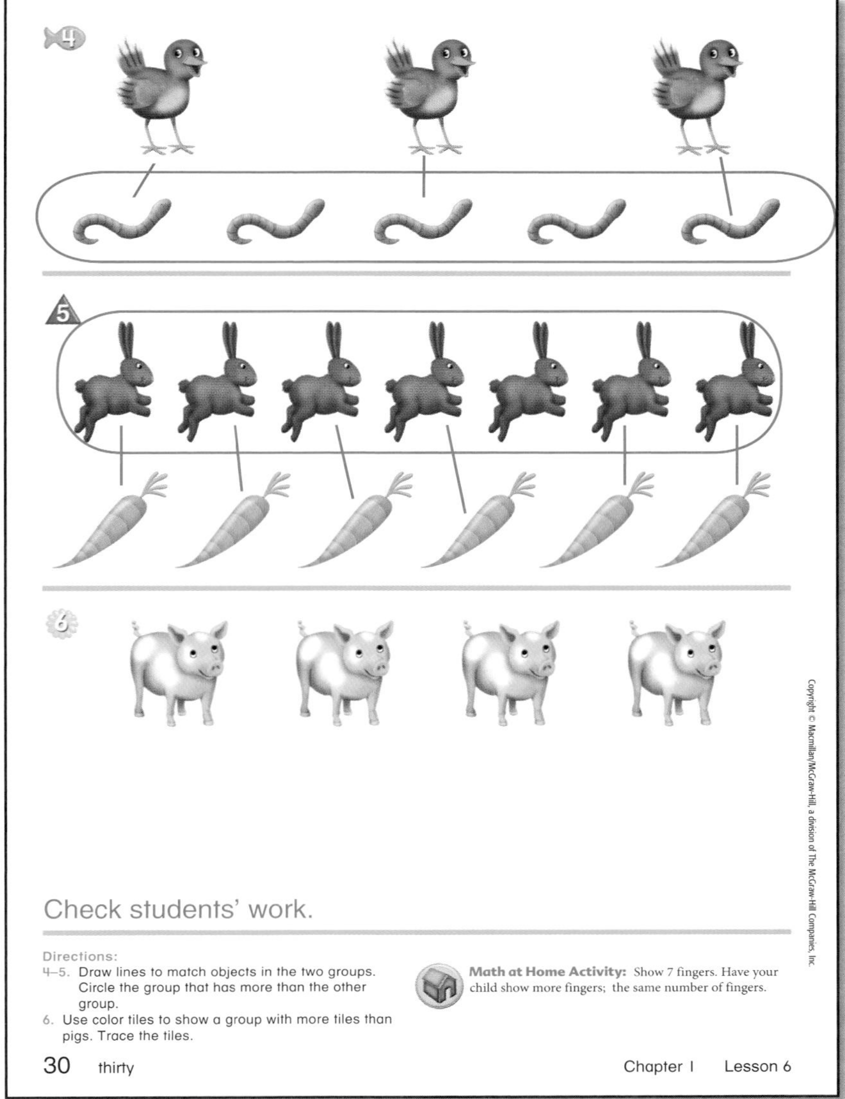

3 Practice

Guided Practice

- Direct students to p. 29.
- Have students draw a line from each dog to a bone.
- Discuss the sizes of the two sets of objects.
- Ask students to circle the group that has more objects.
- Work through Exercises 2-3 as a class.

Independent Practice

Have students turn to p. 30. Explain the directions. Have students work independently on the exercises 4-6.

4 Assess

Formative Assessment

Have students discuss what they know about sizes of groups.

- **How do we know if groups have the same number of objects?** We can match the objects in the groups. **How do we know if one group has more than the other group?** Match items 1:1. The group with more has extra.
- Show students six color tiles. Have them use counters to make a group with more and explain their work.

Quick Check **Are students still struggling to count and write 1, 2, and 3?**

If Yes → Small Group Options (p. 29B)

If No → Independent Work Options (p. 29B)

 CRM Skills Practice Worksheet (p. 28)

CRM Enrich Worksheet (p. 30)

LESSON 1-7

Less Than

Lesson Planner

Objective

Use one-to-one correspondence to identify a group with less.

Vocabulary

less than

Review Vocabulary

more than, same number

Resources

Materials: chart paper, balls

Manipulatives: connecting cubes, attribute buttons, counters, color tiles

Literature Connection: *Bat Jamboree* by Kathi Appett

Alternate Lesson: Use *Stack, Tell, Spin, and Win* on pages 126–127 of *Math Their Way* for practice in one-to-one correspondence to determine more than or less than. Use *IMPACT Mathematics*: Unit A to provide practice with identifying groups with less.

Teacher Technology

TeacherWorks

Focus on Math Background

Comparing quantities using one-to-one correspondence to determine the group that has less is preparation for comparing numbers with symbols for *more than* (>) and *less than* (<).

One–to-one correspondence reinforces the concepts of *same* and *equal* when the groups are of the same number. It also introduces the concept of inequality for more and less. Teaching separate lessons on *more than* and *less than* will give students more time to internalize each concept and their relationship.

Using quantity as a comparison is related to sorting and classifying by size, size of group, and capacity or volume.

Using a pan scale to show the unbalance of objects is a visual and kinesthetic way for students to see the concept of *more than*, and *less than*, and inequality.

Daily Routine

Use these suggestions before beginning the lesson on p. 31.

5-Minute Check

(Reviews Lesson 1-6)

1. Make two unequal sets using attribute buttons. Are these sets the same? no Which set has more? Sample answer: the set with several buttons
2. Repeat with different sets.
3. Add a pair of equal sets to help students understand the three concepts: more than, less than, same number.

Problem of the Day

Draw two stick figures on the chalkboard holding six and three balloons respectively. Do the figures have the same number of balloons? no Which figure has more than the other? the figure with six balloons

LINE UP Have students with short hair line up on one side of the room. Have students with long hair line up on the other side of the room. Have students in each group pair up to determine which group has less.

Building Math Vocabulary

Make two sets with attribute buttons. Make one set larger than the other set.

- Have students count each group of buttons.
- **How are the groups different?** One is smaller.
- Tell students that another way to say that one group is smaller is to say that it is **less than** the other group.

Visual Vocabulary Cards

Use Visual Vocabulary Card 20 to reinforce the vocabulary introduced in this lesson. (The Define/Example/Ask routine is printed on the back of each card.)

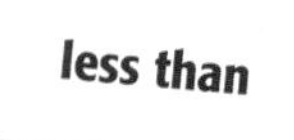

Differentiated Instruction

Small Group Options

Option 1 KINESTHETIC 

Below/Approaching Level 

Materials: pencils, erasers

- Hand each student groups of pencils and erasers.
- Have students pair a pencil and an eraser.
- Ask students to identify which group has less than the other.
- Repeat with different numbers of pencils and erasers.

Option 2 SOCIAL, KINESTHETIC 

English Language Learners ELL

Core Vocabulary: if, does not have more, wearing

Common Use Verb: stand up

Do Math This strategy uses Simon Says to show more/less than.

- Model the game. Say "Simon says, ***stand up*** if you are wearing red." Say: *"There are more/less students wearing red."*
- Introduce *less* as "does not have more" and continue game, focusing on less and more.

Simon says: Stand up if you have more than three buttons on your shirt.

Independent Work Options

Option 1 LOGICAL, LINGUISTIC

Early Finishers OL AL

Materials: connecting cubes

- Give each pair of students connecting cubes. Have them separate the cubes into sets by color.
- Ask them to count the number of cubes in each set.
- Ask students to identify which set or color has less buttons than the others.

Option 2

Student Technology

Math Online macmillanmh.com

 Math Adventures

Option 3

Learning Station: Art (p. 13G)

Direct students to the Art Learning Station for opportunities to explore and extend the lesson concept.

*Strategies for teaching **English Language Learners** are found in each lesson in the Teacher Edition.*

Leveled Lesson Resources

Reteach (p. 31) BL

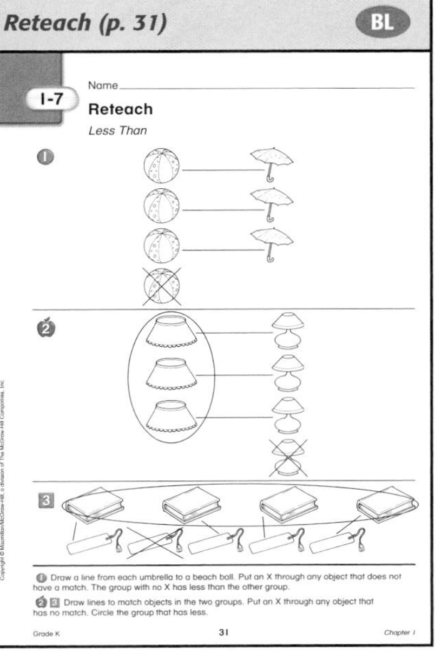

Name

1-7 Reteach

Less Than

1 Draw a line from each umbrella to a beach ball. Put an X through any object that does not have a match. The group with no X has less than the other group.

2 3 Draw lines to match objects in the two groups. Put an X through any object that has no match. Circle the group that has less.

Grade K 31 Chapter 1

Skills Practice (p. 32) OL

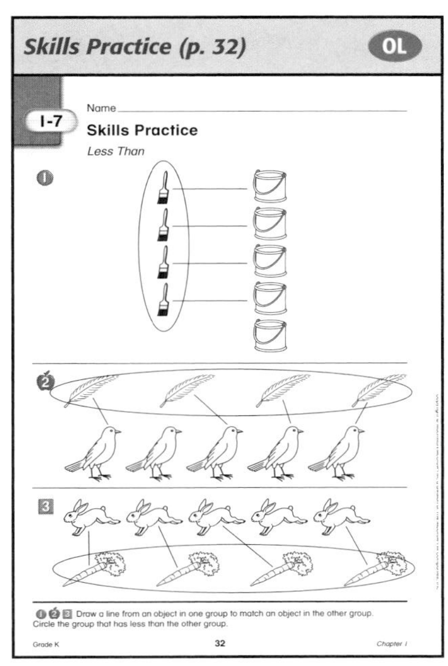

Name

1-7 Skills Practice

Less Than

1 2 3 Draw a line from an object in one group to match an object in the other group. Circle the group that has less than the other group.

Grade K 32 Chapter 1

Enrich (p. 34) AL

Name

1-7 Enrich

Gone Fishing

The hooks are colored.

Draw a line to match each fish to a hook. Color the group that has less than the other group.

Grade K 34 Chapter 1

Homework Practice (p. 33) OL

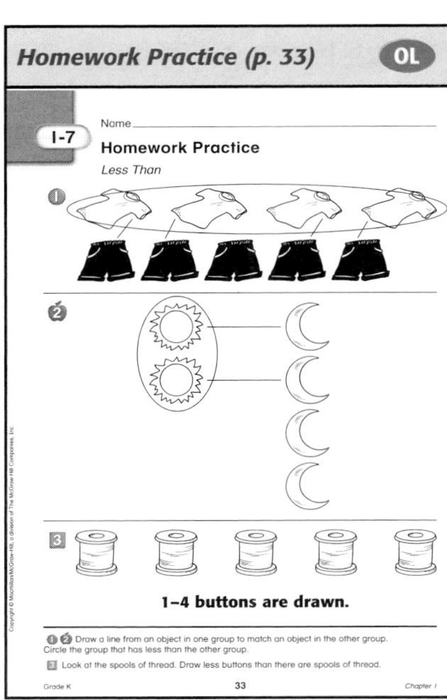

Name

1-7 Homework Practice

Less Than

1–4 buttons are drawn.

1 2 Draw a line from an object in one group to match an object in the other group. Circle the group that has less than the other group.

3 Look at the spools of thread. Draw less buttons than there are spools of thread.

Grade K 33 Chapter 1

1 Introduce

Circle Time

Activity Choice 1 • Literature

Bat Jamboree by Kathi Appett

- Read and discuss the book, focusing on the math vocabulary **more than, *less than*,** and **same number.**
- Represent a number on chart paper by presenting bat cut-outs. Have students represent a number that is the same as your number using bat cut-outs.
- Have students represent a number more than your number using bat cut-outs. Lead a discussion of the differences between students' bats and use *less than* in the comparisons.

Activity Choice 2 • Hands-On

Materials baggies of cubes with different amounts of cubes from one to nine

- Make a group with four buttons and a group with less than four buttons.
- Have students match one button from the first group with one button from the second group.
- Explain that there are not enough buttons in the second group to match each in the first. The second group has less than the first.
- Distribute baggies of cubes that hold various numbers of cubes from one to nine.
- Have partners compare groups of cubes in the baggies. Have students match cubes to determine which group has less than the other.
- Switch partners for more practice with less.

2 Teach

- Direct children to p. 31.
- Identify coats and scarves at the top of the page.
- Remind students that less than means that there are not as many items in one group as in another group.
- Looking at the group of coats and the group of scarves, ask students to draw a line from a coat in one group to a scarf in the other group. Observe matching one to one.
- **What do you notice about each group?** Sample answer: The groups are not the same.
- **Does one group have less (or fewer) objects?** yes
- Circle the group that is less or has fewer objects.

BL Alternate Teaching Strategy

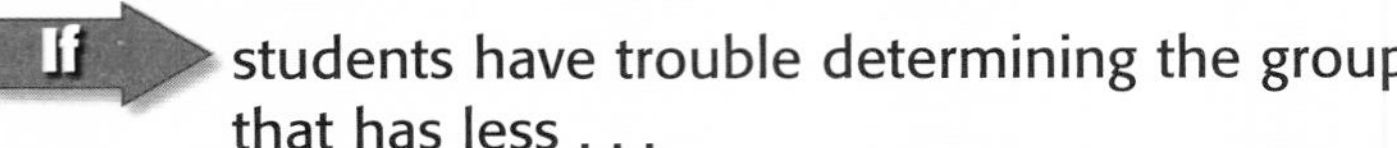

If students have trouble determining the group that has less . . .

Then use one of these reteach options.

1. CRM **Daily Reteach Worksheet** (p. 31)
2. **Find the Group with Less** Have a group of balls that has less than a group of students.
   - Hand each student a ball until all the balls have been distributed.
   - **Which group has less: the group of balls or group of students?** Balls have less because there are not enough for each student to have one.

COMMON ERROR!

Students may draw two lines to the same picture and conclude that two unequal groups are equal. Have students move objects in a group when counting.

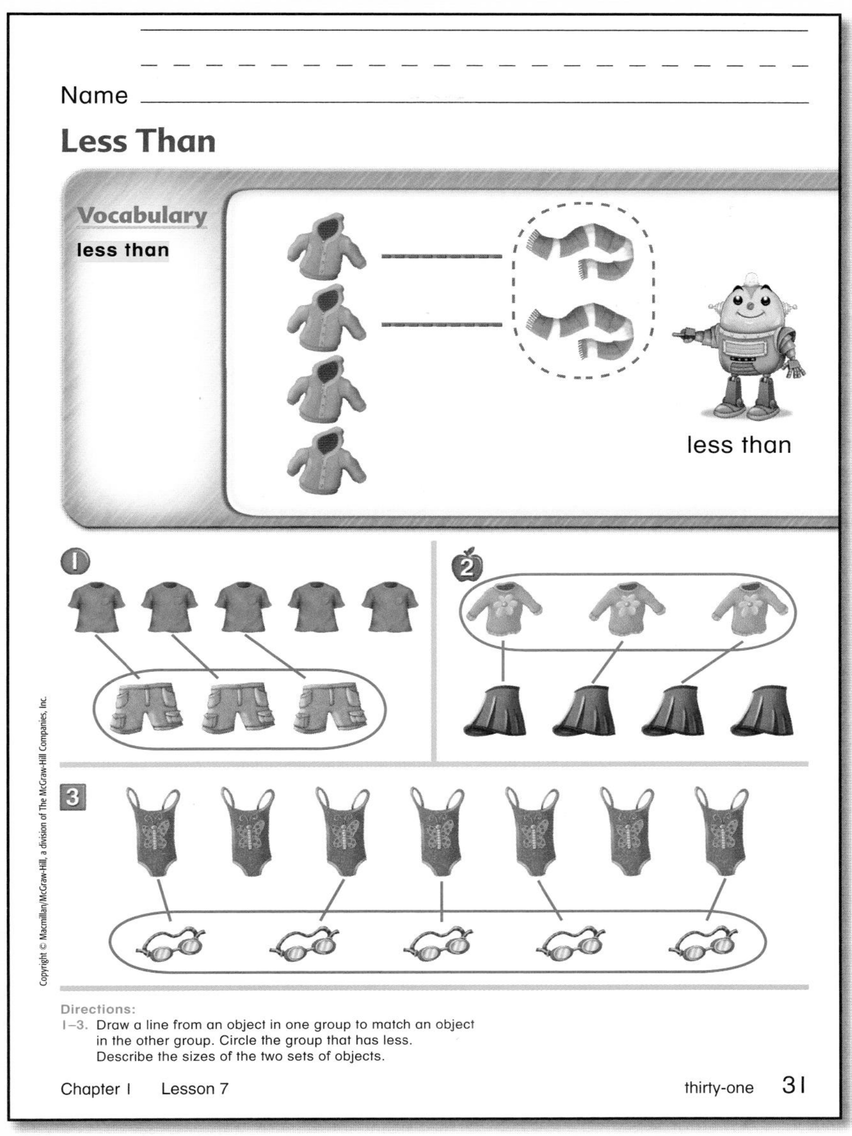

Name
Less Than
Vocabulary
less than
less than
Directions:
1–3. Draw a line from an object in one group to match an object in the other group. Circle the group that has less. Describe the sizes of the two sets of objects.
Chapter 1 Lesson 7 thirty-one 31

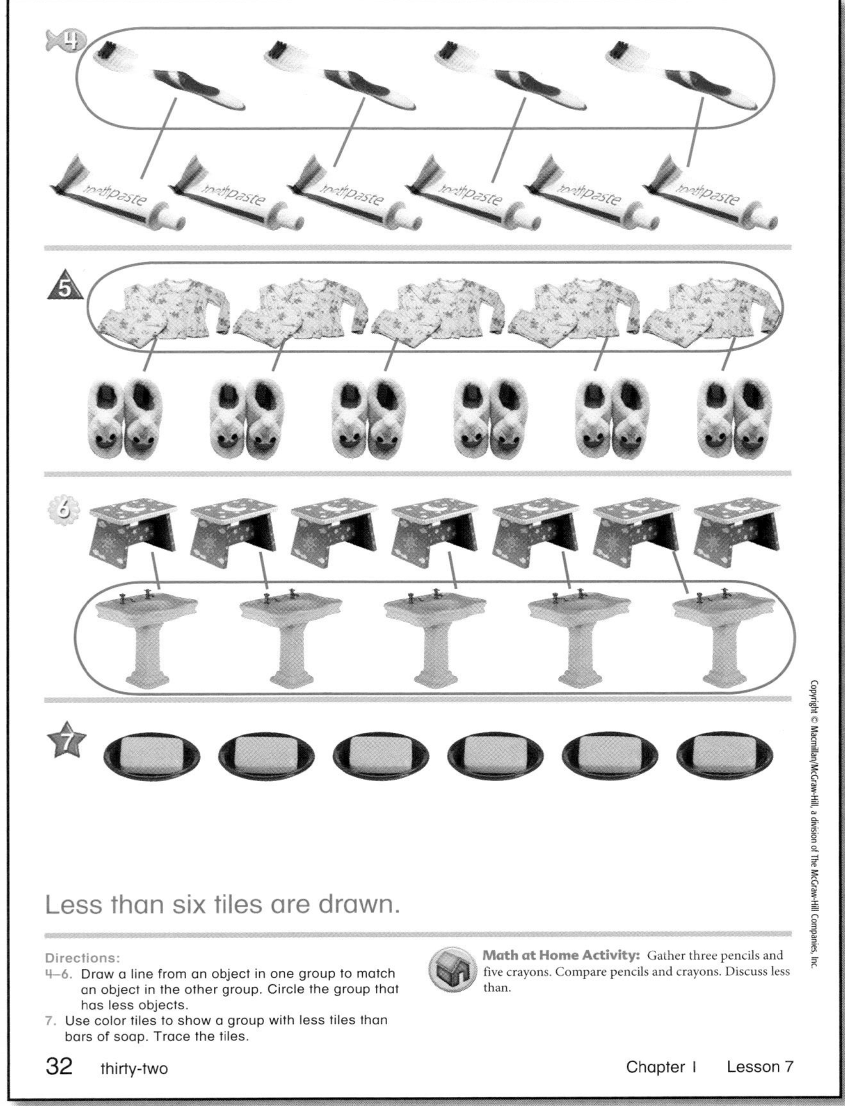

Less than six tiles are drawn.
Directions:
4–6. Draw a line from an object in one group to match an object in the other group. Circle the group that has less objects.
7. Use color tiles to show a group with less tiles than bars of soap. Trace the tiles.
Math at Home Activity: Gather three pencils and five crayons. Compare pencils and crayons. Discuss less than.
32 thirty-two Chapter 1 Lesson 7

3 Practice

Guided Practice

- Direct students to p. 31.
- Have students draw a line from a shirt in one group to shorts in the other group.
- Discuss the sizes of the two sets of objects.
- Ask students to circle the group that has less objects.
- Work through Exercises 2–3 as a class.

Independent Practice

Have students turn to p. 32. Explain the directions. Have students work independently on the exercises.

4 Assess

Formative Assessment

- Have students discuss the concept of less than.
- **How do we know if one group has less than the other?** Match 1:1. The group with less does not have as many.
- Show students eight counters. Have them use color tiles to make a group with less. Have them explain their work.

Quick Check **Are students still struggling to determine groups that have less?**

If Yes → Small Group Options (p. 31B)

If No → Independent Work Options (p. 31B)

CRM Skills Practice Worksheet (p. 32)

CRM Enrich Worksheet (p. 34)

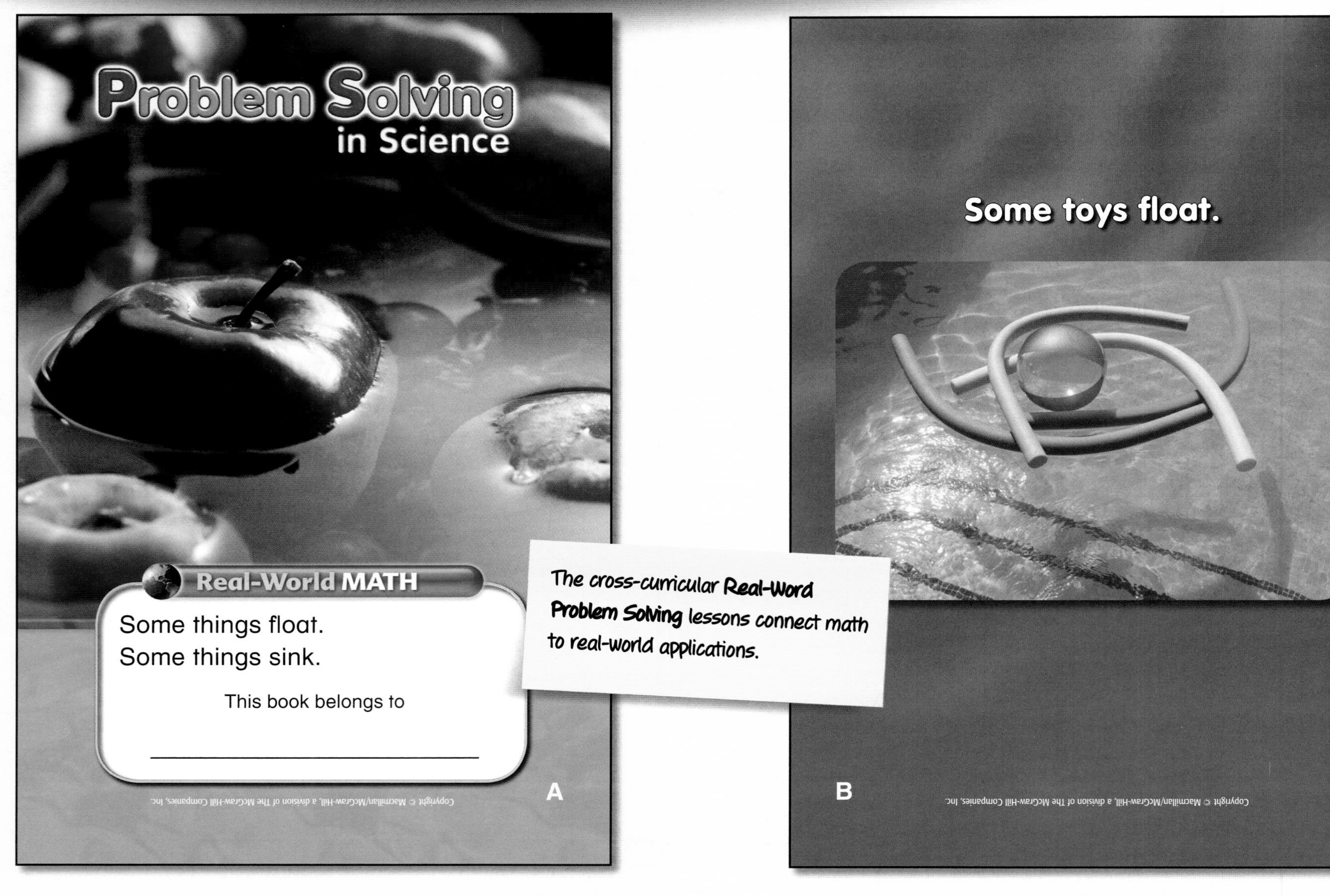

Lesson Planner

Objective

Sort objects by whether they float or sink.

National Standard

Students learn about the properties of objects and materials.

Activate Prior Knowledge

Before you turn students' attention to the pages, discuss how some objects float and others sink when put in water.

- Share with students that when objects float, they are near the surface of the water. When objects sink, they are on the bottom.
- **What do you notice about the objects in the sink?** The grapes sink and the apples float.
- **What are some objects that float in water?** Sample answers: toys with air inside them, a beach ball, some pieces of wood
- **What are some objects that sink in water?** Sample answers: shoes, metal toy cars, marbles, magnets

Silverware sinks.
C

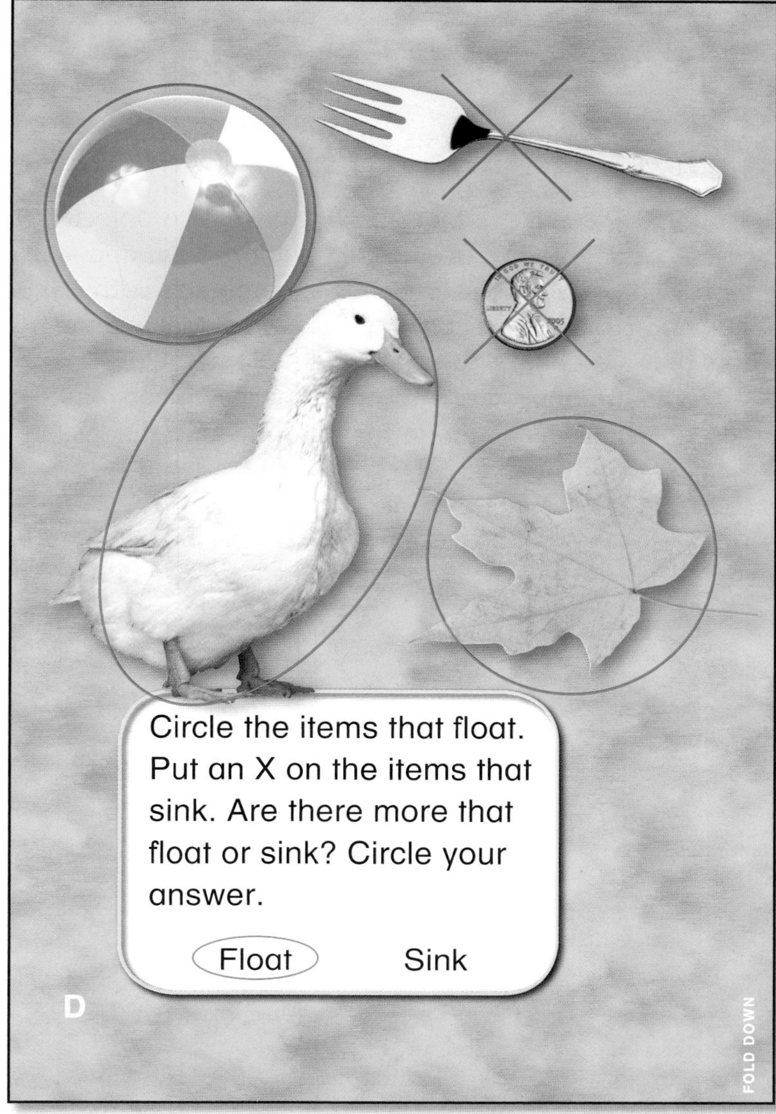

Circle the items that float. Put an X on the items that sink. Are there more that float or sink? Circle your answer.
Float
Sink
D
FOLD DOWN

Create the Book

Guide students to create their book.

- Have them fold the page in half.
- Ask them to write their name on page A.
- Explain that page A is the front cover and page D is the back cover. If necessary, have them practice flipping through the book in order.
- Guide them in reading the information and word problems on each of the pages.

Use the Student Pages

Have students discuss other examples of pool toys that will float and sink on page B.

Page C Ask students if they have ever helped someone wash dishes. Discuss the different dishes that float and sink.

Page D Discuss the objects on the page. Help students count the number of objects that sink and float to determine whether there are more objects that float or sink.

WRITING IN MATH Have students spend five minutes drawing objects that float and five minutes drawing objects that sink. At the end of the 10 minutes, have students count the objects they drew in each group. Ask them to draw a circle around the group with more and a box around the group with less. If groups have the same number, have students underline each group.

FOLDABLES Dinah Zike's Foldables

Use these lesson suggestions for incorporating the Foldables during the chapter.

Lesson 1-6 Place four objects in one case, two objects in the second case and use the terms *more than* and *less than* to describe the sets. Change the objects within the sets and continue practicing these terms. Make some sets that are equal and use the term *same*. Allow students the opportunity to make their own sets and describe them using the terms introduced in the lessons.

Chapter 1 Project

Sort Classroom Objects

Lead a discussion on the results of the completed chapter project with the class.

Vocabulary Review

Review chapter vocabulary using one of the following options.

- **Visual Vocabulary Cards** (13, 20, 25, 39)
- **eGlossary** at macmillanmh.com

The **Chapter Review/Test** can be used for practice or assessment. Five different forms of summative assessment are also found in the Chapter Resource Masters.

Data-Driven Decision Making

Based on the results of the Chapter/Review Test, use the following to review concepts that continue to present students with problems.

Exercises	State/Local Standards	What's the Math?	Error Analysis	Resources for Review
1		Sort and classify objects by attribute.	Omits drawing a line. Draws line to wrong match.	CRM Chapter 1 Resource Masters (Reteach Worksheets) Math Online Concepts in Motion Math Adventures
2		Compare sets of objects.	Omits drawing a line between two objects.	
3		Identify which set is less than the other.	Omits drawing a line. Omits circling group showing which is less.	

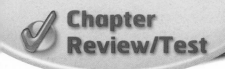

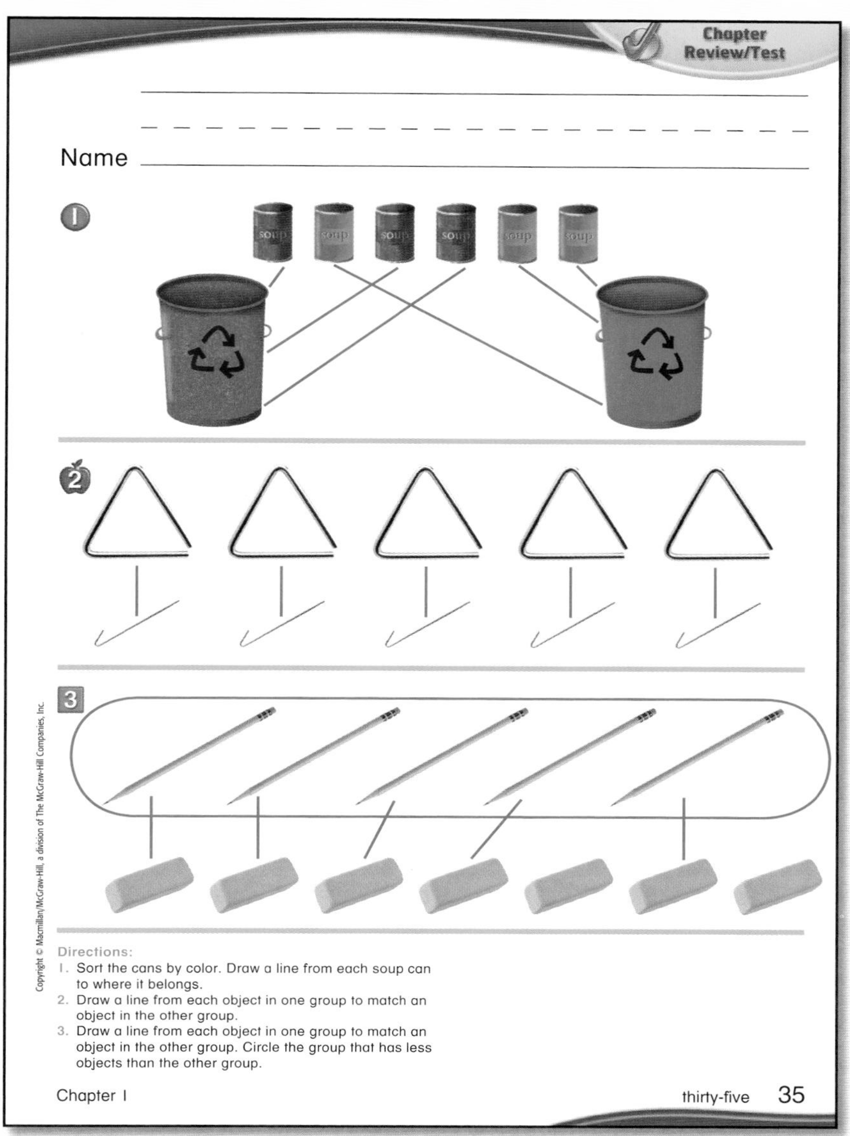

Chapter Review/Test

Name

1

2

3

Directions:
1. Sort the cans by color. Draw a line from each soup can to where it belongs.
2. Draw a line from each object in one group to match an object in the other group.
3. Draw a line from each object in one group to match an object in the other group. Circle the group that has less objects than the other group.

Chapter 1 thirty-five 35

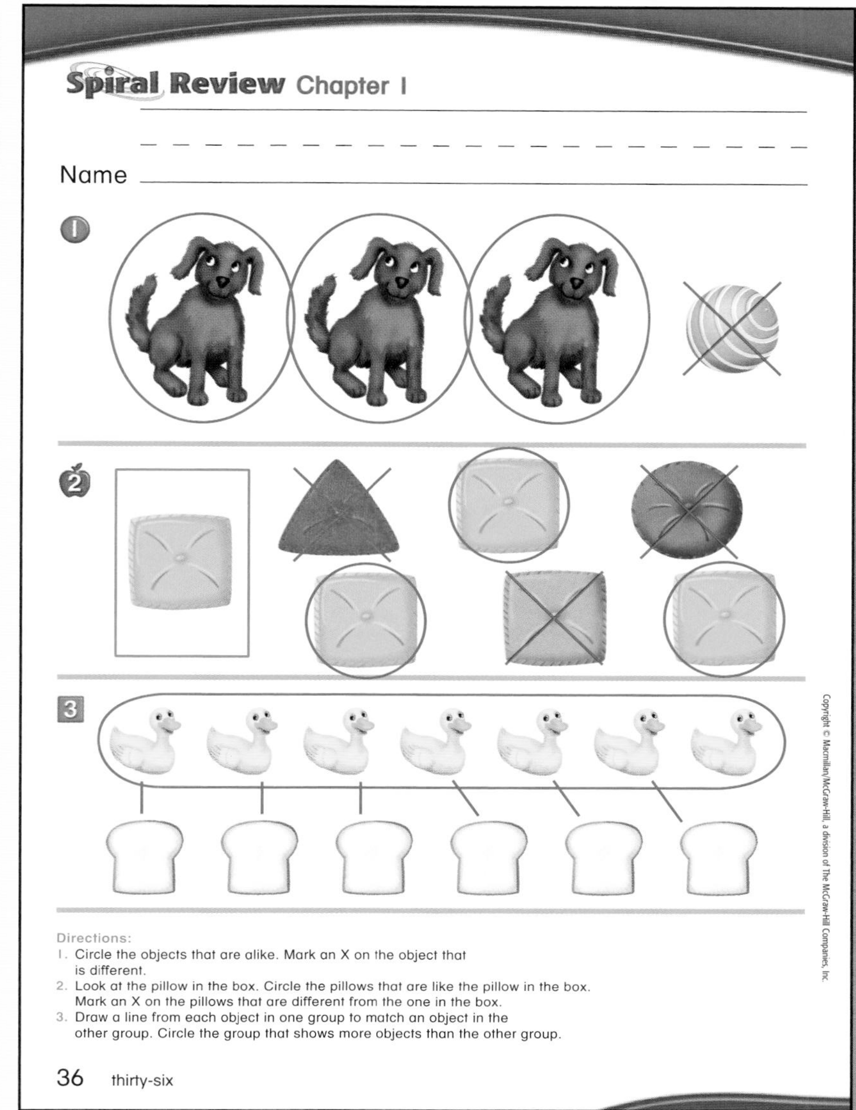

Spiral Review Chapter 1

Name

1

2

3

Directions:
1. Circle the objects that are alike. Mark an X on the object that is different.
2. Look at the pillow in the box. Circle the pillows that are like the pillow in the box. Mark an X on the pillows that are different from the one in the box.
3. Draw a line from each object in one group to match an object in the other group. Circle the group that shows more objects than the other group.

36 thirty-six

Summative Assessment

Use these alternate leveled chapter tests to differentiate assessment for the specific needs of your students.

Leveled Chapter 1 Tests			
Form	**Type**	**Level**	**CRM Pages**
1	Multiple Choice	BL	44–45
2A	Multiple Choice	OL	46–47
2C	Multiple Choice	OL	48–49
2D	Free Response	AL	50–51

BL = below/approaching grade level
OL = on grade level
AL = above/beyond grade level

Spiral Review

Reviews Chapter 1

Objective: Review and assess mastery of skills and concepts from Pre-Kindergarten.

Resources for Review

Based on student results, refer to these lessons for remediation.

- **Exercise 1: Lesson 1-1** (p. 17),
- **Exercise 2: Lesson 1-4** (p. 23),
- **Exercise 3: Lesson 1-6** (p. 29),

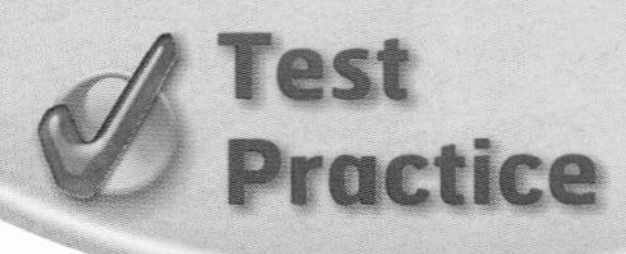

Chapter 1

Formative Assessment

- You can use Student Edition pp. 37-38 to benchmark student progress.
- Additional practice pages can be found in Chapter 1 Resource Masters.

Chapter 1 Resource Masters
Cumulative Test Practice

- Multiple Choice format (pp. 44–49)
- Free Response format (pp. 50–51)

Create additional practice worksheets or tests.

Math Online For additional practice visit macmillanmh.com.

Test-Taking Tips

For the Teacher

- It may be helpful to review the vocabulary words and provide examples.
- Tell students to work on one question at a time.

For the Student

- Tell students where to put their name on their test. Be sure to tell students to write their first and last name on their test.
- Remind students to listen carefully as you read each question before they choose an answer.

Test Practice gives students an opportunity to practice the kinds of questions found on state assessments

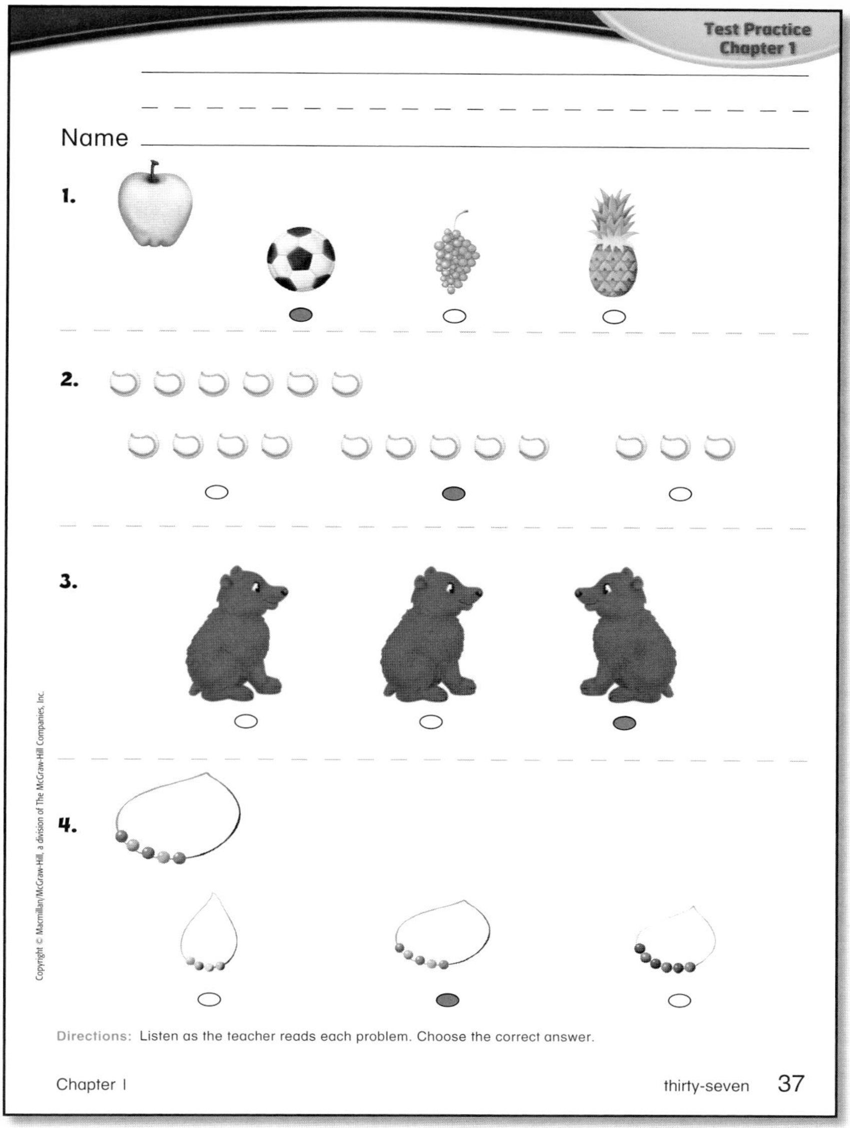
Test Practice
Chapter 1
Name
1.
2.
3.
4.
Directions: Listen as the teacher reads each problem. Choose the correct answer.
Chapter 1
thirty-seven 37

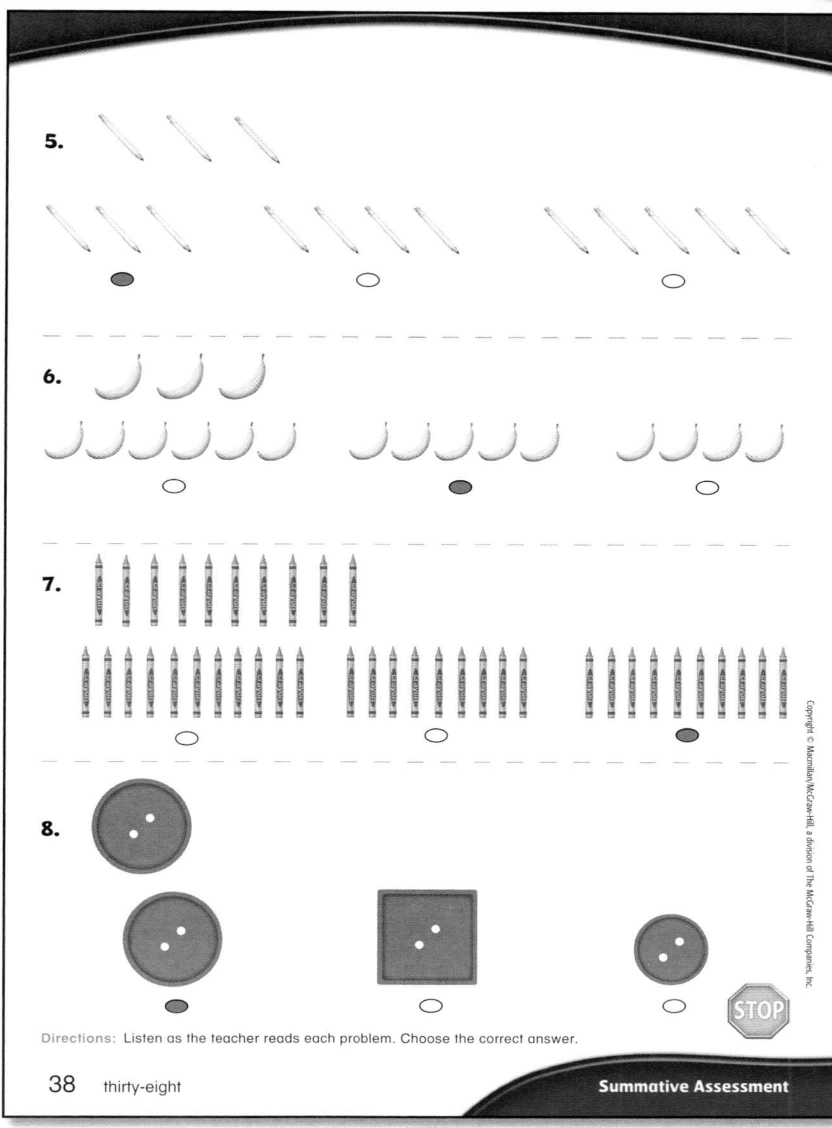
5.
6.
7.
8.
STOP
Directions: Listen as the teacher reads each problem. Choose the correct answer.
38 thirty-eight
Summative Assessment

Test Directions for Teachers

Read the following directions to students before they begin. Then read each question followed by a pause to allow students time to work and choose an answer. The first test item can be worked as a class example.

- **Write your name at the top of the page.**
- **I am going to read each question to you. Listen carefully to the entire question before you choose an answer.**

1. Look at the objects. Find the object below that does not belong. Mark the object that does not belong.
2. Look at the baseballs. Mark the group has 1 less baseballs.
3. Look at the bears. Mark the bear that is different.
4. Look at the necklace. Mark the necklace that has the same number of beads.

- **Turn the page over.**

5. Look at the group of pencils. Mark the group that shows the same number.
6. Look at the bananas. Mark the group has 2 more bananas.
7. Look at the group of crayons. Mark the group that the same number of crayons.
8. Look at the button. Mark the button that is the same shape and size.

Chapter Overview

Chapter-at-a-Glance

In Chapter 2, students will read, write, order, and compare numbers 0–5.

Lesson		Math Objective	State/Local Standards
2-1	**Numbers 1, 2, and 3** (pp. 43–44)	Name, recognize, and count the numerals 1, 2, and 3 using concrete objects and illustrations.	
2-2	**Read and Write 1, 2, and 3** (pp. 45–46)	Recognize and write the numerals 1, 2 and 3.	
2-3	**Numbers 4 and 5** (pp. 47–48)	Name, recognize, and count the numerals 4 and 5 using concrete objects and illustrations.	
2-4	**Read and Write 4 and 5** (pp. 49–50)	Recognize and write the numerals 4 and 5.	
2-5	**Problem-Solving Strategy: Draw a Picture** (pp. 53–54)	Name, recognize, and count the numerals 1, 2, 3, 4, and 5 using concrete illustrations.	
2-6	**Read and Write 0** (pp. 55–56)	Recognize and write the numeral 0.	
2-7	**Compare Numbers 0 to 5** (pp. 57–58)	Use one-to-one correspondence and counting to compare groups and determine which has more, less, or whether the groups are the same.	
2-8	**Order Numbers 0 to 5** (pp. 59–60)	Order numbers from 0 to 5 in sequence using illustrations.	

Use Numbers 0 to 5

BIG Idea Students begin to understand that numbers explain the world around them and that items in sets can be counted.

- For example, a set of five items has more items in it than a set of four items.
- Students will also begin to understand that the numbers zero through five represent a rational ordering and counting of items.

Algebra Students prepare for algebra by laying the foundation for solving inequalities by comparing and ordering numbers. Lessons 2-7 and 2-8

GK-FP1 *Number and Operations:* **Representing, comparing, and ordering whole numbers and joining and separating sets**

Children use numbers, including written numerals, to represent quantities and to solve quantitative problems, such as counting objects in a set, creating a set with a given number of objects, comparing and ordering sets or numerals by using both cardinal and ordinal meanings, and modeling simple joining and separating situations with objects. They choose, combine, and apply effective strategies for answering quantitative questions, including quickly recognizing the number in a small set, counting and producing sets of given sizes, counting the number in combined sets, and counting backward.

Skills Trace
Vertical Alignment

Pre-Kindergarten

In Pre-K students learned to:
- Count by ones to 10 or higher.
- Name "how many" are in a group of up to three (or more) objects without counting (e.g., recognizing two or three crayons in a box).

Kindergarten

During this chapter, students learn to:
- Understand the relationship between numbers and quantities.
- Count, represent, and name number of objects up to five.
- Compare and order numbers.

After this chapter, students will learn to:
- Identify and create simple patterns.

First Grade

In first grade, students will learn to:
- Describe and extend a pattern.
- Count, read, write, compare, and order whole numbers to 20.
- Explain the reasoning used and justify the procedures selected.
- Count, read, and write whole numbers to 100.
- Compare and order whole numbers to 100.

Backmapping and Vertical Alignment McGraw-Hill's *Math Connects* program was conceived and developed with the final results in mind: student success in Algebra 1 and beyond. The authors, using the **NCTM Focal Points and Focal Connections** as their guide, developed this brand new series by backmapping from Algebra 1 concepts, and vertically aligning the topics so that they build upon prior skills and concepts and serve as a foundation for future topics.

Math Vocabulary

The following math vocabulary words for Chapter 2 are listed in the glossary of the ***Student Edition***. You can find interactive definitions in 13 languages in the ***eGlossary*** at macmillanmh.com.

count (p. 43)

1 2 3

five (p. 47) 5

four (p. 47) 4

number (p. 45)

one (p. 43)

1

order (p. 59)

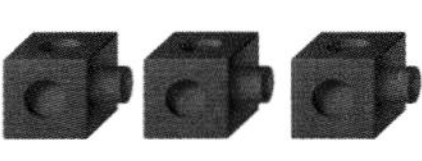

These numbers are in order from smallest to largest.

three (p. 43)

3

two (p. 43)

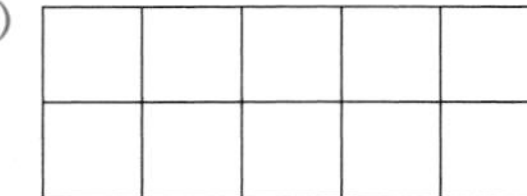

2

zero (p. 55)

Visual Vocabulary Cards Use Visual Vocabulary Card 29 to introduce and reinforce the vocabulary in this chapter. (The Define/Example/Ask routine is printed on the back of each card.)

order

Chapter Planner

Suggested Pacing		
Instruction	Review and Assessment	TOTAL
8 days	2 days	**10 days**

Diagnostic Assessment
Are You Ready? (p. 40)

	Lesson 2-1 (Pacing: 1 day)	Lesson 2-2 (Pacing: 1 day)	Lesson 2-3 (Pacing: 1 day)
Lesson/ Objective	**Numbers 1, 2, and 3** (pp. 43–44) **Objective:** Name, recognize, and count the numerals 1, 2, and 3 using concrete objects and illustrations.	**Read and Write 1, 2, and 3** (pp. 45–46) **Objective:** Recognize and write the numerals 1, 2, and 3.	**Numbers 4 and 5** (pp. 47–48) **Objective:** Name, recognize, and count the numerals 4 and 5 using concrete objects and illustrations.
State/Local Standards			
Math Vocabulary	**count, one, two, three**	**number**	**four, five**
Lesson Resources	**Materials** empty coffee can with plastic lid, number strips, crayons, number cards **Manipulatives** two-colored counters, color tiles **Other Resources** CRM Leveled Worksheets (pp. 6–9) Daily Reteach Problem of the Day	**Materials** cups, pencils, cards, chart paper, markers, pictures with objects **Manipulatives** two-colored counters **Other Resources** CRM Leveled Worksheets (pp. 10–13) Daily Reteach Problem of the Day	**Materials** drawing paper, crayons, pictures of objects, shaker **Manipulatives** counters, connecting cubes, color tiles **Other Resources** CRM Leveled Worksheets (pp. 14–17) Daily Reteach Problem of the Day
Technology Math Online	Math Adventures	Math Adventures	Math Song Track 4 Math Adventures
Reaching All Learners	English Learners, p. 43B ELL Below Level, p. 43B BL Early Finishers, p. 43B OL AL	English Learners, p. 45B ELL Gifted and Talented, p. 45B AL Early Finishers, p. 45B OL AL	English Learners, p. 47B ELL Below Level, p. 47B BL Early Finishers, p. 47B OL AL
Alternate Lesson	*Math Their Way*, pp. 168–178	*Math Their Way*, pp. 177–178	*Math Their Way*, pp. 168–178

KEY

BL Below/Approaching Level	OL On Level	AL Above/Beyond Level	ELL English Learners
SE Student Edition	TE Teacher Edition	CRM Chapter 2 Resource Masters	CD-Rom
Transparency	Flip Chart	Real-World Problem Solving Library	

Use Numbers 0 to 5

	Lesson 2-4 (Pacing: 1 day)	Lesson 2-5 (Pacing: 1 day)	Lesson 2-6 (Pacing: 1 day)
Lesson/ Objective	**Read and Write 4 and 5** (pp. 49–50) **Objective:** Recognize and write the numerals 4 and 5.	Problem-Solving Strategy **Draw a Picture** (pp. 53–54) **Objective:** Name, recognize, and count the numerals 1, 2, 3, 4, and 5 using concrete illustrations.	**Read and Write 0** (pp. 55–56) **Objective:** Recognize and write the numeral 0.
State/Local Standards			
Math Vocabulary			**zero**
Lesson Resources	**Materials** cards, pencils, chart paper, markers, crayons, picture with objects **Manipulatives** connecting cubes **Other Resources** CRM Leveled Worksheets (pp. 18–21) Daily Reteach Problem of the Day Math Song. Track 4	**Materials** stuffed animals **Manipulatives** two-colored counters **Other Resources** CRM Leveled Worksheets (pp. 22–26) Daily Reteach Problem of the Day *Community Helpers*	**Materials** pencils, picture of animals **Manipulatives** connecting cubes **Other Resources** CRM Leveled Worksheets (pp. 27–30) Daily Reteach Problem of the Day
Technology Math Online	Math Adventures		Math Adventures
Reaching All Learners	English Learners, p. 49B ELL Gifted and Talented, p. 49B AL Early Finishers, p. 49B OL AL	English Learners, p. 53B ELL Below Level, p. 53B BL Early Finishers, p. 53B OL AL	English Learners, p. 55B ELL Below Level, p. 55B BL Early Finishers, p. 55B OL AL
Alternate Lesson	*Math Their Way*, pp. 177–178		*Math Their Way*, p. 47

Formative Assessment
Mid-Chapter Check (p. 51)

Game Time: Rainbow Crossing (p. 52)

Chapter Planner

	Lesson 2-7 (Pacing: 1 day)	Lesson 2-8 (Pacing: 1 day)
Lesson/ Objective	**Compare Numbers 0 to 5** (pp. 57–58) **Objective:** Use one-to-one correspondence and counting to compare groups and determine which has more, less, or whether the groups are the same.	**Order Numbers 0 to 5** (pp. 59–60) **Objective:** Order numbers from 0 to 5 in sequence using illustrations.
State/Local Standards		
Math Vocabulary		**order**
Lesson Resources	**Materials** paper, pencils, crayons, stapler **Manipulatives** two-colored counters **Other Resources** CRM Leveled Worksheets (pp. 31–34) Daily Reteach Problem of the Day	**Materials** 0–5 number cards, paper, pencils, crayons **Manipulatives** two-colored counters, connecting cubes **Other Resources** CRM Leveled Worksheets (pp. 35–38) Daily Reteach Problem of the Day
Technology Math Online	Math Song Track 4 Math Adventures Concepts in Motion	Math Song Track 4 Math Adventures Concepts in Motion
Reaching All Learners	English Learners, p. 57B ELL Below Level, p. 57B BL Early Finishers, p. 57B OL AL	English Learners, p. 59B ELL Gifted and Talented, p. 59B AL Early Finishers, p. 59B OL AL
Alternate Lesson	*Math Their Way*, p. 130 *IMPACT* Mathematics: Unit B	*Math Their Way*, p. 44 *IMPACT* Mathematics: Unit B

Problem Solving in Social Studies (p. 61)

Summative Assessment
- Chapter Review/Test (p. 63)
- Test Practice (p. 65)

Assessment Options

Diagnostic Assessment

- SE *Option 1:* Are You Ready? (p. 40)
- *Option 2:* Online Quiz (macmillanmh.com)
- CRM *Option 3:* Diagnostic Test (p. 40)

Formative Assessment

- TE Alternate Teaching Strategies (every lesson)
- TE Writing in Math (every lesson)
- TE Line Up (every lesson)
- SE Mid-Chapter Check (p. 51)
- CRM Mid-Chapter Test (p. 41)

Summative Assessment

- SE Chapter Review/Test (p. 63)
- SE Test Practice (p. 65)
- CRM Leveled Chapter Tests (pp. 46–53)
- CRM Cumulative Test Practice (p. 54)
- CRM Listening Assessment (p. 44)
- CRM Oral Assessment (p. 42)
- Exam*View*® Assessment Suite
- Advanced Tracker

McGraw-Hill Professional Development

Targeted professional development has been articulated throughout ***McGraw-Hill's Math Connects*** *Program*. The **McGraw-Hill Professional Development Video Library** provides short videos that support the **NCTM Focal Points and Focal Connections**. For more information, visit macmillanmh.com.

Model Lessons

Instructional Strategies

What the Research Says . . .

According to *In Adding It Up: Helping Children Learn Mathematics* (2002), the U. S. mathematics education literature makes a distinction between the natural numbers (1, 2, 3, and so on) and the whole numbers (0, 1, 2, 3, and so on). The recognition that zero should be considered a legitimate number—rather than the absence of number—was an important intellectual achievement in the history of mathematics. As an idea, zero is present in the earliest schooling, but as a number, zero can be a significant obstacle for some students and teachers. "Zero is nothing," some people say. In fact, zero communicates that there is not any of some type of thing. As you work through this chapter, make sure students understand that zero is the *absence* of cubes, muffins, or balls.

Teacher Notes

Learning Stations

Cross-Curricular Links

Reading

individual | KINESTHETIC 

Hold Up Fingers

- Listen to the story.
- Hold up how many fingers.

Teacher Note: Read slowly so students can think about how many fingers to hold up. Check the number of fingers students are showing for each number.

Materials:

- *Roar: A Noisy Counting Book* by Pamela Duncan Edwards

Science

small group | KINESTHETIC

Count Natural Objects

- Go outside with your five bags.
- Count one leaf, two stones, three twigs, four blades of grass, and five acorns.
- Put the objects in your bags.
- Draw pictures of the objects on your bags.

Teacher Note: Make sure there are leaves, stones, twigs, acorns, and grass outside for students to collect. Instruct students on outdoor safety rules. Have students work in pairs.

Materials:

- lunch bags
- crayons
- leaves, grass, stones, twigs, and acorns

Health

small group | AUDITORY

Counting Teammates and Playing

- Line up.
- Count off from one to five.
- Listen for the number.
- Walk forward that many steps.

Teacher Note: Be sure students count off from one to five accurately. Each group of five students will be a team. When teams are formed, call a number from zero to five. Have teams come forward that many steps.

Materials:

- none

Art

Make a Picture

- Draw 10 pictures.
- Glue zero to five beans, beads, or buttons on each picture.
- Group the pictures by how many beans, beads, or buttons.
- Write the number of beans, beads, or buttons.

Teacher Note: Check that students are counting accurately.

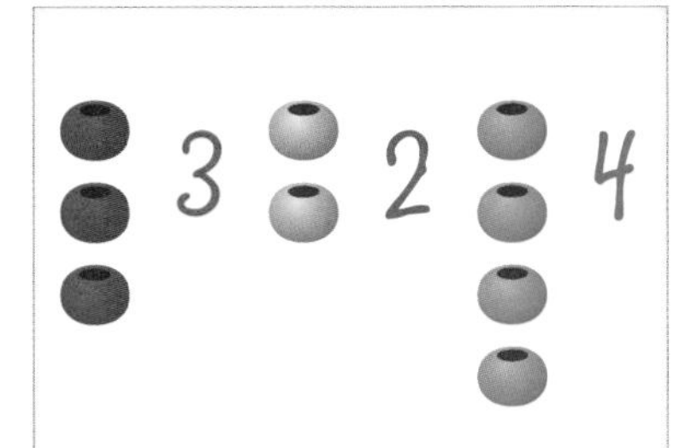

Materials:

- drawing paper
- crayons
- glue
- beans, beads, buttons

Language Arts

Tell Stories

- Look at the pictures.
- Work with a partner.
- Tell stories about the animals or objects in the pictures.
- Use numbers zero to five in your story.

Teacher Note: Use photos or pictures that clearly show one to five animals or objects.

Materials:

- photographs or pictures

Calendar Time

Days of the Month

- Show students a classroom calendar.
- Point to the numbers as students count the days.
- Write today's date on the board. Ask students if they recognize the number. Show students the number in the written date and the number on the calendar.
- Have volunteers follow your lead.
- Have students find all dates with the numbers zero, one, two, three, four, and five in it.

Teacher Note: Point out that the days of the month happen in order and that they are numbered each month starting at the number one.

Introduce the Chapter

Real World: School Days in a Week

Share with students that they will learn to read, write, put in order, and compare the numbers zero to five.

- Write the days that students attend school, Monday through Friday, on the chalkboard.
- Write the numbers one to five for each school day, with one for Monday, two for Tuesday, and so on.
- Read the numbers and point to them.
- Hold up your fingers and count with students. Start with the little finger as the number one.
- Have students hold up their fingers and count each number.
- Have students say the corresponding day as you read the numbers on the chalkboard.

Use the Student Page

Have students turn to p. 39. Guide students to discuss the images on the page and answer the Explore questions.

Key Vocabulary

Introduce key vocabulary in the chapter using the routine below.

Define: You can count items to find out how many there are.
Example: I count three racoons in the picture.
Ask: What items can you count?

Diagnostic Assessment

Check for students' prerequisite skills before beginning the chapter.

- **Option 1:** ***Are You Ready for Chapter 2?***
  SE Student Edition, p. 40
- **Option 2:** ***Online Assessment Quiz***
  Math Online macmillanmh.com
- **Option 3:** ***Diagnostic Test***
  CRM Chapter 2 Resource Masters, p. 40

RTI (Response to Intervention)

Apply the Results Based on the results of the diagnostic assessment on p. 40, use the chart on the next page to address individual needs before and during the chapter.

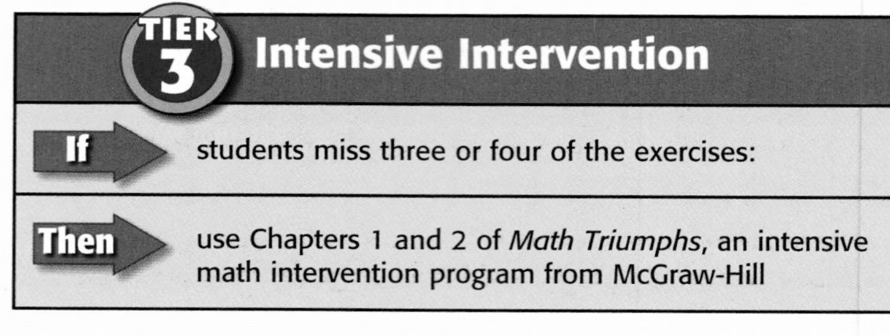

TIER 3	Intensive Intervention
If	students miss three or four of the exercises:
Then	use Chapters 1 and 2 of *Math Triumphs*, an intensive math intervention program from McGraw-Hill

FOLDABLES Study Organizer — Dinah Zike's Foldables

Guide students to create an Accordion Book Foldable graphic organizer to order numbers 0–5.

1. Fold four pieces of paper into hamburgers. However, fold one side one half inch shorter than the other side.

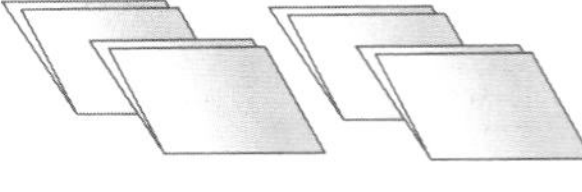

2. Fold this tab forward over the shorter piece, and then fold it back away from the shorter piece of paper.

3. Glue together to form an accordion by gluing a straight edge of one section into the valley of another section.

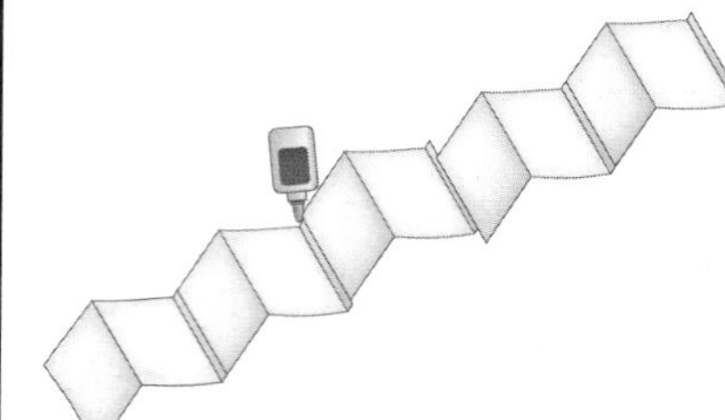

4. Write one number on the top left side of each of the three sections, beginning with number 1, and have students find and place pictures on the appropriate sections to illustrate each number.

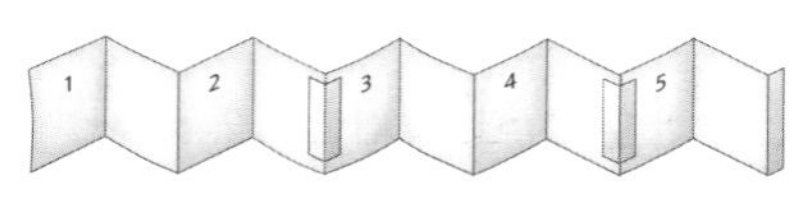

When to Use It *Lessons 2-2, 2-4, 2-5, and 2-6 (Additional instructions for using the Foldable with these lessons are found on pp. 51 and 63.)*

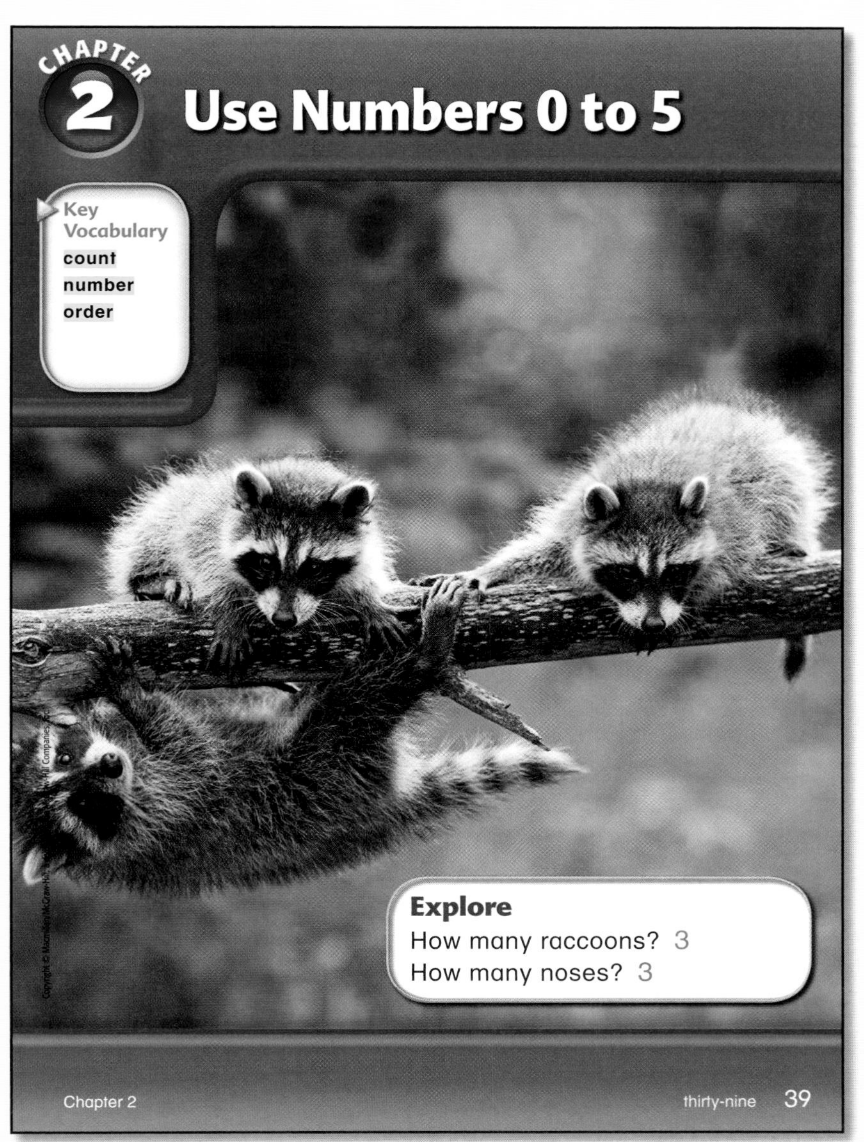

How many raccoons? 3
How many noses? 3

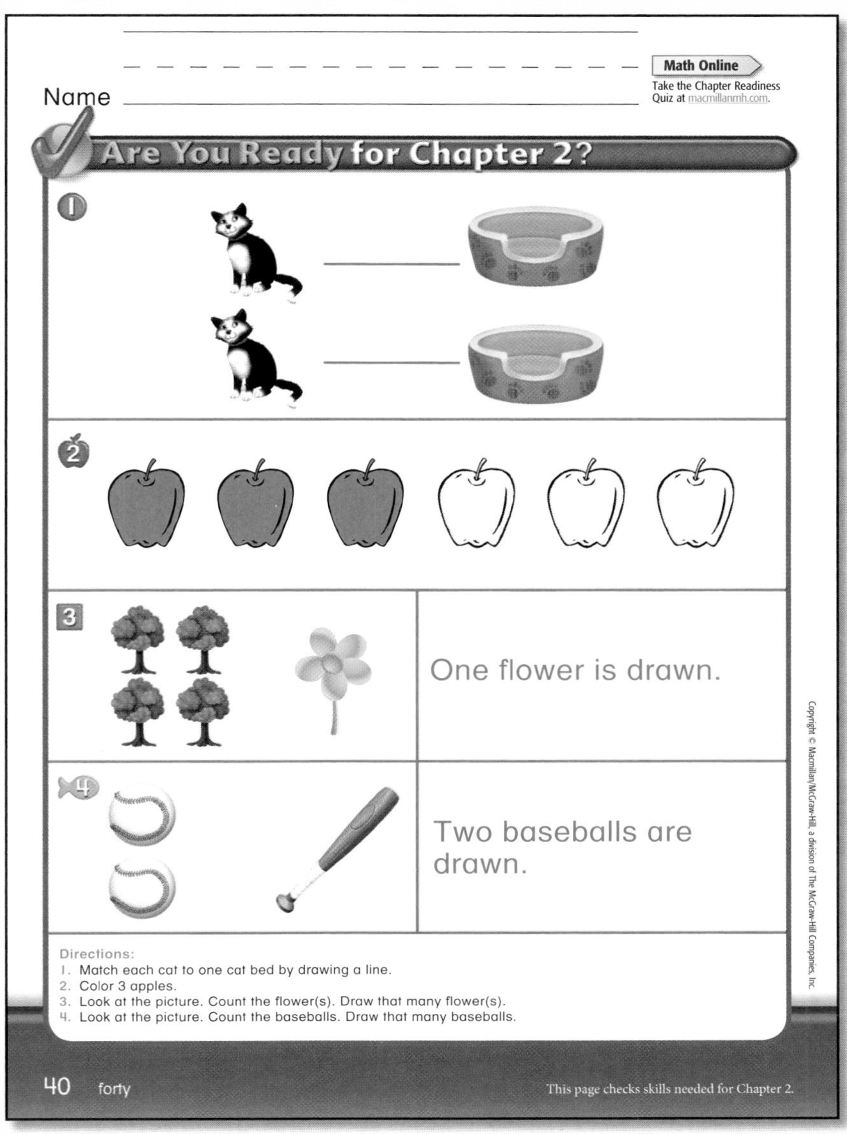

Name
Math Online
Take the Chapter Readiness Quiz at macmillanmh.com.
Are You Ready for Chapter 2?
One flower is drawn.
Two baseballs are drawn.
Directions:
1. Match each cat to one cat bed by drawing a line.
2. Color 3 apples.
3. Look at the picture. Count the flower(s). Draw that many flower(s).
4. Look at the picture. Count the baseballs. Draw that many baseballs.
40 forty
This page checks skills needed for Chapter 2.

RTI (Response to Intervention)

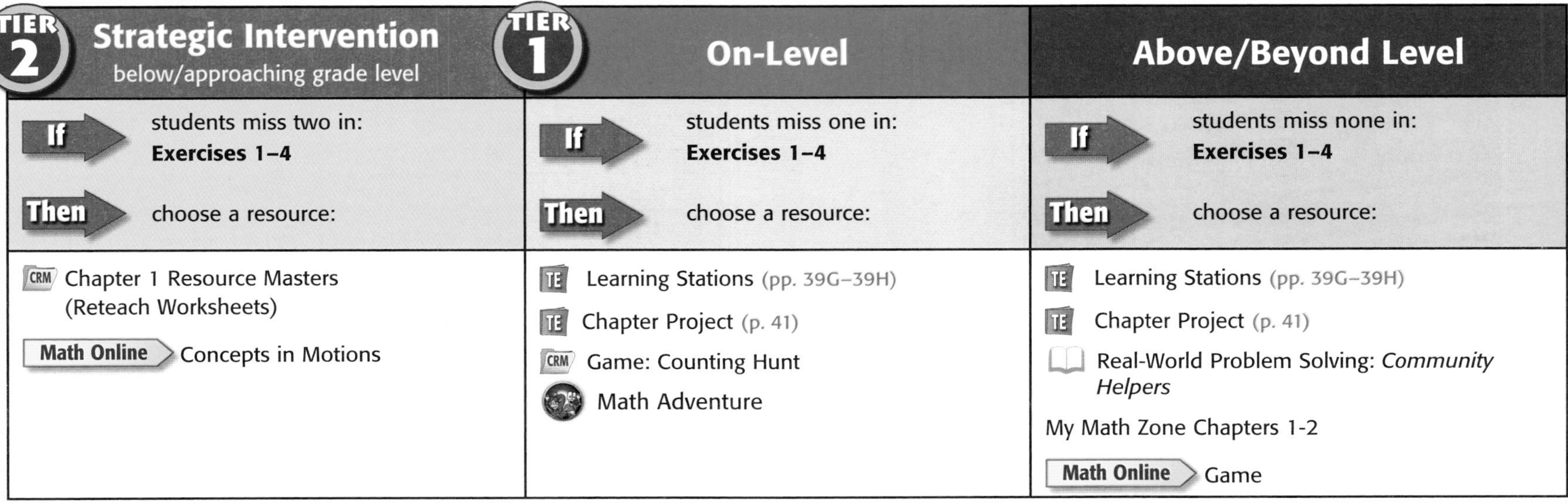

TIER 2 Strategic Intervention below/approaching grade level	TIER 1 On-Level	Above/Beyond Level
If students miss two in: **Exercises 1–4**	**If** students miss one in: **Exercises 1–4**	**If** students miss none in: **Exercises 1–4**
Then choose a resource:	**Then** choose a resource:	**Then** choose a resource:
CRM Chapter 1 Resource Masters (Reteach Worksheets) Math Online Concepts in Motions	TE Learning Stations (pp. 39G–39H) TE Chapter Project (p. 41) CRM Game: Counting Hunt Math Adventure	TE Learning Stations (pp. 39G–39H) TE Chapter Project (p. 41) Real-World Problem Solving: *Community Helpers* My Math Zone Chapters 1-2 Math Online Game

WRITING IN ▶MATH

Starting the Chapter
Ask students to use their Math Journals and draw something they have seen with one to five pieces or parts. For example, students could draw their shirts and draw five buttons. Have them put numbers near the objects, such as one near the shirt and five near the buttons. They could also draw and count classroom objects.

Chapter 2 Project

Create a Mural

Have students create a mural to illustrate their understanding of numbers from zero to five.

- Explain that each student or group of students is responsible for one part of a mural.
- Give the mural a theme, such as a barnyard.
- Have students draw objects that belong with the theme. Have them draw a number of objects and write the number with the picture.

Chapter 2 Literature List

Lesson	Book Title	Author
2-1	**Moo, Baa, La La La!**	Sandra Boynton
2-2	**Mama Cat Has Three Kittens**	Denise Fleming
2-3	**Where the Wild Things Are**	Maurice Sendak
2-4	**Ten Red Apples**	Virginia Miller
2-5	**Five Little Kittens**	Nancy Jewell
2-6	**Ten Red Apples**	Virginia Miller
2-7	**One Monkey Too Many**	Jackie French Koller
2-8	**Five Little Monkeys Jumping on the Bed**	Eileen Christelow
Any	**1, 2, 3; How Many Animals Can You See?**	Emilie Boon
Any	**1, 2, 3, To the Zoo**	Eric Carle
Any	**At the Edge of the Woods: A Counting Book**	Cynthia Cotten

ELL National ESL Standards Alignment for Chapter 2			
Lesson, Page	**ESL Standard**	**Modality**	**Level**
2-1, p. 43B	Goal 1, Standard 3, e	Auditory	Beginning
2-2, p. 45B	Goal 2, Standard 2, e	Auditory/Spatial	Intermediate
2-3, p. 47B	Goal 1, Standard 3, g	Kinesthetic, Social	Intermediate
2-4, p. 49B	Goal 1, Standard 3, b	Intrapersonal, Social	Beginning
2-5, p. 53B	Goal 2, Standard 2, i	Intrapersonal	Intermediate
2-6, p. 55B	Goal 2, Standard 3, k	Visual, Social	Intermediate
2-7, p. 57B	Goal 1, Standard 3, d	Visual, Social	Intermediate
2-8, p. 59B	Goal 2, Standard 1, e	Visual	Intermediate
2-1, p. 43B	Goal 1, Standard 3, e	Auditory	Beginning

The National ESL Standards can be found in the Teacher Reference Handbook.

English

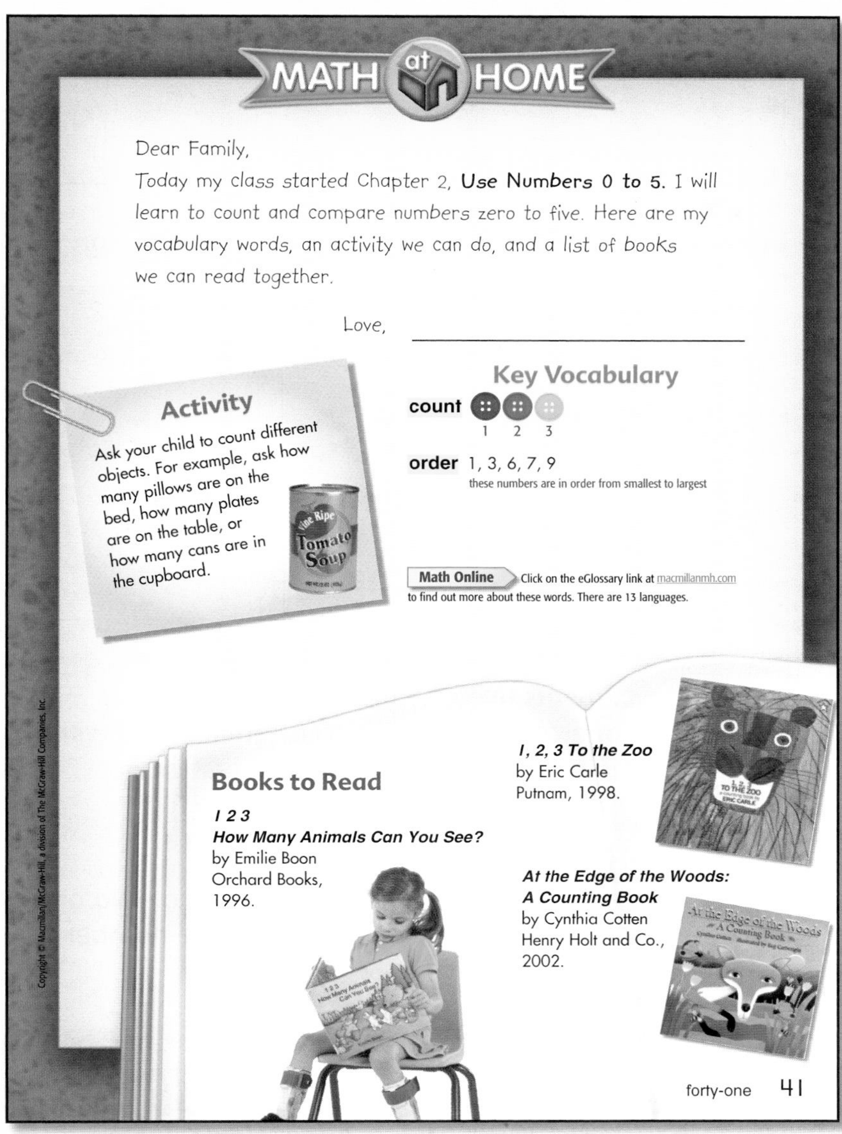

MATH at HOME

Dear Family,

Today my class started Chapter 2, **Use Numbers 0 to 5**. I will learn to count and compare numbers zero to five. Here are my vocabulary words, an activity we can do, and a list of books we can read together.

Love, ______________________

Activity

Ask your child to count different objects. For example, ask how many pillows are on the bed, how many plates are on the table, or how many cans are in the cupboard.

Key Vocabulary

count 1 2 3

order 1, 3, 6, 7, 9
these numbers are in order from smallest to largest

Math Online Click on the eGlossary link at macmillanmh.com to find out more about these words. There are 13 languages.

Books to Read

1 2 3 How Many Animals Can You See?
by Emilie Boon
Orchard Books, 1996.

1, 2, 3 To the Zoo
by Eric Carle
Putnam, 1998.

At the Edge of the Woods: A Counting Book
by Cynthia Cotten
Henry Holt and Co., 2002.

Español

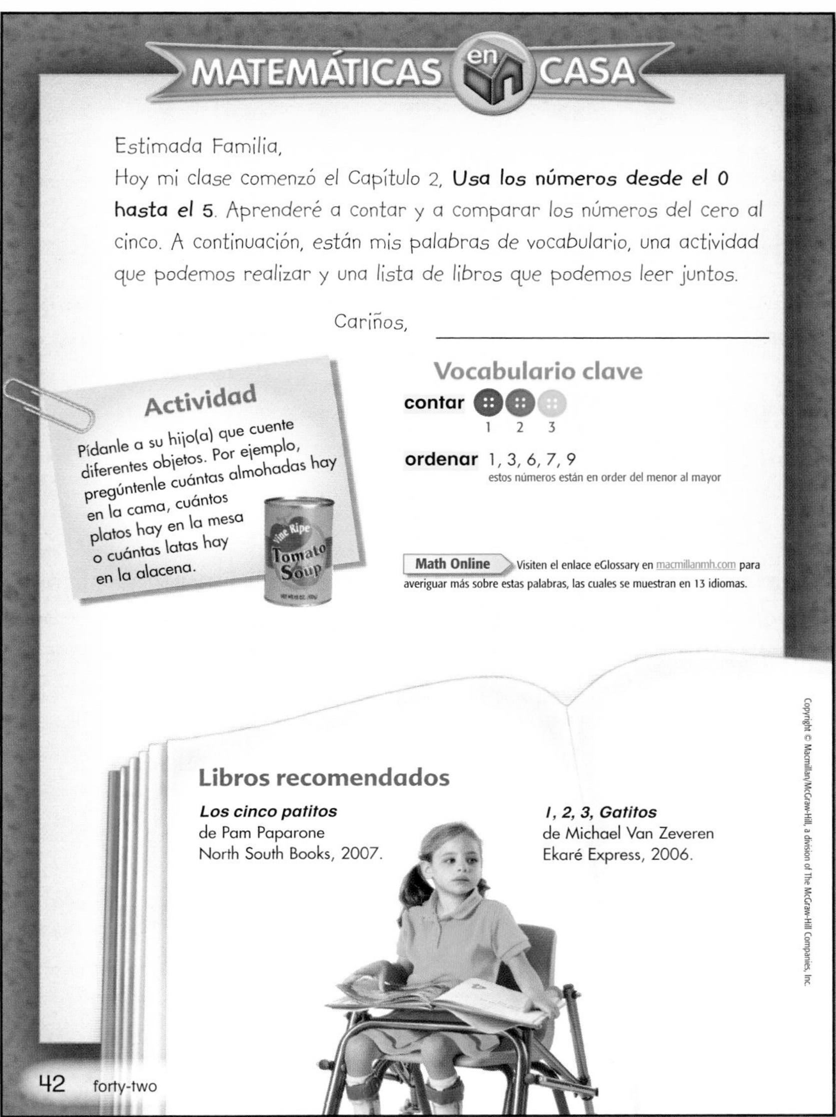

MATEMÁTICAS en CASA

Estimada Familia,

Hoy mi clase comenzó el Capítulo 2, **Usa los números desde el 0 hasta el 5**. Aprenderé a contar y a comparar los números del cero al cinco. A continuación, están mis palabras de vocabulario, una actividad que podemos realizar y una lista de libros que podemos leer juntos.

Cariños, ______________________

Actividad

Pídanle a su hijo(a) que cuente diferentes objetos. Por ejemplo, pregúntenle cuántas almohadas hay en la cama, cuántos platos hay en la mesa o cuántas latas hay en la alacena.

Vocabulario clave

contar 1 2 3

ordenar 1, 3, 6, 7, 9
estos números están en order del menor al mayor

Math Online Visiten el enlace eGlossary en macmillanmh.com para averiguar más sobre estas palabras, las cuales se muestran en 13 idiomas.

Libros recomendados

Los cinco patitos
de Pam Paparone
North South Books, 2007.

1, 2, 3, Gatitos
de Michael Van Zeveren
Ekaré Express, 2006.

- Read the Math at Home letter on p. 41 with the class and have each child sign it.
- Send home copies of the Math at Home letter with each student.
- Use the Spanish letter on p. 42 for students with Spanish-speaking parents or guardians.

Read-Aloud Anthology

For an optional reading activity to introduce this chapter's math concepts, see the Read-Aloud Anthology on p. TR25.

LESSON 2-1

Numbers 1, 2, and 3

Lesson Planner

Objective

Name, recognize and count the numerals 1, 2, and 3 using concrete objects and illustrations.

Vocabulary

count, **one**, **two**, **three**

Resources

Materials: empty coffee can with plastic lid, number strips, crayons, number cards
Manipulatives: two-colored counters, color tiles
Literature: *Moo, Baa, La La La!* by Sandra Boynton
Alternate Lesson: Adapt *The Number Stations* on pages 168–178 of *Math Their Way* to provide practice in naming and counting the quantities 1, 2, and 3.
Teacher Technology
TeacherWorks

Focus on Math Background

The ability to count is a precursor to being able to add and subtract numbers. Students will use manipulatives to count. They will also count common objects in pictures and as realia. These counting experiences will help students connect representations to numbers, an essential math skill.

Daily Routine

Use these suggestions before beginning the lesson on p. 43.

5-Minute Check

(Reviews Lesson 1-7)
Have students use connecting cubes to decide whether one pencil is more than, the same number as, or less than two pencils.

Problem of the Day

Show students five crayons. Have students use one-to-one correspondence to create a group with the same number of crayons as the first group.

LINE UP Ask students to line up in groups of two or three. Ask volunteers to count the number of students in each group.

Building Math Vocabulary

Materials: magnetic manipulatives, marker board

- Tell students that we **count** to find how many.
- Put one magnetic manipulative on a marker board. Count **one** counter and show how many one is by coloring one box on the board.
- Repeat the activity with **two** and **three** magnetic manipulatives.

Differentiated Instruction

Small Group Options

Option 1 VISUAL

Below/Approaching Level BL

Materials: identical pattern blocks

- Put out one block on a table. Represent this quantity verbally by saying "one." Put out two blocks. Say, "one, two." Put out three blocks. Say, "one, two, three."
- Clear the table.
- Put out one block and ask students how many. Count with students. Repeat for two blocks and then three blocks.

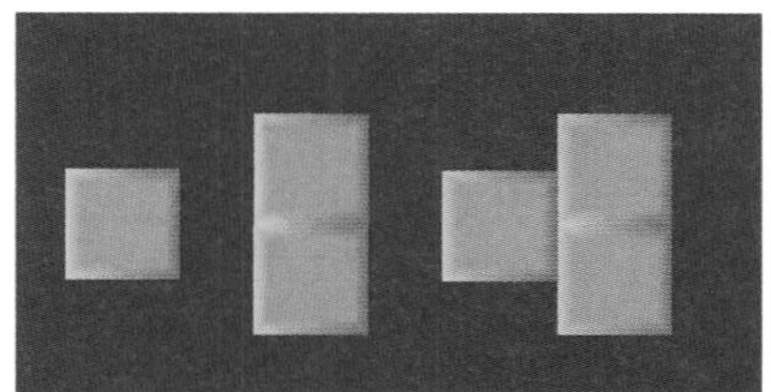

Option 2 AUDITORY

English Language Learners ELL

Materials: 1–3 number cards
Core Vocabulary: one, two, three
Common Use Verb: show

Hear Math This strategy teaches numbers 1, 2, and 3.

- Show the one card. Say: "one." Have students repeat. Repeat with the two and three cards.
- Show one finger, touch it, and say: "**One.**" Have students repeat. Say: "***Show* one** finger." Repeat for other numbers. Vary pace and sequence.

Independent Work Options

Option 1 LINGUISTIC

Early Finishers OL AL

Materials: classroom objects

- Have students lay out classroom objects in a group of one.
- Have students choose a partner to find other objects in the room that show the same amount.
- Then have them repeat the activity with groups of two and three.

Option 2

Student Technology

Math Online macmillanmh.com

Math Adventures

Option 3

Learning Station: Reading (p. 39G)

Direct students to the Reading Learning Station for opportunities to explore and extend the lesson concept.

Leveled Lesson Resources

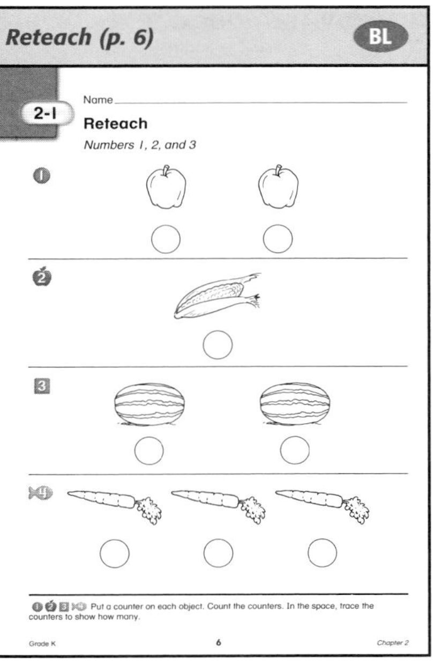

Reteach (p. 6) BL

2-1 Name
Reteach
Numbers 1, 2, and 3

Put a counter on each object. Count the counters. In the space, trace the counters to show how many.

Grade K 6 Chapter 2

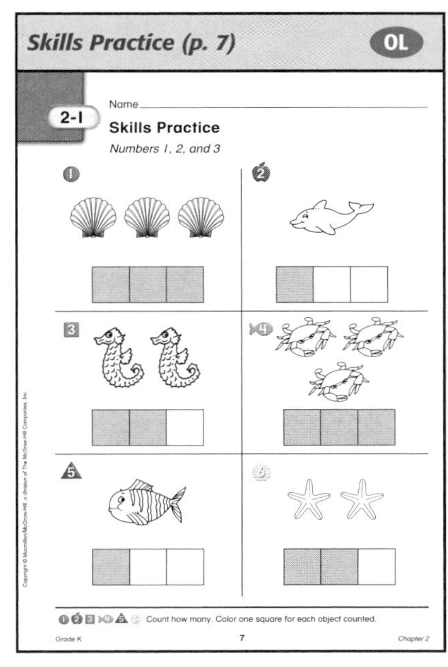

Skills Practice (p. 7) OL

2-1 Name
Skills Practice
Numbers 1, 2, and 3

Count how many. Color one square for each object counted.

Grade K 7 Chapter 2

Enrich (p. 9) AL

2-1 Name
Enrich
Birthday Bash

1

2

3

Identify how old each child is by counting the candles on the cake. Write the number of candles.

Grade K 9 Chapter 2

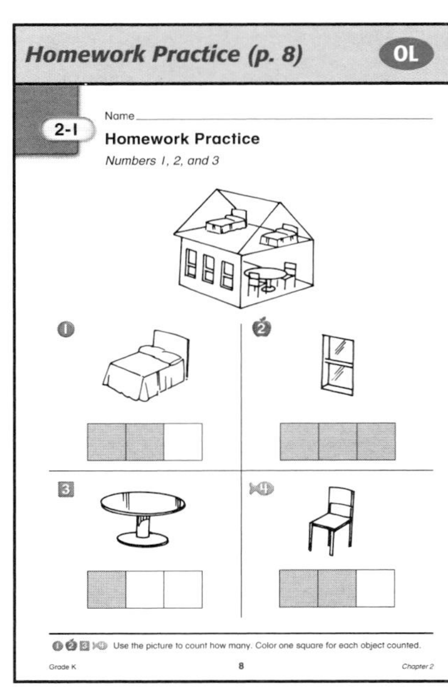

Homework Practice (p. 8) OL

2-1 Name
Homework Practice
Numbers 1, 2, and 3

Use the picture to count how many. Color one square for each object counted.

Grade K 8 Chapter 2

1 Introduce

Circle Time

Activity Choice 1 • Literature

Moo, Baa, La La La!
by Sandra Boynton

Materials: two-colored counters

- Read the book aloud having students use counters to **count** each type of animal except for the last two pages.
- Show the second to last page. Model counting the dogs in the picture with the same colored counter, represent the quantity verbally by counting to two. Continue counting by placing the same colored counters on each type of animal.
- Show the last page. Have students count animals by the same method. Ask which group(s) has **one**, **two**, or **three** animals.

Activity Choice 2 • Hands-On

Materials: counters, coffee can

- Give each student one counter.
- **How many counters did I give you?** one
- Have students count to check.
- **What is something in our room that we have one of?** Sample answers: door, sink, block center, bathroom, clock, teacher
- Invite students to walk to that item and match it to their counter.
- Explain that when we count we start with *one*. Have students listen to what *one* sounds like as you count it and drop it in the coffee can.
- Allow each student to drop their counter in the coffee can as they count and say "one."
- Give each student two counters and repeat activity. Explain that when we count we say "one, two." Two is one more than one.
- Give each student three counters and repeat activity.

2 Teach

- Direct students to the top of p. 43.
- Tell students to look at the edge of the bathtub. Represent the quantity verbally by counting the towel draped across the tub with students, having them point as they count. Repeat for the bottle of shampoo. Reiterate the number *one*.
- **What other object is there one of?** one bathtub
- Have students point to the bathtub as they count.
- Tell students to look at the objects inside the bathtub. Count the two whales with students, having them point as they count. Reiterate the number two.
- **What other object are there two of in the bathtub?** two ducks
- Have students point to each duck as they count.
- Count the three tugboats with students, having them point as they count. Reiterate the number three.
- **What other object are there three of in the bathtub?** three goldfish
- Have students point to each goldfish as they count.

BL Alternate Teaching Strategy

If students have trouble recognizing an amount of one, two, or three objects . . .

Then use one of these reteach options.

1 CRM **Daily Reteach Worksheet** (p. 6)

2 **Show a Model** Provide students with cards that show one to three dots, stars, or cubes.

- Have students count the objects, then say the numbers.
- Have students lay a counter on each object on the card and count again, practicing number one, two, and three.

COMMON ERROR!

Students may count numbers out of order. Continue to practice rote counting to a rhythm or a song.

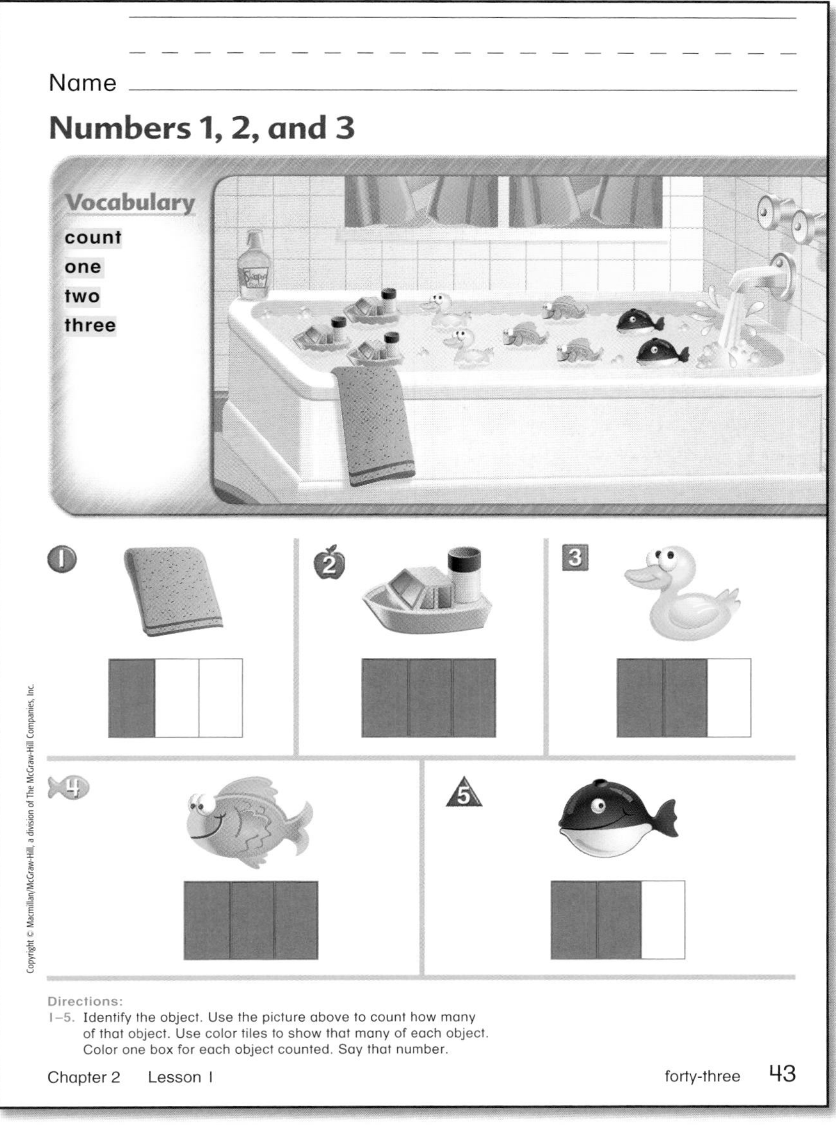

Name
Numbers 1, 2, and 3
Vocabulary
count
one
two
three
Directions:
1–5. Identify the object. Use the picture above to count how many of that object. Use color tiles to show that many of each object. Color one box for each object counted. Say that number.
Chapter 2 Lesson 1
forty-three 43

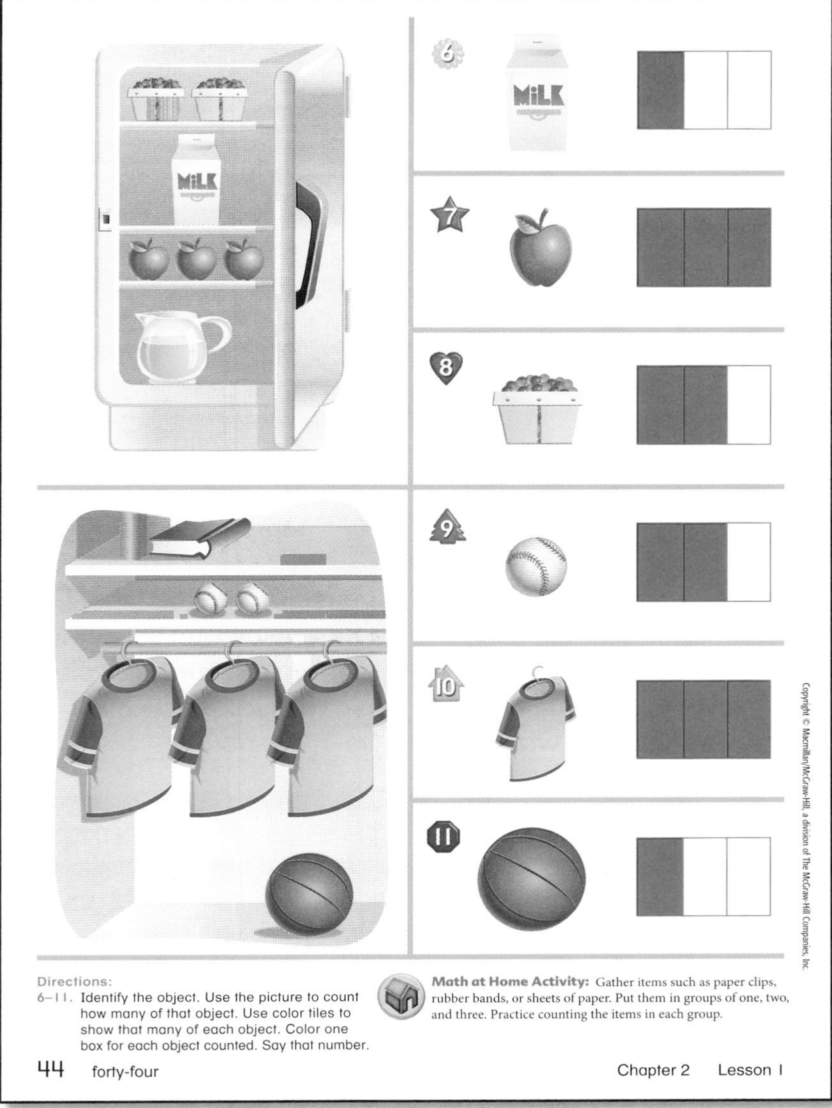

MILK
Directions:
6–11. Identify the object. Use the picture to count how many of that object. Use color tiles to show that many of each object. Color one box for each object counted. Say that number.
Math at Home Activity: Gather items such as paper clips, rubber bands, or sheets of paper. Put them in groups of one, two, and three. Practice counting the items in each group.
44 forty-four
Chapter 2 Lesson 1

3 Practice

Guided Practice

- Direct students to p. 43.
- Identify each object in Exercises 1–5 with students.
- Use the picture at the top of the page to count how many of that object with students.
- Have students use color tiles to show the number, then color one square for each object counted.
- Have students say the number.

Independent Practice

Have students turn to p. 44. Explain the directions. Have students work independently on the exercises.

4 Assess

Formative Assessment

- Display a picture with one, two, or three objects.
- Have students count the number of objects.
- Have students hold up that many fingers.

Quick Check **Are students still struggling to recognize, name, and count numbers one, two, and three?**

If Yes → Small Group Options (p. 43B)

If No → Independent Work Options (p. 43B)

CRM Skills Practice Worksheet (p. 7)

CRM Enrich Worksheet (p. 9)

LESSON 2-2 Read and Write 1, 2, and 3

Lesson Planner

Objective
Recognize and write the numerals 1, 2, and 3.

Vocabulary
number

Resources
Materials: cups, pencils, cards, chart paper, markers, pictures with objects
Manipulatives: two-colored counters
Literature: *Mama Cat Has Three Kittens* by Denise Fleming
Alternate Lesson: Use *Recording at the Number Stations* on pages 177–178 of *Math Their Way* for practice in recognizing and writing numbers 1, 2, and 3.

Teacher Technology
TeacherWorks

Focus on Math Background

In these early stages of counting, offer experiences in *discrete objects*, which may be handled as they are counted. Watch students count to be sure they have one-to-one correspondence when they count. This lesson will provide students with many counting, recognizing, and representing opportunities of one, two, and three in varied settings.

Daily Routine

Use these suggestions before beginning the lesson on p. 45.

5-Minute Check
(Reviews Lesson 2-1)

1. Have students show something in the room there is only one of.
2. Have students show a group of two objects and a group of three objects.

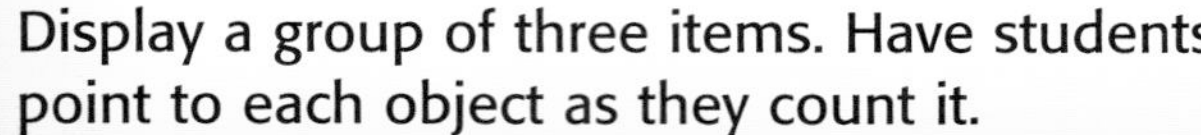

Problem of the Day
Display a group of three items. Have students point to each object as they count it.

LINE UP Assign students numbers one, two, or three to trace in the air. Have students line up by ones, then twos, then threes. Have students "erase" their numbers so they do not bump into them.

Building Math Vocabulary
Materials: chart paper, markers, two-colored counters

- Tell students that a **number** is a way to show how many.
- Write numbers one, two, and three on the chart paper.
- Count one counter, then show the number one on the paper.
- Repeat with numbers two and three, asking students to point to the number that represents how many counters.

Differentiated Instruction

Small Group Options

Option 1 Gifted and Talented AL

VISUAL

Materials: classroom objects, drawing paper, crayons

- Have students use one color to draw identical objects in groups of one, two, and three, and have them symbolically describe their drawing by writing the number for each group.
- Have students draw different objects with different colors in groups of three, two, and one on the back of the paper, and write the number for each group.

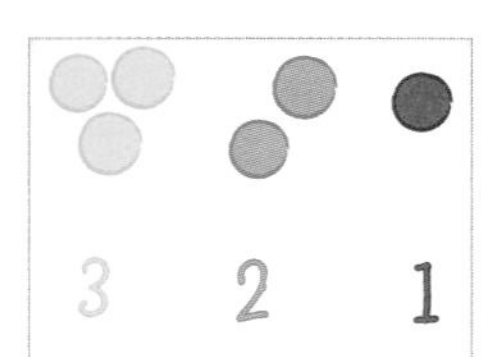

Option 2 English Language Learners ELL

AUDITORY/SPATIAL

Materials: poster paper, marker, lined paper, pencils
Core Vocabulary: straight line down, around
Common Use Verb: make

Write Math This strategy vocalizes writing 1, 2, and 3.

- Repeat rhymes chorally: "**Straight line down** from the sun, That's the way to ***make*** a one." "***Around*** *and back like a railroad track, Two, two, two!* ***Around*** *the tree and* ***around*** *the tree, That's the way to* **make** *a three."*
- Extend activity by having students act out rhymes.

Independent Work Options

Option 1 Early Finishers OL AL

LINGUISTIC

Materials: connecting cubes, paper, pencils

- Have students lay out identical connecting cubes in groups of one, two, and three.
- Have them symbolically describe the cubes by writing the numbers that match each group on paper.
- Have students lay out different colored connecting cubes in groups of one, two, and three.
- Tell them to write the numbers that match each group on the back of the paper.

Option 2 Student Technology

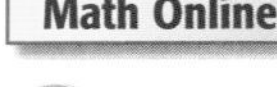

macmillanmh.com

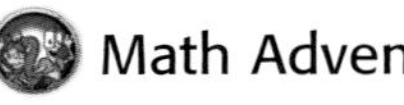

Math Adventures

Option 3 Learning Station: Science (p. 39G)

Direct students to the Science Learning Station for opportunities to explore and extend the lesson concept.

Leveled Lesson Resources

Reteach (p. 10) BL

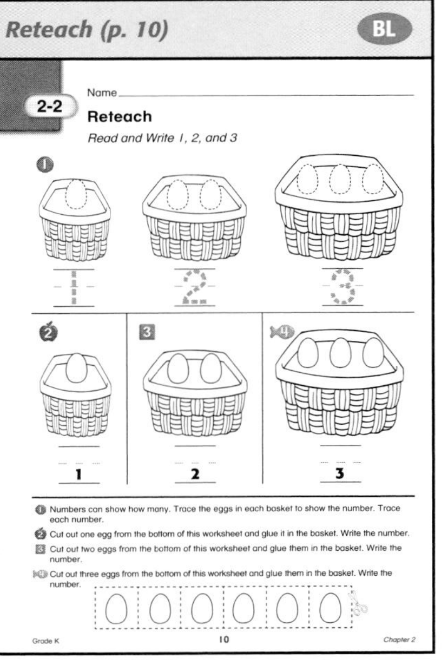

2-2 Name

Reteach

Read and Write 1, 2, and 3

1 Numbers can show how many. Trace the eggs in each basket to show the number. Trace each number.
2 Cut out one egg from the bottom of this worksheet and glue it in the basket. Write the number.
3 Cut out two eggs from the bottom of this worksheet and glue them in the basket. Write the number.
4 Cut out three eggs from the bottom of this worksheet and glue them in the basket. Write the number.

Grade K 10 Chapter 2

Skills Practice (p. 11) OL

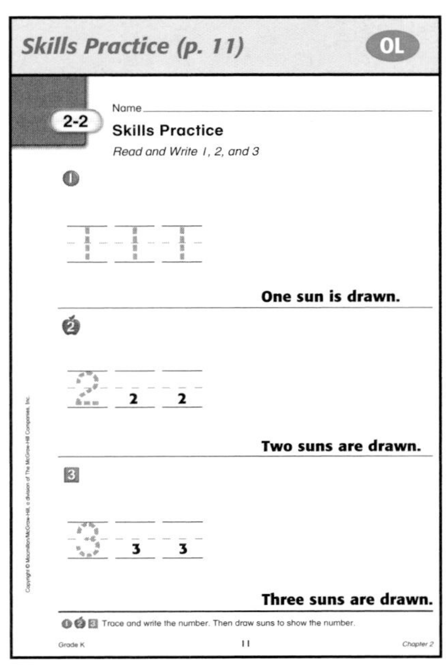

2-2 Name

Skills Practice

Read and Write 1, 2, and 3

1 One sun is drawn.
2 Two suns are drawn.
3 Three suns are drawn.

1 2 3 Trace and write the number. Then draw suns to show the number.

Grade K 11 Chapter 2

Enrich (p. 13) AL

2-2 Name

Enrich

Flower Power

Count the number of petals on each flower. Write the number in the middle of each flower.

Grade K 13 Chapter 2

Homework Practice (p. 12) OL

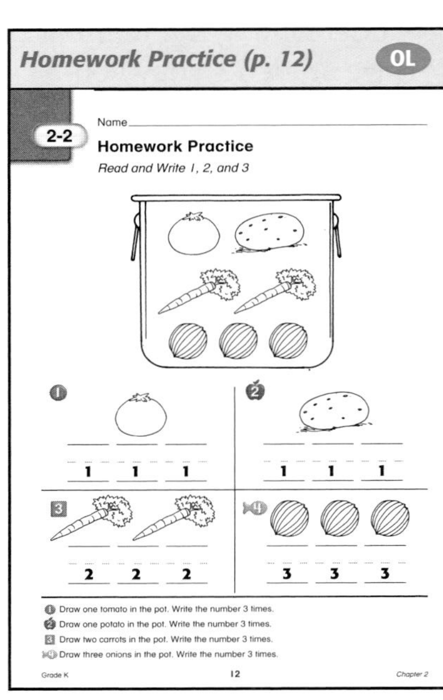

2-2 Name

Homework Practice

Read and Write 1, 2, and 3

1 Draw one tomato in the pot. Write the number 3 times.
2 Draw one potato in the pot. Write the number 3 times.
3 Draw two carrots in the pot. Write the number 3 times.
4 Draw three onions in the pot. Write the number 3 times.

Grade K 12 Chapter 2

1 Introduce

Activity Choice 1 • Literature

Mama Cat Has Three Kittens
by Denise Fleming

Materials: two-colored counters, cups, pencils, cards

- Read the book aloud, discussing situations that involve one, two, and three kittens. Write the **numbers** on the chalkboard. Symbolically describe the situation by drawing the correct number of kittens by each number.
- Give pairs of students six counters and three cups. Have one partner put one, two, or three counters in the cups. Have the other partner write the numbers on cards.
- Have partners mix cups and cards and trade.
- Ask partners to take turns matching counters with numbers and checking each other's work.

Activity Choice 2 • Hands-On 

Materials: chart paper, markers

- Write the word *one* and the number one next to it on paper. Ask a volunteer to put one dot next to the word and number.
- **What things come in ones?** Sample answers: nose, chin, mouth, head
- Model writing the number one on the chalkboard. Have students copy you by writing the number one in the air.
- Repeat the activity with the number two.
- **What things come in twos?** Sample answers: eyes, ears, hands, feet, gloves, shoes
- Repeat the activity with the number three.
- **What can you do in threes?** Sample answers: hop, jump, clap

2 Teach

- Direct students to top of p. 45.
- Name and count the objects in the park with students.
- Have students name as many objects as they can that appear only one time in the picture.

BL Alternate Teaching Strategy

 students are continuing to struggle writing numbers one, two, and three and corresponding those numbers with amounts . . .

 use one of these reteach options.

1 CRM **Daily Reteach Worksheet** (p. 10)

2 **Show a Model** Make number strips of dotted outlines of numbers one, two, and three with pictures of triangles corresponding to the numbers.

- Have students count the objects, say each number, then write the numbers.
- Continue until students can write the numbers and correspond the numbers with amounts.

COMMON ERROR!

Students may write numbers two and three backwards. Provide opportunities to trace the numbers using crayons, markers, and finger paint, and to write them from models.

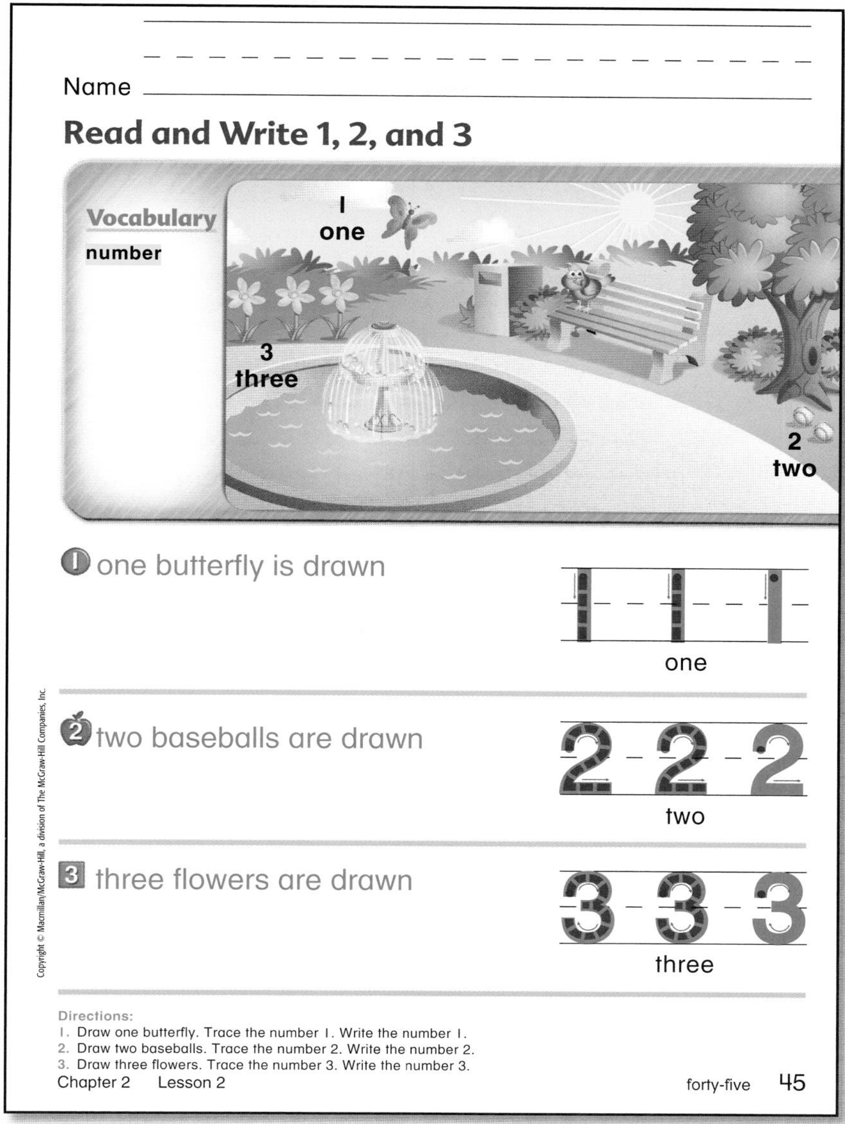

Name
Read and Write 1, 2, and 3
Vocabulary
number
1
one
3
three
2
two
one butterfly is drawn
one
two baseballs are drawn
two
three flowers are drawn
three
Directions:
1. Draw one butterfly. Trace the number 1. Write the number 1.
2. Draw two baseballs. Trace the number 2. Write the number 2.
3. Draw three flowers. Trace the number 3. Write the number 3.
Chapter 2 Lesson 2
forty-five 45

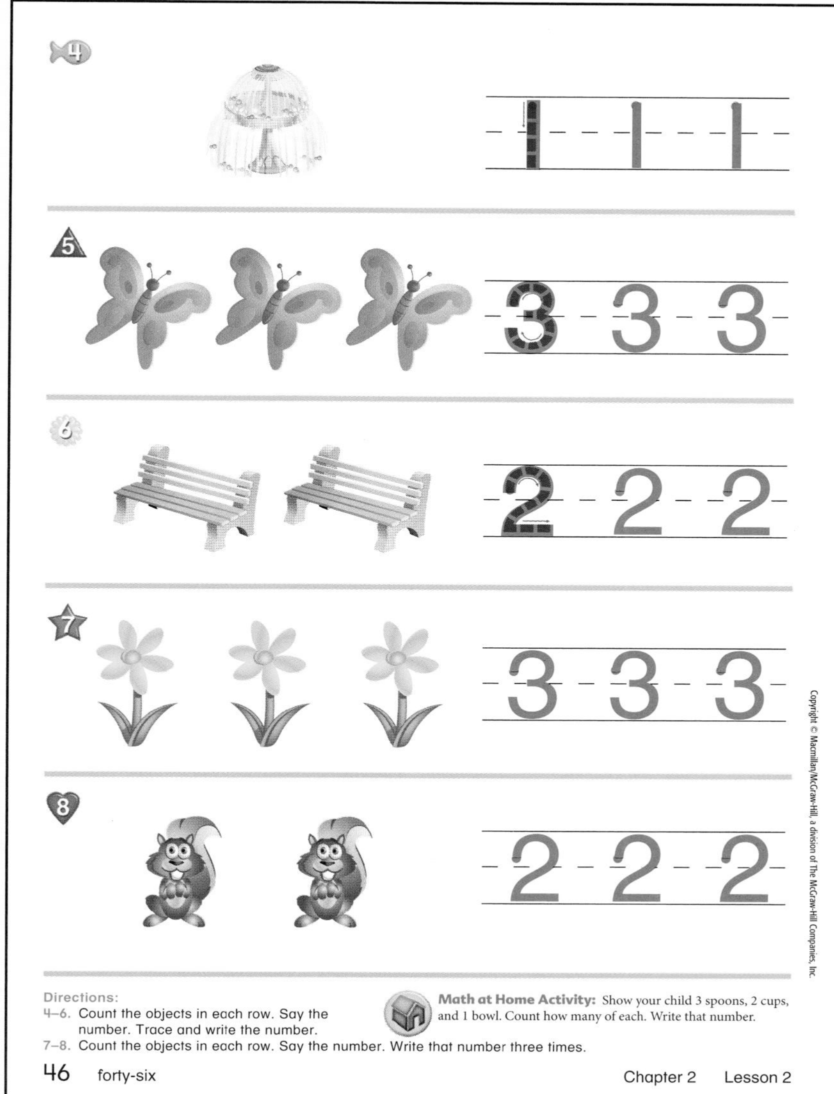

Directions:
4–6. Count the objects in each row. Say the number. Trace and write the number.
7–8. Count the objects in each row. Say the number. Write that number three times.
Math at Home Activity: Show your child 3 spoons, 2 cups, and 1 bowl. Count how many of each. Write that number.
46 forty-six
Chapter 2 Lesson 2

3 Practice

Guided Practice

- Direct students to p. 45. Have students place 1, 2, or 3 cubes by the appropriate groups of objects in the park.
- Have students say the number in Exercise 1 and draw one butterfly.
- Guide students in writing the number one, tracing the dashed lines. Then have students write the number using the green dot and arrows as guides.
- Repeat the activity for Exercises 2 and 3.

Independent Practice

Have students turn to p. 46. Explain the directions. Have students work independently on the exercises.

4 Assess

Formative Assessment

- Display a picture with one, two, and three objects.
- Have students count the number of objects, then write the number that corresponds to the picture.

Quick Check **Are students still struggling to read and write the numbers one, two, and three?**

If Yes → Small Group Options (p. 45B)

If No → Independent Work Options (p. 45B)

CRM Skills Practice Worksheet (p. 11)

CRM Enrich Worksheet (p. 13)

LESSON 2-3

Numbers 4 and 5

Lesson Planner

Objective

Name, recognize and count the numerals 4 and 5 using concrete objects and illustrations.

Vocabulary

four, **five**

Resources

Materials: drawing paper, crayons, pictures of objects, shaker

Manipulatives: counters, connecting cubes, color tiles

Literature Connection: *Where the Wild Things Are* by Maurice Sendak

Alternate Lesson: Adapt *The Number Stations* on pages 168–178 of *Math Their Way* to provide practice in naming and counting the quantities 4 and 5.

Teacher Technology

TeacherWorks • Math Songs Track 4 Lesson Plan

Focus on Math Background

The ability to count is a precursor to being able to add and subtract numbers. Counting experiences will help students connect representations to numbers, an essential math skill.

Students start by counting from one to three. Moving on to counting four and five objects leads to the ability to count to larger numbers. Grouping objects in fours and fives also affords students the opportunity to group and compare.

Daily Routine

Use these suggestions before beginning the lesson on p. 47.

5-Minute Check

(Reviews Lesson 2-2)

1. Show students one pencil. Have them count with you.
2. Write the number one on the chalkboard.
3. Repeat the activity with two, then three.

Problem of the Day

Ask students questions about objects in the classroom that can be answered with the numbers one, two, or three. Start by asking how many teachers are in the room. After students answer each question, have them count the objects aloud to check their answers.

Ask students to line up in groups of two, three, four, or five.

Building Math Vocabulary

Materials: chart paper, markers, two-colored counters

- Draw **four** circles on the board and count them aloud. Count again with students.
- Draw **five** stars on the board and count them aloud with students. Count again with students.
- Have students place four counters in a group and count them.
- Have students place five counters in a group and count them.

Differentiated Instruction

Small Group Options

Option 1 Below/Approaching Level BL

VISUAL

Materials: dot cards 4 and 5, two-colored counters

- Put dot cards facedown on a table. Have a student choose a card, flip it over, and count the dots.
- Have students symbolically describe the dots by placing that many counters below the card and counting aloud.

Option 2 English Language Learners ELL

KINESTHETIC, SOCIAL

Materials: 100 of any small object (cubes, buttons, etc.)
Core Vocabulary: walk heel to toe, four, five
Common Use Verb: find

Do Math This strategy uses group learning to practice finding 4 and 5.

- Form teams of four, single file, four steps from the chalkboard.
- Put small objects in front of the classroom.
- Demonstrate walking **heel to toe** to get objects.
- Shouting: "**Find four.**" The front students take four heel-to-toe steps to the objects, collect 4 things and takes them behind their line. Then that player shouts to the next player: "**Find four!**" The first team to finish wins.
- Repeat for: "**Find five!**"

Independent Work Options

Option 1 Early Finishers OL AL

VISUAL-SPATIAL

Materials: stickers, markers

- Write the numbers four and five on a sheet of paper.
- Have students place the correct amount of stickers next to the numbers.

Option 2 Student Technology

Math Online macmillanmh.com

Math Songs "Here is the Beehive" Track 4

Option 3 Learning Station: Reading (p. 39G)

Direct students to the Reading Learning Station for opportunities to explore and extend the lesson concept.

Leveled Lesson Resources

Reteach (p. 14) BL

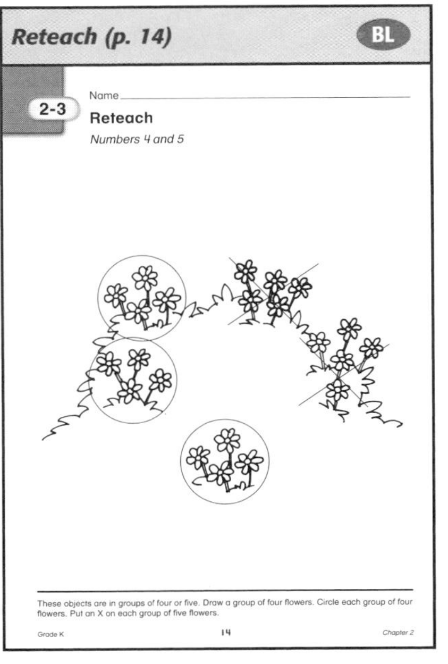

Skills Practice (p. 15) OL

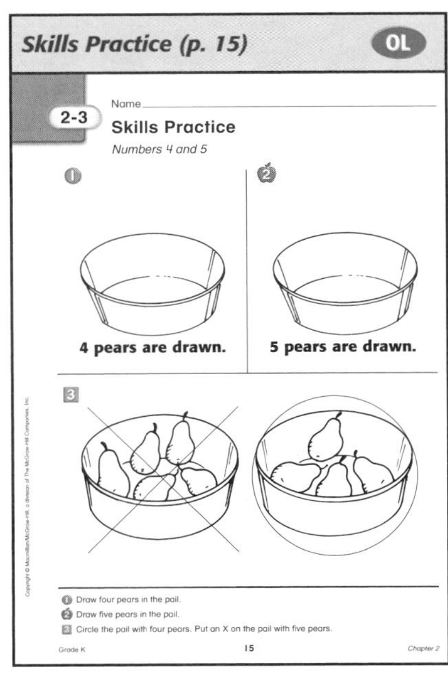

Enrich (p. 17) AL

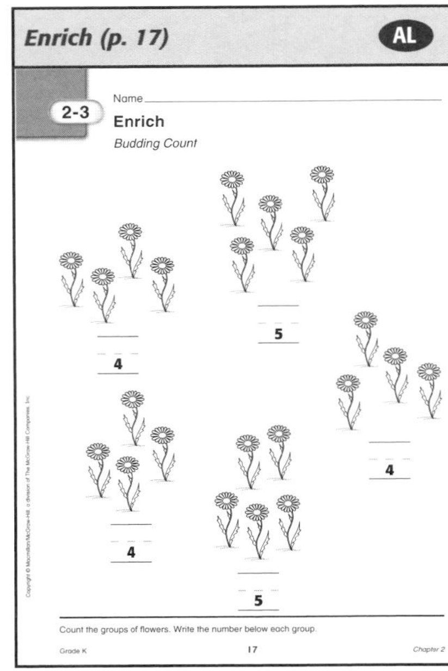

Homework Practice (p. 16) OL

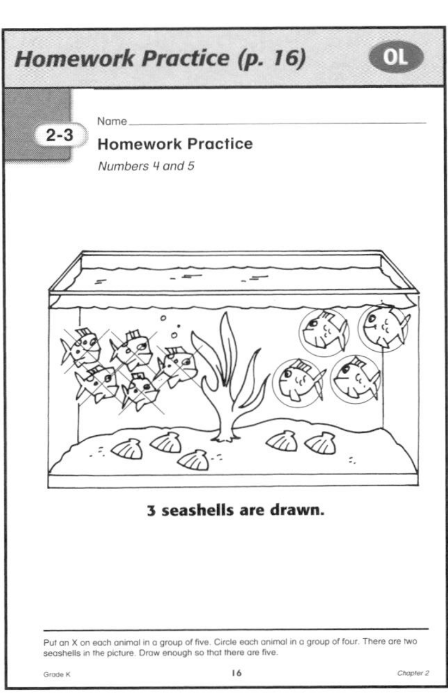

1 Introduce

Circle Time

Activity Choice 1 • Literature

Where the Wild Things Are
by Maurice Sendak
Materials: drawing paper, crayons

- Read the book aloud. Count the number of wild things on pp. 8–9. Ask how many wild things are on subsequent pages.
- Next, draw groups of **four** and **five** objects on the board. Have students verbally describe the objects by identifying the total number in each group.
- Have students draw a picture of an island with either four or five creatures. Have students form a circle. Have a volunteer share his or her picture, then point to another student to say whether the picture has four or five creatures. The student who guesses shares next.

Activity Choice 2 • Hands-On

- Review numbers one, two, and three using counters and showing the quantities.
- Put four counters in a shaker.
- Shake them out and ask students how many counters were in the shaker. Count them together.
- Have students drop the counters one at a time in the shaker while counting.
- Tell students that four is one more than three.
- Repeat the activity with five counters.
- Be sure to say that five is one more than four.
- Repeat using four or five counters randomly.
- Allow time for students to use the counters in small groups, counting out four and five.

2 Teach

- Direct students to the top of p. 47.
- Count the four bears on the left side with students. Have each student point to each bear as they verbally describe the number the bear represents.
- Have students place a blue connecting cube on each bear.
- Reiterate the number four.
- Count the five bears on the right side of the page with students. Have each student point to each bear as they name the number the bear represents.
- Have students place a red connecting cube on each bear.
- Reiterate the number five.

BL Alternate Teaching Strateg

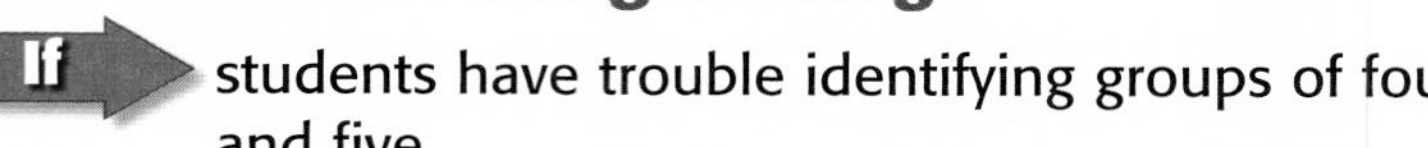

If students have trouble identifying groups of four and five . . .

Then use one of these reteach options.

1 CRM **Daily Reteach Worksheet** (p. 14)

2 **Use Pictures** Provide students with a picture of four objects and a picture of five objects.
- Have students place color tiles on each picture as they count objects from one to four.
- Tell students to clap from one to four and one to five. Model the clapping.
- Have students find four and five objects in the classroom.

COMMON ERROR!

Students may reverse four and five when counting. Provide a number line that has visuals that show a group of four and a group of five.

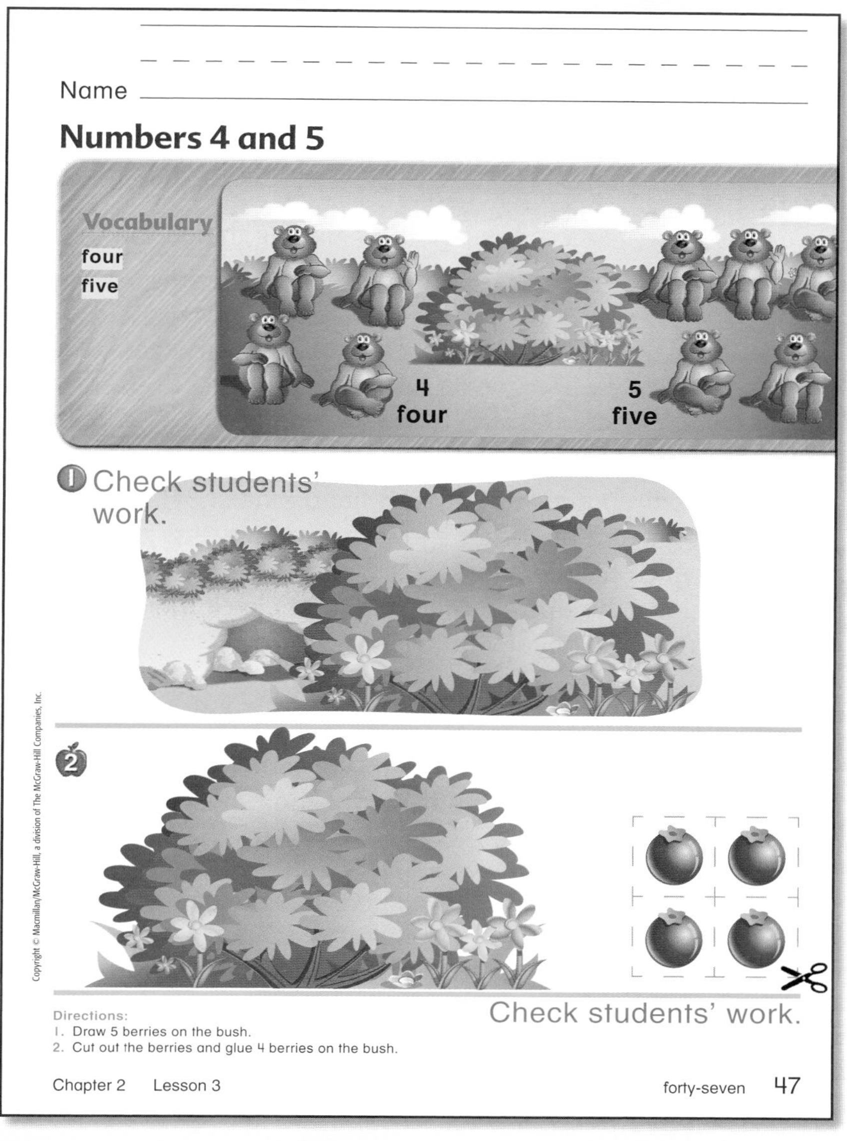
Name

Numbers 4 and 5

1 Check students' work.

2

Check students' work.

Directions:
1. Draw 5 berries on the bush.
2. Cut out the berries and glue 4 berries on the bush.

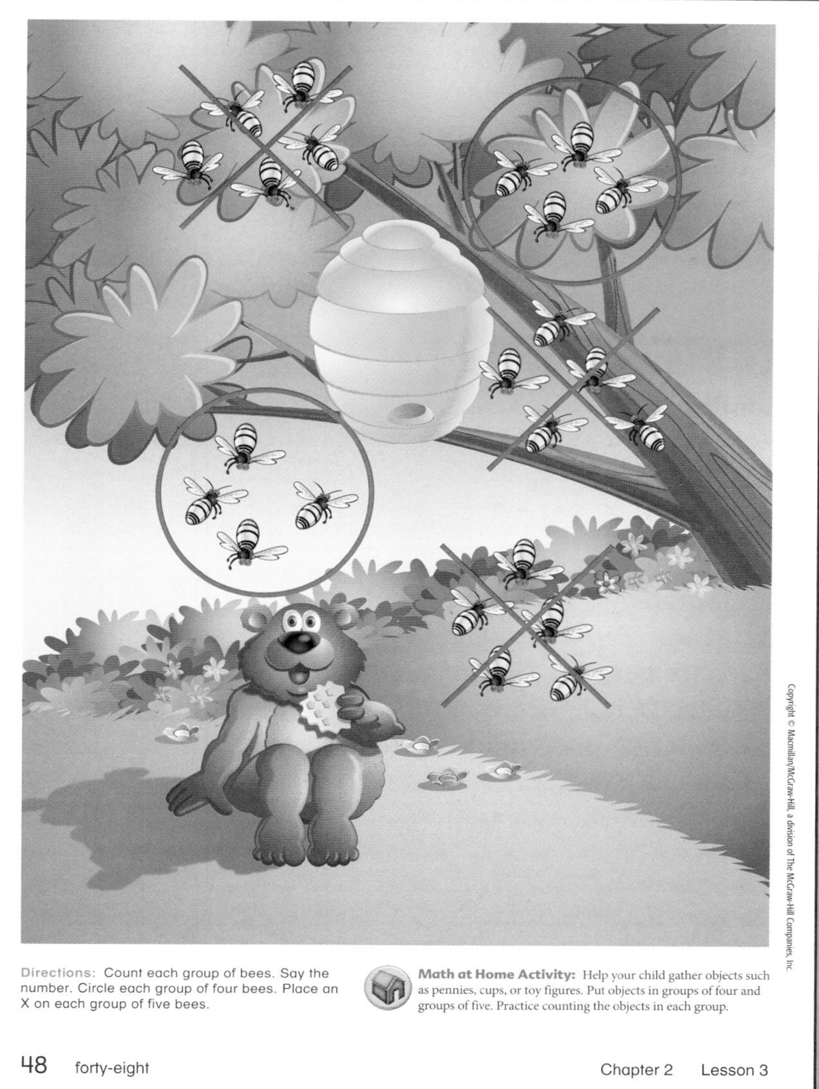
Directions: Count each group of bees. Say the number. Circle each group of four bees. Place an X on each group of five bees.

Math at Home Activity: Help your child gather objects such as pennies, cups, or toy figures. Put objects in groups of four and groups of five. Practice counting the objects in each group.

3 Practice

Guided Practice

- Direct students to Exercise 1 on p. 47.
- Explain that some bears eat berries. Have students count out five counters to represent berries. Have them draw five berries on the bush.
- Direct students to Exercise 2.
- Have students count the four berries beside the bush. Have them cut and glue each berry on the bush and count the berries again.

Independent Practice

Have students turn to p. 48. Explain the directions. Have students work independently on the exercise.

4 Assess

Formative Assessment

- Display a picture with four objects and five objects.
- Ask students to identify four objects, then five objects.
- Have them count to check their answers.
- Have students show a group of four and five using counters.

Quick Check **Are students still struggling with ways to make four and five?**

If Yes → Small Group Options (p. 47B)

If No → Independent Work Options (p. 47B)

CRM Skills Practice Worksheet (p. 15)

CRM Enrich Worksheet (p. 17)

LESSON 2-4

Read and Write 4 and 5

Lesson Planner

Objective

Recognize and write the numerals 4 and 5.

Review Vocabulary

number

Resources

Materials: cards, pencils, chart paper, markers, crayons, picture with objects
Manipulatives: connecting cubes
Literature: *Ten Red Apples* by Virginia Miller
Alternate Lesson: Use *Recording at the Number Stations* on pages 177–178 of *Math Their Way* for practice in recognizing and writing numerals 4 and 5.

Teacher Technology
TeacherWorks • Math Songs Track 4 Lesson Plan

Focus on Math Background

As students learn to count objects and to name the number represented by a group, they understand that each object is counted only one time but that objects can be counted in any order. They also understand that the last number said is the total number of objects.

Daily Routine

Use these suggestions before beginning the lesson on p. 49.

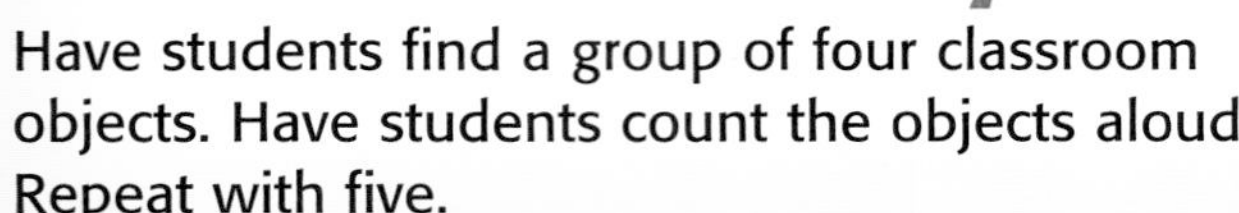

5-Minute Check

(Reviews Lesson 2-3)
Hold up a picture in each hand, one showing four dogs and the other showing five dogs. Ask students which picture shows four dogs. Have them count aloud the dogs in that picture to check their answer. Repeat with five.

Problem of the Day

Have students find a group of four classroom objects. Have students count the objects aloud. Repeat with five.

LINE UP Have students write numbers four and five on cards. Have students hold up their four card as they line up. Have students hold up their five card when in line.

Review Math Vocabulary

Materials: cards, markers

- Write **numbers** one to five on cards. Mix the cards. Give five students a number card.
- Have each student use a finger to tap their nose the number of times that matches the number on their cards.
- Tell the rest of the class to count aloud as each student taps.
- Give five different students a number card. Repeat the activity.

Differentiated Instruction

Small Group Options

Option 1 Gifted and Talented AL

VISUAL

Materials: 1–5 number cards, counters, cups

- Give each small group a set of 1–5 number cards, five counters, and a cup.
- Have one student put one to five counters in a cup, shake the cup, then spill the counters. Have another student symbolically describe the number by finding the card that matches the number of counters. Have the group count aloud to check answers.

Option 2 English Language Learners ELL

INTRAPERSONAL, SOCIAL

Core Vocabulary: down, once more, a flag
Common Use Verb: stop

Hear Math This strategy vocalizes writing numbers 4 and 5.

- Draw the number four in the air. Say: "Come **down** and back and **down once more**, that's the way you make a four." For five, say: "Come **down** and around, put **a flag** on top. See what you have got … FIVE!"

Independent Work Options

Option 1 Early Finishers OL AL

KINESTHETIC-SPATIAL

Materials: paper, crayons, scissors

- Have students draw and cut out objects, such as circles.
- Ask them to put the objects into groups of one, two, three, four, and five.
- Have students symbolically describe the objects by writing the number next to each group.

Option 2 Student Technology

 Math Songs "Here is the Beehive" Track 4

Option 3 Learning Station: Health (p. 39G)

Direct students to the Health Learning Station for opportunities to explore and extend the lesson concept.

Leveled Lesson Resources

Reteach (p. 18) BL

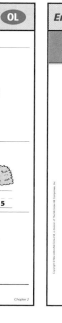

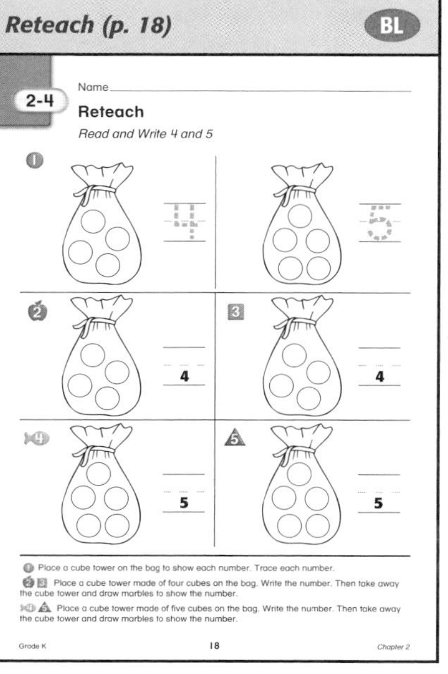

2-4 Name
Reteach
Read and Write 4 and 5

① Place a cube tower on the bag to show each number. Trace each number.
② ③ Place a cube tower made of four cubes on the bag. Write the number. Then take away the cube tower and draw marbles to show the number.
④ ⑤ Place a cube tower made of five cubes on the bag. Write the number. Then take away the cube tower and draw marbles to show the number.

Grade K 18 *Chapter 2*

Skills Practice (p. 19) OL

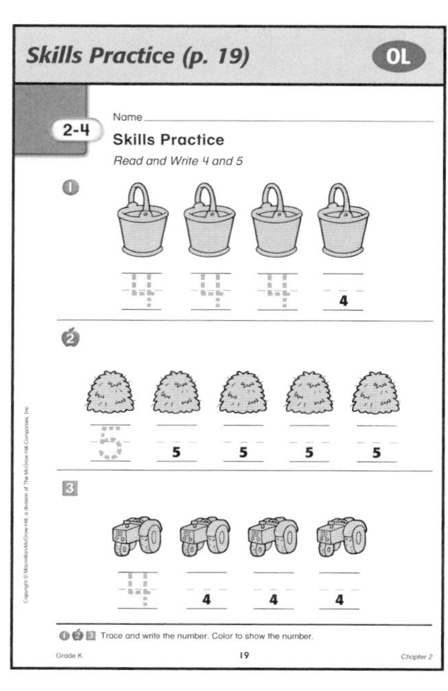

2-4 Name
Skills Practice
Read and Write 4 and 5

① ② ③ Trace and write the number. Color to show the number.

Grade K 19 *Chapter 2*

Enrich (p. 21) AL

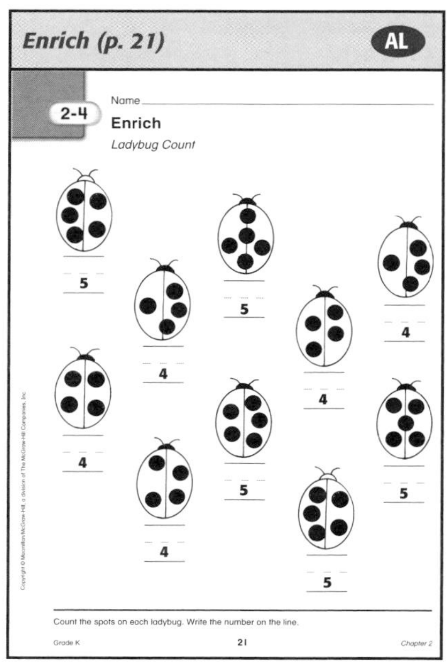

2-4 Name
Enrich
Ladybug Count

Count the spots on each ladybug. Write the number on the line.

Grade K 21 *Chapter 2*

Homework Practice (p. 20) OL

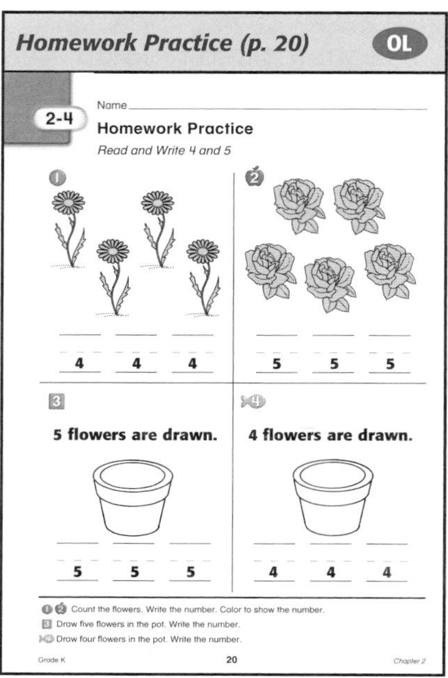

2-4 Name
Homework Practice
Read and Write 4 and 5

③ 5 flowers are drawn.
④ 4 flowers are drawn.

① ② Count the flowers. Write the number. Color to show the number.
③ Draw five flowers in the pot. Write the number.
④ Draw four flowers in the pot. Write the number.

Grade K 20 *Chapter 2*

1 Introduce

Circle Time

Activity Choice 1 • Literature

Ten Red Apples (pp. 1–12)
by Virginia Miller

- Read the book aloud, having students symbolically describe the **numbers** by writing them and putting the correct number of counters next to the numbers.
- Draw a group of four and five apples on the chalkboard. Write the numbers four and five. Have students match the groups and numbers.
- Have pairs write numbers one to five on five cards and draw one to five apples on five cards. Put the two piles of cards facedown.
- Have pairs take turns showing two cards. Explain that a player gets a point if the cards match, and the winner is the first to get five points.

Activity Choice 2 • Hands-On 

Materials: connecting cubes, chart paper, markers

- Ask students to use connecting cubes to make groups of four.
- Model writing a number four. Have students write the number four in the air.
- Repeat with number five.
- Write the number four on chart paper.
- Ask students to hold up a train of four connecting cubes.
- Repeat with the number five.
- Invite students to write the numbers on the chart paper.

2 Teach

Direct students to the top of p. 49.

- Discuss the construction site and what is occurring.
- Talk about each item.
- Direct students to the four orange cones. Verbally describe the cones by counting them with students. Emphasize *four* and describe how it is written. Have students write the number *four* in the air.
- Count the bricks with students. Emphasize *five* and describe how it is written. Have students write the number *five* in the air.

BL Alternate Teaching Strategy

If students have trouble counting objects and writing the numbers . . .

Then use one of these reteach options.

1 CRM **Daily Reteach Worksheet** (p. 18)

2 **Use Manipulatives** Put a container with sand in front of each student.

- Have students drop four marbles in the sand. Tell them to write the number of marbles in the sand four times.
- Repeat the activity with five marbles, writing in the sand five times.

! COMMON ERROR!

Students may write numbers backwards. Give them numbers to trace, and provide opportunities for extra practice using round-ended toothpicks or pipe cleaners.

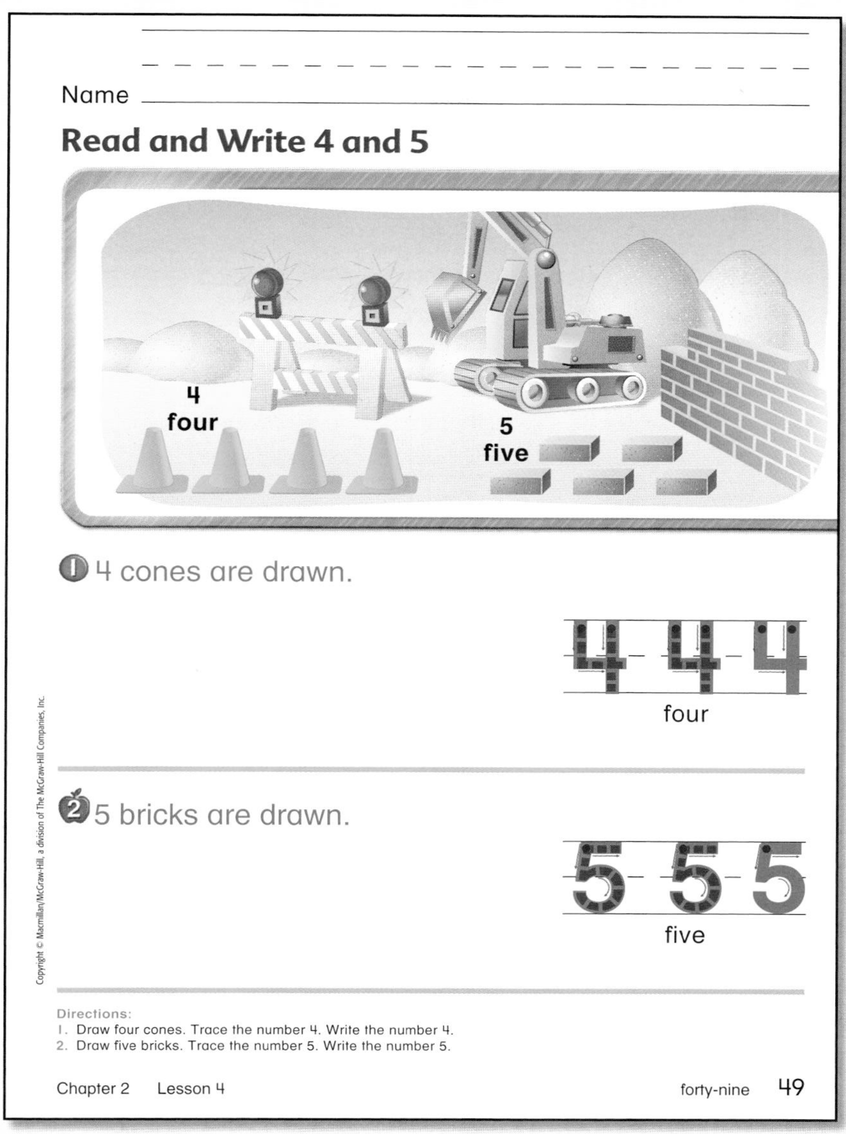

Name
Read and Write 4 and 5
4
four
5
five
1 4 cones are drawn.
4 4 4
four
2 5 bricks are drawn.
5 5 5
five
Directions:
1. Draw four cones. Trace the number 4. Write the number 4.
2. Draw five bricks. Trace the number 5. Write the number 5.
Chapter 2 Lesson 4 forty-nine 49

3
STOP STOP STOP STOP STOP
5 5 5
4
4 4 4
5
4 4 4
6
5 5 5
7
4 4 4
Directions:
3–5. Count the objects in each row. Say the number. Trace and write the number.
6–7. Count the objects in each row. Write that number three times.
Math at Home Activity: Make groups of 4 and 5 using cereal or macaroni. Have your child count how many in each group and write that number.
50 fifty Chapter 2 Lesson 4

3 Practice

Guided Practice

- Direct students to the top of p. 49. Have them look at the orange cones and count them.
- For Exercise 1, have students draw that many cones in the empty space. Have students trace the number four and write it beside their drawing.
- For Exercise 2, direct students to look at the bricks and count them. Have students draw that many bricks in the empty space. Have students trace the number five and write it beside their drawing.

Independent Practice

Have students turn to p. 50. Explain the directions. Have students work independently on the exercises.

4 Assess

Formative Assessment

- Display a picture with four objects.
- Have students count the items and write the number.
- Repeat with a picture of five objects.

Quick Check **Are students still struggling to read and write the numbers four and five?**

If Yes → Small Group Options (p. 49B)

If No → Independent Work Options (p. 49B)

CRM Skills Practice Worksheet (p. 19)

CRM Enrich Worksheet (p. 21)

Mid-Chapter Check

Lessons 2-1 to 2-4

Formative Assessment

Use the Mid-Chapter Check to assess students' progress in the first half of the chapter.

ExamView Assessment Suite Customize and create multiple versions of your Mid-Chapter Check and the test answer keys.

FOLDABLES® Dinah Zike's Foldables

Use these lesson suggestions for incorporating the Foldables during the chapter.

Lesson 2-2 Make and glue together three sections of the Foldable Number Line. Write one number on the top left side of each section, beginning with number one, and have students find and place pictures on the appropriate sections to illustrate each number. Students can draw or use magazines, catalogs, advertisements, or worksheets.

Lesson 2-4 Make and glue two more sections to the Foldable Number Line. Have students write the numbers four and five on the top left side of each of the two sections. Then have students find and place pictures on the appropriate sections to illustrate each number. Students can draw or use magazines, catalogs, advertisements, or worksheets.

Name ______________

1

3

2

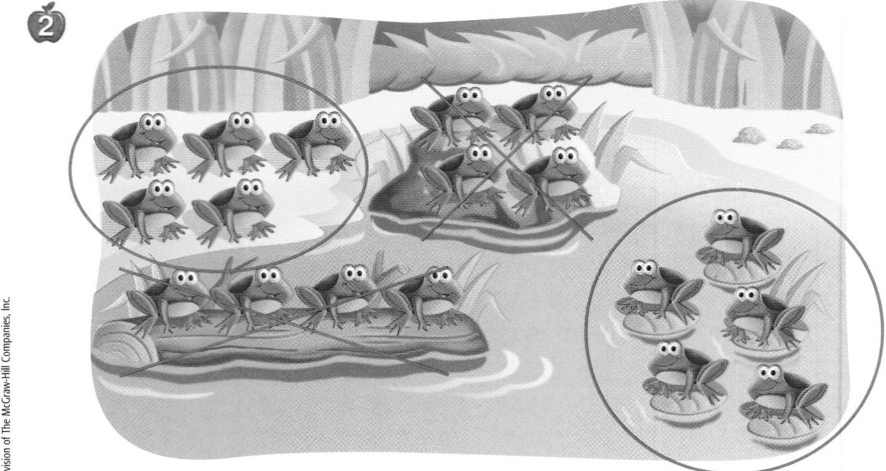

3

5

Directions:
1. Count each object. Color a box for each object counted. Write the number.
2. Circle each group of five frogs. Place an X on each group of four frogs.
3. Count the objects. Write the number.

Data-Driven Decision Making

Based on the results of the Mid-Chapter Check, use the following resources to review concepts that continue to give students problems.

Exercises	State/Local Standards	What's the Math?	Error Analysis	Resources for Review
1 **Lesson 2-2**		Understand relationship between numbers and quantities. Read and write the numerals up to 3.	Does not color correct number of boxes. Counts incorrectly. Writes wrong number.	CRM Chapter 2 Resource Masters (Reteach Worksheets) Math Online Concepts in Motion Math Adventures
2 **Lesson 2-3**		Understand relationship between numbers and quantities. Name, recognize, and count numbers to 5.	Does not circle frogs in group of five. Does not "X" each frog in a group of four.	
3 **Lesson 2-4**		Recognize and write numbers up to 5.	Counts incorrectly. Writes wrong number.	

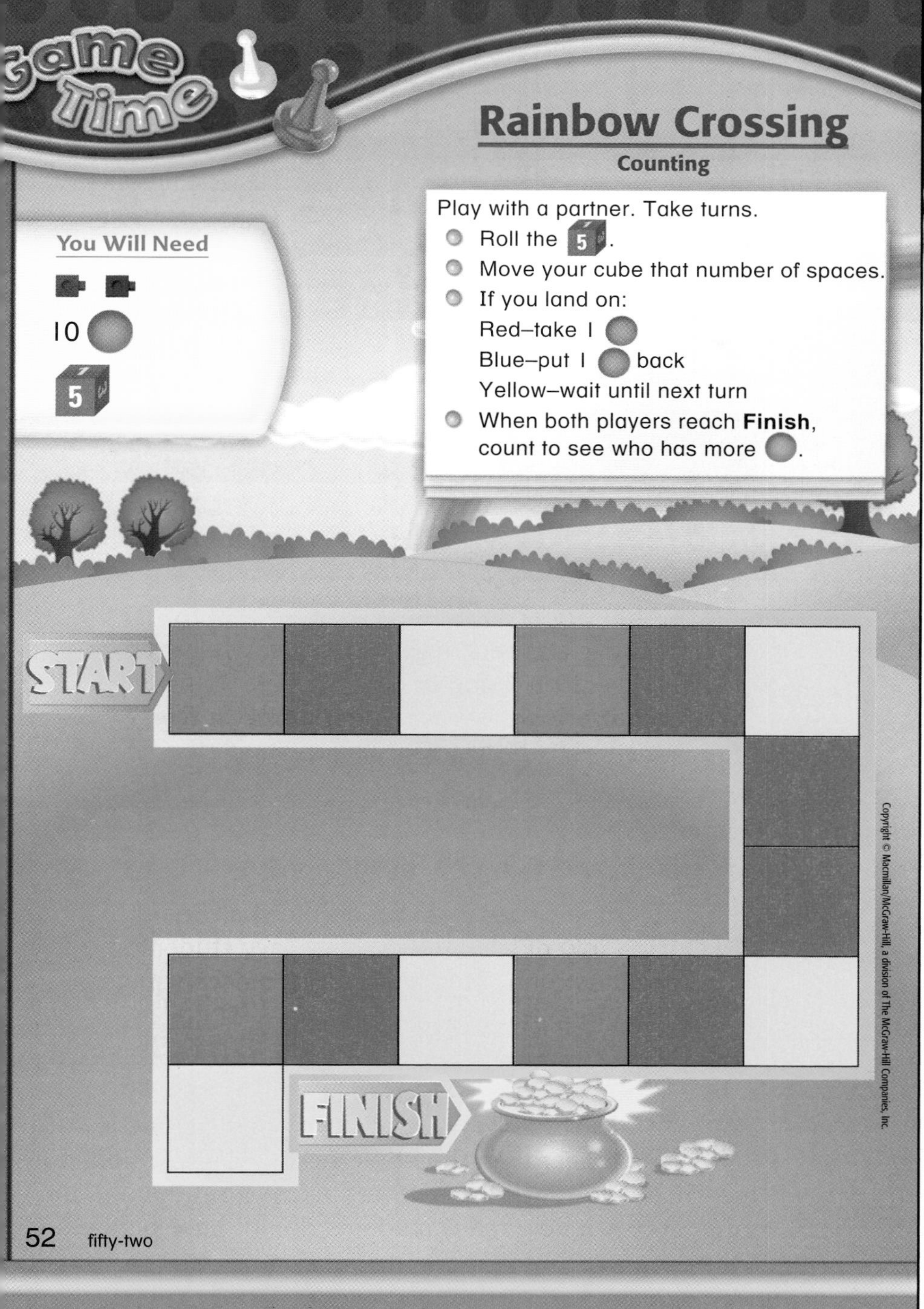
Rainbow Crossing

Counting

You Will Need

10

Play with a partner. Take turns.

- Roll the .
- Move your cube that number of spaces.
- If you land on:

  Red–take 1

  Blue–put 1 back

  Yellow–wait until next turn
- When both players reach **Finish**, count to see who has more .

START

FINISH

52 fifty-two

Rainbow Crossing

Math Concept: Counting

Manipulatives: 0–5 number cube, connecting cubes, 10 two-colored counters

Introduce the game on page 52 to your students to play as a class, in small groups, or at a learning work-station to review concepts introduced in this chapter.

Instructions

- Have students roll the number cube to decide who goes first.
- Have players take turns rolling the number cube and moving their cube that number of squares.
- Tell players that if they land on red to take one counter, if they land on blue they put one counter back, and if they land on yellow they do nothing because yellow is a resting space.
- The game can also be played with beans, macaroni, or cereal.
- When both players reach *Finish*, have them count their counters, with the winner having more counters.

Extend the Game

Have students continue playing, but change the rules so that the student with *less* counters wins.

Differentiated Practice

Use these leveling suggestions to differentiate the game for all learners.

Level	Assignment
BL **Below/Approaching Level**	Have students play in pairs.
OL **On Level**	Have students play the game with the rules as written.
AL **Above/Beyond Level**	Have students assign a rule for the yellow space, so that counters are added or subtracted on the three color spaces: yellow, red, and blue.

2-5 Problem-Solving Strategy
Draw a Picture

Lesson Planner

Objective

Name, recognize, and count the numerals 1, 2, 3, 4, and 5 using concrete illustrations.

Resources

Literature Connection: *Five Little Kittens* by Nancy Jewell

Teacher Technology

TeacherWorks

Real-World Problem Solving Library
Math and Social Studies: *Community Helpers*
Use these leveled books to reinforce and extend problem-solving skills and strategies.

Leveled for:

- OL On Level
- ELL Sheltered English
- SP Spanish

For additional support, see the Real-World Problem Solving Teacher Guide.

On-level title is available in classroom Big Book.

Daily Routine

Use these suggestions before beginning the lesson on p. 53.

5-Minute Check

(Reviews Lesson 2-4)

1. **What are some things that come in fours?** Sample answers: legs on a table, wheels on a car, legs on a dog or cat
2. **What are some things that come in fives?** Answers will vary. Sample answers: toes, fingers

Problem of the Day

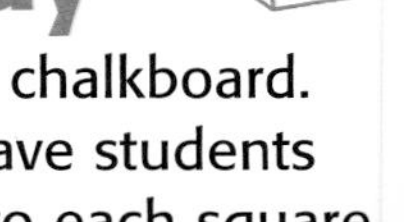

Draw three circles in a row on the chalkboard. Draw a row of four stars below. Have students draw lines connecting each circle to each square. Which group has more? stars

LINE UP As students line up, make sure one line is longer than the other. Ask students to hold out their hands to touch the partners across from them in the other line. Ask how many students do not have partners.

Differentiated Instruction

Small Group Options

Option 1 Below/Approaching Level BL

VISUAL

Materials: drawing paper, crayons

- Using only one sheet of paper, have two students each draw a row of objects. Ask a third student to draw lines to connect the objects in the rows.
- Have students verbally describe which row has more and how they know.
- Have students switch roles.

Option 2 English Language Learners ELL

INTRAPERSONAL

Materials: five pictures of objects in groups of one to five
Core Vocabulary: picture, finger, underneath
Common Use Verb: draw

Write Math This strategy teaches using pictures to solve problems.

- Post a picture of a set of objects from one to five. Students show the amount on their fingers.
- Write the number underneath the picture.
- Have students write the number and draw a matching picture. Students may count aloud to check their answers.

Independent Work Options

Option 1 Early Finishers OL AL

VISUAL

Materials: paper, crayons, scissors, glue, construction paper with bows drawn on it

- Give each student a piece of construction paper with one to five outlines of bows drawn on it.
- Have students draw and color squares as boxes for presents. Tell students to draw the number of squares needed to put one bow on each box.
- After students have drawn and colored their boxes, have them cut out the bows.
- Have students glue one bow on each box to check that they drew the correct number of boxes.

Option 2 Student Technology

Math Online macmillanmh.com

Option 3 Learning Station: Art (p. 39H)

Direct students to the Art Learning Station for opportunities to explore and extend the lesson concept.

Leveled Lesson Resources

Reteach (pp. 22–23) BL

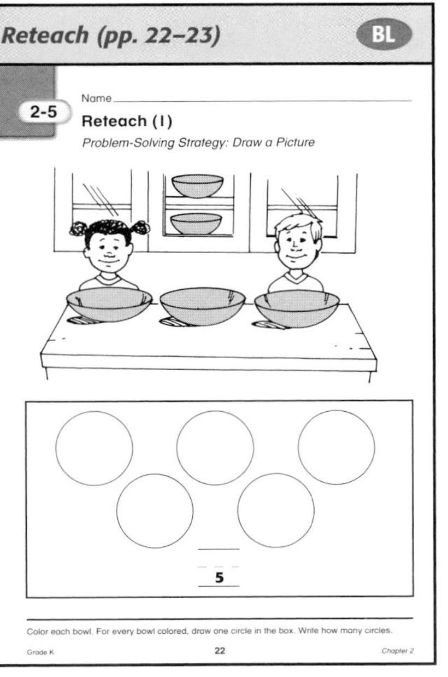
2-5 Name
Reteach (1)
Problem-Solving Strategy: Draw a Picture

5

Color each bowl. For every bowl colored, draw one circle in the box. Write how many circles.

Grade K 22 *Chapter 2*

Skills Practice (p. 24) OL

2-5 Name
Skills Practice
Problem-Solving Strategy: Draw a Picture

1

Each child caught one butterfly. Trace a line from each net to a butterfly. Draw one circle for each butterfly that was *not* caught. Write how many butterflies were *not* caught.

Grade K 24 *Chapter 2*

Enrich (p. 26) AL

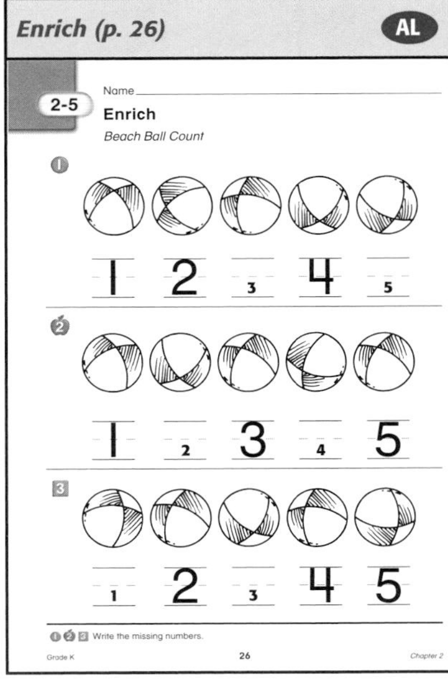
2-5 Name
Enrich
Beach Ball Count

1. 1 2 3 4 5
2. 1 2 3 4 5
3. 1 2 3 4 5

1 2 3 Write the missing numbers.

Grade K 26 *Chapter 2*

Homework Practice (p. 25) OL

2-5 Name
Homework Practice
Problem-Solving Strategy: Draw a Picture

1. 2
2. 3

1. Each frog caught one bug. Draw a line from each frog to a bug. Draw one circle for each bug that was *not* caught. Write how many bugs were *not* caught.
2. Each bee sat on one flower. Draw a line from each flower to a bee. Draw one circle for each bee. Write how many bees.

Grade K 25 *Chapter 2*

1 Introduce

Circle Time

Activity Choice 1 • Literature

Five Little Kittens by Nancy Jewell

- Read the story aloud, counting the kittens in each picture.
- Have students symbolically describe objects by drawing a picture of their favorite animal four times.
- Open the book to a page that shows a picture of five kittens.
- **How many kittens are on the page?** five
- **How many more kittens are there than the animals you drew on your page?** one
- Tell students another way to know how many more is by drawing a figure to represent the objects they are counting.
- Draw 4 triangles to represent students' four animals, 5 circles for the kittens, and draw a line from each triangle to each circle. Ask students to tell which set has more.

Activity Choice 2 • Hands-On

- Display five stuffed animals. Choose four students and ask them to each stand near one animal.
- **How many animals are there?** five
- **How many students are standing near an animal?** four
- **How many more animals are there than students?** one
- Tell students that another way to find out how many animals are left is to match picture:
- Symbolically describe the objects by drawing on the chalkboard five triangles to represent each stuffed animal and four circles to represent each student.
- Have a student draw a line from each triangle to each circle. Ask the students to tell how many are left.

2 Teach

Drawing a picture to solve a problem helps students visualize the problem. Their drawings do not need to be detailed. Drawing simple representations gives students time to focus on the problem.

Understand Review what students know and what they need to find for each problem.

Plan Have students discuss their strategy for solving the problems.

Solve Guide students to draw a picture to solve the problem. Discuss the picture with the students, explaining the game the children are playing. Have students count each fishing line and determine how many ducks can be caught with the fishing lines.

Check Have students look back at the problem to be sure that the answers fit what they already know about the problem.

BL Alternate Teaching Strategy

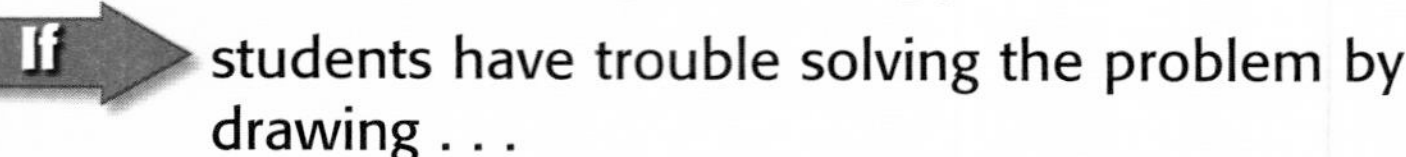

If students have trouble solving the problem by drawing . . .

Then use one of these reteach options.

1. CRM **Daily Reteach Worksheet** (p. 22)
2. **Use Manipulatives** Have students use manipulatives.
   - Give students counters.
   - Have them match the counters to the lines they drew.
   - As they pick up the counters, they can describe them verbally by counting.

COMMON ERROR!

Students may want to draw two lines from each child so that each duck is "caught." Remind them that each duck can only be caught once. You might have students draw the lines from the ducks to the children.

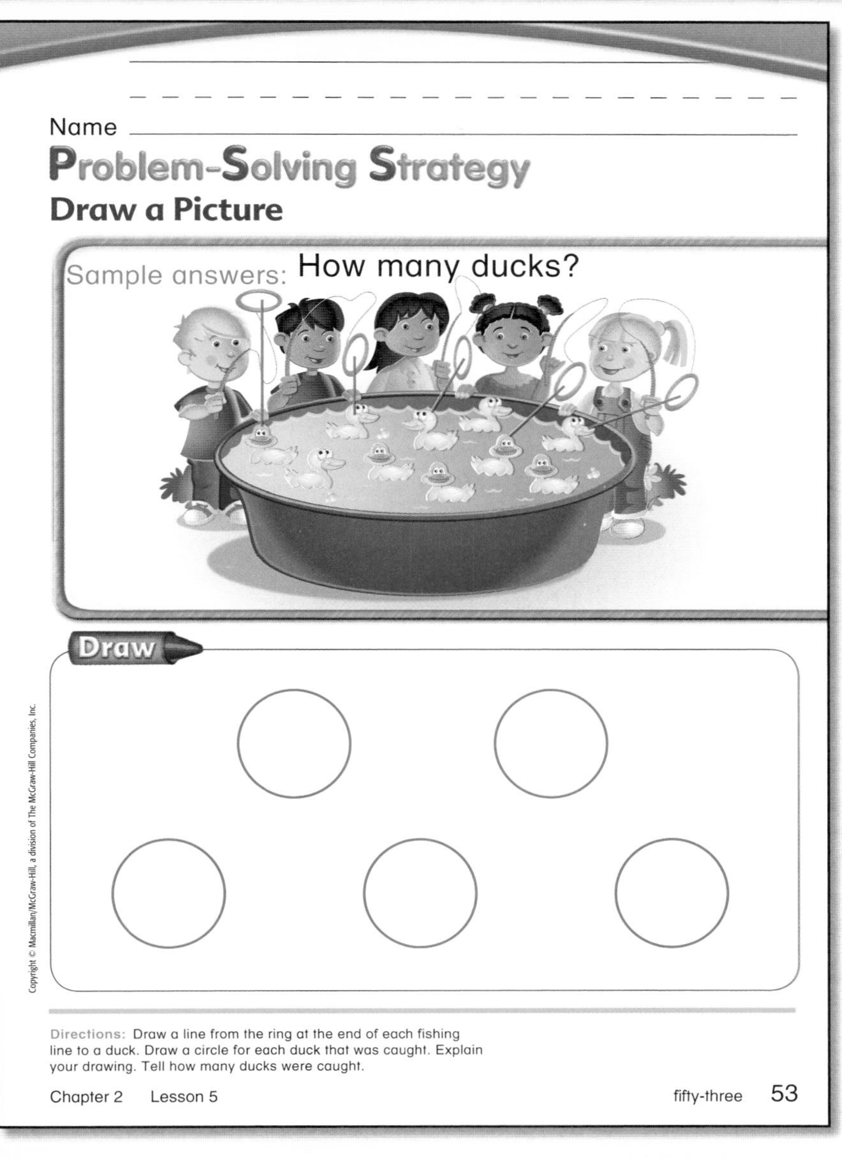

Name
Problem-Solving Strategy
Draw a Picture
Sample answers:
How many ducks?
Draw
Copyright © Macmillan/McGraw-Hill, a division of The McGraw-Hill Companies, Inc.
Directions: Draw a line from the ring at the end of each fishing line to a duck. Draw a circle for each duck that was caught. Explain your drawing. Tell how many ducks were caught.
Chapter 2 Lesson 5
fifty-three 53

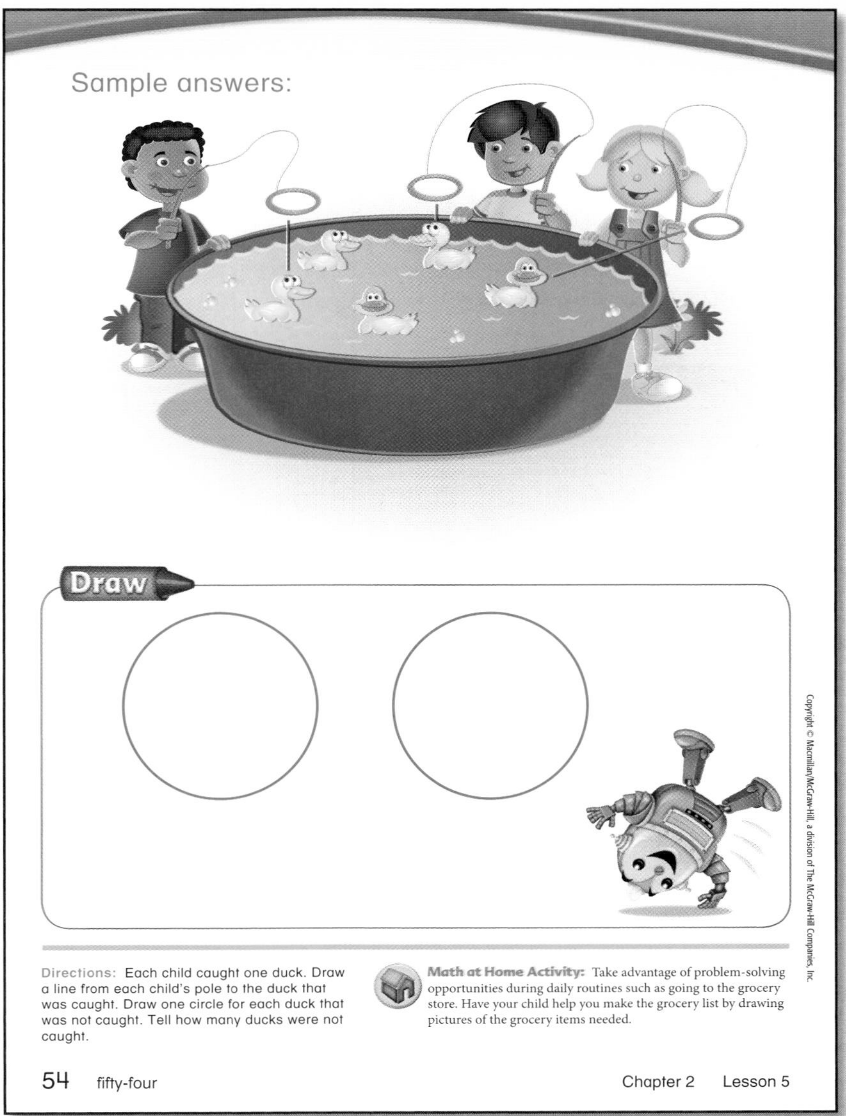

Sample answers:
Draw
Copyright © Macmillan/McGraw-Hill, a division of The McGraw-Hill Companies, Inc.
Directions: Each child caught one duck. Draw a line from each child's pole to the duck that was caught. Draw one circle for each duck that was not caught. Tell how many ducks were not caught.
Math at Home Activity: Take advantage of problem-solving opportunities during daily routines such as going to the grocery store. Have your child help you make the grocery list by drawing pictures of the grocery items needed.
54 fifty-four
Chapter 2 Lesson 5

3 Practice

Guided Practice

Direct students to the bottom of p. 53. Have students draw a circle for each duck that was caught. Ask students to explain their drawings and tell how many ducks were caught.

Independent Practice

Have students turn to p. 54 and work independently.

- Be sure students understand that they are drawing to find out the number of ducks that were *not* caught, rather than the number caught.
- Remind students to draw a line from each child's pole to one duck. There should only be one line from each pole.
- Ask students to tell what would happen if one more child caught a duck. Ask them what would draw to solve this problem.
- Have students determine other materials that could be used to solve this problem.

4 Assess

Formative Assessment

On the chalkboard, draw a row of six dogs and a row of four people. Tell students each dog walker wants to walk a dog.

- Have students draw a picture to solve the problem and explain their drawing.
- **How many dogs will not have a walker?** two

Quick Check **Are students continuing to struggle with drawing to solve problems?**

If Yes → Small Group Options (p. 53B)

If No → Independent Work Options (p. 53B)

CRM Skills Practice Worksheet (p. 24)

CRM Enrich Worksheet (p. 26)

LESSON 2-6

Read and Write 0

Lesson Planner

Objective

Recognize and write the numeral 0.

Vocabulary

zero

Resources

Materials: pencils, picture of animals
Manipulatives: connecting cubes
Literature: *Ten Red Apples* by Virginia Miller
Alternate Lesson: Adapt *Numeral Sequence Cards* on page 47 of *Math Their Way* for practice in recognizing and writing zero.

Teacher Technology
TeacherWorks • Concepts in Motion • Math Songs Track 4 Lesson Plan

Focus on Math Background

Students develop their number sense gradually. Most children first develop number sense by working with concrete objects. The concept of zero representing a lack of objects is clearer to students when they recognize one-to-one correspondence between numbers and quantities of objects.

Daily Routine

Use these suggestions before beginning the lesson on p. 55.

5-Minute Check

(Reviews Lesson 2-5)
Show a line of six cats and a line of four fish. How many cats will not get a fish? How can you check your answer? Two; Draw a picture to show each cat that did not get a fish. Draw lines from cats to fish. Count cats not connected.

Problem of the Day

Show the number 4 and four number cubes. Have students write the number that shows one more and add that many cube(s) to represent that number.

LINE UP Ask students who have zero pockets to line up. Ask students who have zero shoelaces to line up. Continue with zero items so all students line up.

Building Math Vocabulary

Materials: cup with a zero written on it

- Ask students how many elephants are in the room, then how many swimming pools are in the room.
- Ask volunteers to make up questions that have **zero** as the answer.
- Hand a volunteer the zero cup. Ask the student to find zero crayons.
- Ask the class to stand and jump zero times and to sing zero songs. Ask them to laugh zero times.
- Emphasize that zero is the number we use to tell how many when there are none.

Differentiated Instruction

Small Group Options

Option 1 Below/Approaching Level (BL)

VISUAL

Materials: identical small marshmallows

- Have each student take one marshmallow at a time and put it on their desk.
- Have students verbally describe them by counting the number of marshmallows until there are five total.
- Tell students to remove all of their marshmallows.
- **How many marshmallows are left?** zero

Option 2 English Language Learners (ELL)

VISUAL, SOCIAL

Core Vocabulary: none, zero, make a fist
Common Use Verb: see

Write Math This strategy helps students visualize the shape of zero as a first.

- Model one finger, two fingers, etc. Ask: "How many fingers do you ***see***?" Show a closed fist. Ask: "How many fingers do you ***see***?"
- Say: "**None**. When you **make a fist**, you ***see* zero** fingers."

Independent Work Options

Option 1 Early Finishers (OL) (AL)

KINESTHETIC-SPATIAL

Materials: paper, crayons

- Have students write the numbers zero to five on a piece of paper.
- Have them represent the numbers by drawing a simple object to show each quantity above each number.
- Point out that there should be no objects above the zero.

Option 2 Student Technology

Math Online macmillanmh.com

Math Adventures

Option 3 Learning Station: Language Arts (p. 39H)

Direct students to the Language Arts Learning Station for opportunities to explore and extend the lesson concept.

Leveled Lesson Resources

Reteach (p. 27) (BL)

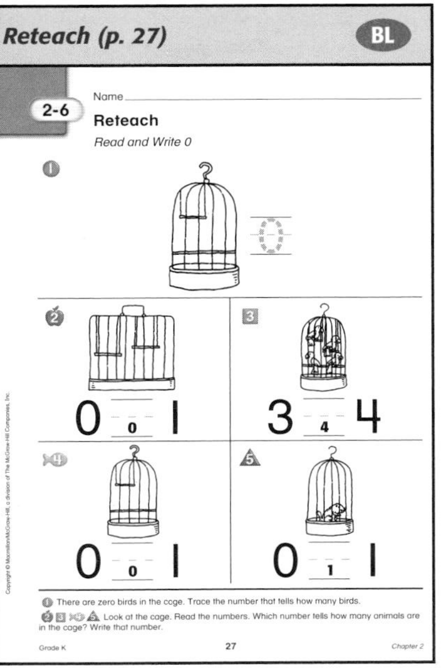

2-6 Name ______
Reteach
Read and Write 0

Skills Practice (p. 28) (OL)

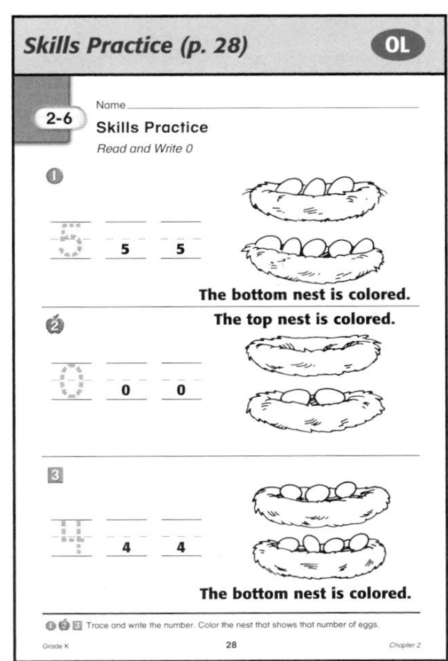

2-6 Name ______
Skills Practice
Read and Write 0

The bottom nest is colored.
The top nest is colored.
The bottom nest is colored.

Enrich (p. 30) (AL)

2-6 Name ______
Enrich
Ice Cream Count

Homework Practice (p. 29) (OL)

2-6 Name ______
Homework Practice
Read and Write 0

This jar is colored.
This jar is colored.
This jar is colored.

1 Introduce

Activity Choice 1 • Literature

Ten Red Apples
by Virginia Miller

- Show students the first two pages.
- **How many red apples do you see?** zero
- Write a **zero** on the chalkboard. Explain that the number *zero* describes how many red apples are shown on the tree. Contrast this tree with several trees that follow.
- Demonstrate *zero* as a concept in various contexts such as an empty pencil holder and an empty box of crayons.
- Ask students to distinguish between situations that represent zero and those that represent other numbers.

Activity Choice 2 • Hands-On

Materials: connecting cubes

- Have students work in pairs.
- Give one student in each pair some connecting cubes. Ask the student to give the cubes to his or her partner.
- Have the student describe the cubes by asking him or her how many connecting cubes the first student now has in hand.
- Tell students that after you give away all the cubes, you have none, or zero. Write a zero on the chalkboard and say "zero."

2 Teach 

- Direct students to p. 55.
- Identify the machines with balls.
- Direct students to the first machine.
- Have students use cubes to show how many balls are in the machine.
- **How many balls do you see?** five Have students explain how they know.
- Count with students. Have students represent the number five by tracing it with their finger.
- Have students use cubes to show four balls, three balls, two balls, and one ball.
- Have students tell how many balls are in each machine and to explain how they know.
- Count the balls with the students.
- Have students trace the numbers with their fingers.
- **How many balls are in the last machine?** zero
- Emphasize the last machine as having zero balls. Say that zero is the number we use to tell how many when there are none.

BL Alternate Teaching Strategy

If students have trouble reading, writing, and understanding zero . . .

Then use one of these reteach options.

1 CRM **Daily Reteach Worksheet** (p. 27)

2 **Demonstrate Zero** Wave to the students. Ask how many waving hands they see.
- Put your hands behind your back. Ask how many waving hands they see now.
- Ask how many giraffes are in the room.

COMMON ERROR!
Students may not think of zero as being the same thing as nothing. Provide two-colored counters for students to count. Then take them away and ask how many are left.

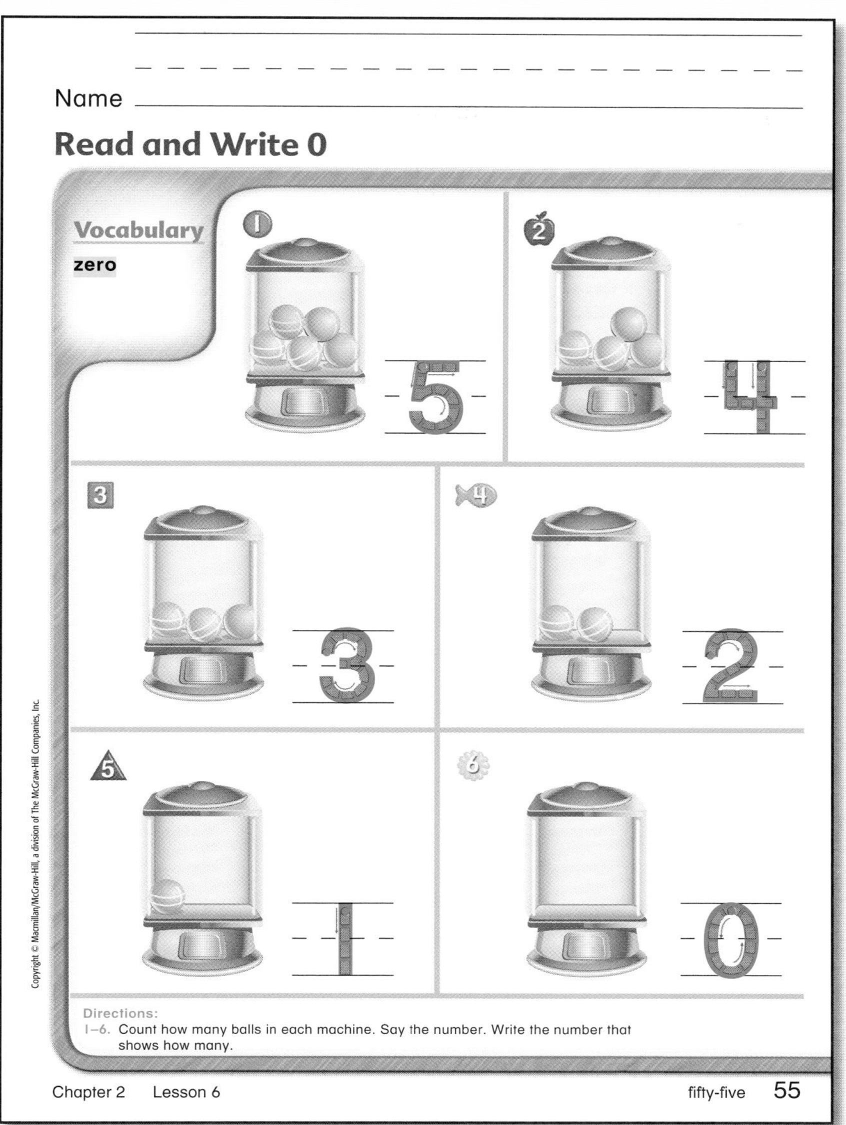

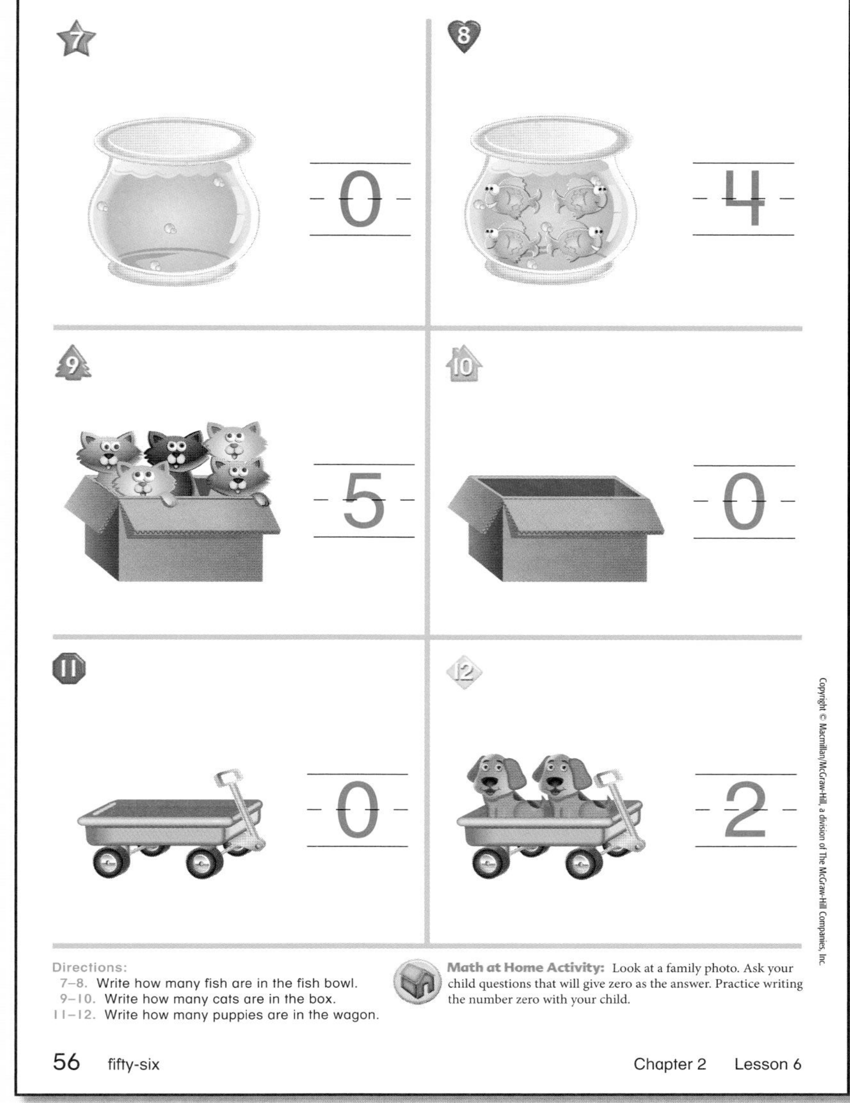

3 Practice

Guided Practice

- Direct students to p. 55.
- Again, count how many balls are in each machine with students.
- Tell students to write, next to each machine, the number that shows how many balls are in each machine.
- Have students count numbers zero to five in order by pointing to each machine and saying the number of balls aloud, starting with the last machine with zero balls.

Independent Practice

Have students turn to p. 56. Explain the directions. Have students work independently on the exercises.

4 Assess

Formative Assessment

- Show students a picture of several animals and the same picture without any animals.
- Ask how many animals are in each picture.
- Have students write the number zero on the picture without any animals.

Quick Check **Are students still struggling to read and write zero?**

If Yes → Small Group Options (p. 55B)

If No → Independent Work Options (p. 55B)

 Skills Practice Worksheet (p. 28)

CRM Enrich Worksheet (p. 30)

LESSON **2-7**

Compare Numbers 0 to 5

Lesson Planner

Objective

Use one-to-one correspondence and counting to compare groups and determine which has more, less, or whether the groups are the same.

Review Vocabulary

count

Resources

Materials: paper, pencils, crayons, stapler
Manipulatives: two-colored counters
Literature: *One Monkey Too Many* by Jackie French Koller
Alternate Lesson: Use the game *Squares* on page 130 of *Math Their Way* to provide practice for one-to-one correspondence and comparing groups to determine more or less.
Use *IMPACT Mathematics*: Unit B to provide practice with comparing groups of numbers.

Teacher Technology
TeacherWorks • Concepts in Motion • Math Songs Track 4 Lesson Plan

Focus on Math Background

Students may be familiar with numbers up to five and have little difficulty counting. However, they may have difficulty developing a mental picture of quantities for each number. Have them draw pictures of items that correspond to numbers to help them visualize quantities.

Daily Routine

Use these suggestions before beginning the lesson on p. 57.

5-Minute Check

(Reviews Lesson 2-6)
Ask students what the number zero means. Have them represent zero using crayons or pencils.

Problem of the Day

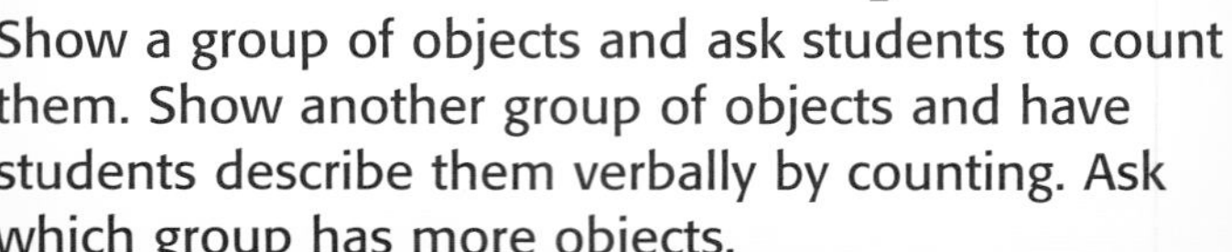

Show a group of objects and ask students to count them. Show another group of objects and have students describe them verbally by counting. Ask which group has more objects.

LINE UP Distribute pencils to students. Ask students with two pencils to line up. Tell students with more than two pencils to line up. Ask students with less than two pencils to line up.

Review Math Vocabulary

Materials: index cards, markers, rubber stamps

- Make a set of cards with numbers zero to five and a set with zero to five stamps. Shuffle each set.
- Explain that *more* means that one group has a larger number of objects than another group, *less* means that one group has a smaller number of objects than another group, and *the same* means the same or equal number of objects are in both groups.
- Show a number card and a stamp card. Ask volunteers to say the number on the number card and **count** the stamps on the other card.
- Ask if the number is more, less, or equal to the number of stamps.

Differentiated Instruction

Small Group Options

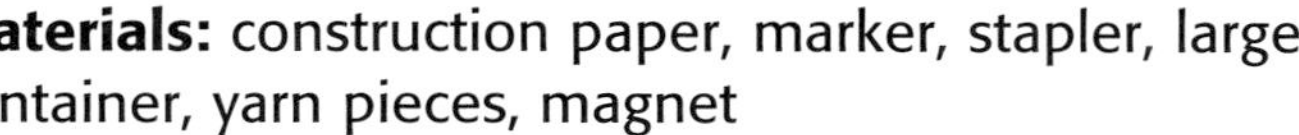

Option 1 Below/Approaching Level BL

VISUAL

Materials: construction paper, marker, stapler, large container, yarn pieces, magnet

- Cut out fish shapes. Write numbers zero to five on each fish and draw that number of dots. Add a staple for the mouth. Put fish into a large container. Tie a magnet on one end of yarn.
- Have students take turns catching a fish with a magnet.
- Have students work in small groups to say which fish has more, less, or same number of dots as other fish.

Option 2 English Language Learners ELL

VISUAL, SOCIAL

Materials: cards with numbers 0–5 and pictures of 0–5 objects, magnets

Core Vocabulary: next to, flip, get to keep

Common Use Verb: take

Do Math This strategy teaches comparing numbers 0–5.

- Lay out cards to play a matching game.
- Students take turns flipping over two cards. If they match, students keep the cards; if not, play continues.

Independent Work Options

Option 1 Early Finishers OL AL

KINESTHETIC-SPATIAL

Materials: paper, colored stickers

- Have students fold their paper in half.
- Ask them to put some stickers on one half of the paper, and then put a different or the same number of stickers on the other half.
- Have students work with partners to describe each other's pictures with the words *more than, less than,* or the *same as/equal to.*

Option 2 Student Technology

Math Online macmillanmh.com

Math Songs "Here is the Beehive" Track 4

Math Adventures

Option 3 Learning Station: Art (p. 39H)

Direct students to the Art Learning Station for opportunities to explore and extend the lesson concept.

Leveled Lesson Resources

Additional support for English Language Learners can be found in the ELL Guide (p. 13). ELL

Reteach (p. 31) BL

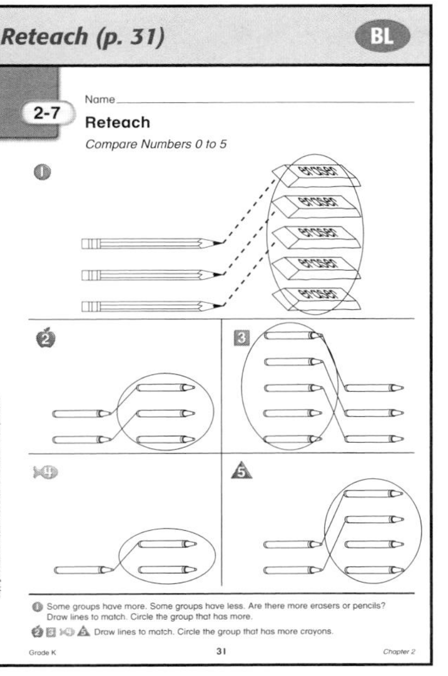

2-7 Name
Reteach
Compare Numbers 0 to 5

1 Some groups have more. Some groups have less. Are there more erasers or pencils? Draw lines to match. Circle the group that has more.
2 3 4 5 Draw lines to match. Circle the group that has more crayons.

Grade K 31 Chapter 2

Skills Practice (p. 32) OL

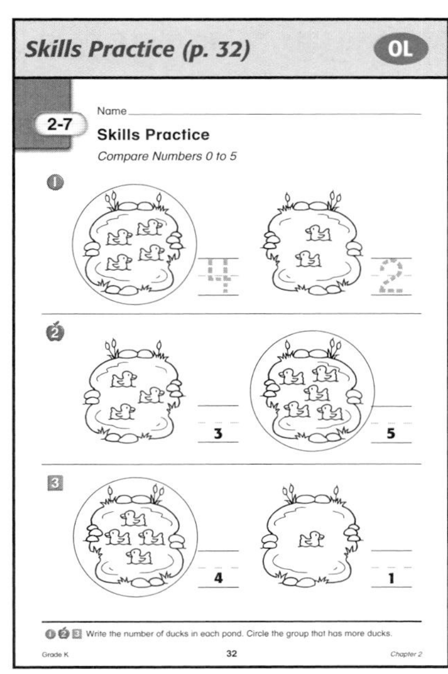

2-7 Name
Skills Practice
Compare Numbers 0 to 5

1 4 2
2 3 5
3 4 1

1 2 3 Write the number of ducks in each pond. Circle the group that has more ducks.

Grade K 32 Chapter 2

Enrich (p. 34) AL

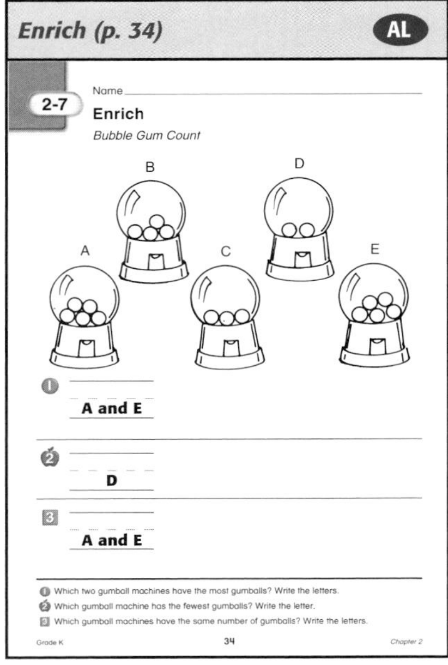

2-7 Name
Enrich
Bubble Gum Count

1 A and E
2 D
3 A and E

1 Which two gumball machines have the most gumballs? Write the letters.
2 Which gumball machine has the fewest gumballs? Write the letter.
3 Which gumball machines have the same number of gumballs? Write the letters.

Grade K 34 Chapter 2

Homework Practice (p. 33) OL

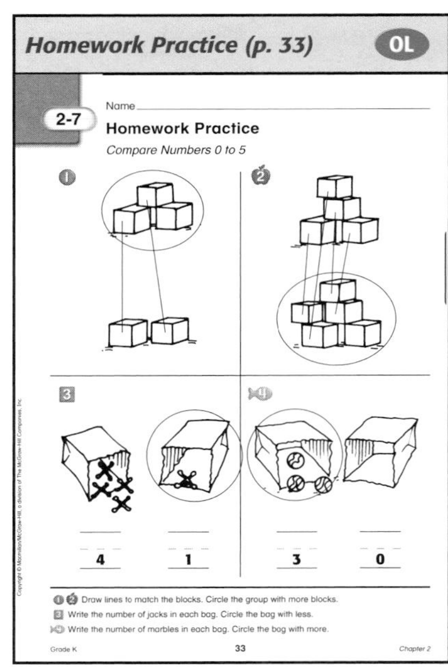

2-7 Name
Homework Practice
Compare Numbers 0 to 5

3 4 1
4 3 0

1 2 Draw lines to match the blocks. Circle the group with more blocks.
3 Write the number of jacks in each bag. Circle the bag with less.
4 Write the number of marbles in each bag. Circle the bag with more.

Grade K 33 Chapter 2

1 Introduce

Circle Time

Activity Choice 1 • Literature

One Monkey Too Many
by Jackie French Koller
Materials: two-colored counters, paper

- Give each student ten counters and a piece of paper. Have students use counters to show, for example, how many monkeys were to ride the bike. Have them use counters to symbolically describe the actual number. Have them **count** aloud as they use each counter.
- Write *less than, more than*, and *same number as* or *equal to* in three columns. Model using these words to compare the numbers *one* and *two*. Discuss the consequences of having "one monkey too many."
- Have students model other situations in the book, using *less, more*, and *the same* or *equal to* compare numbers.

Activity Choice 2 • Hands-On

Materials: counters

- Have students work in small groups.
- Ask them to create four rows of counters as follows: a row with zero counters, a row with one, a row with two, and a row with three.
- Lead them to create the rows one by one.
- Discuss which rows have more counters than others. Use *less* and *more* to compare the rows.
- Have a student choose a row. Verbally represent the row by saying the number, and showing that many counters.
- Tell the student that the two rows are the same or equal.
- Have students repeat the activity with another row.

2 Teach

- Direct students to the top of p. 57.
- Verbally describe the number by counting with students.
- **How many handsaws and pieces of wood do you see?** five, five
- **Does one set have more than the other set, less than the other set, or are the sets the same/equal?** Have students trace the lines matching the handsaws and wood. Explain that the two sets have the same number because we can draw lines to match the handsaws and wood. Have students say "same/equal."
- Repeat with hammers and nails. Have students say "more when referring to the number of hammers."
- Repeat with paintbrushes and paint cans. Have students say "less when referring to the number of paint brushes."

BL Alternate Teaching Strategy

If students have trouble comparing numbers zero to five . . .

Then use one of these reteach options.

1 CRM **Daily Reteach Worksheet** (p. 31)

2 **Use Drawing Books** Staple six pieces of paper together to make a book. Write numbers zero to five on the pages.

- Have students look at each number and draw that many dots in a set. Then have them draw a set of dots with more than, less than, or the same number of dots.
- Have them trade books, match dots, then say if the one set is more than, less than, or if the sets are the same/equal.

COMMON ERROR!

Students may confuse *more, less*, and *same/equal*. Show two sets of one to five connecting cubes. Show one-to-one correspondence and explain *more, less*, and *same/equal*.

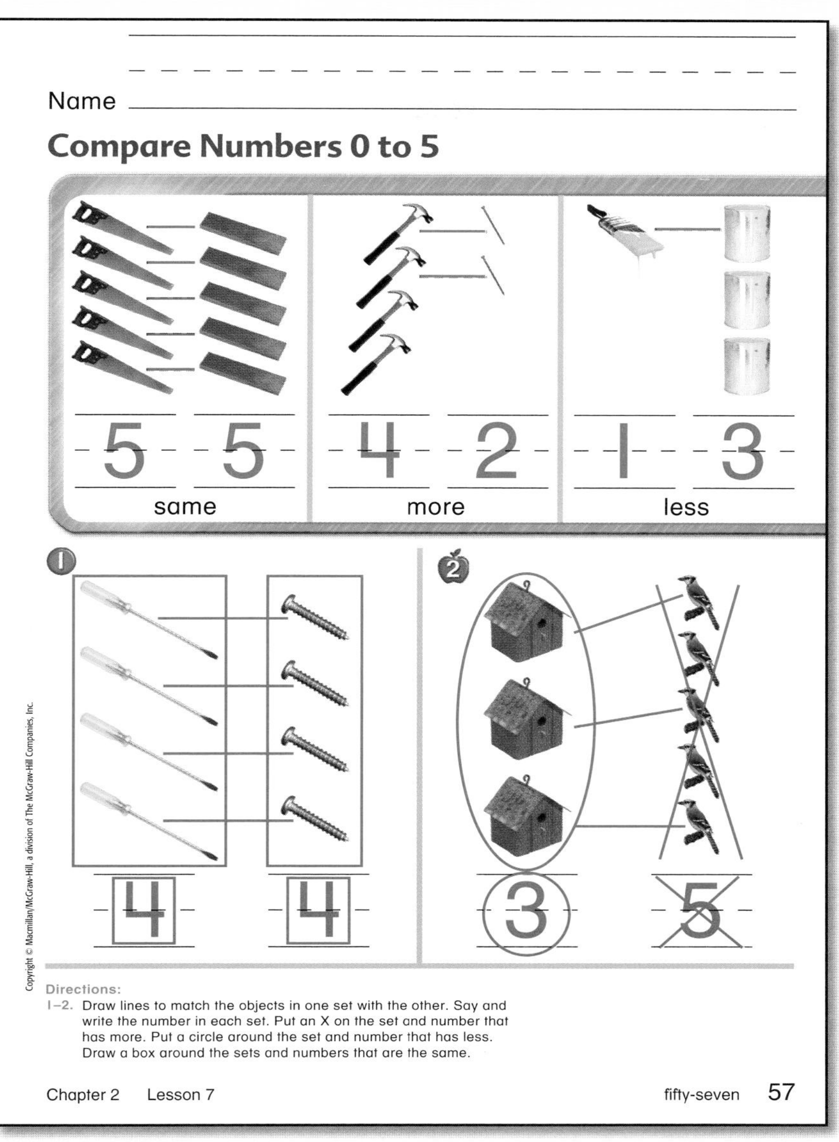

Name

Compare Numbers 0 to 5

5 5 same | 4 2 more | 1 3 less

1. 4 4
2. 3 5

Directions:
1–2. Draw lines to match the objects in one set with the other. Say and write the number in each set. Put an X on the set and number that has more. Put a circle around the set and number that has less. Draw a box around the sets and numbers that are the same.

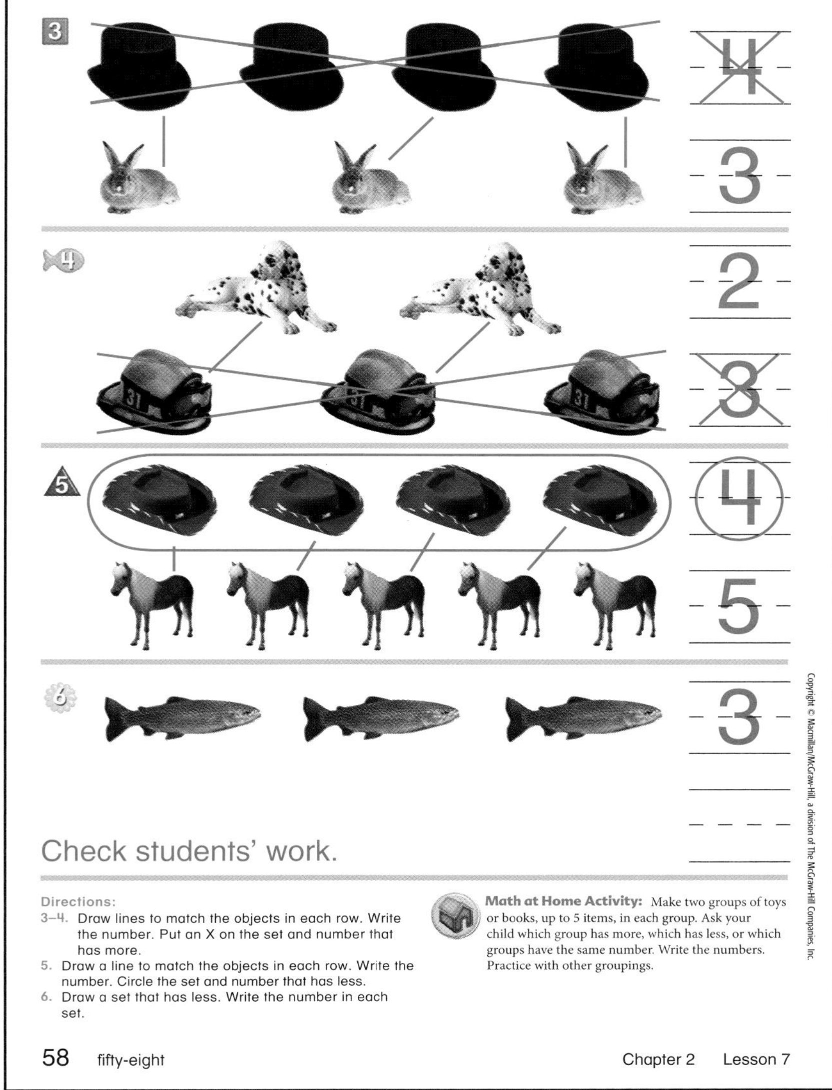

3. 4 3
4. 2 3
5. 4 5
6. 3

Check students' work.

Directions:
3–4. Draw lines to match the objects in each row. Write the number. Put an X on the set and number that has more.
5. Draw a line to match the objects in each row. Write the number. Circle the set and number that has less.
6. Draw a set that has less. Write the number in each set.

Math at Home Activity: Make two groups of toys or books, up to 5 items, in each group. Ask your child which group has more, which has less, or which groups have the same number. Write the numbers. Practice with other groupings.

3 Practice

Guided Practice

- Direct students to Exercise 1 on p. 57. Count the screwdrivers with students. **How many do you see?** four Have students write the number. Repeat with screws.
- Have students draw lines to match the screwdrivers and screws. **Is the number of screwdrivers the same/equal, more, or less than the number of screws? How do you know?** Sample answers: Same number; numbers or lines match.
- Have students put an X on the number and set that has more, a circle around the set that has less, and a box around the sets that are the same/equal.
- Repeat the activity for Exercise 2.

Independent Practice

Have students turn to p. 58. Explain the directions. Have students work independently on the exercises.

4 Assess

Formative Assessment

Draw a row of five circles on the chalkboard or chart paper. Draw a row of three squares below the circles.

- **Which row has more figures?** five circles
- Have students draw a row of triangles with fewer figures than the row of squares, then a row of triangles with the same number as the first row of triangles.

Quick Check **Are students still struggling to compare numbers zero to five?**

If Yes → Small Group Options (p. 57B)

If No → Independent Work Options (p. 57B)

CRM Skills Practice Worksheet (p. 32)

CRM Enrich Worksheet (p. 34)

LESSON 2-8

Order Numbers 0 to 5

Lesson Planner

Objective

Order numbers from 0 to 5 in sequence using illustrations.

Vocabulary

order

Resources

Materials: 0–5 number cards, paper, pencils, crayons
Manipulatives: connecting cubes, two-colored counters
Literature Connection: *Five Little Monkeys Jumping on the Bed* by Eileen Christelow
Alternate Lesson: Adapt *Large Numeral Cards* on page 44 of *Math Their Way* to provide practice in ordering numbers 0 to 5 in sequence.
Use *IMPACT Mathematics*: Unit B to provide practice with ordering numbers.
Teacher Technology
TeacherWorks • Concepts in Motion

Focus on Math Background

Students begin to understand the order of numbers by figuring out where numbers belong in relation to each other. For example, by knowing that the number two is between one and three, students can put those numbers in order. Use a number line to help students understand the order of numbers.

Daily Routine

Use these suggestions before beginning the lesson on p. 59.

5-Minute Check

(Reviews Lesson 2-7)
Show students two groups of crayons. Ask what group has more, what group has less, or if the groups have the same number.

Problem of the Day

Have students draw a picture with more than three birds and less than three flowers.

LINE UP Give each student a number card with a number from zero to five. Ask students to line up in groups of six. Have each group of six count off from zero to five.

Building Math Vocabulary

- Write numbers zero to five on separate pages of a flip chart. Explain that numbers go in **order**. Say that numbers start with zero, then go to one, then go to two, and so on.
- Show students the number zero on the flip chart. Have students say “zero.”
- Show the number one. Tell students they are going to count in order to one. Flip back to zero, have students say “zero,” flip to one, and have students say “one.”
- Repeat for numbers two, three, four, and five.

Visual Vocabulary Cards

Use Vocabulary Card 29 to reinforce the vocabulary introduced in this lesson. (The Define/Example/Ask routine is printed on the back of each card.)

Differentiated Instruction

Small Group Options

Option 1 Gifted and Talented AL

LINGUISTIC

- Tell students a riddle: "What number comes between two and four?" Write the riddle on the chalkboard as: 2 __ 4.
- Have a volunteer represent the answer by writing in the missing number of the riddle.
- Ask students to take turns writing their own number riddles on the chalkboard. Have other students fill in the missing number(s).

Option 2 English Language Learners ELL

VISUAL

Materials: cards with numbers 0–5, number line

Core Vocabulary: side, move to, stand below

Common Use Verb: look

See Math This strategy uses cooperative learning to teach ordering numbers.

- Pass out number cards. Have a student stand underneath his or her matching number on a number line.
- Allow watchers to prompt the student trying to place the number if they need help.
- Repeat for all students as time permits.

Idependent Work Options

Option 1 Early Finishers OL AL

VISUAL-KINESTHETIC

Materials: connecting cubes, paper, pencil

- Have students make trains of connecting cubes, one train each for one, two, three, four, and five.
- Have them mix up the order of their trains.
- Have students trade desks and put the trains in order. Remind students that they can use the connecting cubes to count.
- Have students write the numbers 1, 2, 3, 4, and 5 in order below each train.

Option 2 Student Technology

Math Online macmillanmh.com

Math Songs "Here is the Beehive" Track 4

Math Adventures

Option 3 Learning Station: Health (p. 39G)

Direct students to the Health Learning Station for opportunities to explore and extend the lesson concept.

Leveled Lesson Resources

Additional support for English Language Learners can be found in the ELL Guide (p.17). ELL

Reteach (p. 35) BL

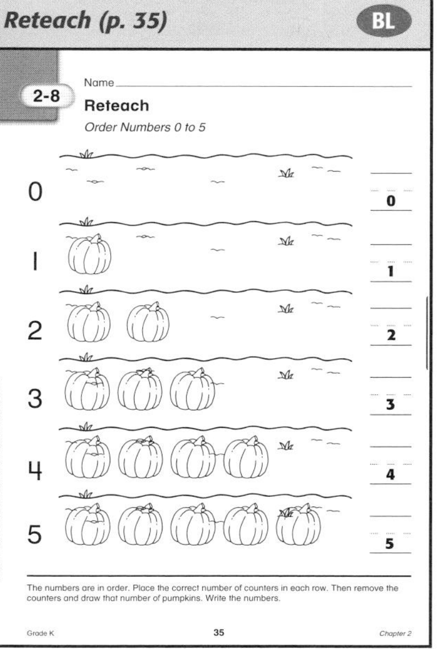

2-8 Name

Reteach

Order Numbers 0 to 5

0, 1, 2, 3, 4, 5

The numbers are in order. Place the correct number of counters in each row. Then remove the counters and draw that number of pumpkins. Write the numbers.

Grade K 35 Chapter 2

Skills Practice (p. 36) OL

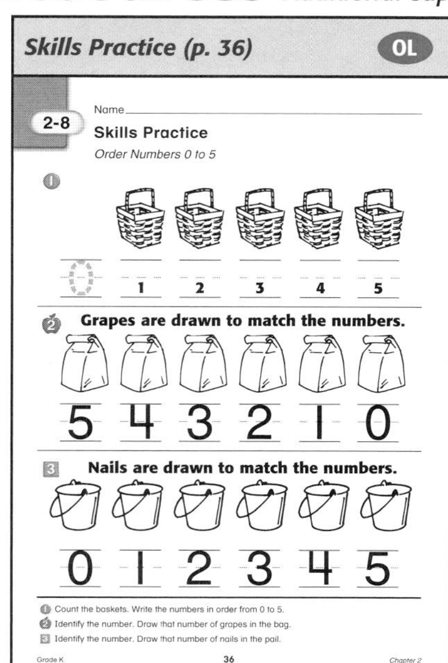

2-8 Name

Skills Practice

Order Numbers 0 to 5

Grapes are drawn to match the numbers.

5 4 3 2 1 0

Nails are drawn to match the numbers.

0 1 2 3 4 5

1. Count the baskets. Write the numbers in order from 0 to 5.
2. Identify the number. Draw that number of grapes in the bag.
3. Identify the number. Draw that number of nails in the pail.

Grade K 36 Chapter 2

Enrich (p. 38) AL

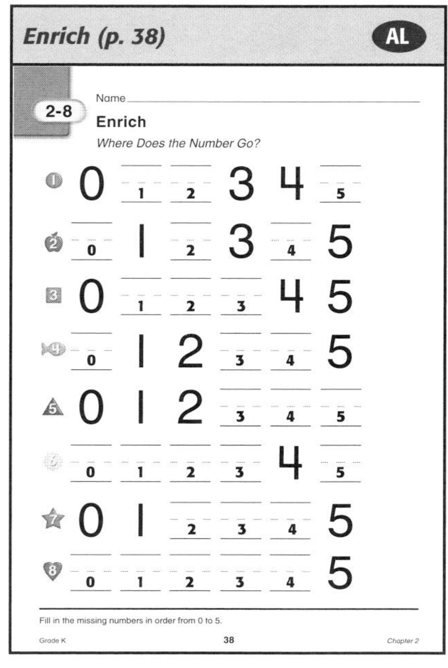

2-8 Name

Enrich

Where Does the Number Go?

0 _ _ 3 4 _

_ 1 _ 3 _ 5

0 _ _ _ 4 5

_ 1 2 _ _ 5

0 1 2 _ _ _

_ _ _ _ 4 _

0 1 _ _ _ 5

_ _ _ _ _ 5

Fill in the missing numbers in order from 0 to 5.

Grade K 38 Chapter 2

Homework Practice (p. 37) OL

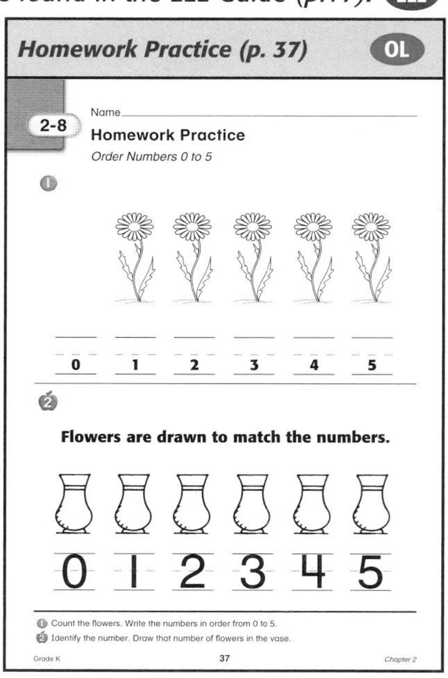

2-8 Name

Homework Practice

Order Numbers 0 to 5

Flowers are drawn to match the numbers.

0 1 2 3 4 5

1. Count the flowers. Write the numbers in order from 0 to 5.
2. Identify the number. Draw that number of flowers in the vase.

Grade K 37 Chapter 2

LESSON 2-8

1 Introduce

Activity Choice 1 • Literature

Five Little Monkeys Jumping on the Bed by Eileen Christelow

- Give each student 15 connecting cubes. Read the story aloud, having students stack cubes to show how many monkeys are jumping on the bed.
- **When the last monkey jumps off the bed, how many monkeys are left on the bed?** zero
- Have students put their stacks in **order** from zero to five and name each number in order.
- Have students form groups of four to six. Give each group member a card with a number from zero to five. Have students make their number with connecting cubes (except zero), and put the cubes in order.

Activity Choice 2 • Hands-On

Materials: two-colored counters

- Have students work in small groups.
- Write the numbers zero through five on the chalkboard.
- Ask students to read the numbers with you as you point to the corresponding numbers.
- Point to zero and ask students to gather that many counters. Continue with the rest of the numbers.
- Point out that, as you say the numbers in order, the amount of counters becomes more.

2 Teach

- Direct students to the top of p. 59.
- Discuss peas and how they grow.
- **How many peas are in the first peapod?** zero
- Have students write the number zero. Remind them that zero is the number that tells how many when there are none.
- Repeat the activity for numbers one to five, verbally representing the peas by counting the peas in the pods and writing the numbers.
- Count zero to five peapods with students, saying the numbers in order.
- Say that when we counted, we named each number in order. Tell them that when we wrote zero to five, we showed the numbers in order. Say that *order* is a special way to name and show numbers.

BL Alternate Teaching Strategy

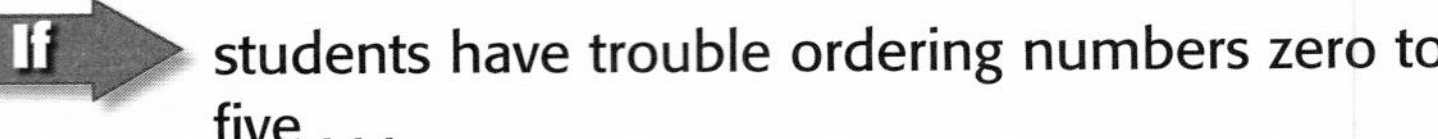

If students have trouble ordering numbers zero to five . . .

Then use one of these reteach options.

1 CRM **Daily Reteach Worksheet** (p. 35)

2 **Use Visuals** Have students form groups of six.

- Show the numbers zero to five in a row on the chalkboard.
- Give each student a card with a number from zero to five.
- Represent the number verbally by counting the number cards zero to five as you point to the number on the chalkboard one at a time, in correct numerical order.
- Have remaining students say the numbers in order.

COMMON ERROR!

Students may confuse the order of the numbers as they count. Provide illustrated groups of objects and their corresponding numbers in order and have students count.

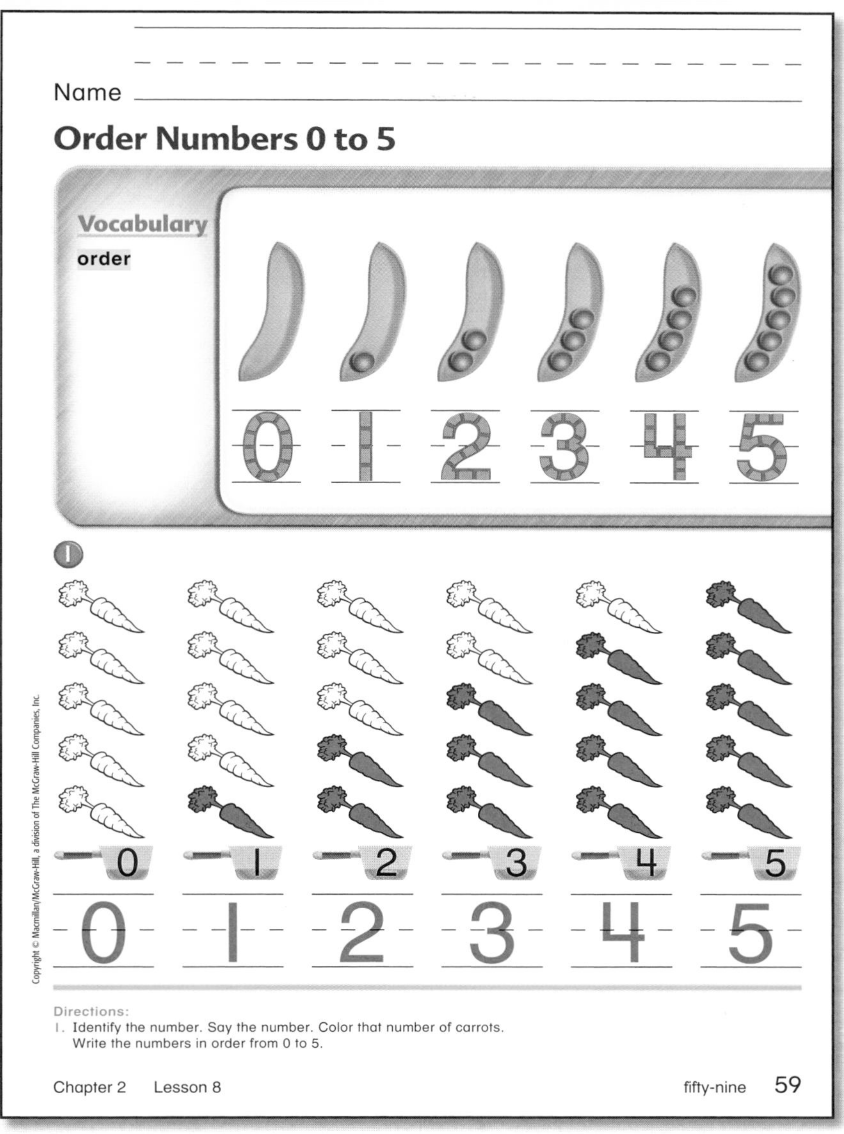

Name
Order Numbers 0 to 5
Vocabulary
order
0 1 2 3 4 5
0 1 2 3 4 5
0 1 2 3 4 5
Directions:
1. Identify the number. Say the number. Color that number of carrots. Write the numbers in order from 0 to 5.
Chapter 2 Lesson 8 fifty-nine 59

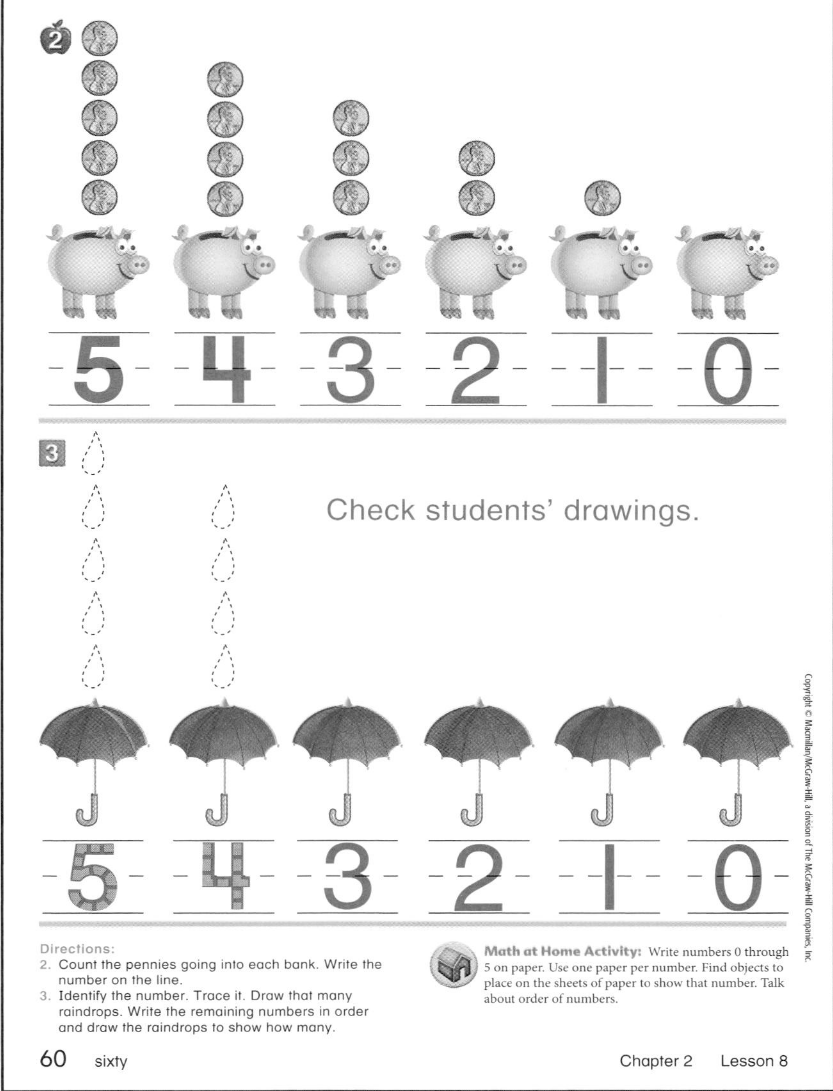

5 4 3 2 1 0
Check students' drawings.
5 4 3 2 1 0
Directions:
2. Count the pennies going into each bank. Write the number on the line.
3. Identify the number. Trace it. Draw that many raindrops. Write the remaining numbers in order and draw the raindrops to show how many.
Math at Home Activity: Write numbers 0 through 5 on paper. Use one paper per number. Find objects to place on the sheets of paper to show that number. Talk about order of numbers.
60 sixty Chapter 2 Lesson 8

3 Practice

Guided Practice

- Direct students to Exercise 1 on p. 59.
- Tells students to say the number on each pan. Then color that number of carrots above each pan.
- Have students write the numbers in order from zero to five.
- **What is the order of the carrots? How do you know?** Sample answers: The order is zero, one, two, three, four, five; we count in order from zero to five.

Independent Practice

Have students turn to p. 60. Explain the directions. Have students work independently on the exercises.

4 Assess

Formative Assessment

- Ask students to write numbers zero to five in order.
- Have students take turns saying the numbers in order.

Quick Check

Are students still having difficulty putting the numbers zero to five in order?

If Yes → Small Group Options (p. 59B)

If No → Independent Work Options (p. 59B)

 Skills Practice Worksheet (p. 36)

CRM Enrich Worksheet (p. 38)

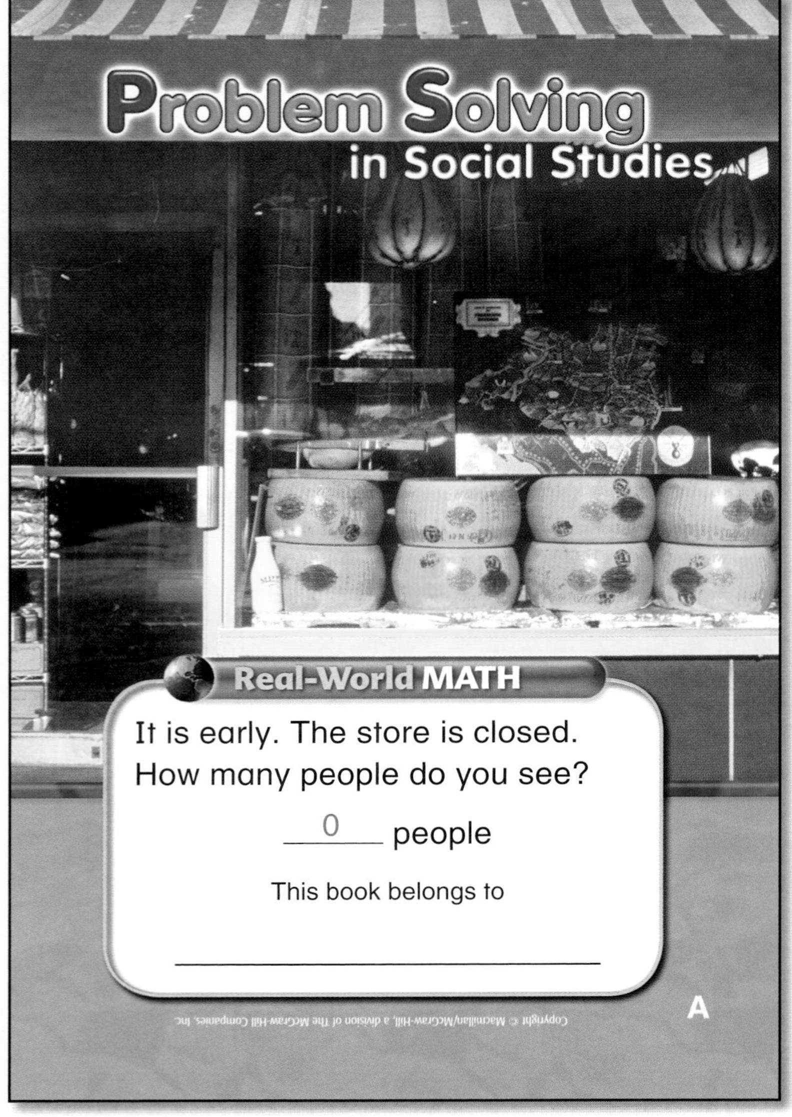

Problem Solving
in Social Studies
Real-World MATH
It is early. The store is closed.
How many people do you see?
0 people
This book belongs to
A
Copyright © Macmillan/McGraw-Hill, a division of The McGraw-Hill Companies, Inc.

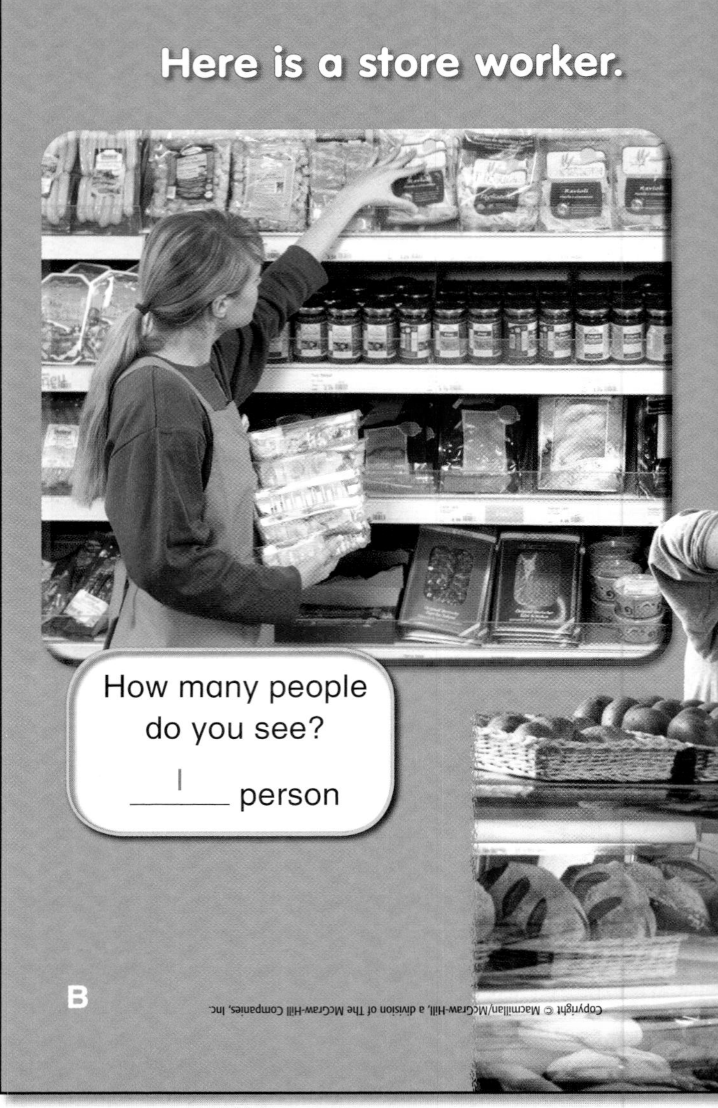

Lesson Planner

Objective

Count objects in the settings of various stores that people use every day.

National Standards 

Students learn how citizens take part in civic life.

Vocabulary

count, one, two, three, four, five

Activate Prior Knowledge

Before you turn students' attention to the pages, discuss grocery stores.

- **What are some different things people count in a grocery store?** Sample answers: fruits, vegetables, muffins, rolls, money to pay for items
- **How are items delivered to a grocery store?** Sample answers: trucks, vans
- **What kinds of foods would need to be transported in a refrigerated truck?** Sample answers: milk, butter, eggs, cheese, yogurt, vegetables, fruit

Here is the baker.
How many people want to buy bread?
2 people
C

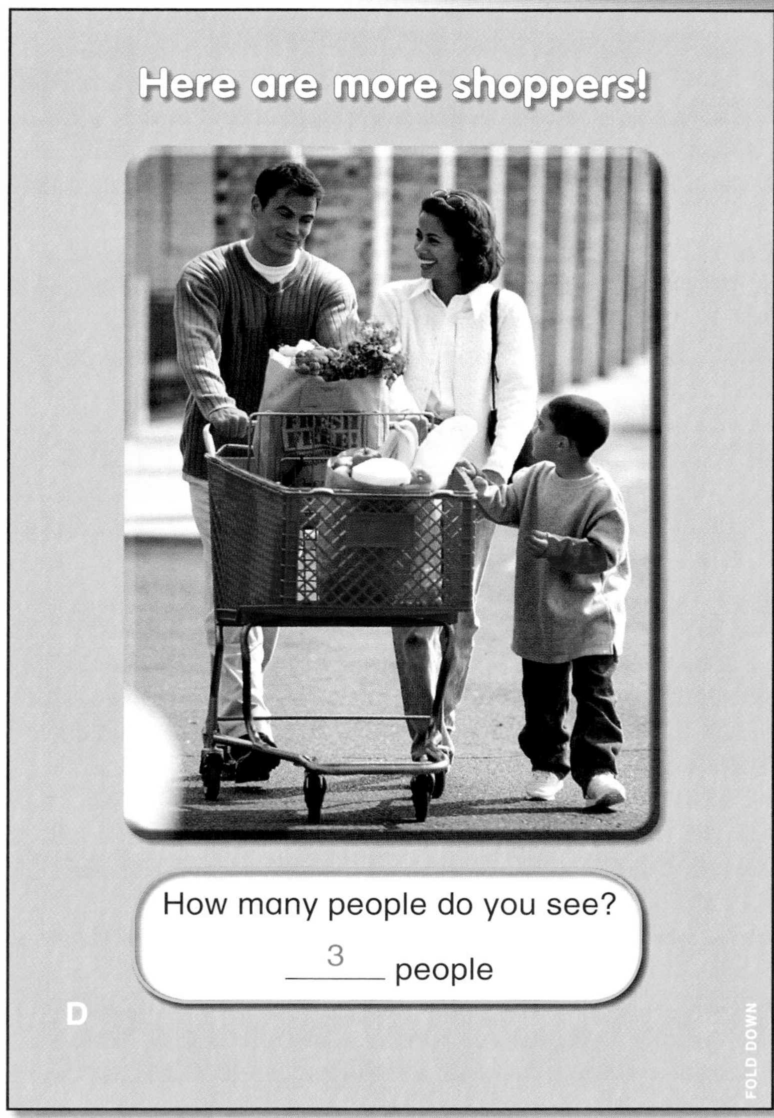

Here are more shoppers!
How many people do you see?
3 people
D
FOLD DOWN

Create the Book

Guide students to create their book.

- Have them fold the page in half.
- Ask them to write their name on page A.
- Explain that page A is the front cover and page D is the back cover. If necessary, have them practice flipping through the book in order.
- Guide them in reading the information and word problems on each of the pages.

Use the Student Pages

Have students work individually or in pairs to solve the word problems on pages B–D.

Page B Have students count the workers.

Page C Have students count the number of people who want to buy bread.

Page D Have students count the total number of people, not just the child or adults.

WRITING IN MATH Have students draw a grocery store scene with items that can be counted. Have students exchange pictures with partners and count objects.

FOLDABLES Dinah Zike's Foldables

Use these lesson suggestions for incorporating the Foldables during the chapter.

Lesson 2-6 Make and glue one more section to the beginning of the Foldable Number Line. Write the number zero on the top left side of the section.

Lesson 2-7 Use the display cases made in chapter one to compare groups of one, two, three, four, or five objects. Determine which groups have more, less, or the same (equal) number of objects.

Chapter 2 Project

Create a Mural

Lead a discussion on the results of the completed chapter project with the class.

Vocabulary Review

Review chapter vocabulary using one of the following options.

- **Visual Vocabulary Card** (29)
- **eGlossary** at macmillanmh.com

Data-Driven Decision Making

Based on the results of the Mid-Chapter Check, use the following to review concepts that continue to present students with problems.

Exercises	State/Local Standards	What's the Math?	Error Analysis	Resources for Review
1 Lesson 2-6		Recognizes and writes the numeral 0.	Counts incorrectly. Is not able to recognize the quantity of 0.	CRM Chapter 2 Resource Masters (Reteach Worksheets) Math Online Concepts in Motion Math Adventures
2 Lesson 2-4		Know larger numbers describe sets with more objects and smaller numbers describe smaller numbers.	Does not draw lines. Counts incorrectly. Does not write number. Xs smaller group.	
3 Lesson 2-8		Understand quantity of zero to five and order and write the numbers.	Writes wrong numbers. Does not color basketballs. Does not color correct number of balls.	

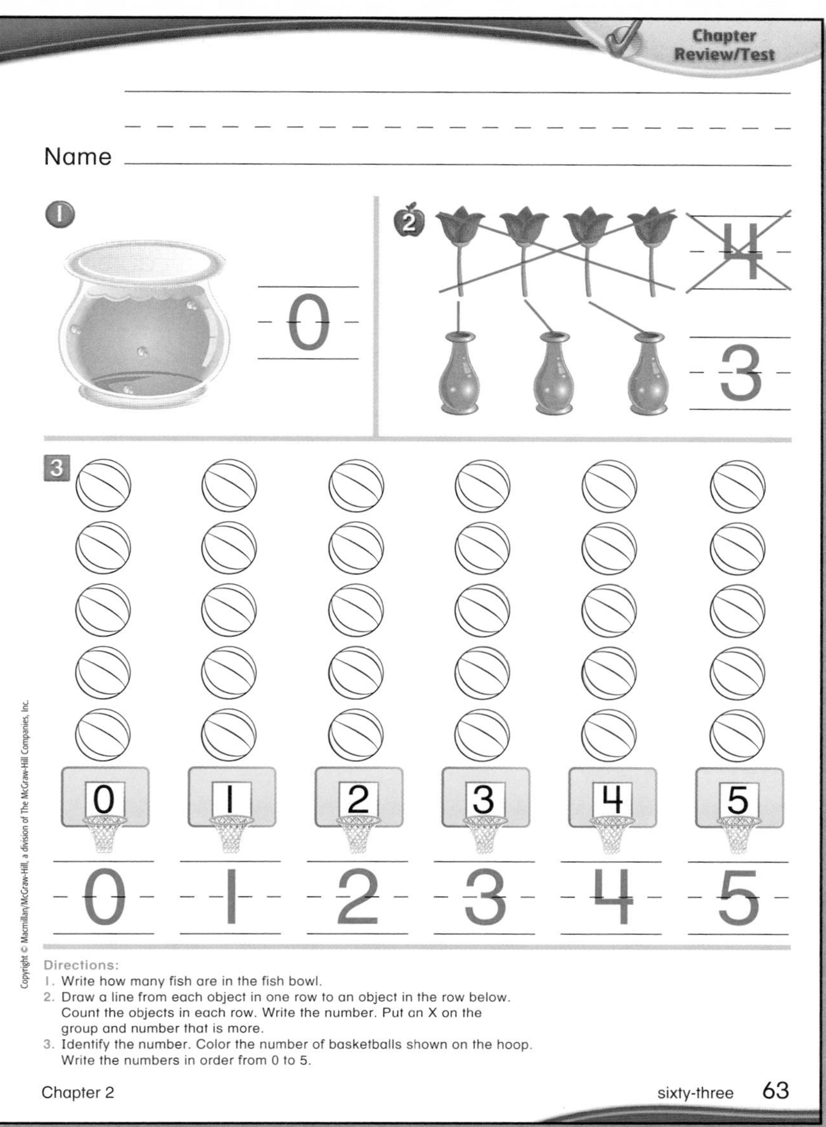

Chapter Review/Test

Name

1 0

2 4 3

3 0 1 2 3 4 5

0 1 2 3 4 5

Directions:
1. Write how many fish are in the fish bowl.
2. Draw a line from each object in one row to an object in the row below. Count the objects in each row. Write the number. Put an X on the group and number that is more.
3. Identify the number. Color the number of basketballs shown on the hoop. Write the numbers in order from 0 to 5.

Chapter 2 sixty-three 63

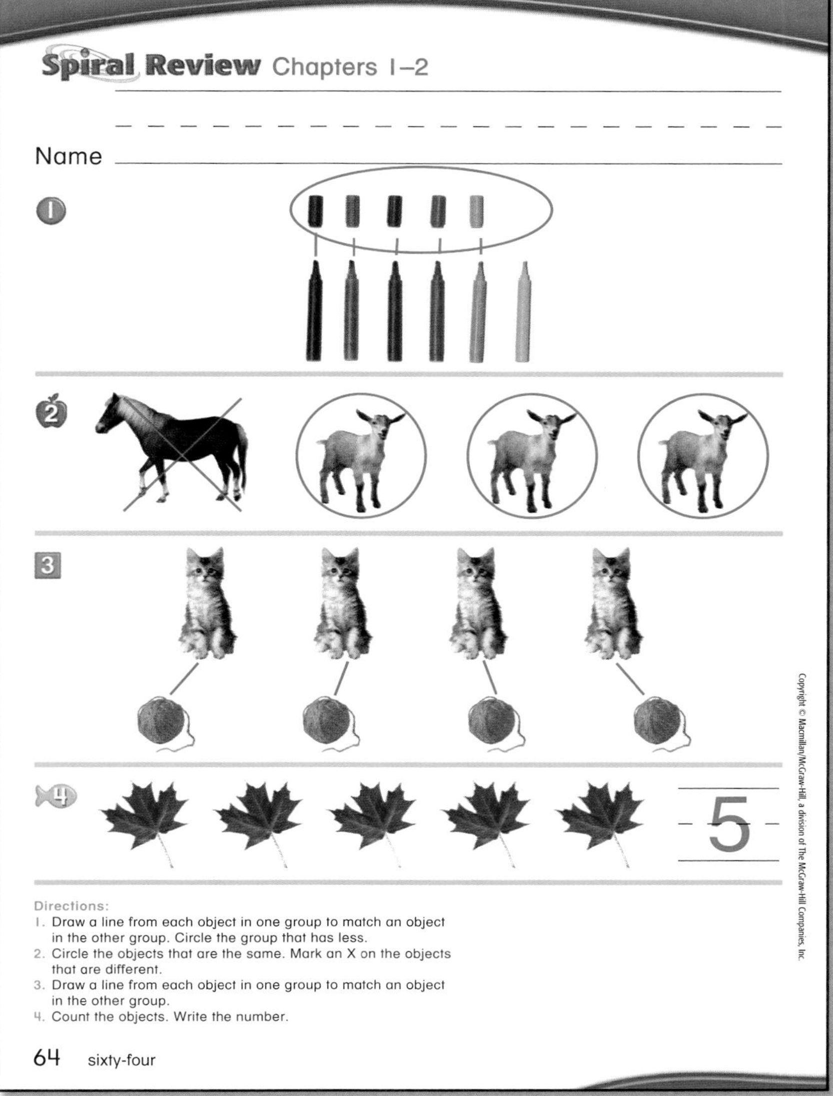

Spiral Review Chapters 1–2

Name

1

2

3

4 5

Directions:
1. Draw a line from each object in one group to match an object in the other group. Circle the group that has less.
2. Circle the objects that are the same. Mark an X on the objects that are different.
3. Draw a line from each object in one group to match an object in the other group.
4. Count the objects. Write the number.

64 sixty-four

Summative Assessment

Use these alternate leveled chapter tests to differentiate assessment for the specific needs of your students.

Leveled Chapter 2 Tests			
Form	**Type**	**Level**	**CRM Pages**
1	Multiple Choice	BL	46–47
2A	Multiple Choice	OL	48–49
2C	Multiple Choice	OL	50–51
2D	Free Response	AL	52–53

BL = below/approaching grade level
OL = on grade level
AL = above/beyond grade level

Spiral Review

Reviews Chapter 1

Objective: Review and assess mastery of skills and concepts from previous chapter.

Resources for Review

Based on student results, refer to these lessons for remediation.

- **Exercise 1: Lesson 1-7** (p. 31),
- **Exercise 2: Lesson 1-1** (p. 17),
- **Exercise 3: Lesson 1-5** (p. 27),
- **Exercise 4: Lesson 2-4** (p. 49),

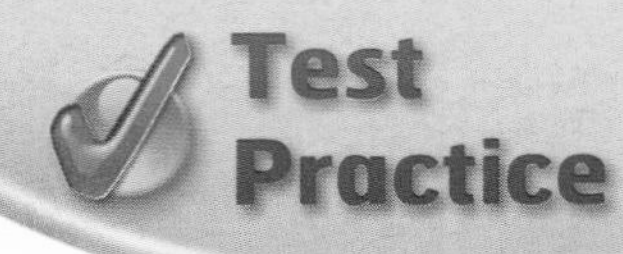

Chapters 1–2

Formative Assessment

- You can use Student Edition pp. 65-66 to benchmark student progress.
- Additional practice pages can be found in Chapter 2 Resource Masters.

Chapter 2 Resource Masters

Cumulative Test Practice

- Multiple Choice format (pp. 46–53)
- Free Response format (pp. 54–55)

Create additional practice worksheets or tests.

Math Online For additional practice visit macmillanmh.com.

Test-Taking Tips

For the Teacher

- It may be helpful to remind students how to count from one to five by pointing to your eyes, ears, and nose while saying, "Eye, eye, ear, ear, nose," then pointing to your eyes, ears, and nose in the same order while saying "one, two, three, four, five."
- Repeat instructions often as some students need to hear information multiple times.

For the Student

- Tell students to be sure they understand what to do before they start answering test questions.
- Encourage students to look over the test before they begin to spot questions that will need more time to do.

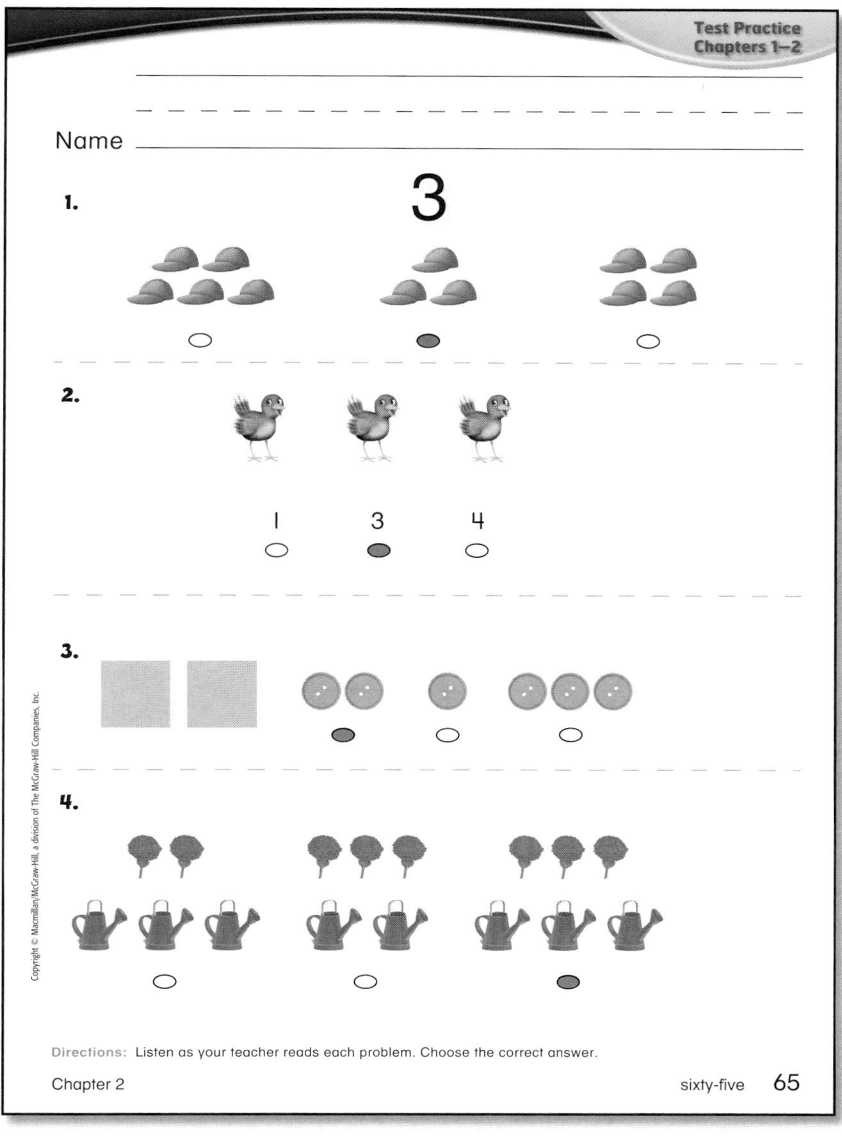

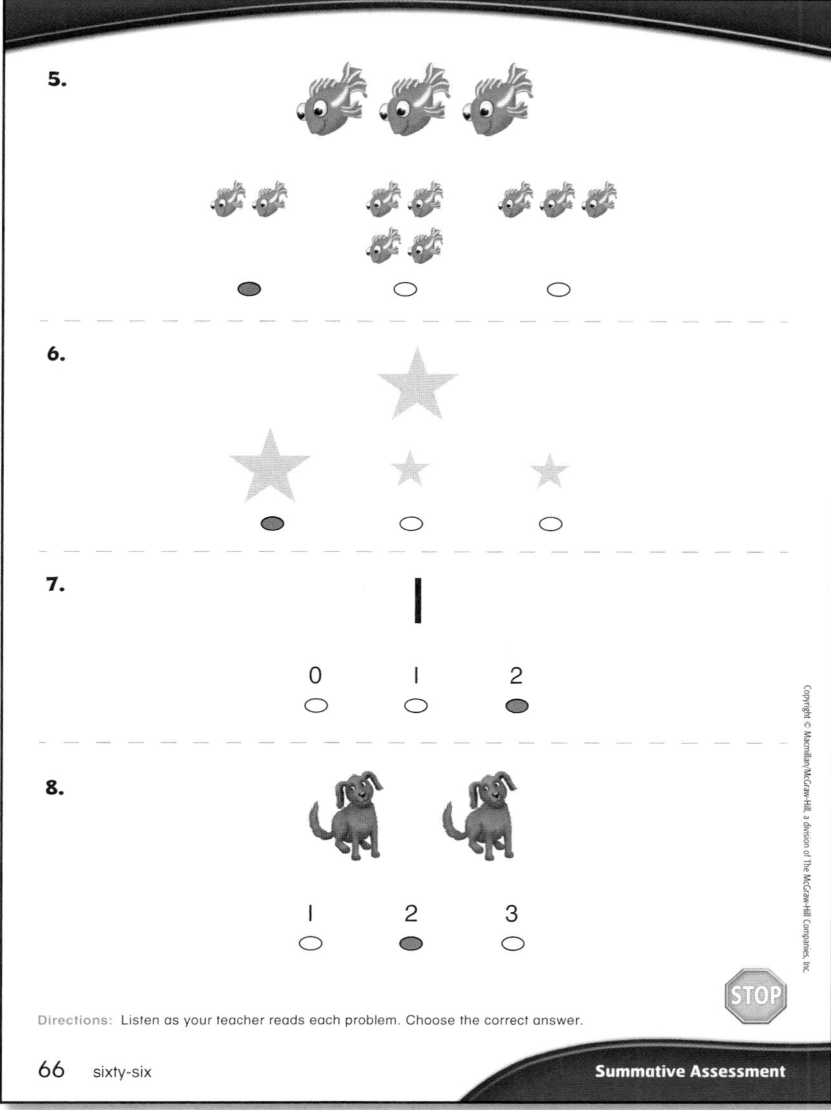

Test Directions for Teachers

Read the following directions to students before they begin. Then read each question followed by a pause to allow students time to work and choose an answer. The first text item can be worked as a class example.

- **Write your name at the top of the page.**
- **I am going to read each question to you. Listen carefully to the entire question before you choose an answer.**

1. Look at the number three. Find the group that has three hats. Mark the group that has three hats.
2. Look at the group of birds. Count the number of birds. Find the number that shows that many birds.
3. Look at the squares. Count the squares. Find the group of buttons that shows the same number of squares. Mark the group of buttons that shows the same number of squares.
4. Look at the groups of flowers and watering cans. Find the group that shows the same or equal number of flowers and watering cans. Mark the group that shows the same or equal number of flowers and watering cans.

- **Turn the page over.**

5. Look at the fish. Count the fish. Find the group of fish that has less. Mark the group that has less fish.
6. Look at the star. Find the star that is the same size. Mark the star that is the same size.
7. Look at the number one. Find the number that is one more. Mark that number.
8. Count the dogs. Find the number that shows how many dogs. Mark the number that shows how many dogs.

Chapter Overview

Chapter-at-a-Glance

In Chapter 3, the emphasis is on identifying patterns; copying and extending color, size, and shape patterns; and comparing patterns.

	Lesson	Math Objective	State/Local Standards
3-1	**Over and Under** (pp. 71–72)	Use the words *over, under, above,* and *below* to describe or place an object with respect to another.	
3-2	**Top, Middle, and Bottom** (pp. 73–74)	Place or find an object that is on the top, middle, or bottom.	
3-3	**Objects: Before and After** (pp. 6)	Describe the order of events or objects or place an object that is before or after.	
3-4	**Identifying Patterns** (pp. 77–78)	Identify, extend, and create patterns.	
3-5	**Object Patterns** (pp. 81–82)	Identify, extend, and create object patterns.	
3-6	**Problem-Solving Strategy: Look for a Pattern** (pp. 83–84)	Solve problems by looking for a pattern.	
3-7	**Sound Patterns** (pp. 85–86)	Identify, extend, and create patterns of sound.	
3-8	**Movement Patterns** (pp. 87–88)	Identify, extend, and create movement patterns.	
3-9	**Predicting Patterns** (pp. 89–90)	Students will use patterns to make predictions.	

Describe Position and Patterns

BIG Idea Patterns are everywhere in the world around us. We see patterns in the clothes we wear, buildings we work in, and the music we listen to. In this chapter, kindergarteners are introduced to working with patterns. Students learn to identify, describe, and extend simple patterns using concrete objects such as color tiles and buttons. Students will be asked to identify, extend, and create patterns of sounds, movement, and concrete models.

Algebra Students begin finding patterns to help them solve problems. Recognizing and using patterns lays the foundation for understanding algebraic functions.
Lesson 3-6

GK-FP6C *Algebra:* Children identify, duplicate, and extend simple number patterns and sequential and growing patterns (e.g., patterns made with shapes) as preparation for creating rules that describe relationships.

Skills Trace

Vertical Alignment

PreKindergarten

In PreK, students learned to:

- Imitate pattern sounds and movements (e.g., clap, stomp, clap, stomp,...).
- Recognizes and reproduces simple patterns of concrete objects (e.g., a string of beads that are yellow, blue, blue, yellow, blue, blue).

Kindergarten

During this chapter, students will learn to:

- Identify, extend, and create patterns of sounds, movements, and concrete models.
- Describe one object in relation to another using formal language such as *over, under, above,* and *below*.

After this chapter, students will learn to:

- Answer questions about picture graphs.
- Compare two-dimensional and three-dimensional objects by common attributes.

First Grade

In first grade, students will learn to:

- Find patterns in numbers, including odd and even.
- Use patterns to develop strategies to solve basic addition and basic subtraction problems.

BackMapping and Vertical Alignment **McGraw-Hill's *Math Connects*** program was conceived and developed with the final results in mind: student success in Algebra 1 and beyond. The authors, using the **NCTM Focal Points and Focal Connections** as their guide, developed this brand new series by back-mapping from Algebra 1 concepts, and vertically aligning the topics so that they build upon prior skills and concepts and serve as a foundation for future topics.

Math Vocabulary

The following math vocabulary words for Chapter 3 are listed in the glossary of the ***Student Edition***. You can find interactive definitions in 13 languages in the ***eGlossary*** at macmillanmh.com.

above, below (p. 71)

after, before (p. 75)

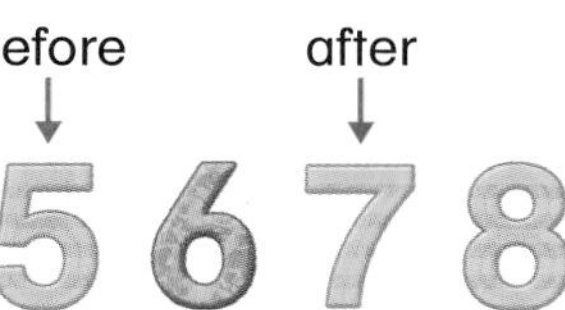

bottom, middle, top (p. 73)

top →
middle →
bottom →

over, under (p. 71)

pattern (p. 77)

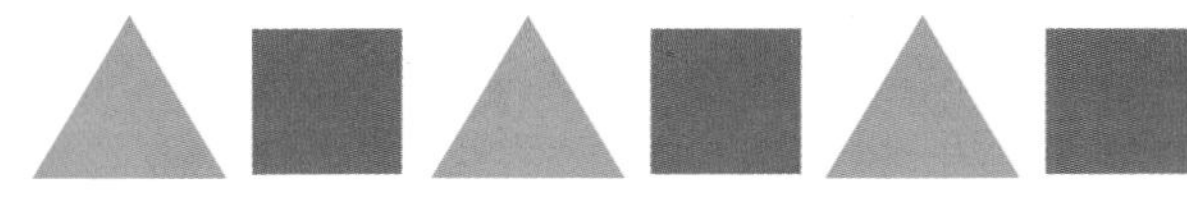

Use **Visual Vocabulary Cards** 2, 4, and 30 to introduce and reinforce the vocabulary in this chapter. (The Define/Example/Ask routine is printed on the back of each card.)

Chapter Planner

Suggested Pacing		
Instruction	Review and Assessment	TOTAL
9 days	2 days	**11 days**

Diagnostic Assessment
Are You Ready? (p. 68)

	Lesson 3-1 (Pacing: 1 day)	Lesson 3-2 (Pacing: 1 day)	Lesson 3-3 (Pacing: 1 day)
Lesson/ Objective	**Over and Under** (pp. 71–72) **Objective:** Use the words *over, under, above,* and *below* to describe or place an object with respect to another.	**Top, Middle, and Bottom** (pp. 73–74) **Objective:** Place or find an object that is on the top, middle, or bottom.	**Before and After** (pp. 75–76) **Objective:** Describe the order of events of objects or determine whether objects are before or after each other.
State/Local Standards			
Math Vocabulary	**over**, **under**, **above**, **below**	**top**, **middle**, **bottom**	**before**, **after**
Lesson Resources	**Materials** pencils, paper, crayons **Manipulatives** pattern blocks, attribute buttons **Other Resources** CRM Leveled Worksheets (pp. 6–9) Daily Reteach Problem of the Day	**Materials** classroom objects, drawing paper, crayons **Manipulatives** color tiles, pattern blocks, connecting cubes **Other Resources** CRM Leveled Worksheets (pp. 10–13) Daily Reteach Problem of the Day	**Materials** drawing paper, crayons, string **Manipulatives** pattern blocks, attribute buttons, connecting cubes, color tiles **Other Resources** CRM Leveled Worksheets (pp. 14–7) Daily Reteach Problem of the Day
Technology Math Online	Math Adventures Concepts in Motion	Math Adventures Concepts in Motion	Concepts in Motion
Reaching All Learners	English Learners, p. 71B ELL Gifted and Talented, p. 71B AL Early Finishers, p. 71B OL AL	English Learners, p. 73B ELL Gifted and Talented, p. 73B AL Early Finishers, p. 73B OL AL	English Learners, p. 75B ELL Gifted and Talented, p. 75B AL Early Finishers, p. 75B OL AL
Alternate Lesson			

KEY

BL Below/Approaching Level
OL On Level
AL Above/Beyond Level
ELL English Learners
SE Student Edition
TE Teacher Edition
CRM Chapter 1 Resource Masters
CD-Rom
Transparency
Flip Chart
Real-World Problem Solving Library

Describe Position and Patterns

	Lesson 3-4 Pacing: 1 day	Lesson 3-5 Pacing: 1 day	Lesson 3-6 Pacing: 1 day
Lesson/ Objective	**Identify Patterns** (pp. 77–78) **Objective:** Identify patterns.	**Object Patterns** (pp. 81–82) **Objective:** Identify, extend, and create patterns of objects.	**Problem-Solving Strategy** **Look for a Pattern** (pp. 83–84) **Objective:** Solve problems by looking for a pattern.
State/Local Standards			
Math Vocabulary	**pattern**		
Lesson Resources	**Materials** black construction paper, white construction paper, classroom objects, crayons, drawing paper **Manipulatives** two-colored counters, connecting cubes, color tiles, pattern blocks **Other Resources** CRM Leveled Worksheets (pp. 18–21) Daily Reteach Problem of the Day	**Materials** drawing paper, crayons, pencils **Manipulatives** pattern blocks, attribute buttons **Other Resources** CRM Leveled Worksheets (pp. 22–26) Daily Reteach Problem of the Day	**Materials** white paper, pencil, crayons, glue, index cards **Manipulatives** attribute buttons, pattern blocks, counters **Other Resources** CRM Leveled Worksheets (pp. 27–30) Daily Reteach Problem of the Day *Desert Patterns*
Technology Math Online	Math Songs Track 1 Math Adventures	Math Songs Track 1 Math Adventures	Math Songs Track 1 Math Adventures
Reaching All Learners	English Learners, p. 77B ELL Below Level p. 77B BL Early Finishers, p. 77B OL AL	English Learners, p. 81B ELL Below Level, p. 81B BL Early Finishers, p. 81B OL AL	English Learners, p. 83B ELL Below Level, p. 83B BL Early Finishers, p. 83B OL AL
Alternate Lesson	*Impact Mathematics*: Unit E	*Impact Mathematics*: Unit E	

Game Time: Leap Frog! (p. 80)

Formative Assessment
Mid-Chapter Check (p. 79)

Chapter Planner

	Lesson 3-7 Pacing: 1 day	Lesson 3-8 Pacing: 1 day	Lesson 3-9 Pacing: 1 day
Lesson/ Objective	**Sound Patterns** (pp. 85–86) **Objective:** Identify, extend, and create sound patterns.	**Movement Patterns** (pp. 87–88) **Objective:** Identify, extend, and create movement patterns.	**Predicting Patterns** (pp. 89–90) **Objective:** Students will use patterns to make predictions.
State/Local Standards			
Math Vocabulary			**predict**
Lesson Resources	**Materials** classroom instruments, pencils **Other Resources** CRM Leveled Worksheets (pp. 31–34) Daily Reteach Problem of the Day	**Other Resources** CRM Leveled Worksheets (pp. 35–38) Daily Reteach Problem of the Day	**Materials** pencils **Manipulatives** pattern blocks **Other Resources** CRM Leveled Worksheets (pp. 39–42) Daily Reteach Problem of the Day
Technology Math Online	Math Songs Track 1	Math Songs Track 1	Math Songs Track 1
Reaching All Learners	English Learners, p. 85B ELL Gifted and Talented, p. 85B AL Early Finishers, p. 85B OL AL	English Learners, p. 87B ELL Below Level, p. 87B BL Early Finishers, p. 87B OL AL	English Learners, p. 89B ELL Below Level, p. 89B BL Early Finishers, p. 89B OL AL
Alternate Lesson		*IMPACT Mathematics*: Unit E	*IMPACT Mathematics*: Unit E

Problem Solving in Art (p. 91)

Summative Assessment
- Chapter Review/Test (p. 93)
- Test Practice (p. 95)

Assessment Options

Diagnostic Assessment

- SE *Option 1:* Are You Ready? (p. 68)
- *Option 2:* Online Quiz (macmillanmh.com)
- CRM *Option 3:* Diagnostic Test (p. 44)

Formative Assessment

- TE Alternate Teaching Strategies (every lesson)
- TE Writing in Math (every lesson)
- TE Line Up (every lesson)
- SE Mid-Chapter Check (p. 79)
- CRM Mid-Chapter Test (p. 45)

Summative Assessment

- SE Chapter Review/Test (p. 93)
- SE Test Practice (p. 95)
- CRM Leveled Chapter Tests (pp. 50–57)
- CRM Cumulative Test Practice (p. 58)
- CRM Listening Assessment (p. 48)
- CRM Oral Assessment (p. 46)
- Exam*View*® Assessment Suite
- Advanced Tracker

Assessment Tips

Sorting is an integral part of the mathematics that kindergarten children will be learning.

- It is important to observe each student on several different occasions because one observation at one given moment is not a good sample.
- Observe each student at least twice in each lesson as they are completing sorting activities.
- The more times a student is observed, the better chance you will have to ascertain whether he/she has a deep understanding of the concept.
- Keep accurate records of each observation.

Teacher Notes

Mc Graw Hill Professional Development

Targeted professional development has been articulated throughout ***McGraw-Hill's Math Connects*** program. The **McGraw-Hill Professional Development Video Library** provides short videos that support the **NCTM Focal Points and Focal Connections.** For more information visit macmillanmh.com.

Model Lessons

Instructional Strategies

Learning Stations

Cross-Curricular Links

Health

pair KINESTHETIC 

Let's Get Moving

- Make this pattern: clap, pat your lap, clap, pat your lap.
- Make new patterns.
- Do other movement patterns.

Teacher Note: Have students copy each others' patterns. Students should perform their patterns one at a time, with the rest of the class joining in when they understand the pattern. Patterns can include standing, sitting, snapping, touching toes, or jumping. Suggest movements that allow all students to participate. If there are students unable to snap their fingers, for example, offer instruction or help students choose another movement.

Materials:

- cards with suggested large movements to use when making patterns

Art

pair | LINGUISTIC 

Name That Pattern

- Look at a pattern.
- Copy the pattern.
- Show the pattern three times.

Teacher Note: Make a small pre-stapled book. On each page, show one unit of a pattern that the student should use to create a repeating pattern. Students can draw their patterns or use stamps or stickers. Students' patterns should always repeat three times.

Materials:

- pre-stapled book with patterns indicated on each page
- markers
- stamps
- stickers

Technology

 pair |  VISUAL 

Creating Patterns

Math Tool Chest:  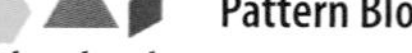 Pattern Blocks

- Choose the Pattern Blocks button.
- Use different shapes and colors to create patterns.
- Create patterns with two and three different shapes or colors.

Teacher Note: Have students use the Pattern Blocks tool to create AB, ABB, AAB, and ABC patterns. Challenge students to create patterns out of different shapes and colors. Have students justify their thinking by explaining a pattern they created on the computer to a classmate. For students who require additional support, provide a variety of patterns for them to copy.

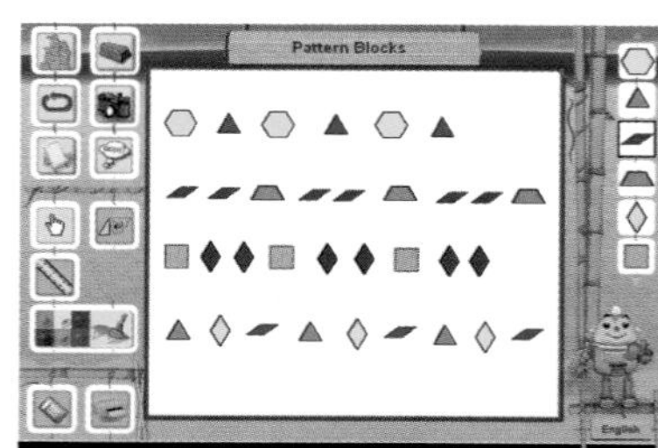

Materials:

- Math Tool Chest

Social Studies

individual | SPATIAL

Missing Colors

- Look at each tray.
- Identify the pattern.
- Determine which colors are missing.
- Lift the cup to see if you are right.
- Repeat with all three trays.

Teacher Note: Make a different pattern of counters on three trays. Cover one to three counters with overturned paper cups so that they are hidden from sight. Make sure that each pattern of counters repeats three times before covering counters. Have students say the pattern of counters aloud before lifting the cup to check their answer.

Materials:

- red and yellow counters
- 3 trays
- paper cups

Reading

individual | LINGUISTIC

How Does It End?

- Look at the paper strip.
- Say what comes next.
- Continue the pattern.

Teacher Note: Show students paper strips with word or letter patterns on them, such as "yes no yes no yes no" or "X O X O X O." Use letters or shapes if words are too difficult. Make sure each pattern repeats three times. Cover the last item in the pattern with a sticky note. Have student say what comes next before lifting the sticky note to check their answer. Have students copy the pattern onto a piece of paper and continue the pattern beyond three units.

Materials:

- sentence strips
- sticky notes
- blank paper strips
- markers

Calendar Time

- Keep track of the weather for an extended amount of time.
- Mark sunny days with a sun and rainy days with a rain cloud.
- Keep note of what changes on rainy days in your classroom. (For example: Put on X on days that you stay inside for recess.)
- At the end of your recording period ask students if they notice a pattern.
- Ask students: If the pattern continues what will we do the next time it rains? Stay inside for recess.

Introduce the Chapter

Real World: Patterns

- Share with students that they are going to learn about patterns.
- Ask two volunteers for an idea of a motion. Put the motions together and have the class follow the pattern.
- Repeat with sounds.

Use the Student Page

Have students turn to p. 67. Guide students to discuss the images on the page and answer the Explore questions.

Key Vocabulary

Introduce the key vocabulary in the chapter using the routine below.

Define: When a set of objects follows an order over and over again, it is a pattern.
Example: A, B, A, B, A, B
Ask: How can you make a pattern using numbers?

Diagnostic Assessment

Check for students' prerequisite skills before beginning the chapter.

- **Option 1:** ***Are You Ready for Chapter 3?***
  SE Student Edition, p. 68
- **Option 2:** ***Online Assessment Quiz***
  Math Online macmillanmh.com
- **Option 3:** ***Diagnostic Test***
  CRM Chapter 3 Resource Masters, p. 44

RTI (Response to Intervention)

Apply the Results Based on the results of the diagnostic assessment on p. 68, use the chart on the next page to address individual needs before and during the chapter.

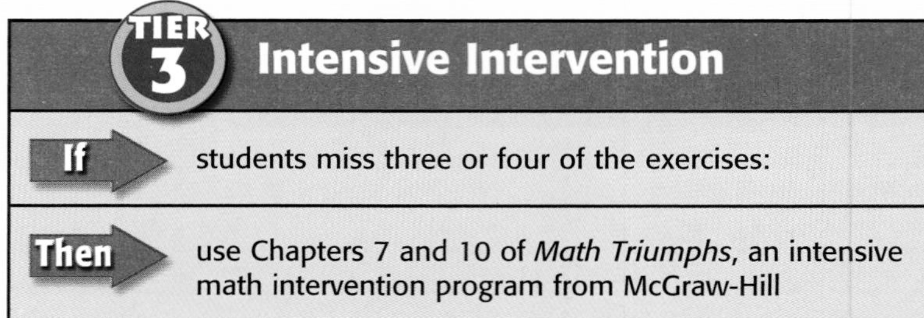

TIER 3 **Intensive Intervention**

If	students miss three or four of the exercises:
Then	use Chapters 7 and 10 of *Math Triumphs*, an intensive math intervention program from McGraw-Hill

Dinah Zike's Foldables

Guide students to create a Flashcard Holder Foldable graphic organizer for making patterns.

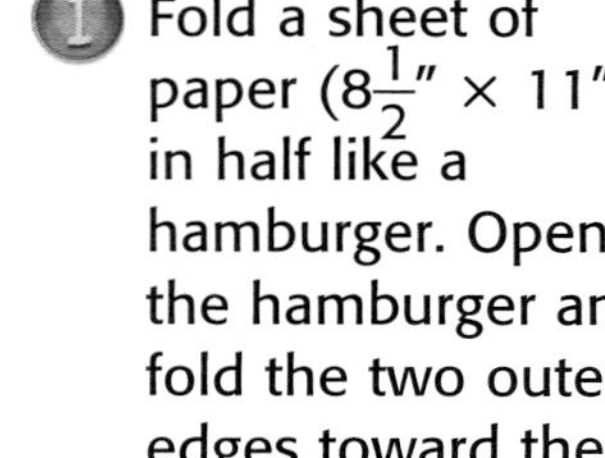

1. Fold a sheet of paper ($8\frac{1}{2}$" × 11") in half like a hamburger. Open the hamburger and fold the two outer edges toward the valley, forming a shutter fold.

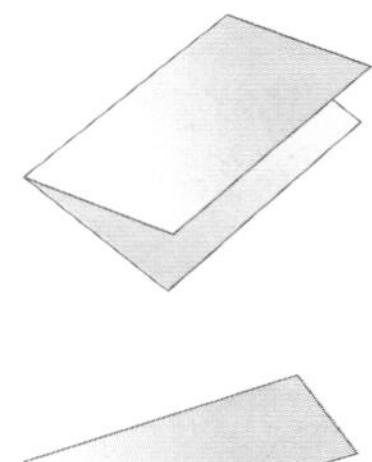

2. Fold one of the inside edges of the shutter back to the outside fold, forming a floppy "L."

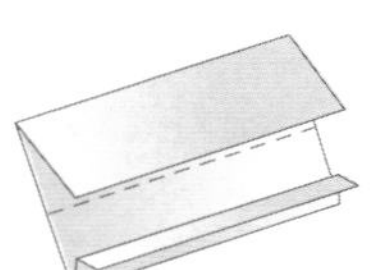

3. Glue the floppy L-tab down to the base so that it forms a strong, straight L-tab. Glue the other shutter side to the front of this L-tab. This forms a tent that is the backboard for displaying flashcards.

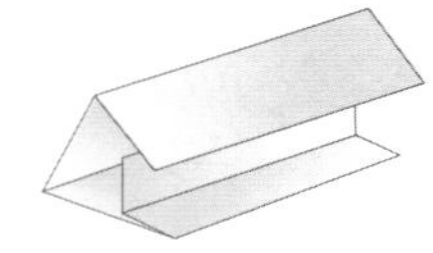

4. Fold the edge of the L-tab up one quarter to one half to form a lip that will keep the student work from slipping off the holder.

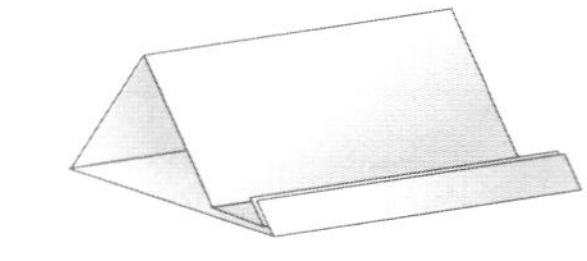

5. Use blue triangles and red circles to make different patterns on the flashcard holder.

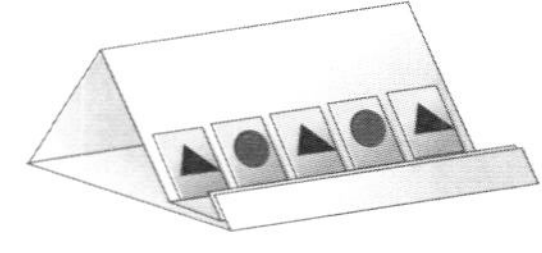

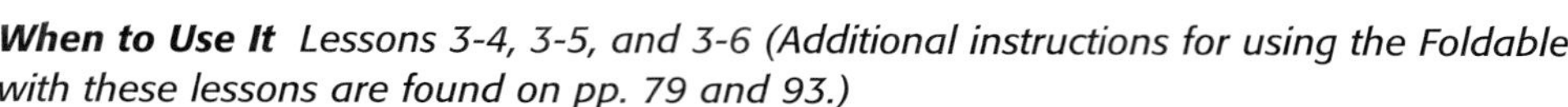

When to Use It *Lessons 3-4, 3-5, and 3-6 (Additional instructions for using the Foldable with these lessons are found on pp. 79 and 93.)*

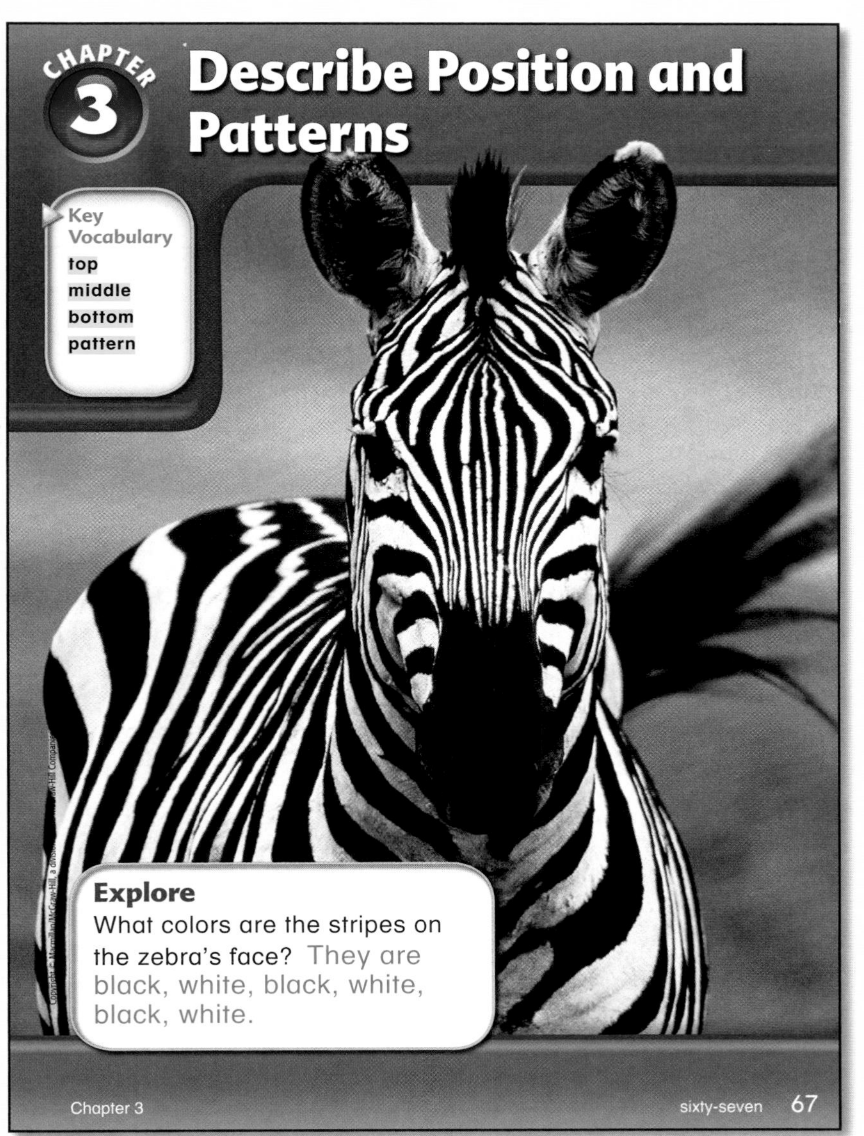

Chapter 3
Describe Position and Patterns
Key Vocabulary
top
middle
bottom
pattern
Explore
What colors are the stripes on the zebra's face? They are black, white, black, white, black, white.
Chapter 3
sixty-seven 67

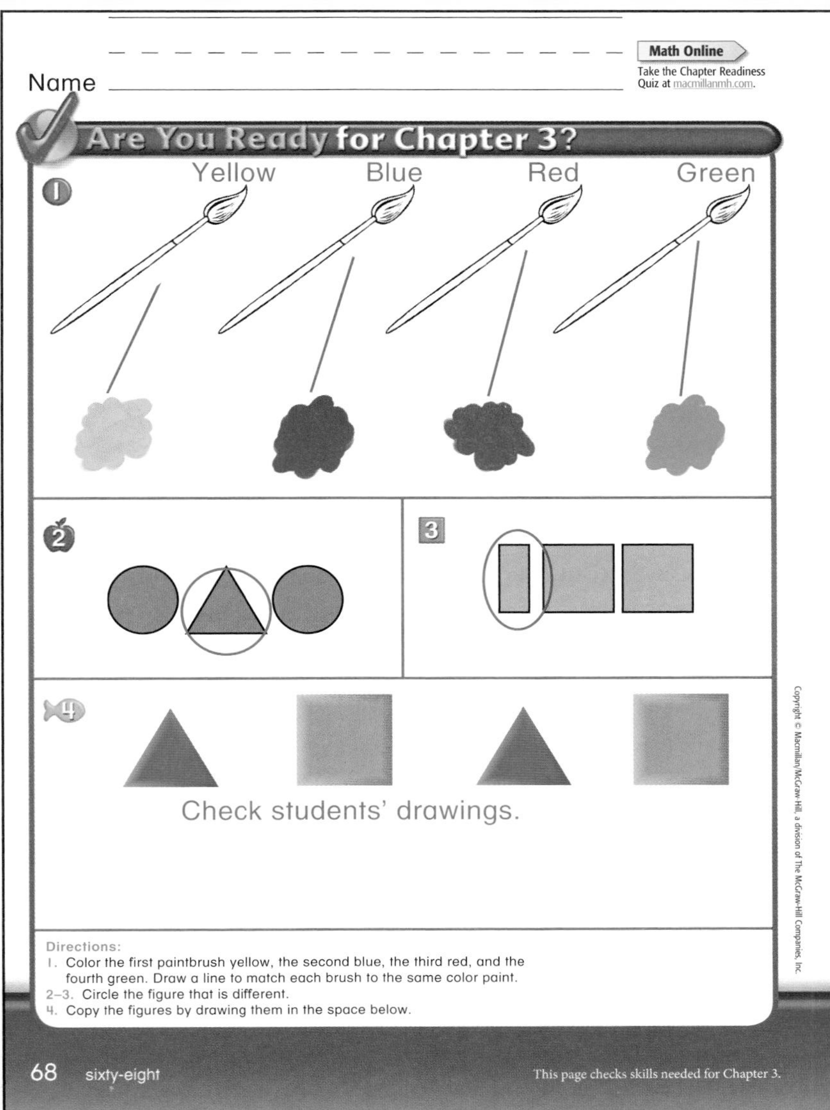

Name
Math Online
Take the Chapter Readiness Quiz at macmillanmh.com.
Are You Ready for Chapter 3?
Yellow
Blue
Red
Green
Check students' drawings.
Directions:
1. Color the first paintbrush yellow, the second blue, the third red, and the fourth green. Draw a line to match each brush to the same color paint.
2–3. Circle the figure that is different.
4. Copy the figures by drawing them in the space below.
68 sixty-eight
This page checks skills needed for Chapter 3.

RTI (Response to Intervention)

TIER 2 Strategic Intervention below/approaching grade level	TIER 1 On-Level	Above/Beyond Level
If students miss two in: **Exercises 1–4** **Then** choose a resource:	**If** students miss one in: **Exercises 1–4** **Then** choose a resource:	**If** students miss none in: **Exercises 1–4** **Then** choose a resource:
CRM Chapter 1 Resource Masters (Reteach Worksheets) Math Online Concepts in Motion	TE Learning Stations (pp. 67G–67H) TE Chapter Project (p. 69) CRM Game: Create a Pattern! Math Adventures My Math Zone Chapters 2-3	TE Learning Stations (pp. 67G–67H) TE Chapter Project (p. 69) Real-World Problem Solving: *Desert Patterns* My Math Zone Chapters 2-3 Math Online Game

WRITING IN ▸ MATH

Starting the Chapter
Have students copy the three patterns they will learn in their Math Journal: object, sound, and physical movement. Then have them draw one example of each.

Chapter 3 Project

Pattern Posters

- Have students create a pattern board. Divide a poster into 4 sections.
- In one section, write the words "over," "under," "above," "below," "top," "middle," "bottom," "before," and "after." Have students draw or glue objects showing the meaning of each word.
- At the top of the other three sections, identify a sound, object, or physical movement pattern. Have students draw or glue objects representing that pattern.
- Hang the posters around the room or in the hall.

Chapter 3 Literature List

Lesson	Book Title	Author
3-1	**Over, Under & Through**	Tana Hoban
3-2	**The Best Bug Parade**	Stuart J. Murphy
3-3	**Parade**	Donald Crews
3-4	**Beep, Beep, Vroom, Vroom!**	Stuart J. Murphy
3-5	**Beep, Beep, Vroom, Vroom!**	Stuart J. Murphy
3-6	**The Button Box**	Margarette S. Reid
3-7	**Beep, Beep, Vroom, Vroom!**	Stuart J. Murphy
3-8	**Bug Dance**	Stuart J. Murphy
3-9	**The Noisy Farm**	Marni McGee
Any	**Jump, Frog, Jump!**	Robert Kalan
Any	**Pattern Fish**	Trudy Harris

ELL National ESL Standards Alignment for Chapter 3

Lesson, Page	ESL Standard	Modality	Level
3-1, p. 71B	Goal 1, Standard 3, b	Visual/Spatial, Kinesthetic	Beginning
3-2, p. 73B	Goal 2, Standard 1, a	Kinesthetic, Linguistic	Intermediate
3-3, p. 75B	Goal 1, Standard 3, i	Linguistic, Logical	Intermediate
3-4, p. 77B	Goal 2, Standard 1, h	Auditory, Kinesthetic	Intermediate
3-5, p. 81B	Goal 1, Standard 3, c	Visual Spatial, Kinesthetic	Intermediate
3-6, p. 83B	Goal 1, Standard 3, d	Kinesthetic	Advance
3-7, p. 85B	Goal 2, Standard 2, e	Auditory, Kinesthetic	Intermediate
3-8, p. 87B	Goal 1, Standard 3, b	Visual/Spatial, Kinesthetic	Intermediate
3-9, p. 89B	Goal 2, Standard 2, j	Logical	Beginning

The National ESL Standards can be found in the Teacher Reference Handbook.

English

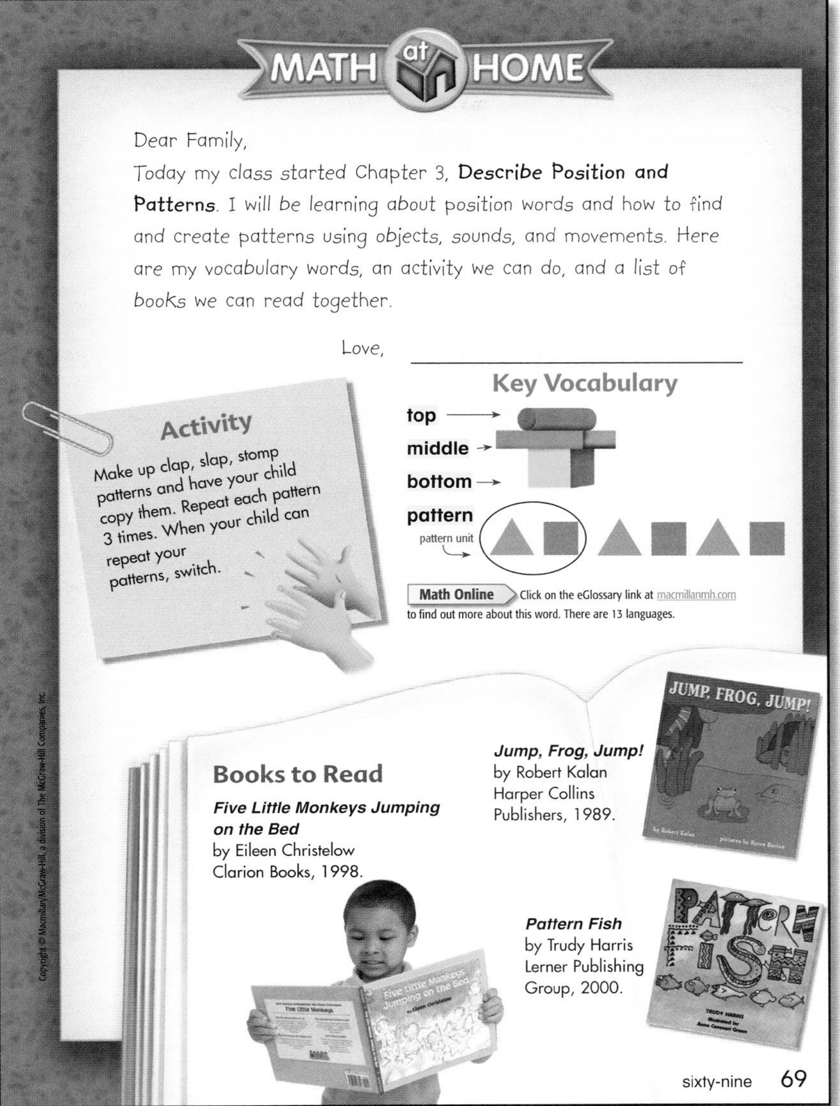

MATH at HOME

Dear Family,

Today my class started Chapter 3, **Describe Position and Patterns**. I will be learning about position words and how to find and create patterns using objects, sounds, and movements. Here are my vocabulary words, an activity we can do, and a list of books we can read together.

Love, ______________

Activity

Make up clap, slap, stomp patterns and have your child copy them. Repeat each pattern 3 times. When your child can repeat your patterns, switch.

Key Vocabulary

top

middle

bottom

pattern

pattern unit

Math Online Click on the eGlossary link at macmillanmh.com to find out more about this word. There are 13 languages.

Books to Read

Five Little Monkeys Jumping on the Bed
by Eileen Christelow
Clarion Books, 1998.

Jump, Frog, Jump!
by Robert Kalan
Harper Collins
Publishers, 1989.

Pattern Fish
by Trudy Harris
Lerner Publishing
Group, 2000.

sixty-nine 69

Español

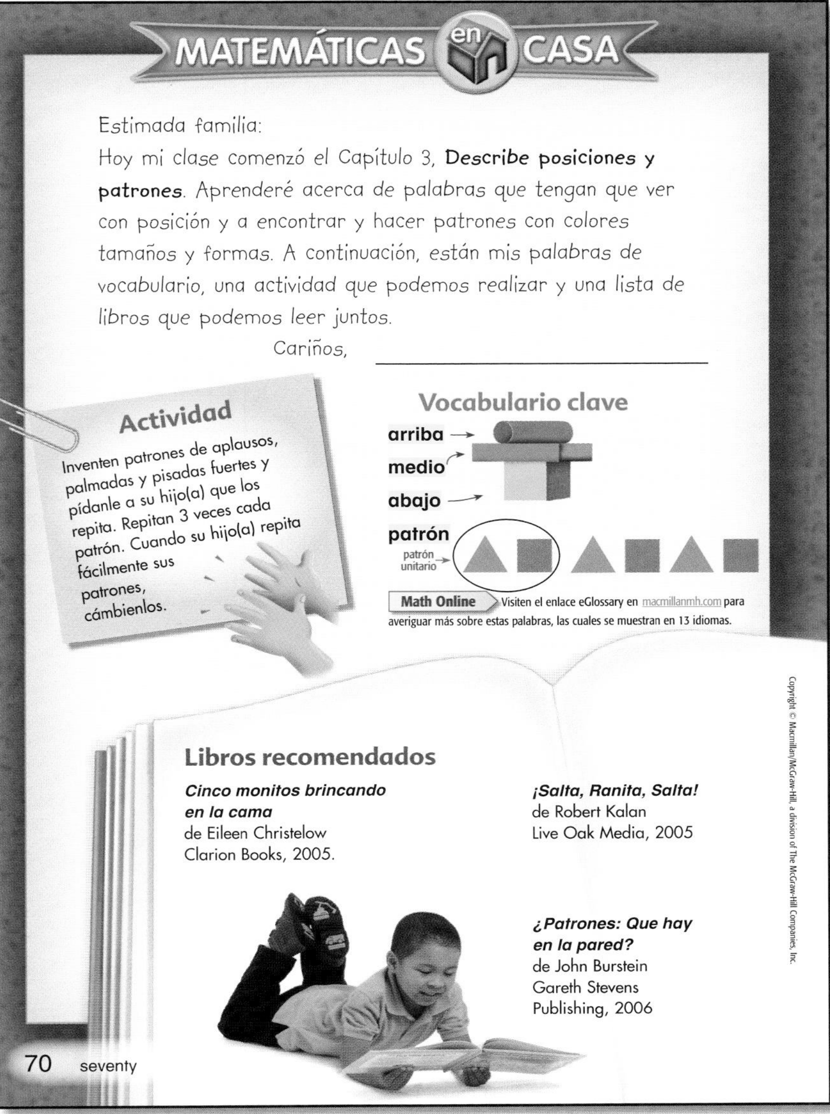

MATEMÁTICAS en CASA

Estimada familia:

Hoy mi clase comenzó el Capítulo 3, **Describe posiciones y patrones**. Aprenderé acerca de palabras que tengan que ver con posición y a encontrar y hacer patrones con colores tamaños y formas. A continuación, están mis palabras de vocabulario, una actividad que podemos realizar y una lista de libros que podemos leer juntos.

Cariños, ______________

Actividad

Inventen patrones de aplausos, palmadas y pisadas fuertes y pídanle a su hijo(a) que los repita. Repitan 3 veces cada patrón. Cuando su hijo(a) repita fácilmente sus patrones, cámbienlos.

Vocabulario clave

arriba

medio

abajo

patrón

patrón unitario

Math Online Visiten el enlace eGlossary en macmillanmh.com para averiguar más sobre estas palabras, las cuales se muestran en 13 idiomas.

Libros recomendados

Cinco monitos brincando en la cama
de Eileen Christelow
Clarion Books, 2005.

¡Salta, Ranita, Salta!
de Robert Kalan
Live Oak Media, 2005

¿Patrones: Que hay en la pared?
de John Burstein
Gareth Stevens
Publishing, 2006

70 seventy

- Read the Math at Home letter on p. 69 with the class and have each student sign it.
- Send home copies of the Math at Home letter with each student.
- Use the Spanish letter on p. 70 for students with Spanish-speaking parents or guardians.

Read-Aloud Anthology

For an optional reading activity to introduce this chapter's math concepts, see the Read-Aloud Anthology on p. TR26.

LESSON 3-1

Over and Under

Lesson Planner

Objective

Students will use the words *over*, *under*, *above*, and *below* to describe or place an object with respect to another.

Vocabulary

over, **under**, **above**, **below**

Resources

Materials: pencils, paper, crayons
Manipulatives: pattern blocks, attribute buttons
Literature Connection: *Over, Under, & Through* by Tana Hoban
Teacher Technology
TeacherWorks • Concepts in Motion

Daily Routine

Use these suggestions before beginning the lesson on p. 71.

5-Minute Check

(Reviews Lesson 2-8)

Put the following numbers in order.

1. 3 2 5 2, 3 5
2. 1 5 4 1, 4, 5
3. 2 4 3 1 1, 2, 3, 4
4. 4 5 2 3 2, 3, 4, 5
5. 5 2 3 1 4 1, 2, 3, 4, 5

Problem of the Day

Ask students to draw five smiley faces. Have them draw four stars above the faces and two flowers under the faces.

LINE UP Have students build connecting cube stacks following your directions. Have students line up when their stack matches your description. Example: *Put a blue connecting cube under your red connecting cube.*

Building Math Vocabulary

- Tell students they will play a game called "Simon Says." Say that Simon says to put their hands **over** their head. Explain over means on top of something else.
- Have students put a book **above** their shoulder. Explain above means the same as over, or on top of something else.
- Have them put their foot **below** their desk. Explain below means on the bottom.
- Have them put their hand **under** their chin. Explain under means the same as below, or something else is on top of it.
- Have students make Simon Says directions using above, below, over, and under.

Differentiated Instruction

Small Group Options

Option 1 LOGICAL

Gifted and Talented AL

Materials: paper, pencil

- Tell students they will be told to draw a picture on their paper using the position words under and over.
- Give the following directions to the students:
  1) Draw a tree. 2) Draw three birds flying over the tree. 3) Draw grass under the tree. 4) Draw two birds in the grass under the tree. 5) Draw the sun over the tree.
- Have students check their pictures while you draw the correct picture one direction at a time.

Option 2 VISUAL/SPATIAL, KINESTHETIC

English Language Learners ELL

Core Vocabulary: letters, shape, over/under

Common Use Verb: look like

See Math This strategy teaches over and under kinesthetically.

- Write "over." Circle the "o" asking: "What does this letter look like?" (Circle)
- Model an o shape with arms overhead and say: "Over." Students repeat.
- Repeat process for "under." To model, bend over, letting interlocked hands swing. Have students lock hands under knees to better illustrate "under."

Independent Work Options

Option 1 KINESTHETIC

Early Finishers AL OL

Materials: paper, crayons

- Tell students they are going to play a game called "I Spy." Explain that all spying must be objects that are above, below, over, or under another object.
- Say that you spy an object. Ex: "I spy something above the chalkboard."
- Have students record what they spied by drawing a picture of it and its location, such as above, below, over, or under something.

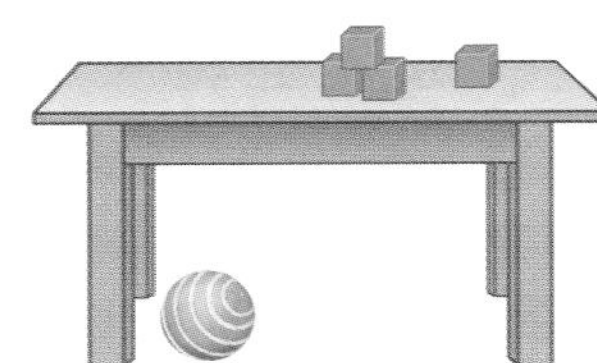

- Repeat the activity, having students take turns saying "I Spy."

Option 2

Student Technology

Math Online macmillanmh.com

Math Adventures

Option 3

Learning Station: Social Studies (p. 67H)

Direct students to the Social Studies Learning Station for opportunities to explore and extend the lesson concept.

Leveled Lesson Resources

Additional support for English Language Learners can be found in the ELL Guide (p. 9). ELL

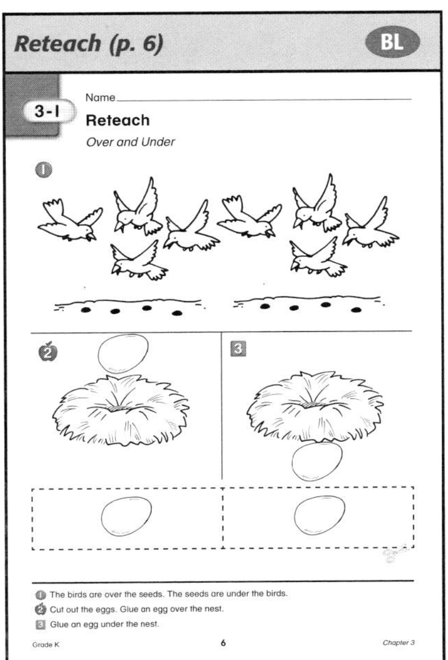

Reteach (p. 6) BL

3-1 Name________

Reteach

Over and Under

1. The birds are over the seeds. The seeds are under the birds.
2. Cut out the eggs. Glue an egg over the nest.
3. Glue an egg under the nest.

Grade K 6 *Chapter 3*

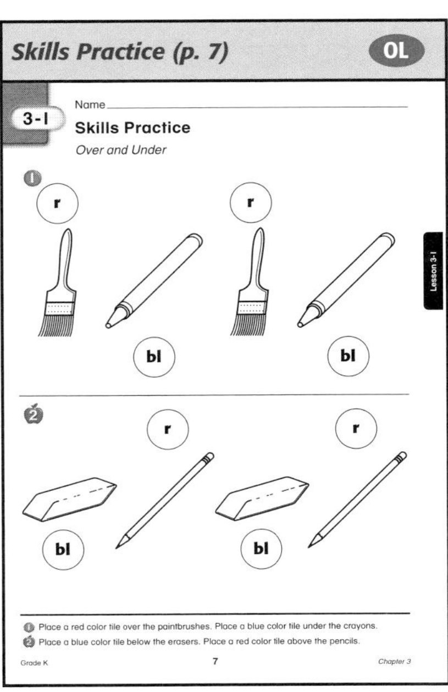

Skills Practice (p. 7) OL

3-1 Name________

Skills Practice

Over and Under

1. Place a red color tile over the paintbrushes. Place a blue color tile under the crayons.
2. Place a blue color tile below the erasers. Place a red color tile above the pencils.

Grade K 7 *Chapter 3*

Enrich (p. 9) AL

3-1 Name________

Enrich

Draw the Directions

Follow the clues to complete the picture.

1. Draw three birds flying over the tree.
2. Draw grass under the tree.
3. Draw two squirrels on the grass under the tree.
4. Draw the sun over the tree
5. Draw three clouds below the sun but above the tree.

Grade K 9 *Chapter 3*

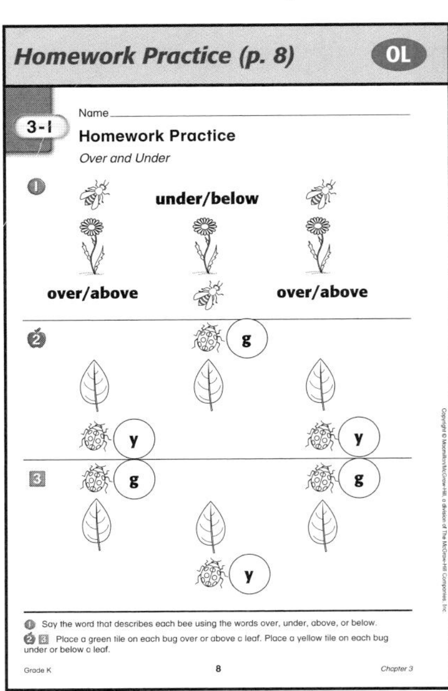

Homework Practice (p. 8) OL

3-1 Name________

Homework Practice

Over and Under

1. Say the word that describes each bee using the words over, under, above, or below.
2. 3. Place a green tile on each bug over or above a leaf. Place a yellow tile on each bug under or below a leaf.

Grade K 8 *Chapter 3*

1 Introduce

Circle Time

Activity Choice 1 • Literature

Over, Under & Through
by Tana Hoban

- Use the pictures to point out what (or who) is over, under, through, in, on, out, etc.
- When possible, have students act out the situation—such as making the bridge shown in the first picture and having another child go under the outstretched arms.
- Ask students to use a crayon (or block) and place it on their desk, hold it above the desk, hold it under the desk, etc.
- At recess, encourage students to find examples of over and under.

Activity Choice 2 • Hands-On

Materials: pattern blocks

- Give each student several pattern blocks.
- Describe how to build a picture on the floor using the pattern blocks. Use the words ***over***, ***under***, ***above***, and ***below***.
- Check their pictures as they build them.
- As time permits, repeat the activity with different pictures.

2 Teach

Direct students to the top of p. 71.

- Ask students to point to the monkey that is near or close to the end of the branch. Tell students that monkey is below or under the branch.
- Ask students if they can point to another monkey that is below or under the branch. Tell students that monkey is far, or the longest distance away from the end of the branch.
- Ask students to point to a monkey that is standing on the branch. Tell students that monkey is above or over the branch.
- Have students point to another monkey that is above or over the branch.

BL Alternate Teaching Strategy

If students have trouble with *over, under, above,* and *below* . . .

Then use one of these reteach options.

1 CRM **Daily Reteach Worksheet** (p. 6)

2 **Use Manipulatives** Hold a string of different attribute buttons vertically.

- Ask questions about the buttons using the words *above, over, under*, or *below*. Ex: "What button is above the round button?" "What button is under the red button?"
- Have students answer the questions using the same words from the question: *above, over, under, and below.*

COMMON ERROR!

Students may reverse the order of the objects when using *over*, *under*, *above*, and *below*. Have them use opposites in two ways to describe objects. For example: The hat is over the head. The head is under the hat.

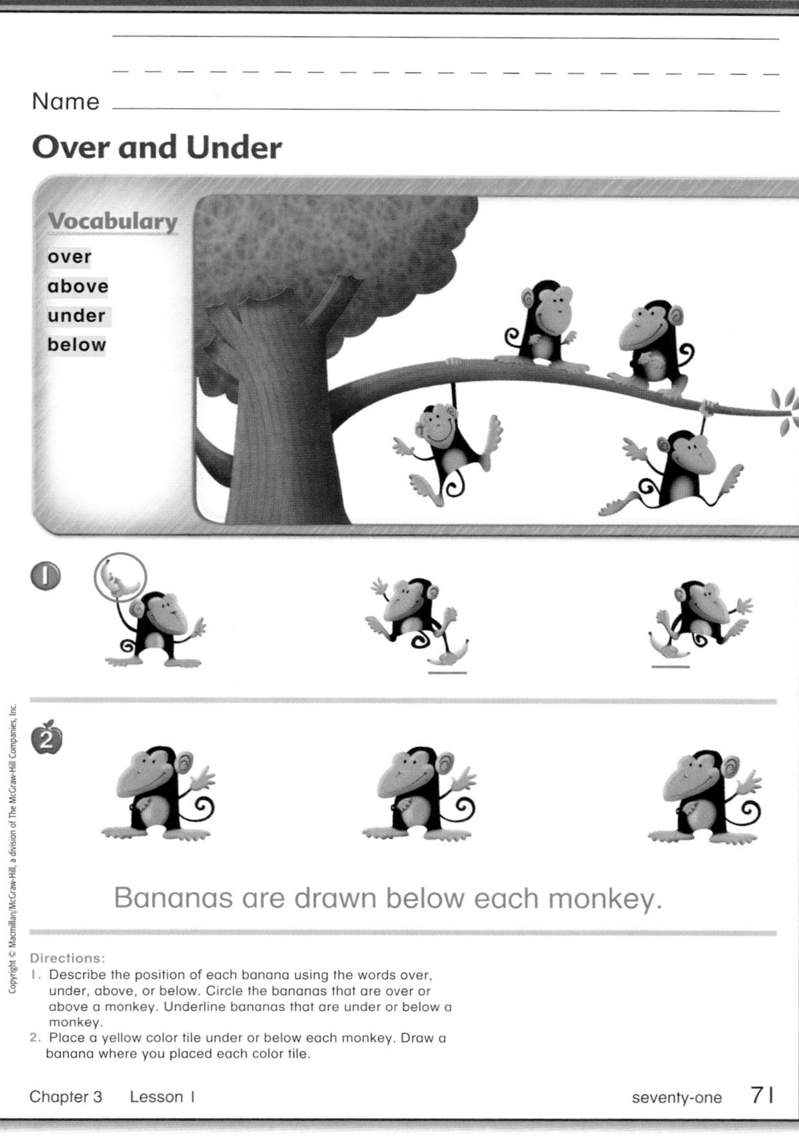

Name

Over and Under

Vocabulary
over
above
under
below

1

2

Bananas are drawn below each monkey.

Directions:
1. Describe the position of each banana using the words over, under, above, or below. Circle the bananas that are over or above a monkey. Underline bananas that are under or below a monkey.
2. Place a yellow color tile under or below each monkey. Draw a banana where you placed each color tile.

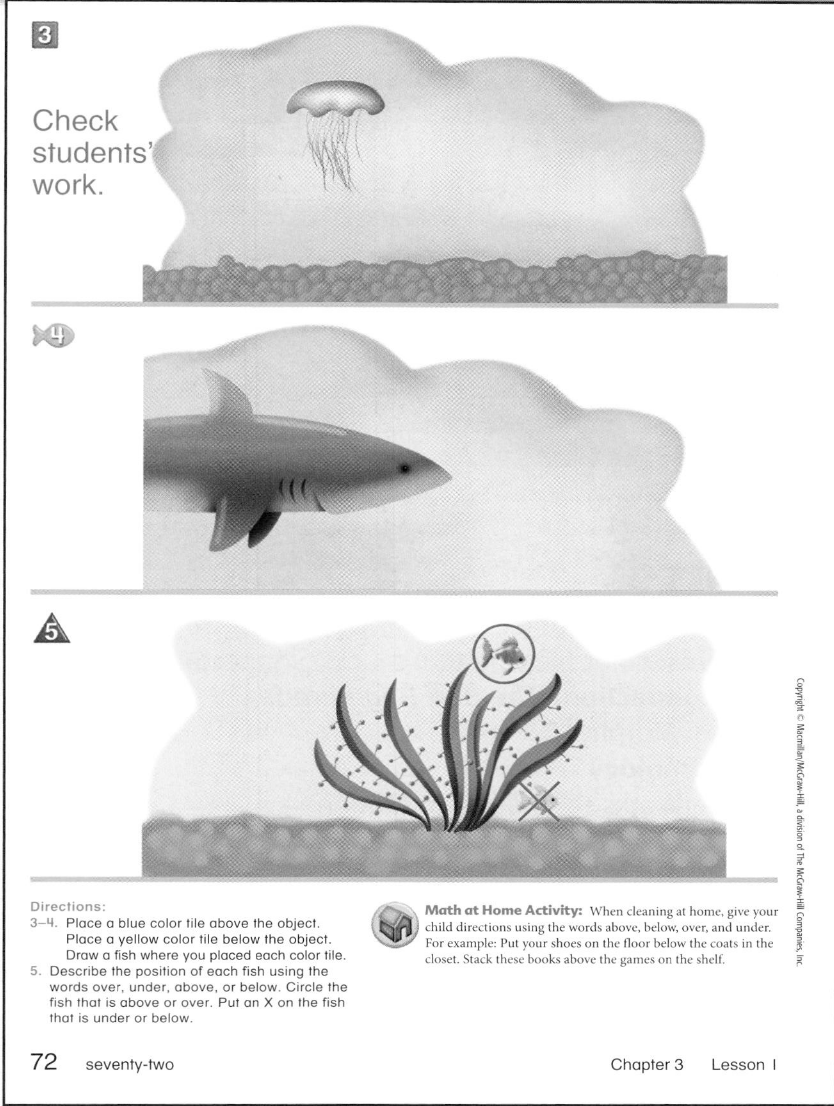

3

Check students' work.

4

5

Directions:
3–4. Place a blue color tile above the object. Place a yellow color tile below the object. Draw a fish where you placed each color tile.
5. Describe the position of each fish using the words over, under, above, or below. Circle the fish that is above or over. Put an X on the fish that is under or below.

Math at Home Activity: When cleaning at home, give your child directions using the words above, below, over, and under. For example: Put your shoes on the floor below the coats in the closet. Stack these books above the games on the shelf.

3 Practice

Guided Practice

- Direct students to p. 71.
- Tell them to circle the bananas being held above or over a monkey. Have them underline bananas being held below or under a monkey.
- In Execise 2 have students place a yellow color tile under or below each monkey.
- Tell them to draw a banana where the students placed each color tile.

Independent Practice

Have students turn to p. 72 and work independently on the exercises.

4 Assess

Formative Assessment

- Show a picture of a forest scene.
- Ask students to describe the picture using the words *over*, *under*, *above*, and *below*.

Quick Check **Are students still struggling to identify over, above, under, and below?**

If Yes → Small Group Options (p. 71B)

If No → Independent Work Options (p. 71B)

CRM Skills Practice Worksheet (p. 7)

CRM Enrich Worksheet (p. 9)

Top, Middle, and Bottom

Lesson Planner

Objective

Students will place or find an object that is on the top, middle, or bottom.

Vocabulary

top, **middle**, **bottom**

Resources

Materials: classroom objects, drawing paper, crayons
Manipulatives: color tiles, pattern blocks, connecting cubes
Literature Connection: *The Best Bug Parade* by Stuart J. Murphy
Teacher Technology
TeacherWorks • Concepts in Motion

Daily Routine

Use these suggestions before beginning the lesson on p. 73.

5-Minute Check

(Reviews Lesson 3-1)

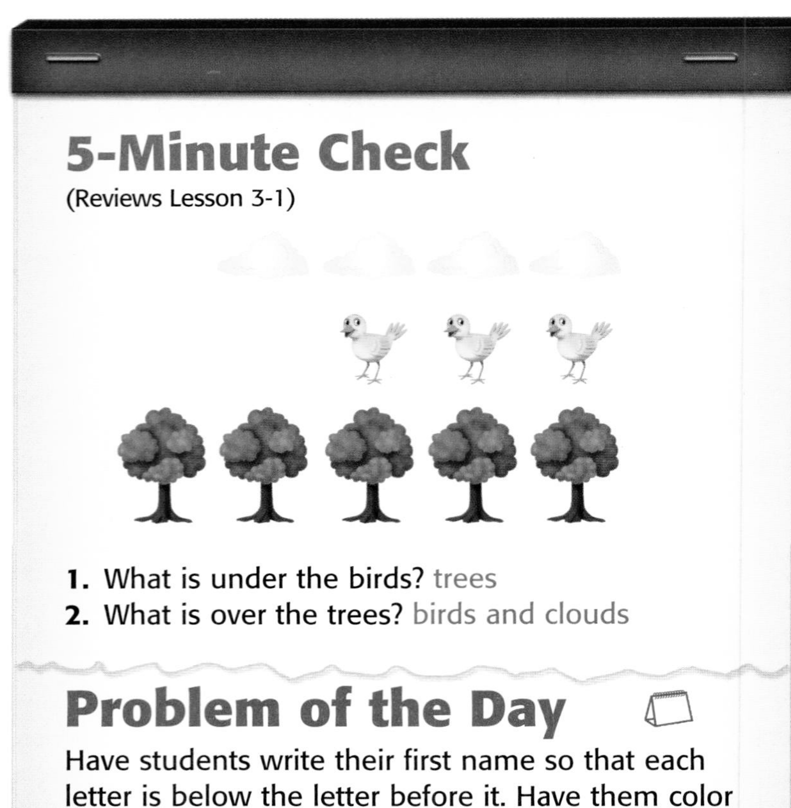

1. What is under the birds? trees
2. What is over the trees? birds and clouds

Problem of the Day

Have students write their first name so that each letter is below the letter before it. Have them color the letters below the first letter and above the last letter red.

LINE UP Have students put their hands on their heads, hips, or feet. Have students touching the top of their body line up. Repeat with middle and bottom.

Building Math Vocabulary

- Show a stack of three connecting cubes. Have students identify the color on **top**. Explain that when something is on top there is nothing else above it.
- Have students identify the color in the **middle**. Explain that something in the middle has something above it and below it.
- Have students identify the color on the **bottom**. Explain that something on the bottom has something above it, but not below it.

Differentiated Instruction

Small Group Options

LOGICAL

Option 1 Gifted and Talented AL

Materials: paper, pencil

- Have students draw three horizontal lines that are the same size on their paper so there is a top line, a middle line, and a bottom line.
- Make sure that there is a space between each line so that the student can draw objects on each line.
- Give the following oral directions:

1) Draw a circle on the bottom line. 2) Draw a square on the top line. 3) Draw a triangle on the middle line. 4) Draw a star next to the circle on the bottom line. 5) Draw an X by the triangle on the middle line. 6) Draw an oval by the square on the top line.

KINESTHETIC, LINGUISTIC

Option 2 English Language Learners ELL

Core Vocabulary: on (top), in (the middle), at (the bottom)

Common Use Verb: are

Do Math This strategy teaches top, middle, and bottom.

- Put your hands on top of your head and say: "My hands are on top." Have students repeat.
- Repeat for waist and feet, using "in the middle" and "at the bottom" as time permits.

Independent Work Options

KINESTHETIC

Option 1 Early Finishers AL OL

Materials: drawing paper, stickers, crayons

- Fold paper so that it is divided into 3 sections that are stacked. Give a folded paper to each student.
- Have students place a different sticker on each section.
- Then have them label the top section, the middle section, and the bottom section.

Option 2 Student Technology

Math Online macmillanmh.com

Math Adventures

Option 3 Learning Station: Art (p. 67G)

Direct students to the Art Learning Station for opportunities to explore and extend the lesson concept.

Leveled Lesson Resources

Additional support for English Language Learners can be found in the ELL Guide (p. 7). ELL

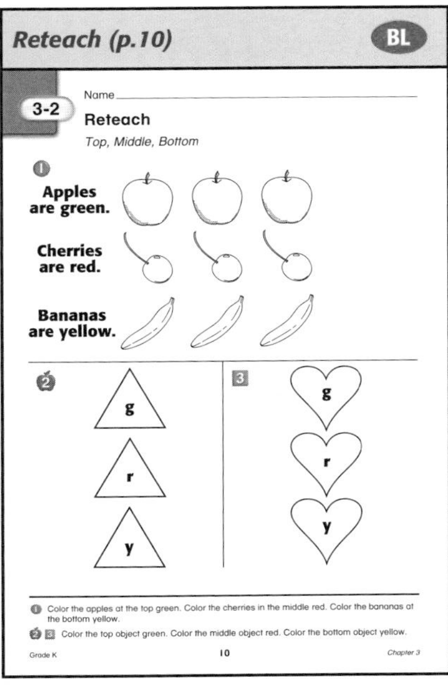

Reteach (p.10) BL

3-2 Name

Reteach

Top, Middle, Bottom

1 Apples are green. Cherries are red. Bananas are yellow.

1 Color the apples at the top green. Color the cherries in the middle red. Color the bananas at the bottom yellow.

2 3 Color the top object green. Color the middle object red. Color the bottom object yellow.

Grade K 10 *Chapter 3*

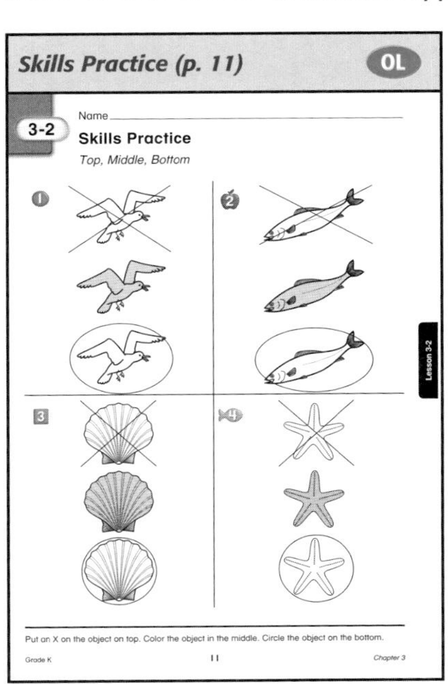

Skills Practice (p. 11) OL

3-2 Name

Skills Practice

Top, Middle, Bottom

Put an X on the object on top. Color the object in the middle. Circle the object on the bottom.

Grade K 11 *Chapter 3*

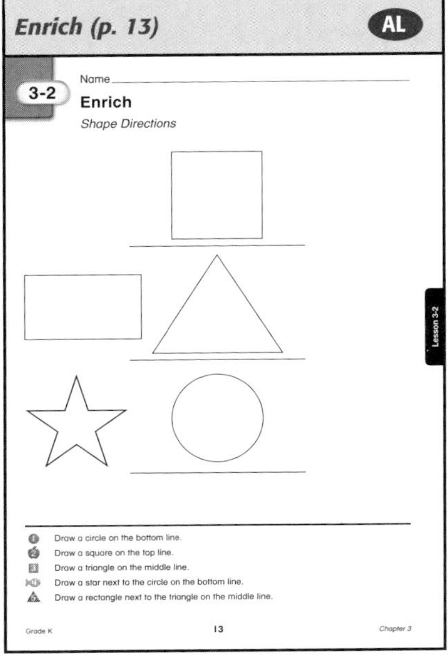

Enrich (p. 13) AL

3-2 Name

Enrich

Shape Directions

1 Draw a circle on the bottom line.

2 Draw a square on the top line.

3 Draw a triangle on the middle line.

4 Draw a star next to the circle on the bottom line.

5 Draw a rectangle next to the triangle on the middle line.

Grade K 13 *Chapter 3*

Homework Practice (p. 12) OL

3-2 Name

Homework Practice

Top, Middle, Bottom

shaded

Put an X on the object on top. Color the object in the middle. Circle the object on the bottom.

Grade K 12 *Chapter 3*

1 Introduce

Circle Time

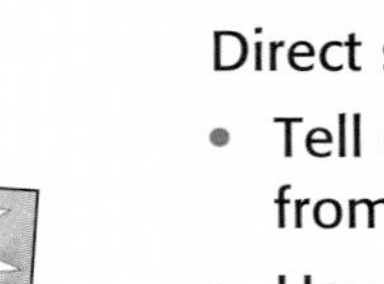

Activity Choice 1 • Literature

The Best Bug Parade by Stuart J. Murphy

- In the chart of big bugs, page 9, what bug is in the middle?
- In the chart of long bugs, page 21, what bug is shown on the top, the bottom, and in the middle?
- In the chart showing short bugs, page 27, what bug is shown on the top, the bottom, and in the middle?
- Students make a stack of 4 cubes—red, blue, green, yellow. Ask students questions about the stack (what color is on the bottom? The top? The middle?
- Extension: Draw a snowperson, describing what goes on the top, middle, and bottom snowballs.

Activity Choice 2 • Hands-On 

Materials: classroom objects
Manipulatives: connecting cubes

- Show students a stack of three classroom objects such as three different colored cups.
- Ask students to identify the color on the **top**, in the **middle**, and on the **bottom**.
- Instruct students to create a cube tower using three cubes. Have them identify the color on the top, in the middle, and on the bottom.
- Have students form pairs. Have partners exchange their cube towers and take turns identifying the color on the top, in the middle, and on the bottom.

2 Teach

Direct students to p. 73.

- Tell students that the mouse sleeping in the top bed is far from the cheese
- Have them point to this mouse.
- Tell students that the mouse sleeping in the middle has a mouse above it and a mouse below it.
- Have them point to the mouse in the middle.
- Tell students that the mouse on the bottom is near, or closest to the cheese.
- Have them point to the mouse on the bottom.

BL Alternate Teaching Strategy

If students have trouble with top, middle, and bottom . . .

Then use one of these reteach options.

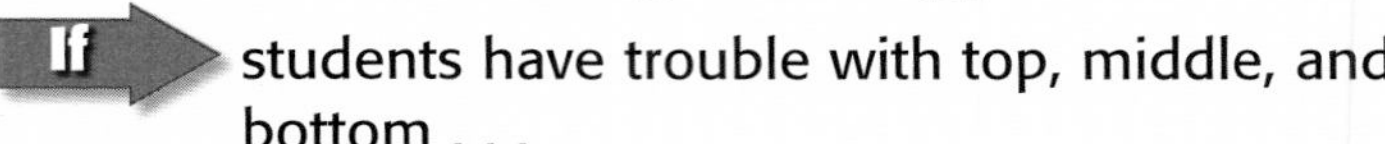

1 CRM **Daily Reteach Worksheet** (p. 10)

2 **Draw a Picture** Have students draw a picture of a rainbow using three colors.
   - Have them identify the color on the top, on the bottom, and in the middle.

COMMON ERROR!

Students may not understand that more than one object can be in the middle. Work with sets greater than three, identifying the top, middle, and bottom.

Name
Top, Middle, and Bottom
Vocabulary
top
middle
bottom
green
yellow
red
Directions: Place a red color tile on the bottom blanket. Place a yellow color tile on the middle blanket. Place a green tile on the top blanket. Color the blankets to match the color tiles.
Chapter 3 Lesson 2 seventy-three 73

Directions:
1–2. Put an X on the object on top.
3. Circle the object on the bottom.
4. Circle the flower on the bottom.
5–6. Put an X on the object in the middle.
Math at Home Activity: Play "I Spy" with your child. Have him or her find things that are on top, in the middle, or on the bottom of something else. Use those words in your description of the object.
74 seventy-four Chapter 3 Lesson 2

3 Practice

Guided Practice

Direct students to p. 73.

Instruct students to place a red color tile on the bottom blanket.

Tell them to place a yellow color tile on the middle blanket.

Have them place a green color tile on the top blanket.

Have them color each blanket to match the color tile that is on it.

Independent Practice

Have students turn to p. 74 and work independently on the exercises.

4 Assess

Formative Assessment

- Stack three different pattern blocks on top of each other.
- Ask students to identify the block on the top, on the bottom, and in the middle.

Quick Check **Are students still struggling to identify top, middle, and bottom?**

If Yes → Small Group Options (p. 73B)

If No → Independent Work Options (p. 73B)

 Skills Practice Worksheet (p. 11)

CRM Enrich Worksheet (p. 13)

LESSON 3-3 Before and After

Lesson Planner

Objective

Describe the order of events of objects or determine whether objects are before or after each other.

Vocabulary

before, **after**

Resources

Materials: paper, crayons, string
Manipulatives: attribute buttons, connecting cubes, pattern blocks, color tiles
Literature Connection: *Parade* by Donald Crews
Teacher Technology
TeacherWorks • Concepts in Motion

Daily Routine

Use these suggestions before beginning the lesson on p. 75.

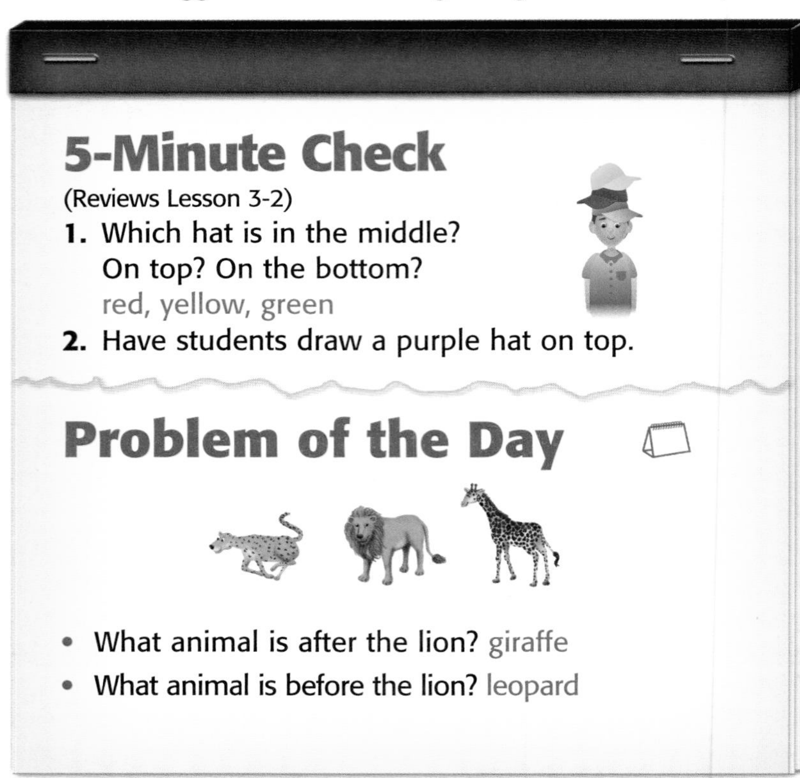

5-Minute Check

(Reviews Lesson 3-2)

1. Which hat is in the middle? On top? On the bottom? red, yellow, green
2. Have students draw a purple hat on top.

Problem of the Day

- What animal is after the lion? giraffe
- What animal is before the lion? leopard

LINE UP Have half the class line up. Ask the other students questions about the positions of the students in line using before and after. For example: "Who is standing before Carlos?" Have students join the line after they answer the question.

Building Math Vocabulary

- Draw a row of three shapes on the chalkboard in this order: star, heart, crescent moon.
- **What comes before the heart?** star
- Explain that when an object comes before a second object, it is in front of that second object.
- **What comes after the heart?** moon
- Explain that when an object comes after another object, it is behind that other object.
- Repeat the activity with other shapes.

Visual Vocabulary Cards

Use Visual Vocabulary Cards 2 and 4 to reinforce the vocabulary introduced in this lesson. (The Define/Example/Ask routine is printed on the back of each card.)

Differentiated Instruction

Small Group Options

Option 1 Gifted and Talented AL

LOGICAL

- Ask three volunteers to go to the front of the room. Have students line up in front of the class, and identify which student is in the front of the line.
- Assign each student a different activity to act out: brushing teeth, eating, throwing a ball. Ask the rest of the class to guess what the student in the middle is doing.
- After the correct answer is given, have them identify the other two activities using this sentence pattern: _____ is the activity before _____. _____ is the activity after _____.

Option 2 English Language Learners ELL

LINGUISTIC, LOGICAL

Core Vocabulary: day, little word, inside the whole word
Common Use Verb: comes after
Talk Math The strategy increases vocabulary and pattern recognition.

- Write the days of the week. Say: "What little word is inside all of these words?" Confirm "day" comes after the other letters.
- Point and say: "Mon." Underline and say "day." Repeat for all days. Continue as a call response with students answering the day.

Independent Work Options

Option 1 Early Finishers AL OL

KINESTHETIC

Materials: paper, crayons

- Have students draw a row of three circles. Identify which circle is first.
- Use the words before and after to instruct them how to color each circle. For example: "Color the circle after the first circle yellow. Color the circle after the yellow circle red. Color the circle before the yellow circle blue."
- Repeat with various shapes and colors.

Option 2 Student Technology

Math Online macmillanmh.com

Option 3 Learning Station: Art (p. 67G)

Direct students to the Art Learning Station for opportunities to explore and extend the lesson concept.

Leveled Lesson Resources

Reteach (p. 14) BL

3-3 Name

Reteach

Before and After

1

2

3

Put an X on the animal that is before the other animals.

Grade K 14 *Chapter 3*

Skills Practice (p. 15) OL

3-3 Name

Skills Practice

Before and After

1 r g

2 g r

3 r g

Put a green tile on the vehicle that comes before the others. Put a red tile on the vehicle that comes after the others.

Grade K 15 *Chapter 3*

Enrich (p. 17) AL

3-3 Name

Enrich

What Shall We Do?

1 **Answers will vary.**

2 **Answers will vary.**

3 **Answers will vary.**

Draw three things that happen before each picture. Label what happens first, second, and third before the last row of pictures.

Grade K 17 *Chapter 3*

Homework Practice (p. 16) OL

3-3 Name

Homework Practice

Before and After

1 y b

2 b y

3 y b

Put a blue tile on the animal that comes before the others. Put a yellow tile on the animal that comes after the others.

Grade K 16 *Chapter 3*

1 Introduce

Circle Time

Activity Choice 1 • Literature

Parade by Donald Crews

- Ask students before and after questions about the story: What came right after the marching band? What came before the antique cars?
- Give students 6 colored blocks to arrange in this order: blue, red, green, yellow, purple, orange. Ask students to hold up the block that comes after the red block and then replace it.

Extension: Students paint or draw a parade and ask a before or after question about their parade for others to solve.

Activity Choice 2 • Hands-On

Manipulatives: string, attribute buttons

- Have students put attribute buttons on a string in this order: red circle, blue triangle, green square. Have them hold up the string, one end in each hand, so that they see the circle in the first position.
- **Which color button comes before the others?** red
- **Which color button comes after the others?** green
- **Which color button comes after the circle and before the square?** blue
- Repeat with other colors.

2 Teach

Direct students to the top of p. 75.

- Have students point to the pig that is near or closest to the food trough. Tell them this pig is before the mud puddle.
- Have students point to the pig that is far from the food trough. Tell them this pig is after the mud puddle.
- **How do you know which pig is before and after the mud puddle?** (Be sure they understand that the pigs are walking toward the pigpen, which makes the second pig come after the first pig.) Both pigs are walking toward the pen, so the one closest to the food trough is before the mud puddle.

BL Alternate Teaching Strategy

If students have trouble with before and after . . .

Then use one of these reteach options.

1  **Daily Reteach Worksheet** (p. 14)

2 **Arrange Connecting Cubes** Tell students they are going to arrange connecting cubes to show *before* and *after*.

- Give each student several connecting cubes of various colors.
- Have students arrange the cubes in rows of three. Give them directions using the words *before* and *after*. For example: In row one, place a red cube before a green cube. Then, place a yellow cube after the green cube.

COMMON ERROR!

Students may struggle with *before* because it can mean “in front of” or “earlier in time.” *After* can mean “behind” or “later in time.” Use a variety of examples for each meaning. Make sure to emphasize that, when talking about objects, *before* means “in front of” and *after* means “behind.”

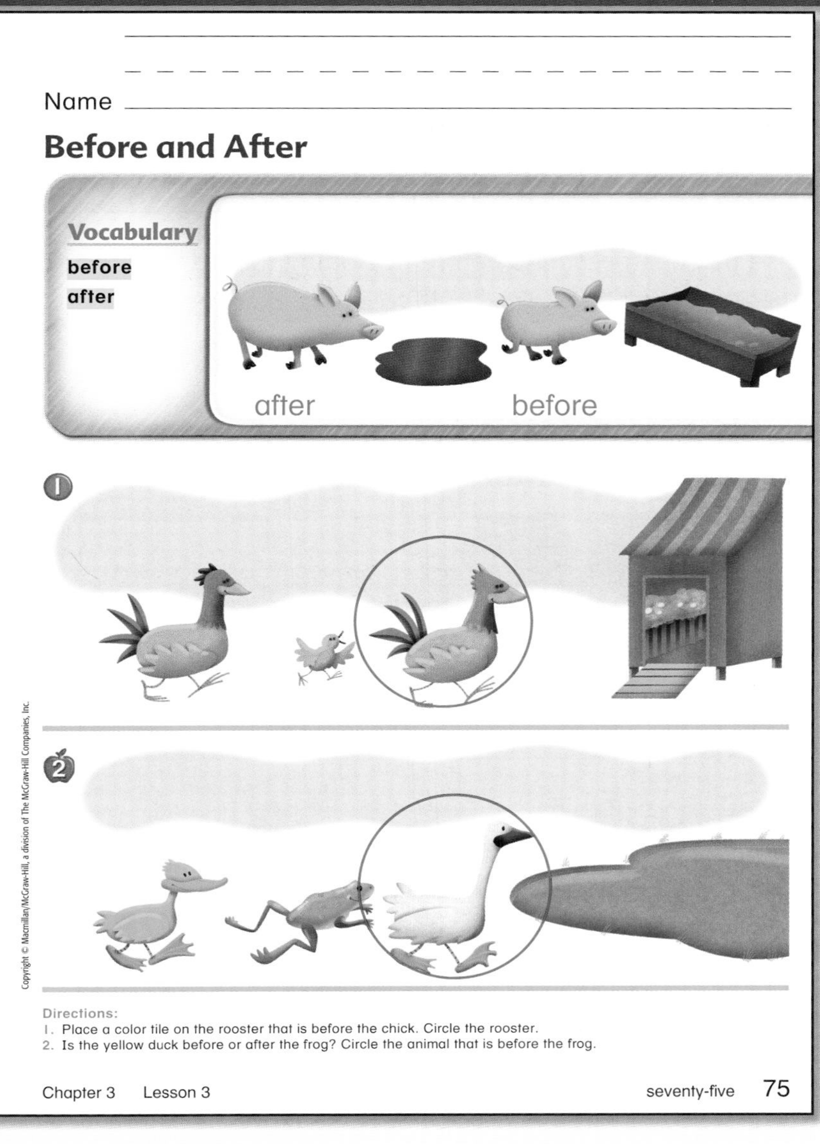

Name
Before and After
Vocabulary
before
after
after
before
Directions:
1. Place a color tile on the rooster that is before the chick. Circle the rooster.
2. Is the yellow duck before or after the frog? Circle the animal that is before the frog.
Chapter 3 Lesson 3
seventy-five 75

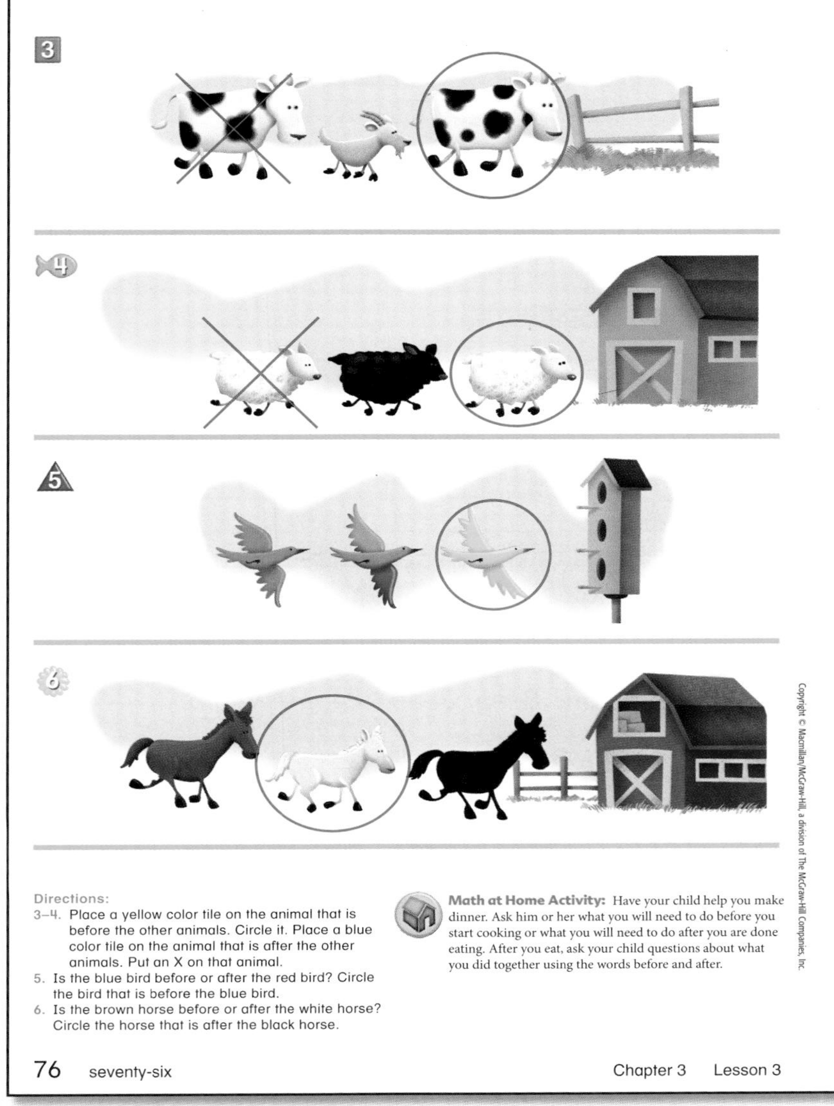

Directions:
3–4. Place a yellow color tile on the animal that is before the other animals. Circle it. Place a blue color tile on the animal that is after the other animals. Put an X on that animal.
5. Is the blue bird before or after the red bird? Circle the bird that is before the blue bird.
6. Is the brown horse before or after the white horse? Circle the horse that is after the black horse.
Math at Home Activity: Have your child help you make dinner. Ask him or her what you will need to do before you start cooking or what you will need to do after you are done eating. After you eat, ask your child questions about what you did together using the words before and after.
76 seventy-six
Chapter 3 Lesson 3

3 Practice

Guided Practice

- Direct students to p. 75.
- **What is happening in the picture in Exercise 1?** The rooster, chick, and rooster are walking to the chicken house.
- Have students place a color tile on the rooster that is before the chick. Have students circle that rooster.
- **What is happening in the picture in Exercise 2?** The duck, frog, and goose are going to the pond.
- Have students point to the yellow duck. Ask students **Is the yellow duck before or after the frog?** after the frog
- Have students circle the animal that is before the frog.

Independent Practice

Have students turn to p. 76 and work independently on the exercises.

4 Assess

Formative Assessment

- Show a person who is about to finish a race and is near the finish line.
- Have students draw a person who will finish the race before the person shown.
- Ask who will finish after the person that was just drawn.

Quick Check **Are students still struggling to identify before and after?**

If Yes → Small Group Options (p.75B)

If No → Independent Work Options (p. 75B)

CRM Skills Practice Worksheet (p. 15)

CRM Enrich Worksheet (p. 17)

LESSON 3-4

Identify Patterns

Lesson Planner

Objective

Students will identify patterns.

Vocabulary

pattern

Resources

Materials: black construction paper, white construction paper, classroom objects, crayons, drawing paper
Manipulatives: two-colored counters, connecting cubes, color tiles, pattern blocks
Literature Connection: *Beep, Beep, Vroom, Vroom!* by Stuart J. Murphy
Alternate Lesson: Use *IMPACT Mathematics:* Unit E to provide practice with identifying patterns.
Teacher Technology
TeacherWorks • Math Songs Track 1

Daily Routine

Use these suggestions before beginning the lesson on p. 77.

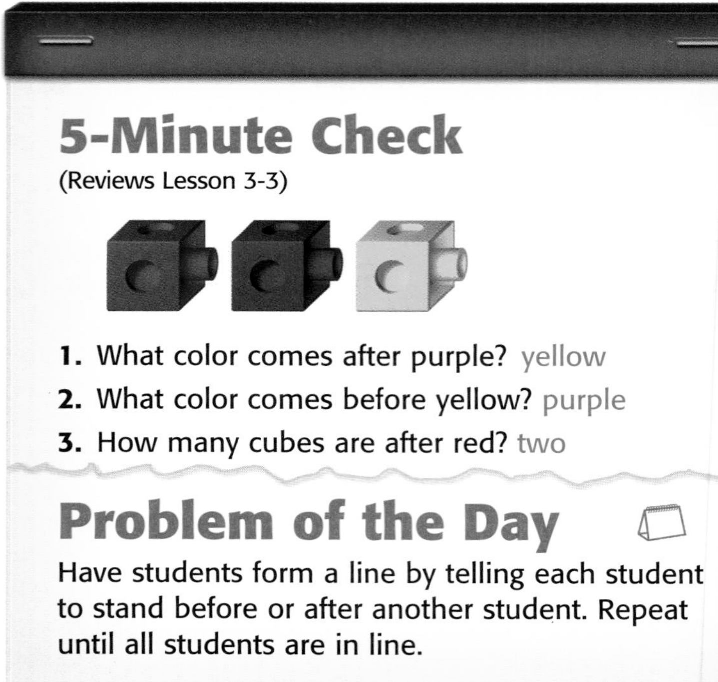

5-Minute Check

(Reviews Lesson 3-3)

1. What color comes after purple? yellow
2. What color comes before yellow? purple
3. How many cubes are after red? two

Problem of the Day

Have students form a line by telling each student to stand before or after another student. Repeat until all students are in line.

LINE UP Have students line up in an AB pattern of boy girl. Explain that they are creating a pattern of objects that are themselves.

Building Math Vocabulary

- Tell students to look at the American flag.
- Ask what they notice about the flag. Point out the red and white striped **pattern**.
- Explain that when colors repeat like on the American flag, it is called a pattern. Explain that patterns can be of colors, objects, numbers, sounds, and motions.
- Tell students that they are going to look at patterns of two objects.
- Ask them to find other patterns in the room. Have volunteers describe their patterns.

Visual Vocabulary Cards

Use Visual Vocabulary Card 30 to reinforce the vocabulary introduced in this lesson.
(The Define/Example/Ask routine is printed on the back of each card.)

Differentiated Instruction

Small Group Options

Option 1 Below/Approaching Level BL

LOGICAL

Materials: patterns from around the house, such as ties, tablecloths, material; pencil, paper, crayons, markers

- Have different object patterns set up on a table in the room. Have students choose an object from the table and extend the pattern on a sheet of paper.
- The students need to draw the pattern and then color the pattern to match the object chosen.
- Have students gather in a group to show their finished work, and have other students try to guess what pattern of objects they copied.

Option 2 English Language Learners ELL

AUDITORY, KINESTHETIC

Core Vocabulary: clap, stomp, watch me

Common Use Verb: repeat

Do Math This strategy helps students recognize patterns.

- Say: "**Watch me**." Clap hands 2 times. Say: "Repeat." Students clap their hands 2 times.
- Continue with new patterns:

  Clap hands once, stomp one foot once (AB)

  Clap 2 times, stomp 2 times (AABB)
- Repeat three times and have students copy the pattern.

Independent Work Options

Option 1 Early Finishers AL OL

LINGUISTIC

Materials: crayons

- Have students draw six squares to create an AB pattern using two colors.
- Have students draw seven triangles to create an AB pattern using two colors.

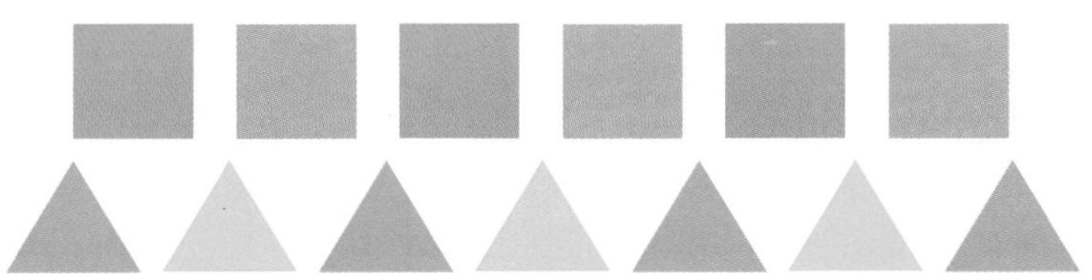

Option 2 Student Technology

Math Online macmillanmh.com

Math Songs "Stars and Stripes" Track 1

Math Tool Chest

Math Adventures

Option 3 Learning Station: Reading (p. 67H)

Direct students to the Reading Learning Station for opportunities to explore and extend the lesson concept.

Leveled Lesson Resources

Additional support for English Language Learners can be found in the ELL Guide (p. 29). ELL

Reteach (p. 18) BL

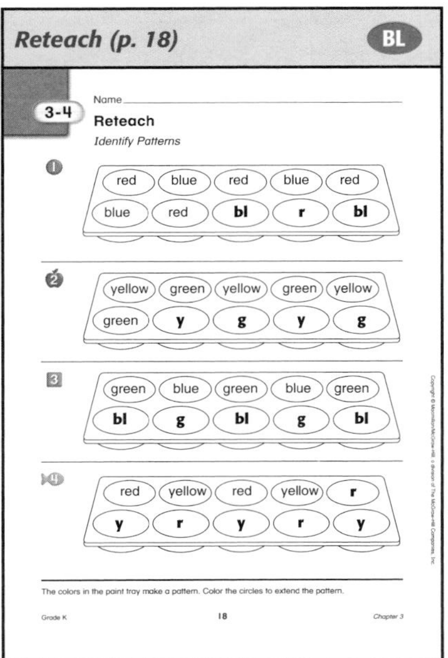

3-4 Name

Reteach

Identify Patterns

1. red, blue, red, blue, red / blue, red, **bl**, **r**, **bl**
2. yellow, green, yellow, green, yellow / green, **y**, **g**, **y**, **g**
3. green, blue, green, blue, green / **bl**, **g**, **bl**, **g**, **bl**
4. red, yellow, red, yellow, **r** / **y**, **r**, **y**, **r**, **y**

The colors in the paint tray make a pattern. Color the circles to extend the pattern.

Grade K 18 Chapter 3

Skills Practice (p. 19) OL

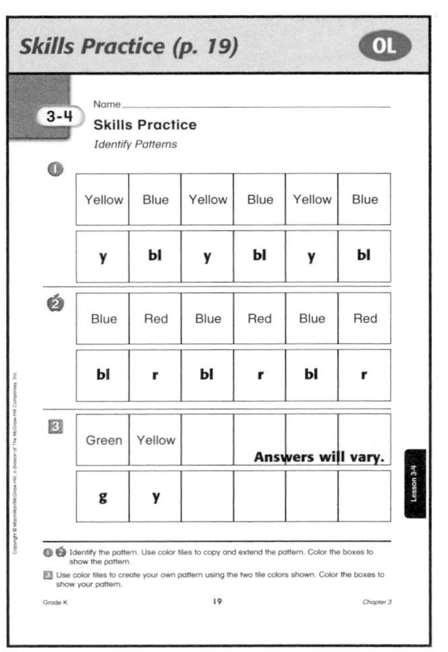

3-4 Name

Skills Practice

Identify Patterns

1.

Yellow	Blue	Yellow	Blue	Yellow	Blue
y	**bl**	**y**	**bl**	**y**	**bl**

2.

Blue	Red	Blue	Red	Blue	Red
bl	**r**	**bl**	**r**	**bl**	**r**

3.

Green	Yellow				
g	**y**				

Answers will vary.

1, 2 Identify the pattern. Use color tiles to copy and extend the pattern. Color the boxes to show the pattern.

3 Use color tiles to create your own pattern using the two tile colors shown. Color the boxes to show your pattern.

Grade K 19 Chapter 3

Enrich (p. 21) AL

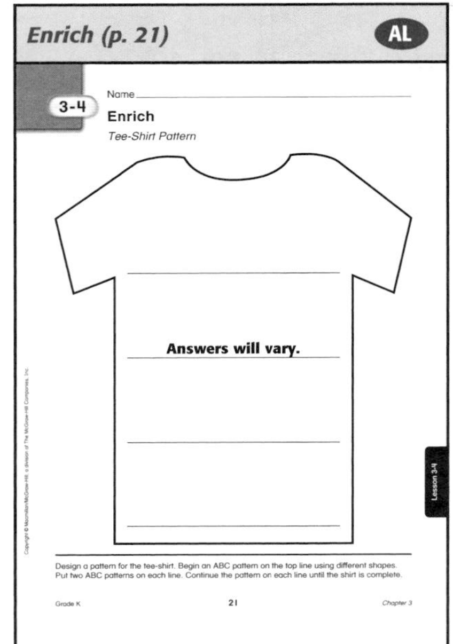

3-4 Name

Enrich

Tee-Shirt Pattern

Answers will vary.

Design a pattern for the tee-shirt. Begin an ABC pattern on the top line using different shapes. Put two ABC patterns on each line. Continue the pattern on each line until the shirt is complete.

Grade K 21 Chapter 3

Homework Practice (p. 20) OL

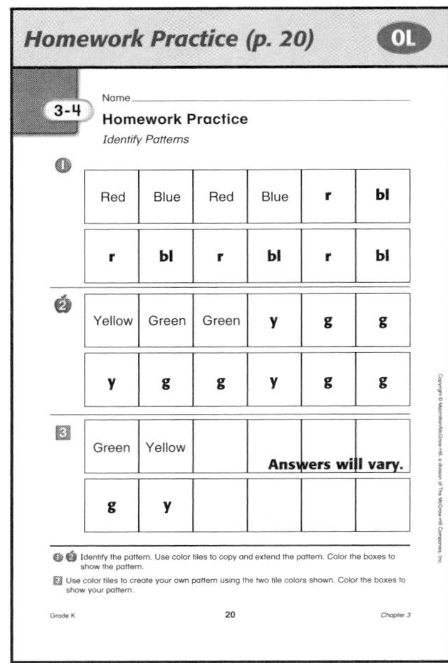

3-4 Name

Homework Practice

Identify Patterns

1.

Red	Blue	Red	Blue	**r**	**bl**
r	**bl**	**r**	**bl**	**r**	**bl**

2.

Yellow	Green	Green	**y**	**g**	**g**
y	**g**	**g**	**y**	**g**	**g**

3.

Green	Yellow				
g	**y**				

Answers will vary.

1, 2 Identify the pattern. Use color tiles to copy and extend the pattern. Color the boxes to show the pattern.

3 Use color tiles to create your own pattern using the two tile colors shown. Color the boxes to show your pattern.

Grade K 20 Chapter 3

1 Introduce

Activity Choice 1 • Literature

Beep, Beep, Vroom, Vroom!
by Stuart J. Murphy

- Identify the pattern Kevin used to place his cars on the shelf (Record it for future reference).
- Identify Dad's pattern, how does it compare to Kevin's?
- Identify Mom's pattern, how does it compare to Kevin's or Dad's patterns?
- Identify Molly's first pattern; how does it compare to Kevin's? What does she need to do to make it match Kevin's pattern?
- What colors are Molly's new cars? Use blocks to find patterns she could make with her new cars.

Activity Choice 2 • Hands-On

Materials: black construction paper, white construction paper, classroom objects
Manipulatives: two-colored counters

- Make a red-yellow AB **pattern** with two-colored counters. Have students copy your pattern.
- **What color would come next?** red
- **How do you know red is next?** Sample answer: Red always follows yellow in this pattern.
- Have students say the color with you, then add to their patterns.
- Have six students come to the front of the room and create an AB pattern using white and black paper.
- Have the class say the colors aloud as they look at the pattern.
- Have students create their own AB patterns using classroom objects.

2 Teach

Direct students to the top of p. 77.

- **What patterns do you see in the picture?** red and green, yellow and green, blue and red
- Remind them that AB patterns are made of two objects. Say that on this page the two objects are two different colors of blocks.

BL Alternate Teaching Strategy

If students have trouble with identifying patterns . . .

Then use one of these reteach options.

1  **Daily Reteach Worksheet** (p. 18)

2 **Use Manipulatives** Have students use connecting cubes of two colors to build a train.

- Have them say the color pattern.
- Have them color the pattern on paper.
- Repeat the activity with two different colors.

3 **TechLink** Have students use Math Tool Chest to help complete the problem-solving exercises.

COMMON ERROR!
Students may incorrectly identify the pattern in a picture. Have them copy and extend the pattern.

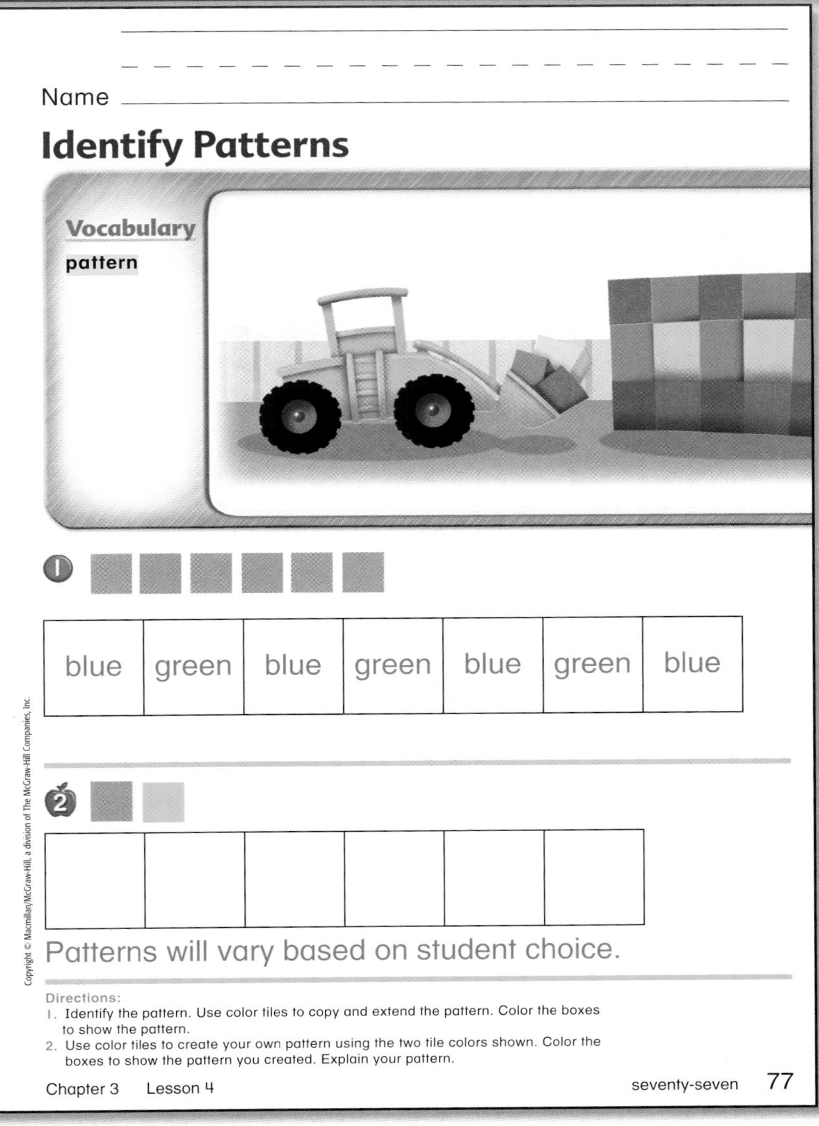
Name

Identify Patterns

Vocabulary
pattern

1

blue	green	blue	green	blue	green	blue

2

Patterns will vary based on student choice.

Directions:
1. Identify the pattern. Use color tiles to copy and extend the pattern. Color the boxes to show the pattern.
2. Use color tiles to create your own pattern using the two tile colors shown. Color the boxes to show the pattern you created. Explain your pattern.

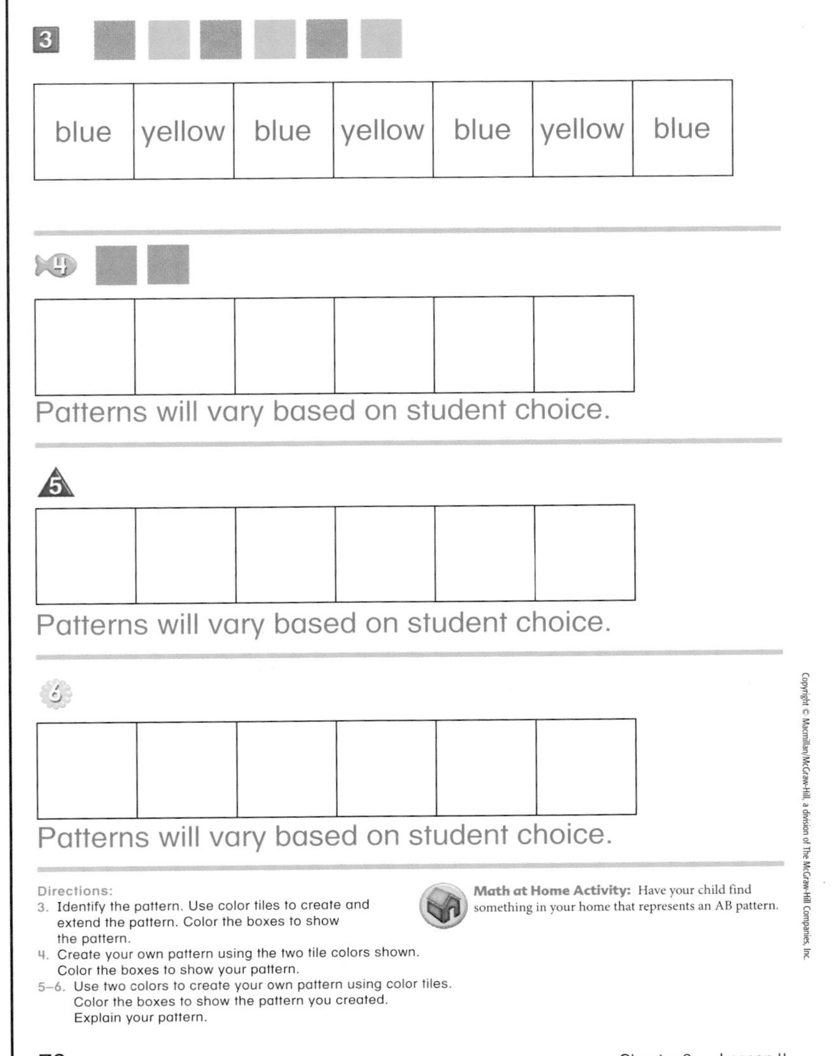
3

blue	yellow	blue	yellow	blue	yellow	blue

4

Patterns will vary based on student choice.

5

Patterns will vary based on student choice.

6

Patterns will vary based on student choice.

Directions:
3. Identify the pattern. Use color tiles to create and extend the pattern. Color the boxes to show the pattern.
4. Create your own pattern using the two tile colors shown. Color the boxes to show your pattern.
5–6. Use two colors to create your own pattern using color tiles. Color the boxes to show the pattern you created. Explain your pattern.

Math at Home Activity: Have your child find something in your home that represents an AB pattern.

3 Practice

Guided Practice

- Direct students to p. 77.
- **What AB pattern do you see in Exercise 1?** blue, green
- Have them use color tiles to copy the pattern and extend it by placing a color tile in the black line box at the end of the row.
- Have students color the boxes below to show the pattern.
- Have them use color tiles to create a pattern using the two color tiles shown in Exercise 2.

Independent Practice

Have students turn to p. 78 and work independently on the exercises.

4 Assess

Formative Assessment

- Show students a color pattern in the room.
- **How would you show this pattern using connecting cubes?** Sample answer: Connect cubes in this order: blue cube, red cube, blue cube, red cube, blue cube, red cube.
- **What color would come next and why?** Sample answer: Blue cube; Blue comes after red in this pattern.

Quick Check **Are students still struggling to identify patterns?**

If Yes → Small Group Options (p. 77B)

If No → Independent Work Options (p. 77B)

CRM Skills Practice Worksheet (p. 19)

CRM Enrich Worksheet (p. 21)

Mid-Chapter Check

Lessons 3-1 to 3-4

Formative Assessment

Use the Mid-Chapter Check to assess student's progress in the first half of the chapter.

ExamView Assessment Suite Customize and create multiple versions of your Mid-Chapter Check and the test answer keys.

FOLDABLES Dinah Zike's Foldables

Have students use the Flashcard Holder Foldable (see p. 67) to review and reinforce the concepts in Lessons 3-1 to 3-4.

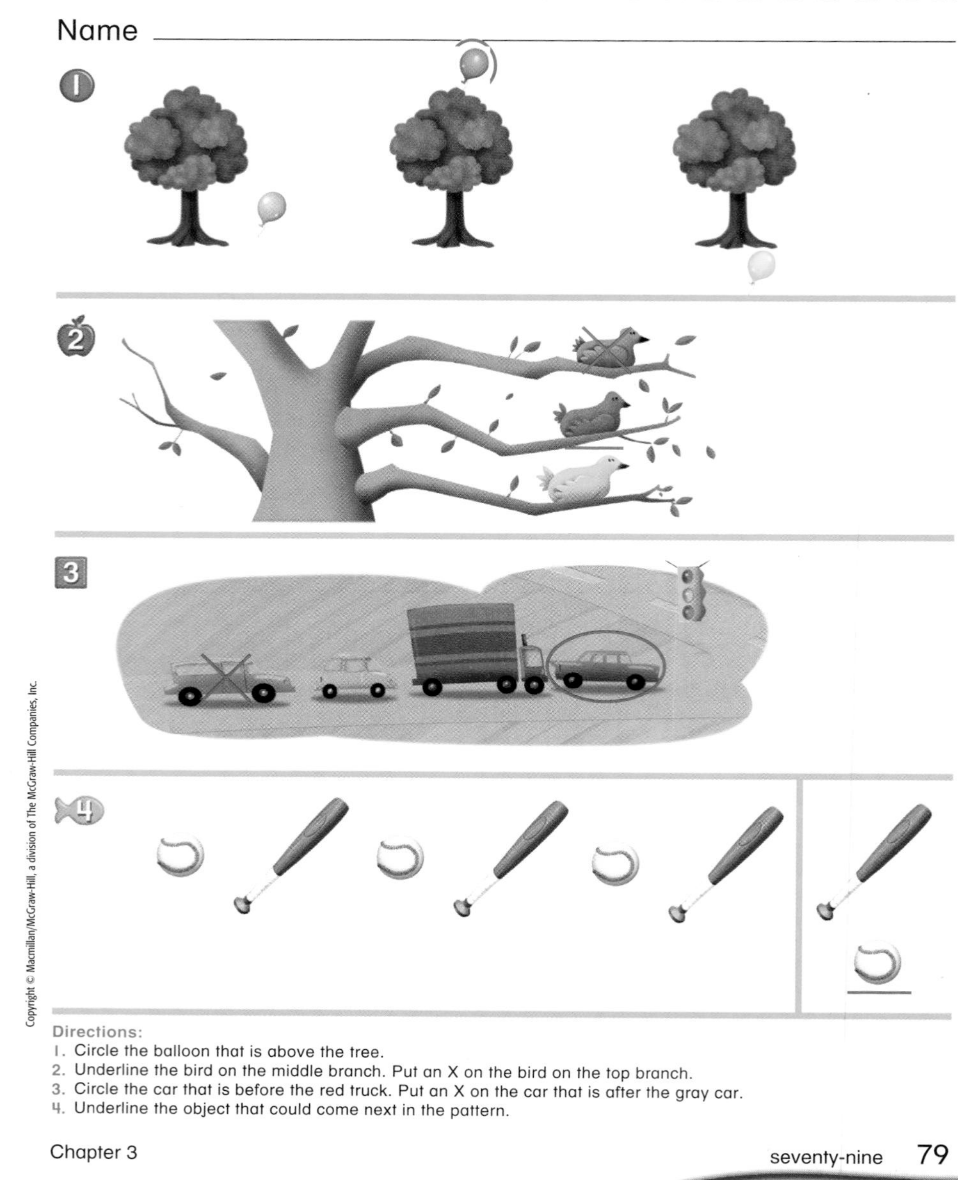

Mid-Chapter Check
Lessons 1-4
Name
Copyright © Macmillan/McGraw-Hill, a division of The McGraw-Hill Companies, Inc.
Directions:
1. Circle the balloon that is above the tree.
2. Underline the bird on the middle branch. Put an X on the bird on the top branch.
3. Circle the car that is before the red truck. Put an X on the car that is after the gray car.
4. Underline the object that could come next in the pattern.
Chapter 3
seventy-nine 79

Data-Driven Decision Making

Based on the results of the Mid-Chapter Check, use the following resources to review concepts that continue to give students problems.

Exercises	State/Local Standards	What's the Math	Error Analysis	Resources for Review
1 Lesson 3-1		Find an object that is over another object.	Circles balloon that is beside or under the tree.	CRM Chapter 3 Resource Masters (Reteach Worksheets) Math Online Concepts in Motion Math Adventures
2 Lesson 3-2		Find an object that is in the top, middle, or bottom.	Does not underline the bird on the middle branch and does not put an x on the correct car.	
3 Lesson 3-3		Find the object that is before or after another object.	Circles more than one object.	
4 Lesson 3-4		Extend patterns.	Reverses the directions.	

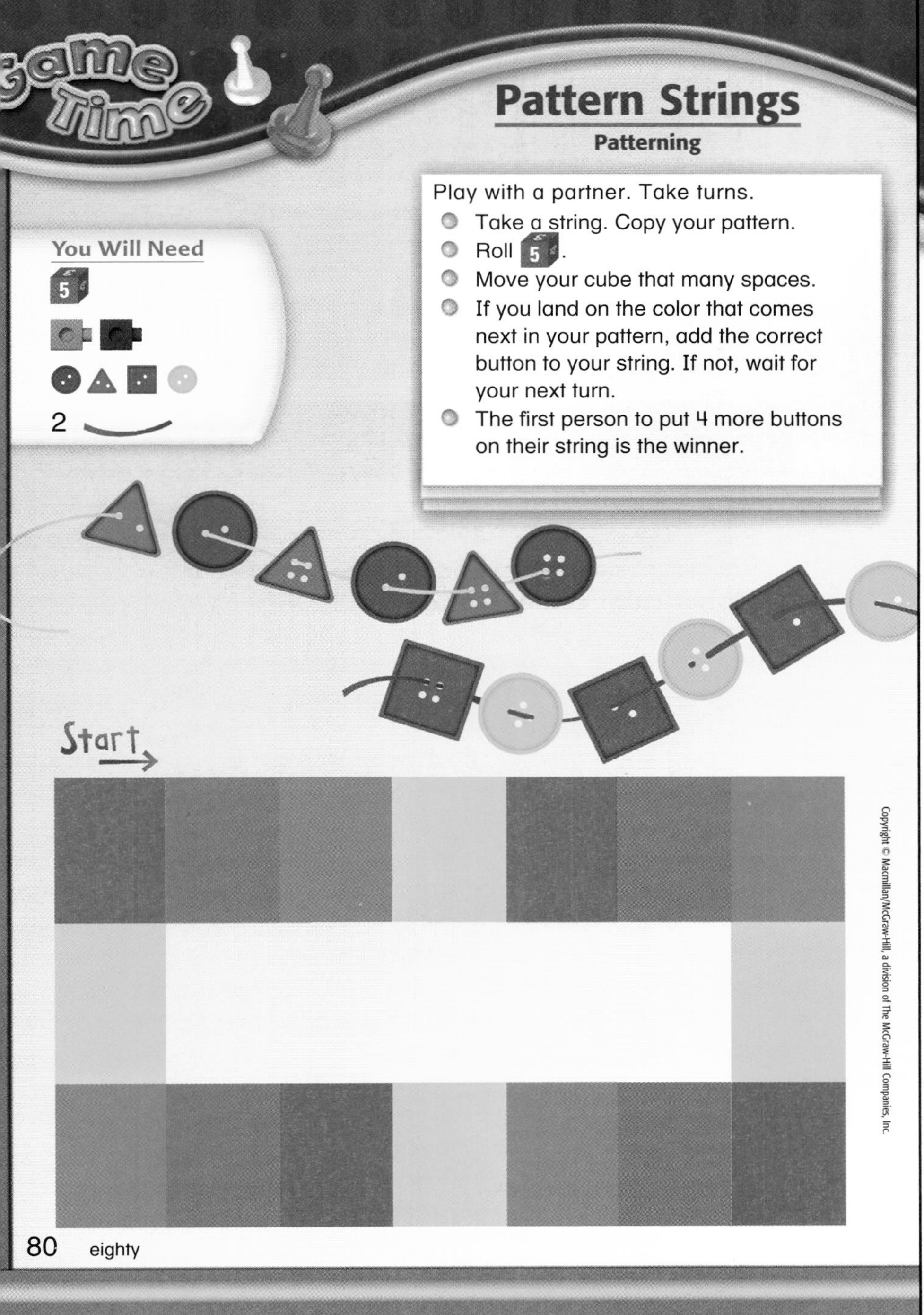
Game Time
Pattern Strings
Patterning
Play with a partner. Take turns.
Take a string. Copy your pattern.
Roll 5.
Move your cube that many spaces.
If you land on the color that comes next in your pattern, add the correct button to your string. If not, wait for your next turn.
The first person to put 4 more buttons on their string is the winner.
You Will Need
2
Start
Copyright © Macmillan/McGraw-Hill, a division of The McGraw-Hill Companies, Inc.
80 eighty

Game Time

Pattern Strings

Math Concept: Patterning

Manipulatives: attribute buttons, purple and orange connecting cube, red number cube

Introduce the game on p. 80 to your students to review concepts introduced in this chapter.

Instructions

- Assign each student a color cube: orange or purple.
- Assign a pattern to each player. Player 1's pattern should be green triangle, blue circle, green triangle, blue circle, green triangle, blue circle. Player 2's pattern should be red square, yellow circle, red square, yellow circle, red square, yellow circle.
- Have students play in pairs and take turns moving their cubes along the path.
- Have players roll the number cube and move their cube that many spaces.
- If players land on the color that comes next in their pattern color, they add the correct button to their string.
- The first player to finish the pattern string wins.

Extend the Game

Have students draw cards with larger numbers instead of rolling a number cube.

Differentiated Practice

Use these leveling suggestions to differentiate the game for all learners.

Level	Assignment
BL Below/Approaching Level	Instead of rolling a number cube, have students move to the next color in their pattern.
OL On Level	Have students play the game with the rules as written.
AL Above/Beyond Level	Play the game again using an ABB pattern.

LESSON **3-5**

Object Patterns

Lesson Planner

Objective

Students will identify, extend, and create patterns of objects.

Review Vocabulary

pattern

Resources

Materials: drawing paper, crayons, pencils
Manipulatives: pattern blocks, attribute buttons
Literature Connection: *Beep, Beep, Vroom, Vroom!* by Stuart J. Murphy
Alternate Lesson: Use *IMPACT Mathematics:* Unit E to provide practice with patterns.
Teacher Technology
TeacherWorks • Concepts in Motion • Math Songs Track 1

Daily Routine

Use these suggestions before beginning the lesson on p. 81

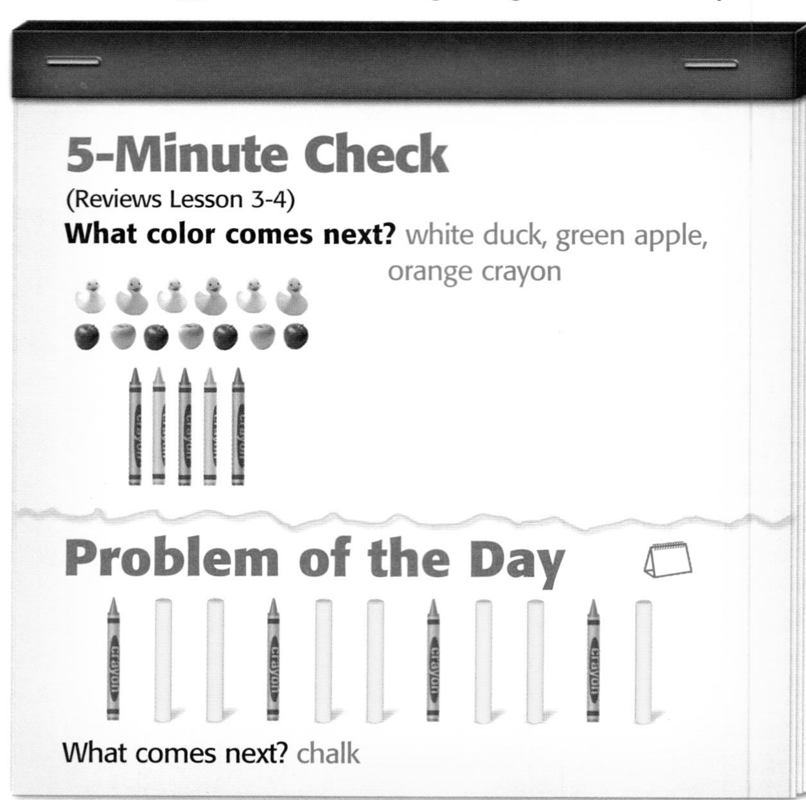

5-Minute Check
(Reviews Lesson 3-4)
What color comes next? white duck, green apple, orange crayon
Problem of the Day
What comes next? chalk

LINE UP Have two students walk forward and one student walk backward to line up. Repeat until all students are in line. Ask what the pattern is.

Review Math Vocabulary

Materials: color tiles

- Tell students that patterns do not have to look the same as the ones from the previous day.
- Explain that anything that repeats is an object **pattern**.
- Create an AAB pattern using color tiles.
- **What part of the pattern repeats?** AAB
- Show students another ABB pattern. Have them identify the repeating part.
- Have students use color tiles to create a pattern using an ABB or AAB pattern. Have them share their pattern with a partner. Have the partner extend the pattern.

Differentiated Instruction

Small Group Options

Option 1 Below/Approaching Level BL

LOGICAL

Materials: pattern blocks, AB patterns written on index cards

- Write a variety of AB patterns on index cards.
- Have index cards with AB patterns written out on each card and pattern blocks on a table for pairs of students to work together.
- Students will choose a card and create the pattern on the card using pattern blocks.
- The students may use shapes or colors to create the pattern. Students need to practice with two or three pattern cards.

Option 2 English Language Learners ELL

SPATIAL, KINESTHETIC

Core Vocabulary: step, hop, do what I do
Common Use Verb: follow
Hear Math This strategy integrates object patterns verbally.

- Have students line up. Say: "***Follow*** me. **Do what I do**."
- Lead while saying and modeling: "**Step**, **step**, **hop**, (repeat)." Have students follow and chant it. Change the pattern to hop, hop, step.
- Change actions for objects, showing ○ ○ □. Repeat with other objects as time permits.

Independent Work Options

Option 1 Early Finishers AL OL

LOGICAL

Materials: construction paper, scissors, glue, small objects such as stickers, cotton balls, toothpicks, paper clips

- Fold construction paper in half. Cut the top half of the fold to flap down and hide the object pattern that students will glue on the bottom half of the fold.
- Give each student a folded and cut piece of paper. Have them glue an ABB or AAB object pattern on the bottom half of the paper, repeating the pattern at least three times.
- Have students use their patterns to ask a partner what comes next in their pattern.
- Have partners take turns showing their pattern and asking what comes next.

Option 2 Student Technology

Math Online macmillanmh.com

Math Songs, "Stars and Stripes" Track 1

Math Adventures

Option 3 Learning Station: Technology (p. 67G)

Direct students to the Technology Learning Station for opportunities to explore and extend the lesson concept.

Leveled Lesson Resources

Additional support for English Language Learners can be found in the ELL Guide (p. 33). ELL

Reteach (p. 22) BL

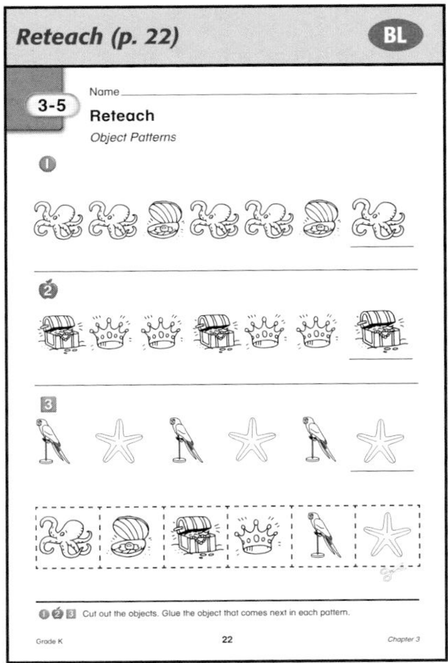

Skills Practice (p. 23) OL

Enrich (p. 25) AL

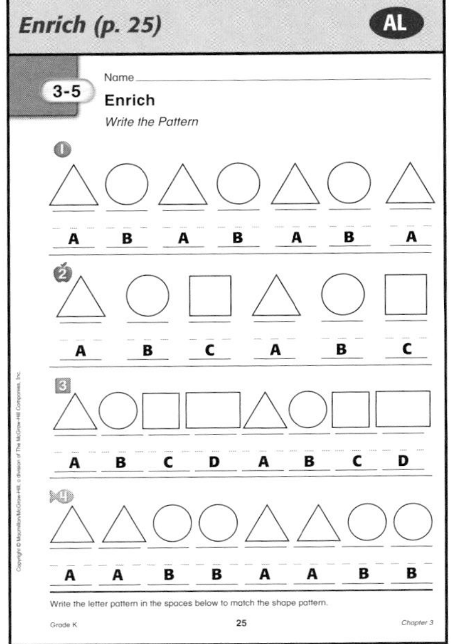

Homework Practice (p. 24) OL

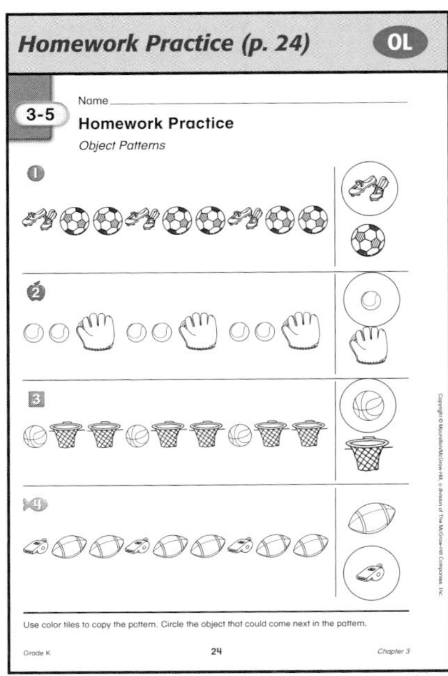

1 Introduce

Circle Time

Activity Choice 1 • Literature

Beep, Beep, Vroom, Vroom!
by Stuart J. Murphy

- Have students work in pairs. Give each pair of students 4 blue blocks, 4 yellow blocks, and 4 red blocks.
- Using the blocks, duplicate the pattern Kevin used to place his cars on the shelf.
- Using the blocks, duplicate Dad's pattern.
- Using the blocks, duplicate Mom's pattern.
- Using the blocks, duplicate Molly's first pattern; how does it compare to Kevin's? Can you quickly change it to match Kevin's pattern?
- What other patterns can be made with the 12 blocks?

Activity Choice 2 • Hands-On

Manipulatives: pattern blocks

- Show students an AB **pattern** made from classroom objects such as blocks.
- **How do you know this is a pattern?** The blocks repeat.
- Show students an AAB pattern made up of the same blocks.
- **Is this a pattern and how do you know?** Yes; the blocks repeat. Have them name the pattern.
- Show students an ABB pattern made up of the same blocks. **Is this a pattern and how do you know?** Yes; the blocks repeat. Have them name the pattern.
- If time permits, have students make their own AAB or ABB pattern.

2 Teach

- Direct students to the top of p. 81.
- Have students identify the pattern of buttons.
- Ask students what button would come next if they were to continue the pattern.
- If students grasp AAB and ABB patterns, show students an ABC pattern. Have them identify the repeating part. Emphasize that there are three different objects in the pattern, rather than two.

BL Alternate Teaching Strategy

If students have trouble with identifying patterns . . .

Then use one of these reteach options.

1 CRM **Daily Reteach Worksheet** (p. 22)

2 **Use Manipulatives** Show students an AAB pattern using attribute buttons.
- Have students say the pattern aloud together, then extend the pattern orally.
- Have students draw and color a picture of the pattern.
- Repeat the activity using an ABB pattern.

COMMON ERROR!

Students may have difficulty recognizing long patterns. Have them say the pattern aloud before extending it, since hearing the pattern can help reinforce the visual pattern.

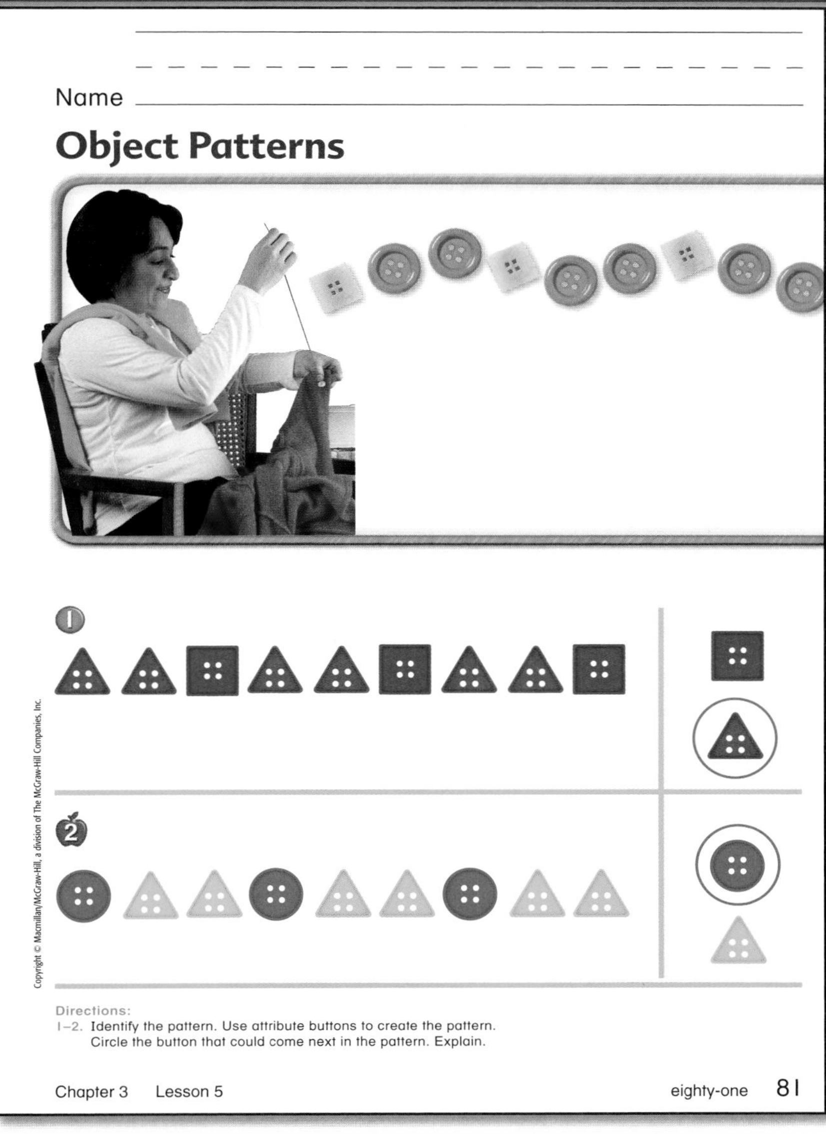

Name
Object Patterns
Directions:
1–2. Identify the pattern. Use attribute buttons to create the pattern. Circle the button that could come next in the pattern. Explain.
Chapter 3 Lesson 5 eighty-one 81

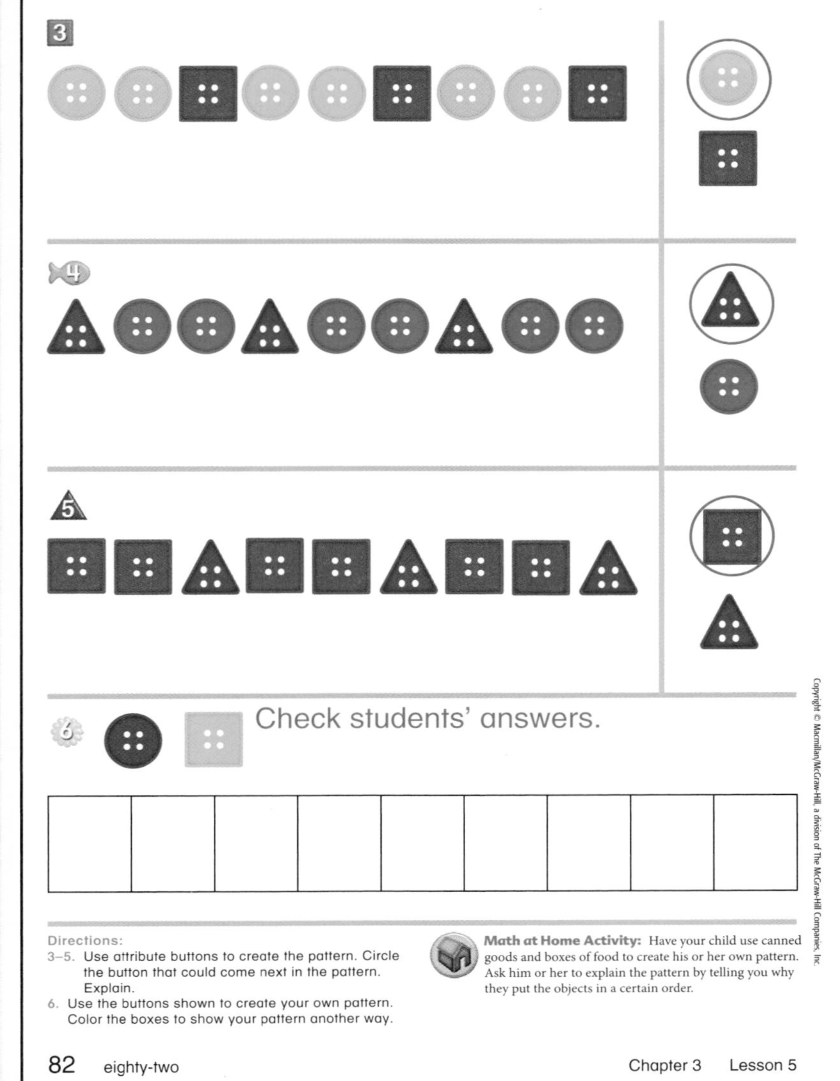

Check students' answers.
Directions:
3–5. Use attribute buttons to create the pattern. Circle the button that could come next in the pattern. Explain.
6. Use the buttons shown to create your own pattern. Color the boxes to show your pattern another way.
Math at Home Activity: Have your child use canned goods and boxes of food to create his or her own pattern. Ask him or her to explain the pattern by telling you why they put the objects in a certain order.
82 eighty-two Chapter 3 Lesson 5

3 Practice

Guided Practice

- Direct students to p. 81.
- **What pattern do you see in the buttons in Exercise 1?** triangle, triangle, square
- Have students use attribute buttons to create the pattern.
- Have students circle the button that could come next in the pattern. triangle
- Repeat this procedure with Exercise 2.

Independent Practice

Have students turn to p. 82 and work independently on the exercises.

4 Assess

Formative Assessment

- Create the pattern pencil-pencil-paper three times.
- **What are the next three parts of the pattern?** pencil, pencil, paper
- Ask students to extend the pattern by showing the next three parts of the pattern.

Quick Check **Are students still struggling to identify, extend, and create patterns of objects?**

If Yes → Small Group Options (p. 81B)

If No → Independent Work Options (p. 81B)

CRM Skills Practice Worksheet (p. 23)

CRM Enrich Worksheet (p. 25)

LESSON 3-6

Problem-Solving Strategy

Look for a Pattern

Lesson Planner

Objective

Identify an AB, ABB, ABC and/or AAB pattern and show it another way.

Resources

Materials: crayons, pencils, white paper, glue, index cards
Manipulatives: attribute buttons, pattern blocks, counters
Literature Connection: *The Button Box* by Margarette S. Reid
Teacher Technology
TeacherWorks • Math Songs Track 1

Real-World Problem Solving Library
Math and Science: *Desert Patterns*
Use these leveled books to reinforce and extend problem-solving skills and strategies.

Leveled for:

- OL On Level
- ELL Sheltered English
- SP Spanish

For additional support see the Real-World Problem Solving Teacher Guide.

On-Level title is available in classroom Big Book.

Daily Routine

Use these suggestions before beginning the lesson on p. 83.

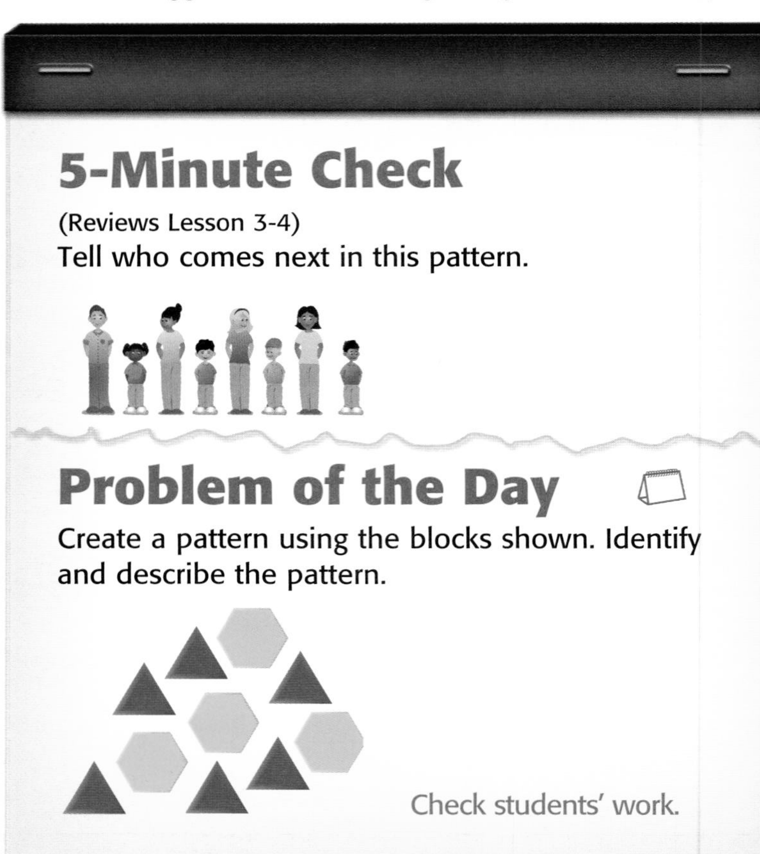

5-Minute Check
(Reviews Lesson 3-4)
Tell who comes next in this pattern.
Problem of the Day
Create a pattern using the blocks shown. Identify and describe the pattern.
Check students' work.

LINE UP Show students which hand is their left hand and which hand is their right. Have students line up if they write with their left hand. Then have students line up if they write with their right hand.

Differentiated Instruction

Small Group Options

Option 1 — Below/Approaching Level (BL)

LINGUISTIC

Materials: connecting cubes, drawing paper, crayons

- Prepare one AB pattern using six connecting cubes.
- Have students model the pattern with connecting cubes. Have students draw and color the pattern.
- If students are ready, have them use nine cubes to create and draw an AAB pattern.

Option 2 — English Language Learners (ELL)

KINESTHETIC

Core Vocabulary: pattern, arms folded, standing straight
Common Use Verb: act out

Do Math This strategy helps students internalize patterning and translation skills and introduces common pattern vocabulary.

- Have students act out different body position patterns, such as: arms folded, standing straight.
- Prompt class to repeat the pattern.
- Allow students to create their own movement patterns.

Independent Work Options

Option 1 — Early Finishers (OL) (AL)

KINESTHETIC

Materials: paper shapes in different colors, paper, glue, markers

- Have students choose nine shapes and glue them in a pattern on their paper.
- Underneath the shape pattern, have students draw the same pattern in a different way.

Option 2 — Student Technology

Math Online macmillanmh.com

Math Songs, "Stars and Stripes" Track 1

Math Adventures

Option 3 — Learning Station: Reading (p. 67H)

Direct students to the Reading Learning Station for opportunities to explore and extend the lesson concept.

Leveled Lesson Resources

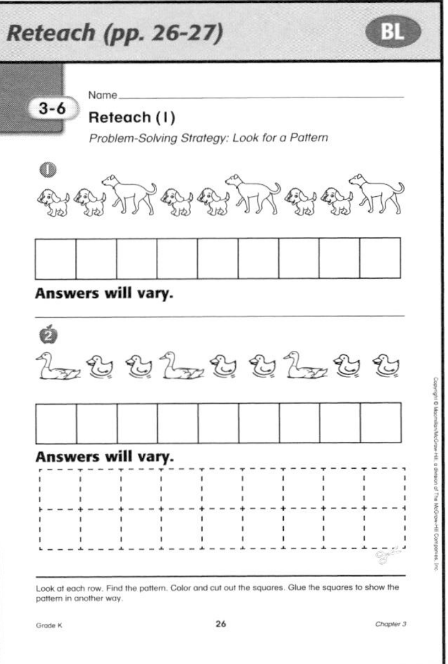
Reteach (pp. 26-27) BL

3-6 Name
Reteach (1)
Problem-Solving Strategy: Look for a Pattern

1
Answers will vary.

2
Answers will vary.

Look at each row. Find the pattern. Color and cut out the squares. Glue the squares to show the pattern in another way.

Grade K 26 Chapter 3

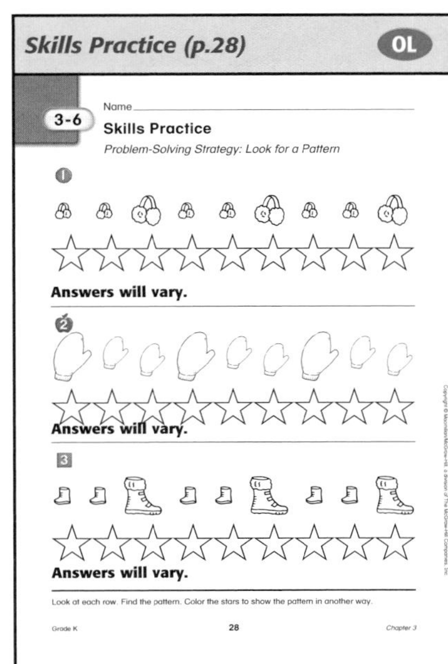
Skills Practice (p.28) OL

3-6 Name
Skills Practice
Problem-Solving Strategy: Look for a Pattern

1
Answers will vary.

2
Answers will vary.

3
Answers will vary.

Look at each row. Find the pattern. Color the stars to show the pattern in another way.

Grade K 28 Chapter 3

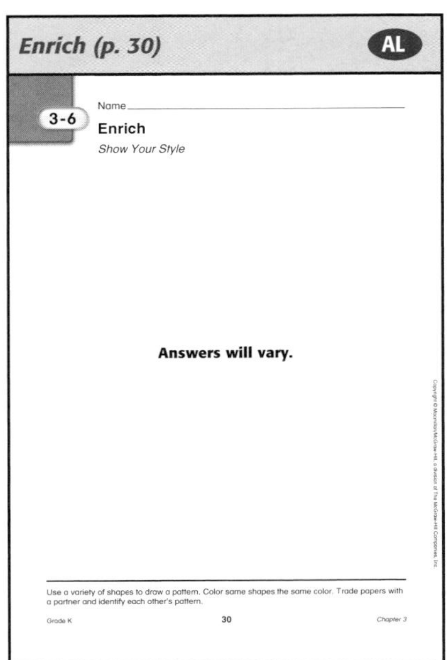
Enrich (p. 30) AL

3-6 Name
Enrich
Show Your Style

Answers will vary.

Use a variety of shapes to draw a pattern. Color same shapes the same color. Trade papers with a partner and identify each other's pattern.

Grade K 30 Chapter 3

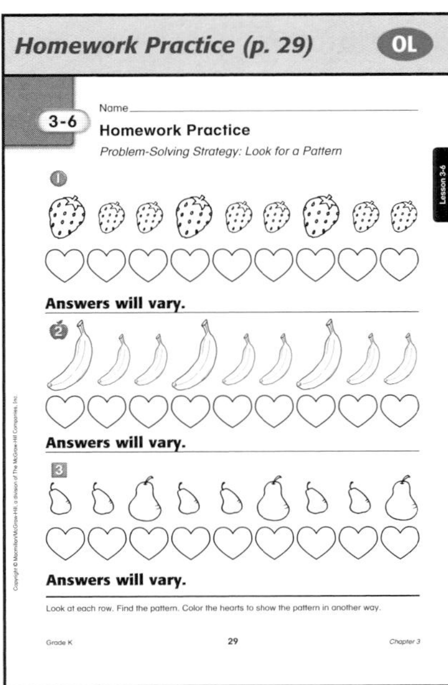
Homework Practice (p. 29) OL

3-6 Name
Homework Practice
Problem-Solving Strategy: Look for a Pattern

1
Answers will vary.

2
Answers will vary.

3
Answers will vary.

Look at each row. Find the pattern. Color the hearts to show the pattern in another way.

Grade K 29 Chapter 3

1 Introduce

Circle Time

Activity Choice 1 • Literature

The Button Box
by Margarette S. Reid

- Give students a button box.
- Ask students to find "sparkly" buttons from the box. Ask them to find buttons covered with cloth.
- Students continue finding similar buttons to those in the story (shanks, uniform, size, color, natural).
- Encourage students to sort the buttons by any characteristics they select. Then ask them to create a pattern using their buttons.
- If time permits, students circulate to each other's patterns and continue the pattern.
- Extension: Patterns can be recorded (or glued) on cards so students can continue the patterns in their free time.

Activity Choice 2 • Hands-On

Manipulatives: attribute buttons, pattern blocks

- String some attribute buttons in a pattern (e.g., AB, AAB, ABB).
- Show students the string. Have them identify and describe the pattern.
- Ask them to use pattern blocks to show the pattern in a different way.
- Ask students how they would use connecting cubes to show the pattern in a different way.

2 Teach

Direct students to the top of p. 83.

Understand Review what students know and what they need to find for the problem.

Plan Have students discuss their strategy for solving the problem.

Solve Guide students to look for a pattern in order to solve the problem. Have students identify and describe the pattern of gingerbread girls. Have students create a way to show the pattern another way by coloring the houses below the pattern.

Check Have students look back at the problem to be sure that the answers fit what they already know about the problem.

BL Alternate Teaching Strategy

If students have trouble showing patterns in different ways . . .

Then use one of these reteach options.

1 CRM **Daily Reteach Worksheet** (pp. 26-27)

2 **Use Shapes** On a sheet of paper, have students draw nine circles in a row and then nine squares under the circles.

- Have them color the circles in a pattern.
- Have them color the squares to show the same pattern in a different way.
- Ask students to draw objects to show the same pattern in a different way.

COMMON ERROR!

Students may have trouble identifying patterns that use only one shape or only one color. Remind students to focus on what makes the items in the pattern different. Focusing on the differences can help students see where repetition occurs.

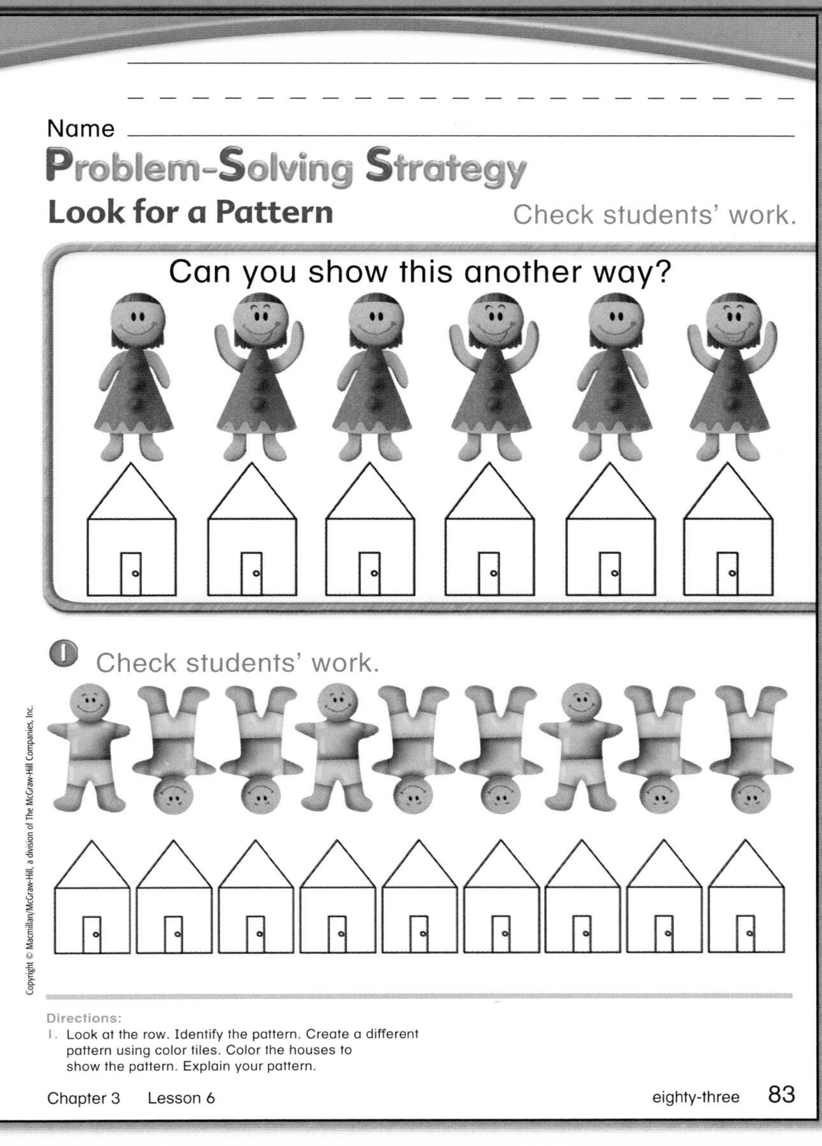

Name ______________________

Problem-Solving Strategy

Look for a Pattern Check students' work.

Can you show this another way?

1 Check students' work.

Directions:
1. Look at the row. Identify the pattern. Create a different pattern using color tiles. Color the houses to show the pattern. Explain your pattern.

Chapter 3 Lesson 6 eighty-three 83

Copyright © Macmillan/McGraw-Hill, a division of The McGraw-Hill Companies, Inc.

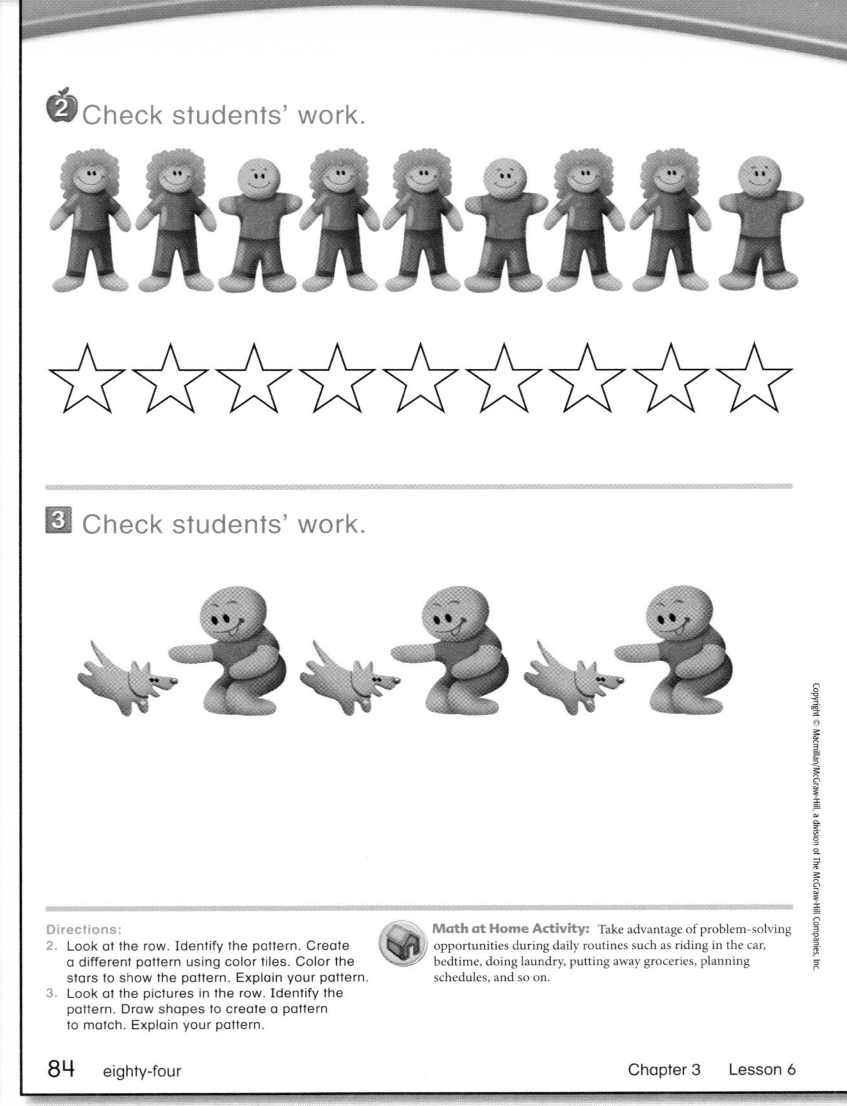

2 Check students' work.

3 Check students' work.

Directions:
2. Look at the row. Identify the pattern. Create a different pattern using color tiles. Color the stars to show the pattern. Explain your pattern.
3. Look at the pictures in the row. Identify the pattern. Draw shapes to create a pattern to match. Explain your pattern.

Math at Home Activity: Take advantage of problem-solving opportunities during daily routines such as riding in the car, bedtime, doing laundry, putting away groceries, planning schedules, and so on.

84 eighty-four Chapter 3 Lesson 6

Copyright © Macmillan/McGraw-Hill, a division of The McGraw-Hill Companies, Inc.

3 Practice

Guided Practice

- Direct students to p. 83.
- Have students describe the gingerbread boys in Exercise 1.
- Have them tell how they could color the houses to show the pattern another way. Sample answer: blue, yellow, yellow, blue, yellow, yellow, blue, yellow, yellow (any ABB pattern)
- Have students color the houses to show their patterns.

Independent Practice

Have students turn to p. 84. Explain the directions. Have students work independently on the exercises.

- Have students tell how cubes or color tiles could be used to show the pattern another way.
- Have students determine another approach or strategy to solving these problems.

4 Assess

Formative Assessment

Show nine counters in an ABB pattern, such as red, yellow, yellow, red, yellow, yellow, red, yellow, yellow.

- **What pattern do you see?** ABB or red, yellow, yellow
- Have students draw the same pattern in a different way.

Quick Check **Are students still struggling to show patterns in a different way?**

If Yes → Small Group Options (p. 83B)

If No → Independent Work Options (p. 83B)

CRM Skills Practice Worksheet (p. 28)

CRM Enrich Worksheet (p. 30)

LESSON 3-7

Sound Patterns

Lesson Planner

Objective

Students will identify, extend, and create sound patterns.

Review Vocabulary

pattern

Resources

Materials: classroom instruments, pencils
Literature Connection: *Beep, Beep, Vroom, Vroom!* by Stuart J. Murphy
Teacher Technology
TeacherWorks • Math Songs Track 1

Daily Routine

Use these suggestions before beginning the lesson on p. 85.

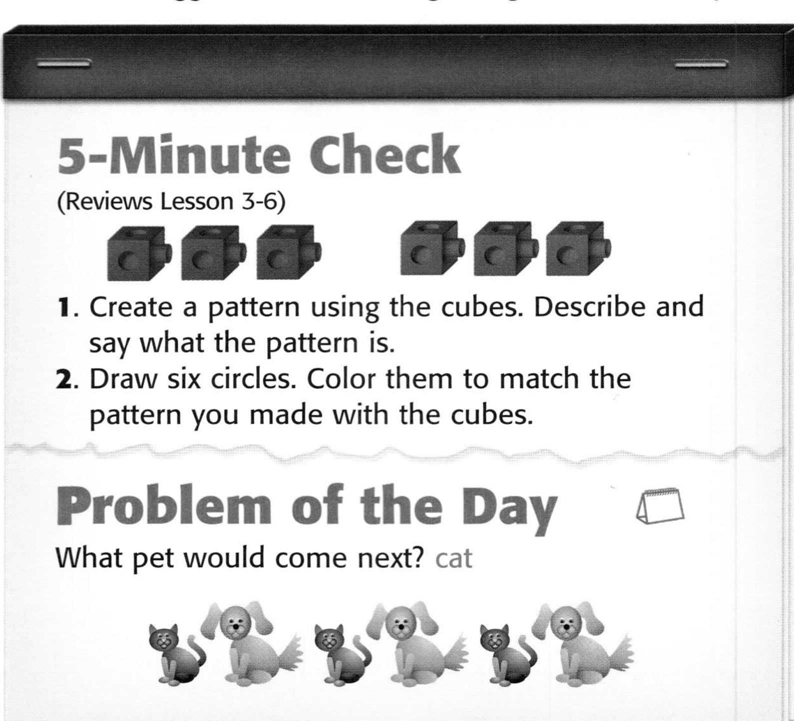

5-Minute Check

(Reviews Lesson 3-6)

1. Create a pattern using the cubes. Describe and say what the pattern is.
2. Draw six circles. Color them to match the pattern you made with the cubes.

Problem of the Day

What pet would come next? cat

LINE UP Have 2 students line up and make the sound of the letter /k/. Have another student line up and make the sound of the letter /s/. Have remaining students line up continuing the sound pattern.

Review Math Vocabulary

Materials: pictures of instruments

- Tell students that they will learn about sound **patterns.**
- Explain that sound patterns are patterns that can be heard, but cannot be seen or touched.
- Explain that you can use images or pictures of instruments to represent sounds, but you cannot see the sounds themselves.
- Ask students to name different ways to make sound patterns.
- Allow students to make up sound patterns and have the rest of the class repeat the patterns.
- Discuss different types of instruments and the kinds of sounds they make.

Differentiated Instruction

Small Group Options

Option 1 Below/Approaching Level BL

KINESTHETIC

Materials: cards with the pictures of a foot stomping and hands snapping, arranged in AB patterns

- Have pairs of students choose a card with an AB, AAB, or ABB pattern with pictures of clapping and stomping. One of the partners chooses a card without letting their partner see their choice.
- The card chosen is then acted out so that the partner can guess the clap, stomp pattern.
- After the partner makes their guess, students switch roles and choose another card.
- When each student has taken a turn, have the students try to make up their own clap, stomp pattern.

Option 2 English Language Learners ELL

AUDITORY, KINESTHETIC

Core Vocabulary: close your eyes, no peeking, carefully
Common Use Verb: listen
Hear Math This strategy connects listening and auditory patterns.

- Say: **"Close your eyes. *Listen* carefully.** No peeking!"
- Clap hands 2 times, pause, repeat. Say: "Repeat what you heard me do." Repeat with a new pattern.

Independent Work Options

Option 1 Early Finishers AL OL

AUDITORY

Materials: tape recorder, classroom instruments

- Have students record a sound pattern on tape using classroom instruments.
- Have the class listen to the tape, determine which instruments were used, and recreate the pattern.

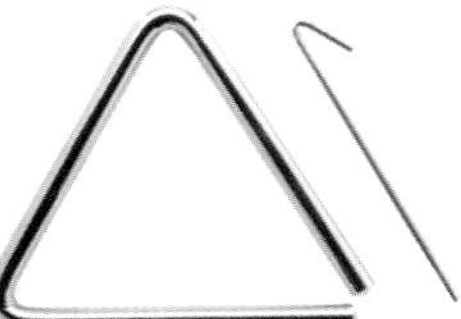

Option 2 Student Technology

Math Online macmillanmh.com
Math Songs, "Stars and Stripes" Track 1

Option 3 Learning Station: Health (p. 67G)

Direct students to the Health Learning Station for opportunities to explore and extend the lesson concept.

Leveled Lesson Resources

Reteach (p. 31) BL

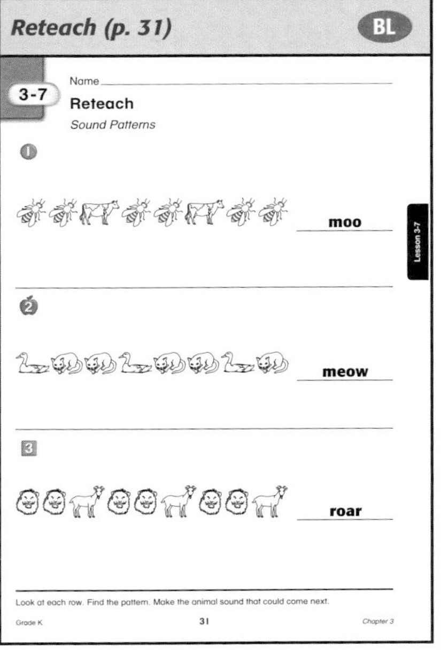

3-7 Name
Reteach
Sound Patterns

1. moo
2. meow
3. roar

Look at each row. Find the pattern. Make the animal sound that could come next.

Grade K 31 Chapter 3

Skills Practice (p. 32) OL

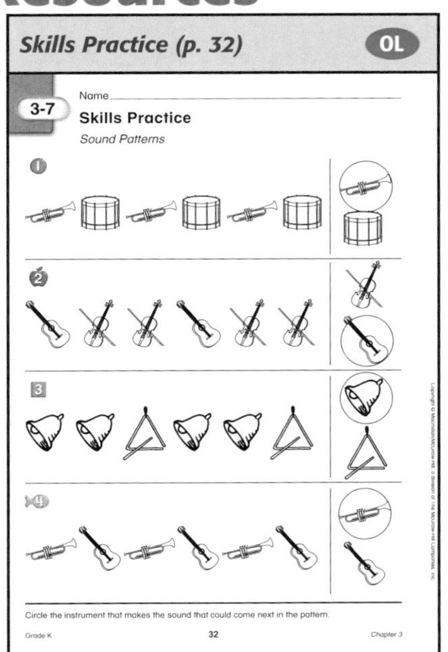

3-7 Name
Skills Practice
Sound Patterns

Circle the instrument that makes the sound that could come next in the pattern.

Grade K 32 Chapter 3

Enrich (p. 34) AL

3-7 Name
Enrich
Snap, Clap

1. snap, clap, snap, clap
2. snap, clap, clap, snap
3. snap, snap, snap, clap
4. clap, clap, snap, snap
5. clap, clap, clap, snap

Act out the above patterns. Snap when you see a circle. Clap when you see a square.

Grade K 34 Chapter 3

Homework Practice (p. 33) OL

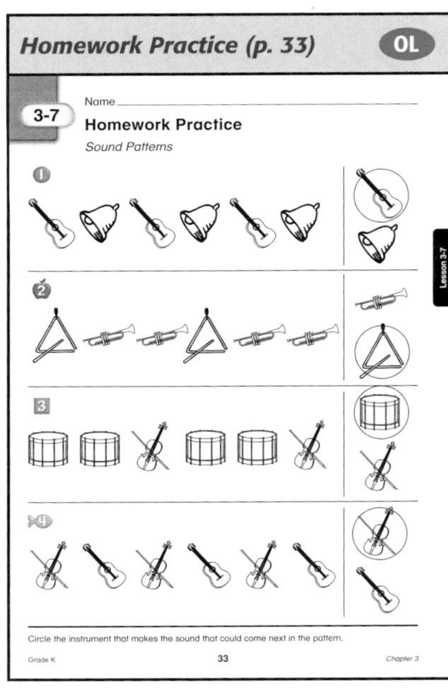

3-7 Name
Homework Practice
Sound Patterns

Circle the instrument that makes the sound that could come next in the pattern.

Grade K 33 Chapter 3

1 Introduce

Circle Time

Activity Choice 1 • Literature

Beep, Beep, Vroom, Vroom! by Stuart J. Murphy

- Revisit this book identifying patterns by the sound for the cars.
- Identify Kevin's pattern by sound (vroom, crash, beep, vroom, crash, beep…).
- Ask students to duplicate Dad's, Mom's, and Molly's first patterns by the sound used for each car.
- Invite students to make up other patterns using "vroom," "crash," and "beep."
- Make sound patterns (snap, snap, clap) and ask students to join you when they identify the pattern.
- Invite students to make sound patterns using musical instruments (triangle, sticks, bell etc.); other students can identify and/or duplicate the patterns.

Activity Choice 2 • Hands-On

Materials: classroom instruments

- Create a sound **pattern** using classroom instruments or other objects that can make noise.
- Ask students to identify the pattern.
- Ask a volunteer to repeat the pattern.
- Create patterns that all students can repeat by clapping your hands and stomping your feet. Practice AB, ABB, and AAB patterns.
- Extend the activity by creating ABC patterns for students to repeat.

2 Teach

Direct students to the top of p. 85.

- **What are the students doing?** playing the recorder and triangle
- Have two students sound out the pattern if a recorder and a triangle are available. If not, have students hum for the recorder sound and say "ding" for the triangle.

BL Alternate Teaching Strategy

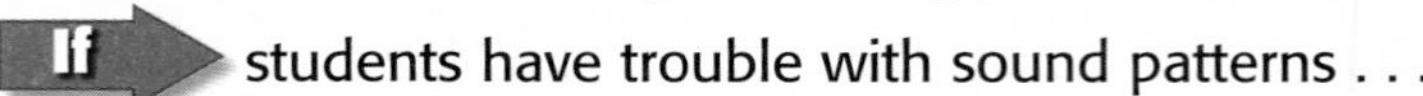

If students have trouble with sound patterns . . .

Then use one of these reteach options.

1 CRM **Daily Reteach Worksheet** (p. 31)

2 **Play a Game** Have students sit with their backs to you.

- Have them listen to sounds created by you and identify them.
- Create sound patterns. Have students repeat the pattern and extend it.

COMMON ERROR!

Students may struggle with sound patterns. Have them associate a picture with each sound before determining the pattern.

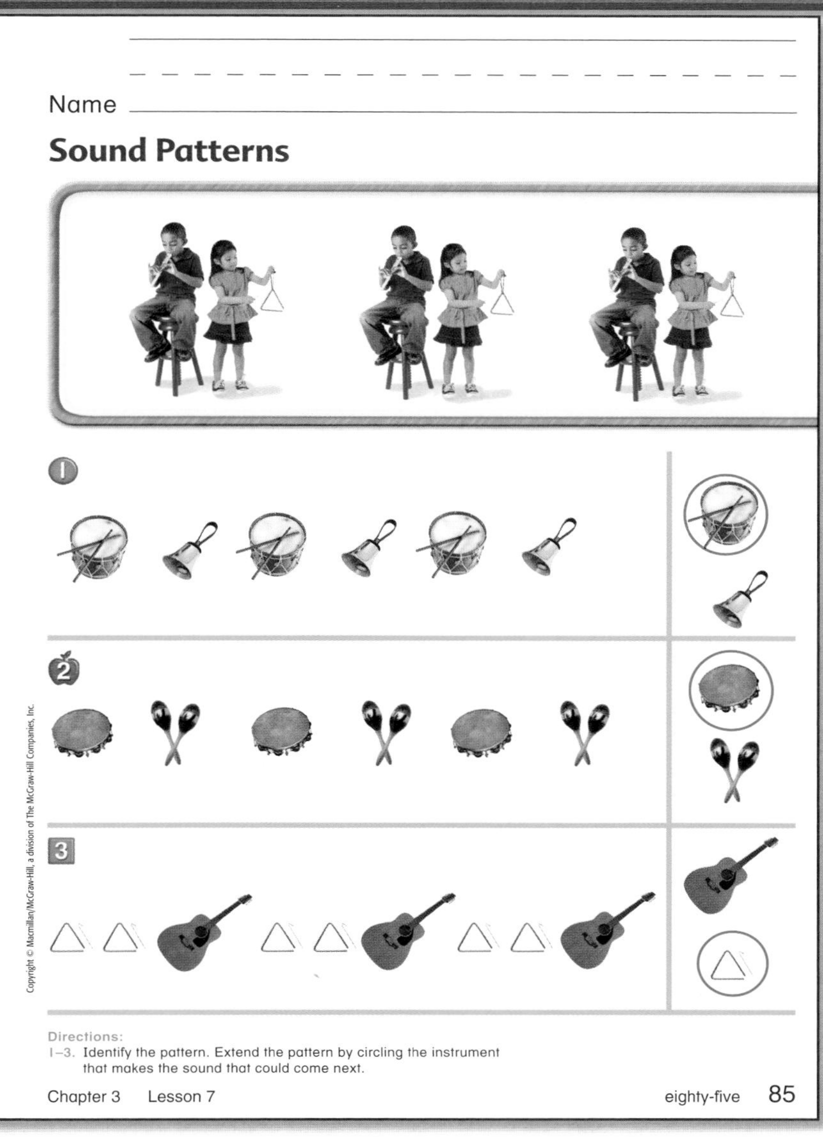

Name
Sound Patterns
Directions:
1–3. Identify the pattern. Extend the pattern by circling the instrument that makes the sound that could come next.
Chapter 3 Lesson 7 eighty-five 85

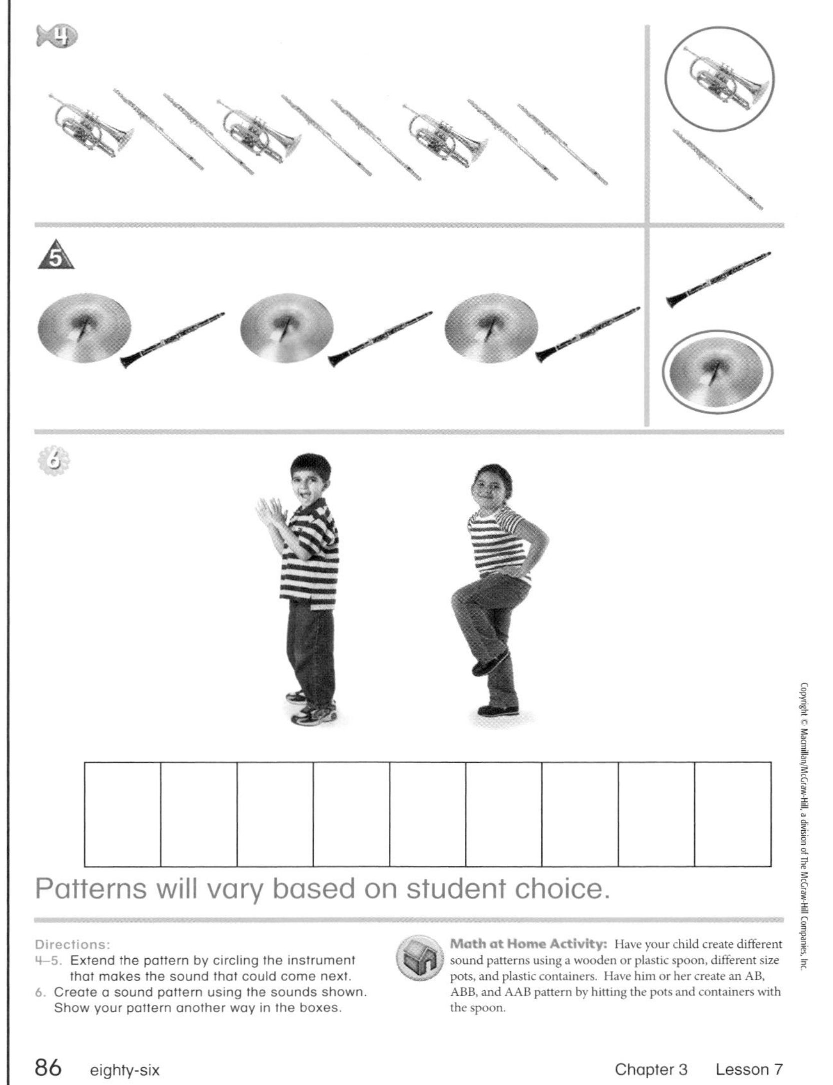

Patterns will vary based on student choice.
Directions:
4–5. Extend the pattern by circling the instrument that makes the sound that could come next.
6. Create a sound pattern using the sounds shown. Show your pattern another way in the boxes.
Math at Home Activity: Have your child create different sound patterns using a wooden or plastic spoon, different size pots, and plastic containers. Have him or her create an AB, ABB, and AAB pattern by hitting the pots and containers with the spoon.
86 eighty-six Chapter 3 Lesson 7

3 Practice

Guided Practice

- Direct students to p. 85.
- Have students identify the instruments in Exercise 1 (drum, bell). Ask volunteers to imitate the sound each instrument makes. Have class sound out the pattern.
- Ask a volunteer what instrument sound would come next. Have the class circle it.
- Continue this activity with Exercises 2 and 3. Identify the tamborine, maracas, triangle, and guitar. If students do not know the sound an instrument makes, help them make the sound or a sound that can stand for it.

Independent Practice

Have students turn to p. 86 and work independently on the exercises. Review the instruments shown (trumpet, flute, cymbal, clarinet).

4 Assess

Formative Assessment

- Tap on a drum once, and then say the student's name twice. Repeat.
- Ask the student to continue the pattern.

Quick Check **Are students still struggling to identify, extend, and create sound patterns?**

If Yes → Small Group Options (p. 85B)

If No → Independent Work Options (p. 85B)

CRM Skills Practice Worksheet (p. 32)

CRM Enrich Worksheet (p. 34)

LESSON 3-8 Movement Patterns

Lesson Planner

Objective

Students will identify, extend, and create patterns of movement.

Review Vocabulary

pattern

Resources

Literature Connection: *Bug Dance* by Stuart J. Murphy
Alternate Lesson: Use *IMPACT Mathematics*: Unit E to provide practice with patterns.
Teacher Technology
TeacherWorks • Math Songs Track 1

Daily Routine

Use these suggestions before beginning the lesson on p. 87.

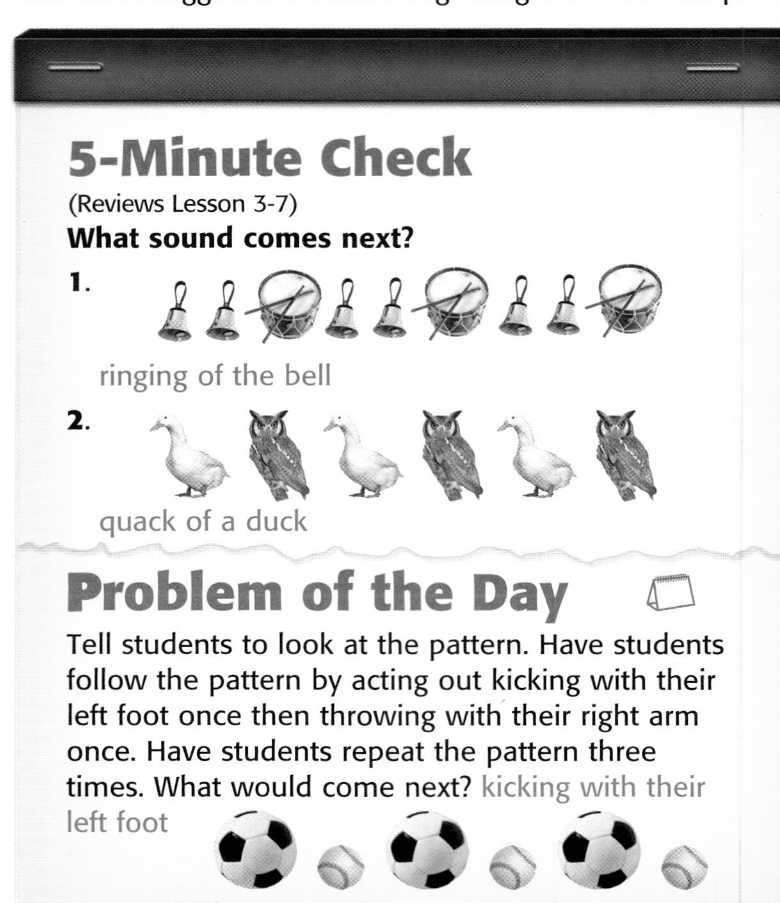

5-Minute Check

(Reviews Lesson 3-7)

What sound comes next?

1. ringing of the bell

2. quack of a duck

Problem of the Day

Tell students to look at the pattern. Have students follow the pattern by acting out kicking with their left foot once then throwing with their right arm once. Have students repeat the pattern three times. What would come next? kicking with their left foot

LINE UP Have students line up in an AB pattern raising their right hand or their left hand repeating the pattern three times. Call out students one at a time to line up and complete the pattern.

Review Math Vocabulary

- Tell students that patterns can be made out of motions, in addition to sounds, colors, or objects. Ask students if they know any songs or dances that have a pattern of motions.
- Invite two students to come to the front of the room and create a movement pattern in an AB pattern.
- Have the class imitate the pattern. Explain that the pattern is a movement **pattern**.
- Work with groups of students and have them create their own movement pattern, using AAB or ABB patterns.

Differentiated Instruction

Small Group Options

Option 1 KINESTHETIC

Below/Approaching Level BL

- Choose 6 students to stand up in front of the class. Quietly tell three of the students to act out a certain action such as raising both hands in the air. Have the other three students act out another action such as standing on one foot. The students need to act out their actions standing in an AB pattern.
- Have the rest of the class extend the pattern predicting what the next action will be. Have the student that answers the question stand up with the line of students and act out the action that completes the pattern.

Option 2 VISUAL/SPATIAL, KINESTHETIC

English Language Learners ELL

Materials: chalk or masking tape
Core Vocabulary: jump, one foot, two feet
Common Use Verb: hop
Talk Math This strategy vocalizes physical patterns.

- Model how to use a hopscotch grid, vocalizing the pattern and naming hop (one foot) and jump (both feet).
- Students take turns using the hopscotch grid, chanting hop, jump, as they go. Repeat as time permits.

Independent Work Options

Option 1 KINESTHETIC

Early Finishers AL OL

- Have each student create a dance that demonstrates a movement pattern.
- Have each student teach the dance to the rest of the group.
- Have all students show the pattern together in a group dance.
- Repeat with other students leading

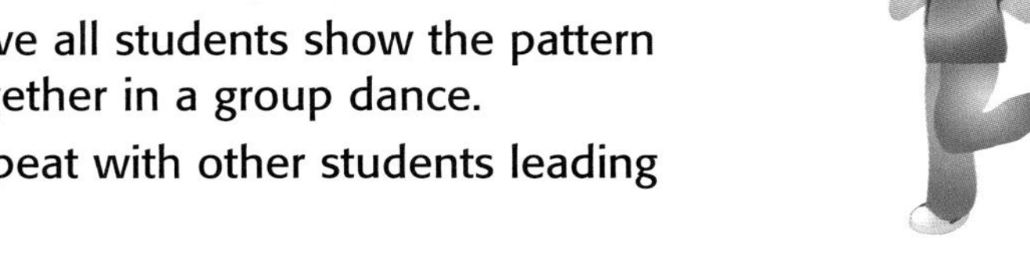

Option 2

Student Technology

Math Online macmillanmh.com

Math Songs, "Stars and Stripes" Track 1

Option 3

Learning Station: Health (p. 67G)

Direct students to the Health Learning Station for opportunities to explore and extend the lesson concept.

Leveled Lesson Resources

Reteach (p. 35) BL

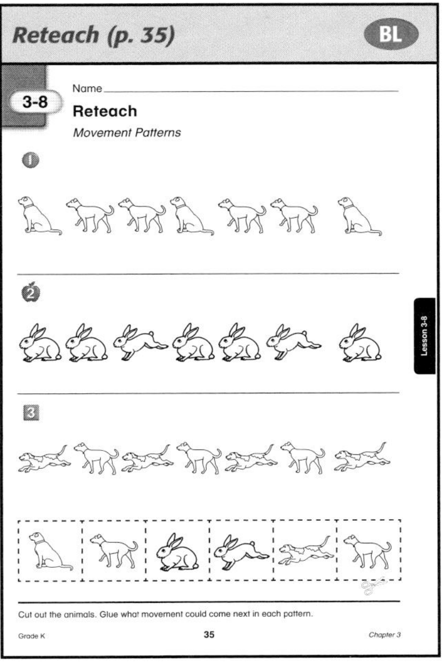

3-8 Name
Reteach
Movement Patterns

Cut out the animals. Glue what movement could come next in each pattern.

Grade K 35 Chapter 3

Skills Practice (p. 36) OL

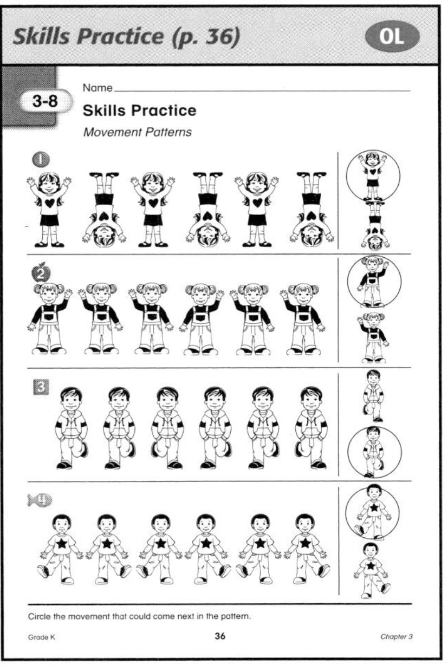

3-8 Name
Skills Practice
Movement Patterns

Circle the movement that could come next in the pattern.

Grade K 36 Chapter 3

Enrich (p. 38) AL

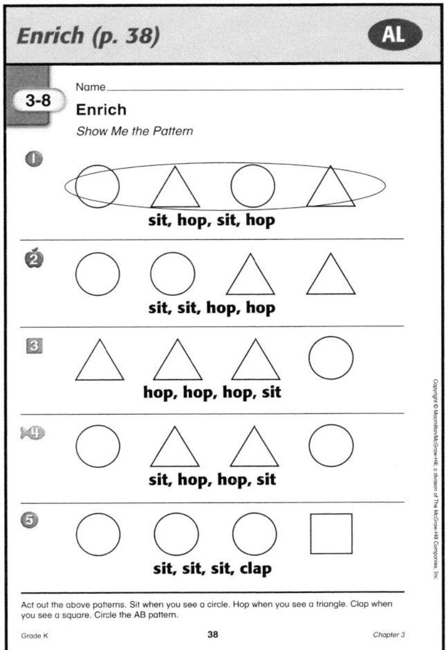

3-8 Name
Enrich
Show Me the Pattern

1. sit, hop, sit, hop
2. sit, sit, hop, hop
3. hop, hop, hop, sit
4. sit, hop, hop, sit
5. sit, sit, sit, clap

Act out the above patterns. Sit when you see a circle. Hop when you see a triangle. Clap when you see a square. Circle the AB pattern.

Grade K 38 Chapter 3

Homework Practice (p. 37) OL

3-8 Name
Homework Practice
Movement Patterns

Circle the movement that could come next in the pattern.

Grade K 37 Chapter 3

1 Introduce

Circle Time

Activity Choice 1 • Literature

Bug Dance by Stuart J. Murphy

- Have students do the dance; use the diagram on pages 8 and 9 to help teach the dance to students.
- Continue the dance emphasizing the fact that the dance repeats after the dancer turns 90° to the right.
- Discuss how centipede feels at the beginning of the story and how he feels at the end.
- Repeat three movements (clap, hands on head, hands on knees, repeat) and ask students to join you when they know the pattern.
- Extension: Encourage students to create repeating dance or exercise movements. Try other dances such as The Bunny Hop.

Activity Choice 2 • Hands-On

- Have students sing the song "Hokey Pokey" and do the motions.
- Explain that in this song, every time they put a body part out or in the circle, they are making a **pattern** of motions or a physical movement pattern.

2 Teach

Direct students to the top of p. 87.

- Have students identify the motions that the girl is doing in the top row.
- Have students act out the pattern.
- Ask students what motion would come next if they continued the pattern.

BL Alternate Teaching Strategy

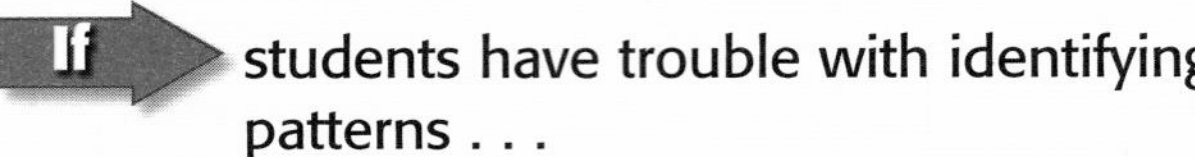

If students have trouble with identifying patterns . . .

Then use one of these reteach options.

1 CRM **Daily Reteach Worksheet** (p. 35)

2 **Copying Movements** Have students copy a movement pattern that you make.

- Add to your movement so that you do two alternating movements, such as take one step to the left, then take one step to the right.
- When students are ready, change the motion to two steps to the left and one step to the right.
- Repeat with other movements.

COMMON ERROR!

If students struggle to make movement patterns, be sure it is not due to lack of coordination. Simplify the movements and describe them with words.

Name
Movement Patterns
Directions:
1–2. Identify the pattern. Extend the pattern by circling the movement that could come next.
Chapter 3 Lesson 8 eighty-seven 87

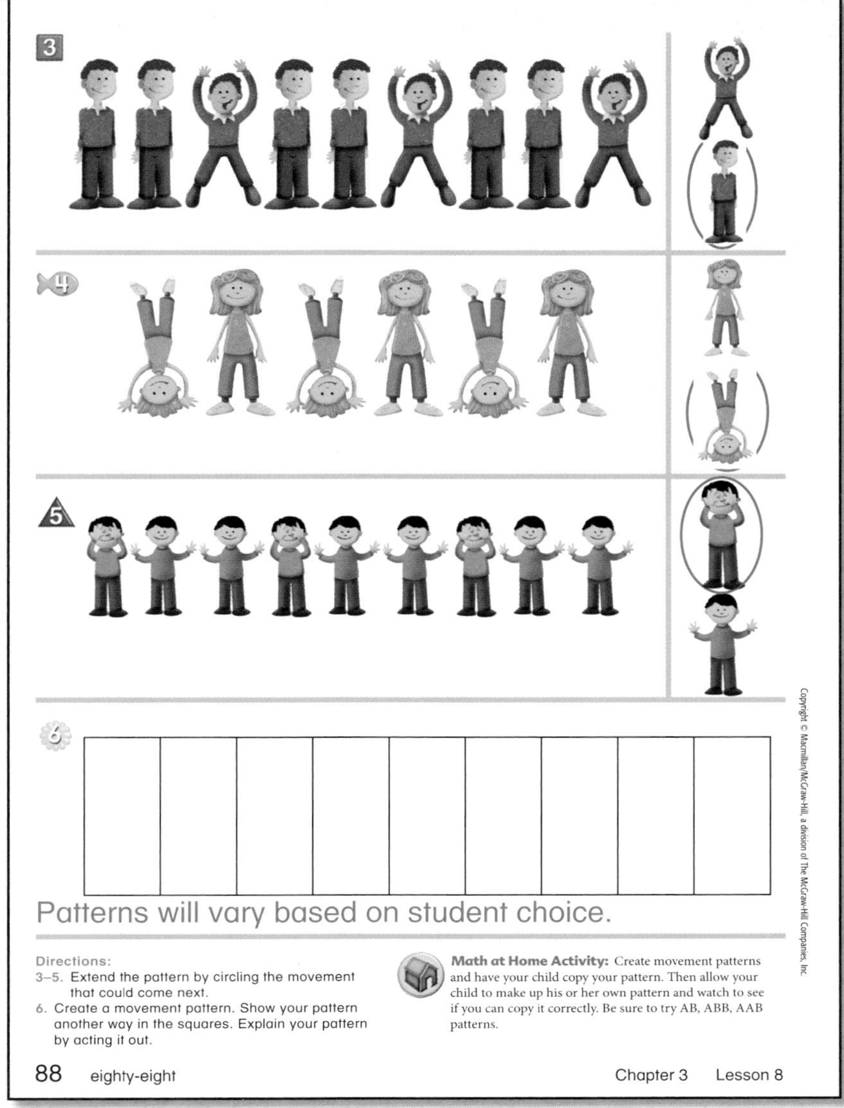

Patterns will vary based on student choice.
Directions:
3–5. Extend the pattern by circling the movement that could come next.
6. Create a movement pattern. Show your pattern another way in the squares. Explain your pattern by acting it out.
Math at Home Activity: Create movement patterns and have your child copy your pattern. Then allow your child to make up his or her own pattern and watch to see if you can copy it correctly. Be sure to try AB, ABB, AAB patterns.
88 eighty-eight Chapter 3 Lesson 8

3 Practice

Guided Practice

- Direct students to p. 87.
- Have students identify the motions in Exercise 1. Ask volunteers if they can imitate the motions the student is doing. Have them act out the whole pattern.
- Ask volunteers what action could come next. Have students circle the motion.
- Repeat this procedure with Exercise 2. Allow students to act out the pattern.

Independent Practice

Have students turn to p. 88 and work independently on the exercises.

4 Assess

Formative Assessment

- Create a hand movement pattern for students to copy and extend, such as hold hands up, clap twice.
- Repeat the activity with AB and AAB patterns.

Quick Check **Are students still struggling to identify, extend, and create physical movement patterns?**

If Yes → Small Group Options (p. 87B)

If No → Independent Work Options (p. 87B)

CRM Skills Practice Worksheet (p. 36)

CRM Enrich Worksheet (p. 38)

LESSON 3-9 Predicting Patterns

Lesson Planner

Objective

Students will use patterns to make predictions.

Vocabulary

predict

Resources

Materials: pencils
Manipulatives: pattern blocks
Literature Connection: *The Noisy Farm* by Marni McGee
Alternate Lesson: Use *IMPACT Mathematics*: Unit E to provide practice with predicting patterns.
Teacher Technology
TeacherWorks • Math Songs Track 1

Daily Routine

Use these suggestions before beginning the lesson on p. 89.

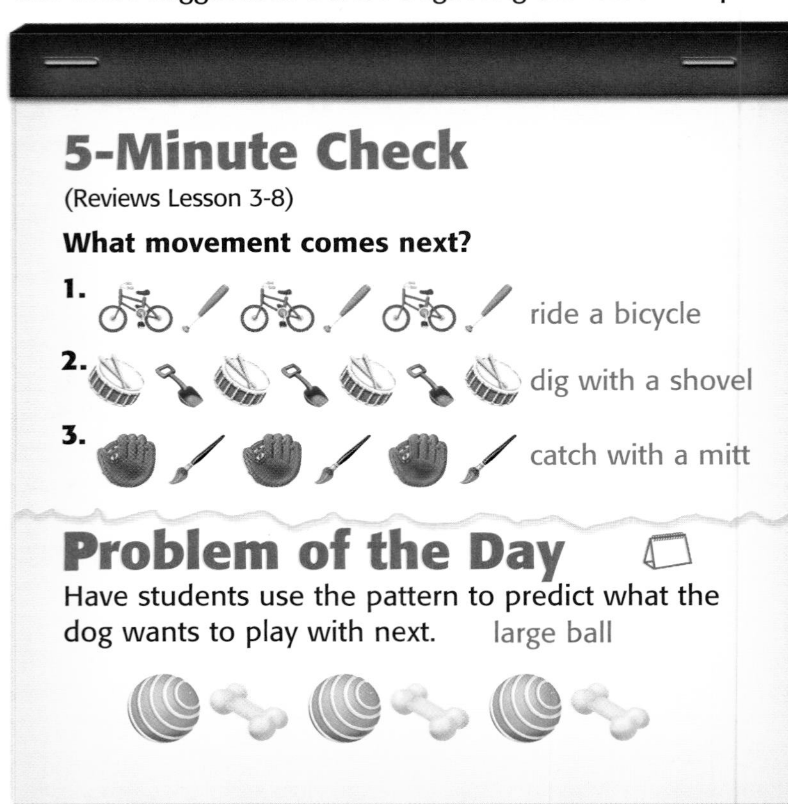

5-Minute Check

(Reviews Lesson 3-8)

What movement comes next?

1. ride a bicycle
2. dig with a shovel
3. catch with a mitt

Problem of the Day

Have students use the pattern to predict what the dog wants to play with next. large ball

LINE UP Write on the chalkboard: If crayon, then boys. If crayon, then girls. Create a green and yellow crayon pattern. Have students predict which comes next. Have boys line up if green and girls if yellow.

Building Math Vocabulary

Discuss how patterns help us **predict** what will happen next. Show this pattern and ask what comes next.

- Tell: If, then we are playing music.
- Tell: If , then we are playing sports.
- Using the patterns, ask students to predict what we will be playing next. sports

Differentiated Instruction

Small Group Options

Option 1 Below/Approaching Level BL

SPATIAL

Materials: pennies, paper, pencils

- Each student should flip the penny ten times, and mark on their paper whether it was heads or tails.
- For the next ten flips, the student should write their predictions of heads or tails. The student should write down what was flipped and compare it to the prediction.
- The students should compare both sets of flipped pennies to see if there is a pattern.

Option 2 English Language Learners ELL

LOGICAL

Materials: paper folded lengthwise with 6 tabs cut and numbered on the front; 2 types of stickers (for dog and car)
Core Vocabulary: under, dog, car
Common Use Verb: will start
See Math This strategy teaches predicting patterns.

- Say: "I ***will start*** a pattern." Tear tabs 1 and 2 off. Say: "Dog, car. This is my pattern."
- Reveal remaining stickers, folding tabs out of the way. Read chorally.
- Fold back tabs to cover stickers. Say: "What is **under** number 5?" dog Repeat with other tabs.

Independent Work Options

Option 1 Early Finishers AL OL

KINESTHETIC

Materials: cotton balls, paper snowflakes, drawing paper, crayons, sticky notes

- Have students create a pattern with the wind (cotton ball for a cloud blowing) and snow (paper snowflakes).
- Have them write: If , then ________. If , then _______.
- Tell them to draw something they would do when it is windy and when it is snowing. Sample answers: fly a kite, go sledding
- Have them draw the activity that others should predict would come next if the pattern continues and cover with sticky notes.
- Have students trade papers and work the problems.

Option 2 Student Technology

Math Online macmillanmh.com

Math Songs, "Stars and Stripes" Track 1

Option 3 Learning Station: Social Studies (p. 67H)

Direct students to the Social Studies Learning Station for opportunities to explore and extend the lesson concept.

Leveled Lesson Resources

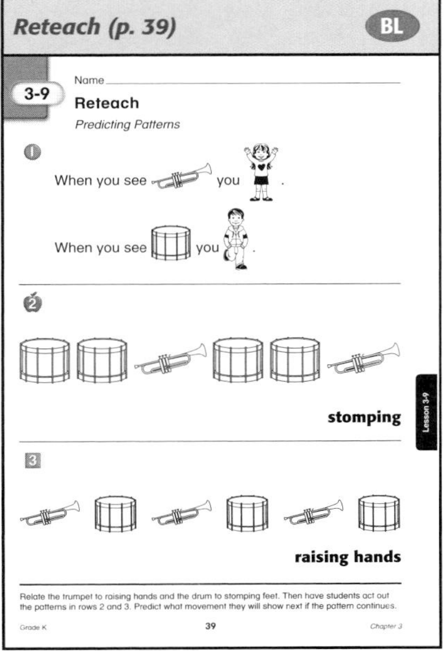

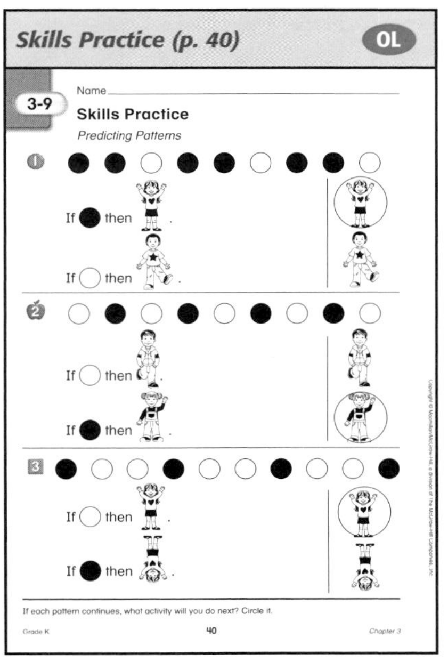

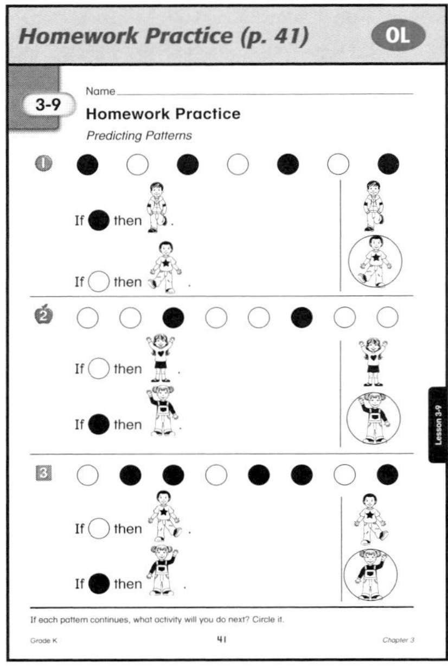

1 Introduce

Circle Time

Activity Choice 1 • Literature

The Noisy Farm by Stuart J. Murphy

- Identify the sounds for each animal or object. Focus on sounds that repeat more than one word (such as "pong, pong, poink" for the bucket or "puck-puck, puckety-puck" for the chickens).
- Invite students to make up animal sound patterns (using purr-purr, puckety-puck, oink-oink!, squeal-squoink!) for others to identify and copy.
- Make sound patterns (snap, snap, clap) and ask students to join you when they identify the pattern.
- Challenge students to predict patterns as you model different sounds.

Activity Choice 2 • Hands-On 

Manipulatives: pattern blocks

- Have students form groups of four.
- Give each group some pattern blocks. Have the class agree on movements that each shape represents. For example, the square means hop one time.
- Have each student take turns creating patterns with their pattern blocks.
- Ask each group to present its pattern, and ask the other groups to **predict** what movement would come next if the pattern continues.
- Then have the class act out the movement pattern.

2 Teach

Direct students to the top of p. 89.

- Have students identify the weather.
- **What do you need when it is sunny?** sunglasses
- **What do you need when it is raining?** umbrella
- Have students identify the weather pattern and predict what comes next.
- **If it is sunny next, what will you need?** sunglasses

BL Alternate Teaching Strategy

If students have trouble with identifying patterns . . .

Then use one of these reteach options.

1 CRM **Daily Reteach Worksheet** (p. 39)

2 Show students an AB pattern of and .

- Tell students if then , and if , then .
- Draw the object that belongs with each part of the pattern below it (below and below).
- Have students predict which item they will need if the pattern continues.
- Challege students to create their own patterns.

COMMON ERROR!

Students may not finish the problems because, after they identify the pattern, they may stop with what comes next. Encourage them to look at the problems in two steps.

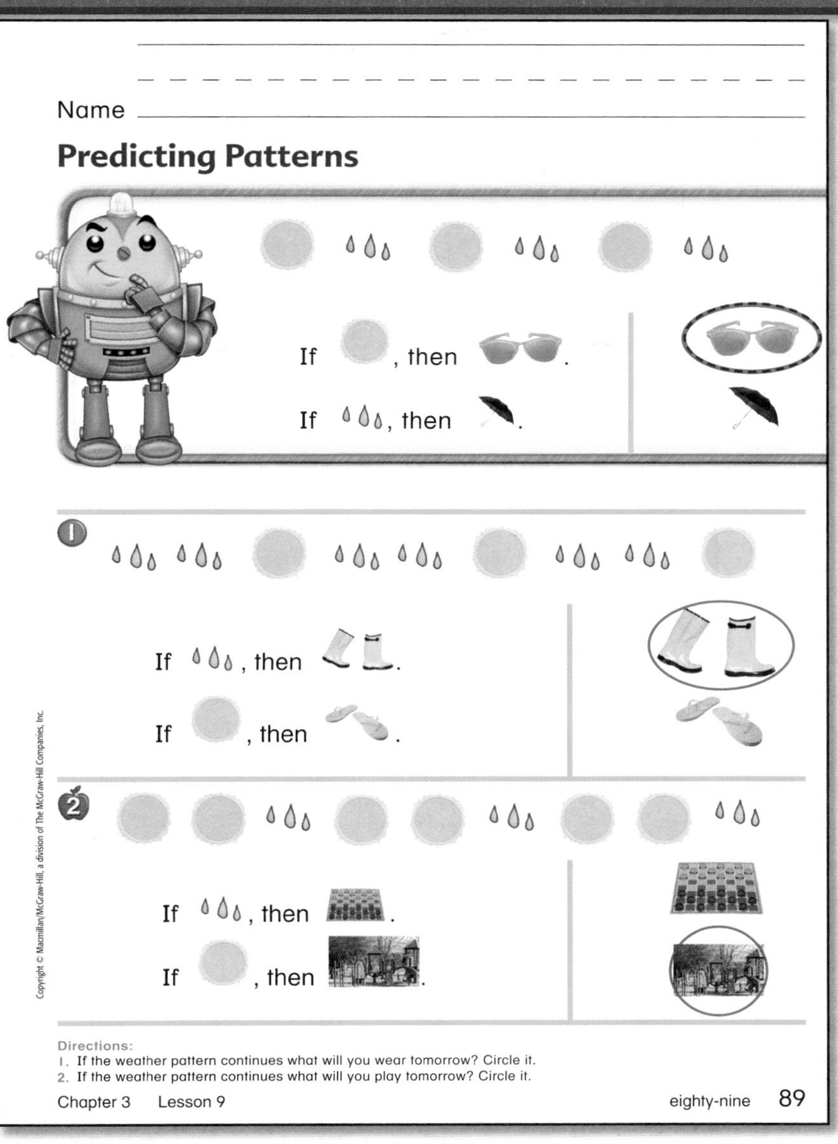

Name

Predicting Patterns

If , then .

If , then .

1

If , then .

If , then .

2

If , then .

If , then .

Directions:
1. If the weather pattern continues what will you wear tomorrow? Circle it.
2. If the weather pattern continues what will you play tomorrow? Circle it.

Chapter 3 Lesson 9 eighty-nine 89

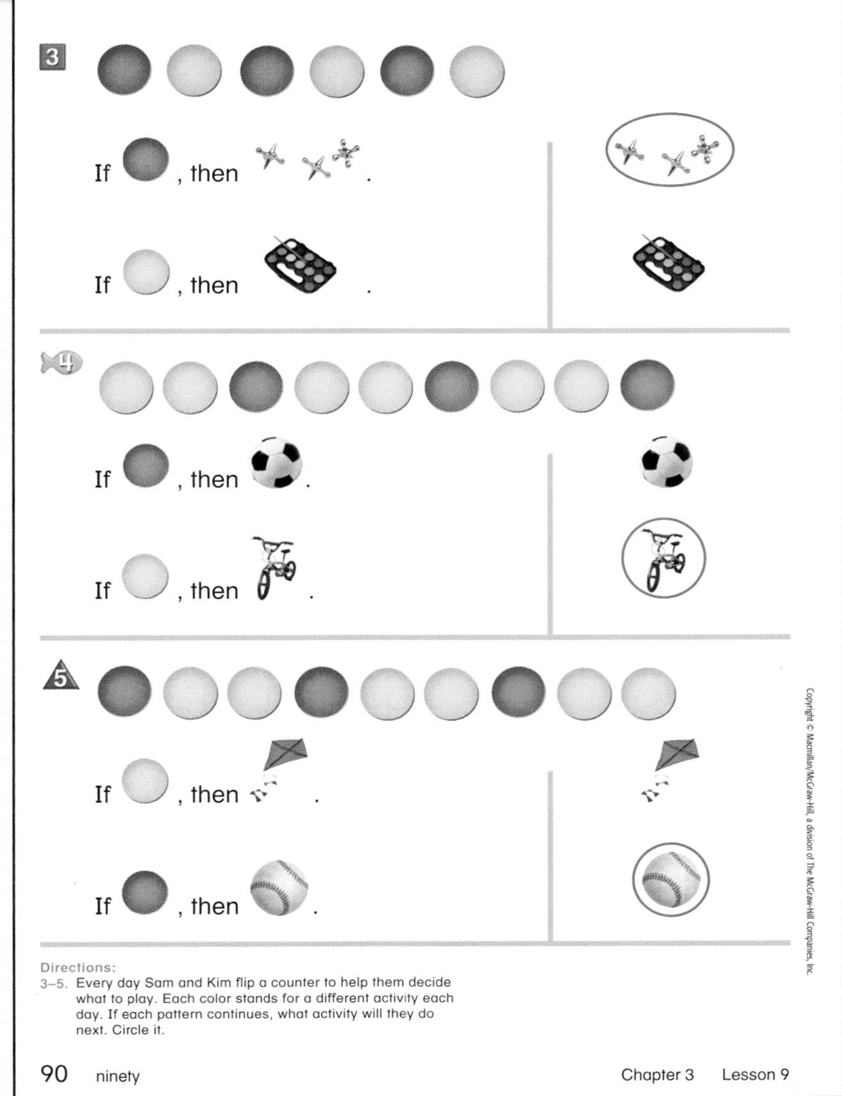

3

If , then .

If , then .

4

If , then .

If , then .

5

If , then .

If , then .

Directions:
3–5. Every day Sam and Kim flip a counter to help them decide what to play. Each color stands for a different activity each day. If each pattern continues, what activity will they do next. Circle it.

90 ninety Chapter 3 Lesson 9

3 Practice

Guided Practice

- Direct students to p. 89.
- Have students identify the weather pattern and what they would wear tomorrow in Exercise 1.
- Have them circle what they will need if the pattern continues.
- Repeat the activity with Exercise 2.

Independent Practice

Have students turn to p. 90 and work independently on the exercises.

4 Assess

Formative Assessment

- Show students the following pattern:  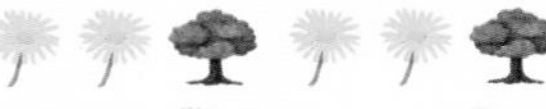
- Tell: If , then . If , then .
- Ask students to predict which animal will come next if the pattern continues.

Quick Check **Are students still struggling to predict patterns?**

If Yes → Small Group Options (p. 89B)

If No → Independent Work Options (p. 89B)

CRM Skills Practice Worksheet (p. 40)

CRM Enrich Worksheet (p. 42)

Problem Solving
in Art
Real-World MATH
Patterns are everywhere!
Let's look in the kitchen.
This book belongs to
TEKS K.13 The student applies Kindergarten mathematics to solve problems connected to everyday experiences and activities in and outside of school.
(A) Identify mathematics in everyday situations.
A

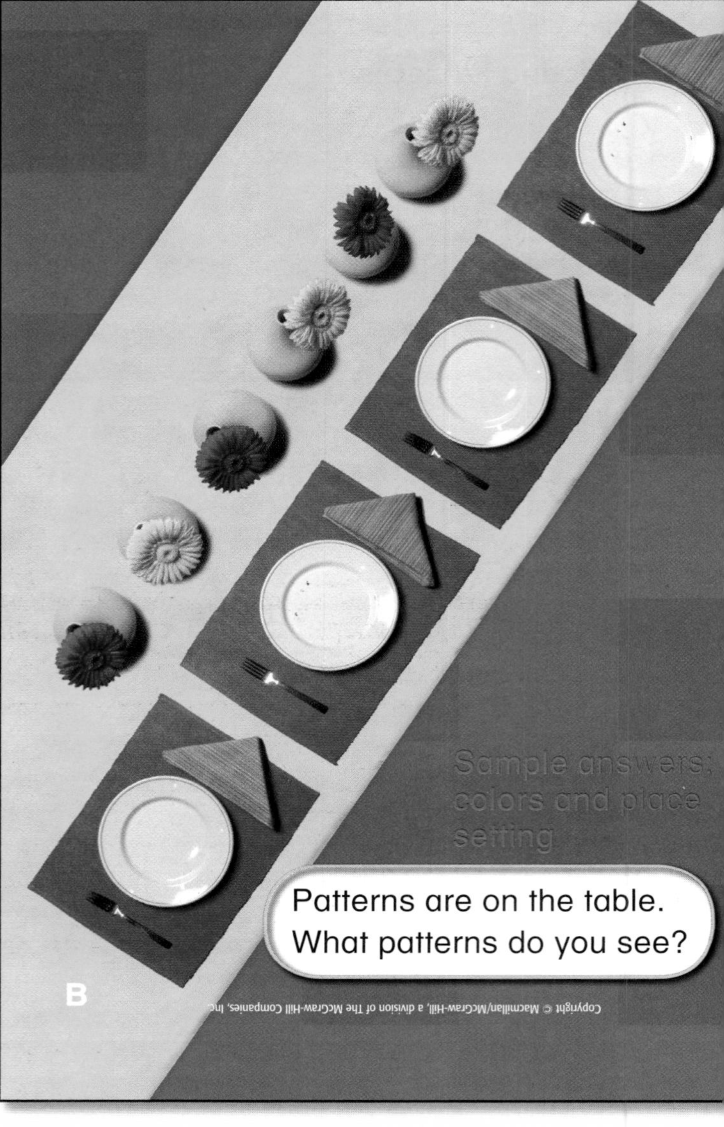

Sample answers: colors and place setting
Patterns are on the table.
What patterns do you see?
B

Lesson Planner

Objectives

To recognize and create patterns from everyday situations and experiences.

National Standards 

Students identify connections and use similarities between the characteristics of the visual arts and other disciplines.

Activate Prior Knowledge

Before you turn students' attention to the pages, discuss collections.

- **Where do you see patterns in your house?** Sample answers: in closets, on furniture
- **Can you think of patterns in the kitchen?** Sample answers: curtains, floor

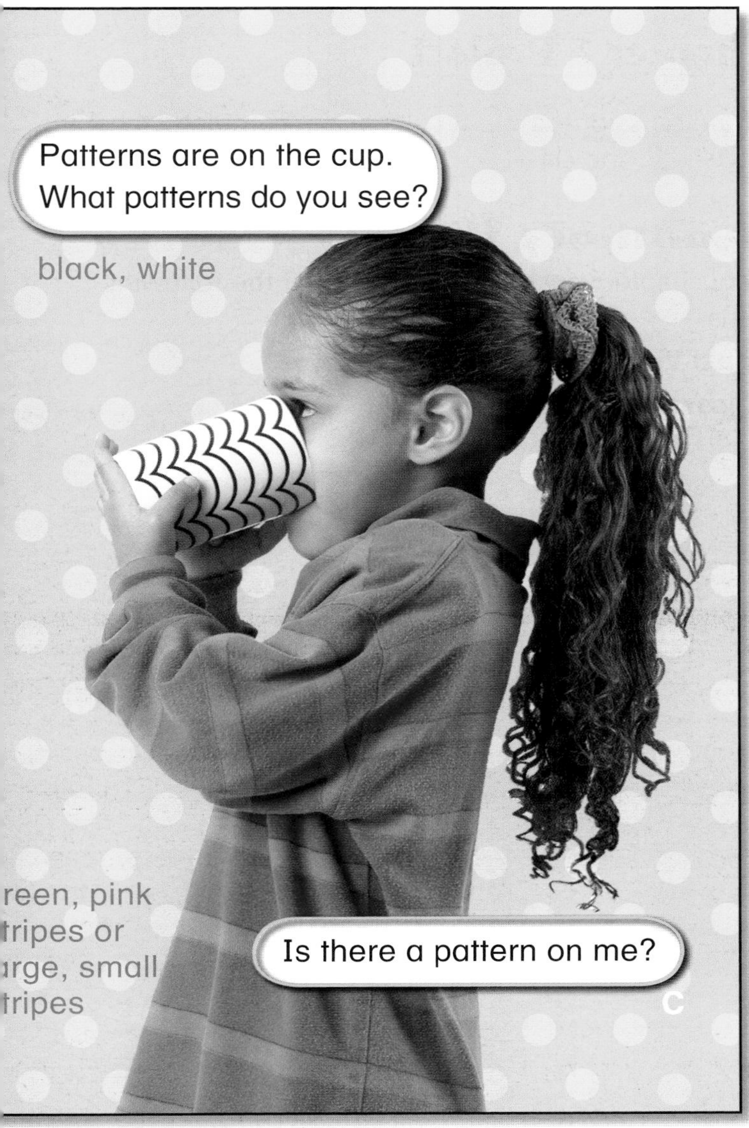

Patterns are on the cup.
What patterns do you see?
black, white
reen, pink
tripes or
rge, small
tripes
Is there a pattern on me?
C

A pattern is on the plate.
What pattern do you see?
dot, leaves
Sample answer: I used red and yellow to show dot and leaves pattern another way.
Color the boxes to show the pattern another way. Explain.
D
FOLD DOWN

Create the Book

Guide students to create their book.

- Have them fold the page in half.
- Ask them to write their name on page A.
- Explain that page A is the front cover and page D is the back cover. If necessary, have them practice flipping through the book in order.
- Guide them in solving the problems on each of the pages.

Use the Student Pages

Have students work individually or in pairs to solve the problems on pages B–D.

Page B Students may not think of place settings as being patterns. Discuss the routine or pattern of setting the table.

Page C Students may notice there is a pattern on the background as well.

Page D Students may struggle with creating a new pattern. Encourage them to be creative and choose a simple pattern (AB, ABB, AAB). Then have them choose color.

WRITING IN MATH Have students write about patterns they find in their bedroom at home.

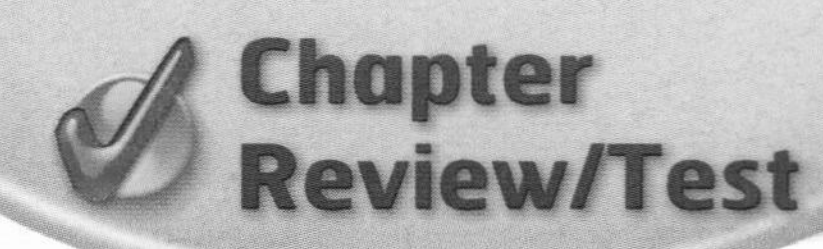

Chapter Review/Test

Dinah Zike's Foldables

Have students use the Flashcard Holder Foldable to review and reinforce the concepts in this chapter. (See p. 67 for instructions.)

Chapter 3 Project

Lead a discussion on the results of the completed chapter projects with the class.

Vocabulary Review

Review chapter vocabulary using one of the following options.

- **Visual Vocabulary Cards (2, 4, 30)**
- **eGlossary** at macmillanmh.com

Data-Driven Decision Making

Based on the results of the Chapter Review/Test, use the following to review concepts that continue to present students with problems.

Exercises	State/Local Standards	What's the Math?	Error Analysis	Resources for Review
1–2 Lessons 3-1 and 3-2		Find an object that is over, under, on top of, in the middle of, or bottom of other objects.	Reverses the directions. Does not correctly follow directions.	CRM Chapter 3 Resource Masters (Reteach Worksheets) Math Online Concepts in Motion Math Adventures
3 Lesson 3-3		Find the object that is before or after another object.	Reverses before and after directions.	
4–5 Lesson 3-4 and 3-5		Identify, create and extend patterns of objects.	Does not correctly identify next object in pattern. Circles both objects.	

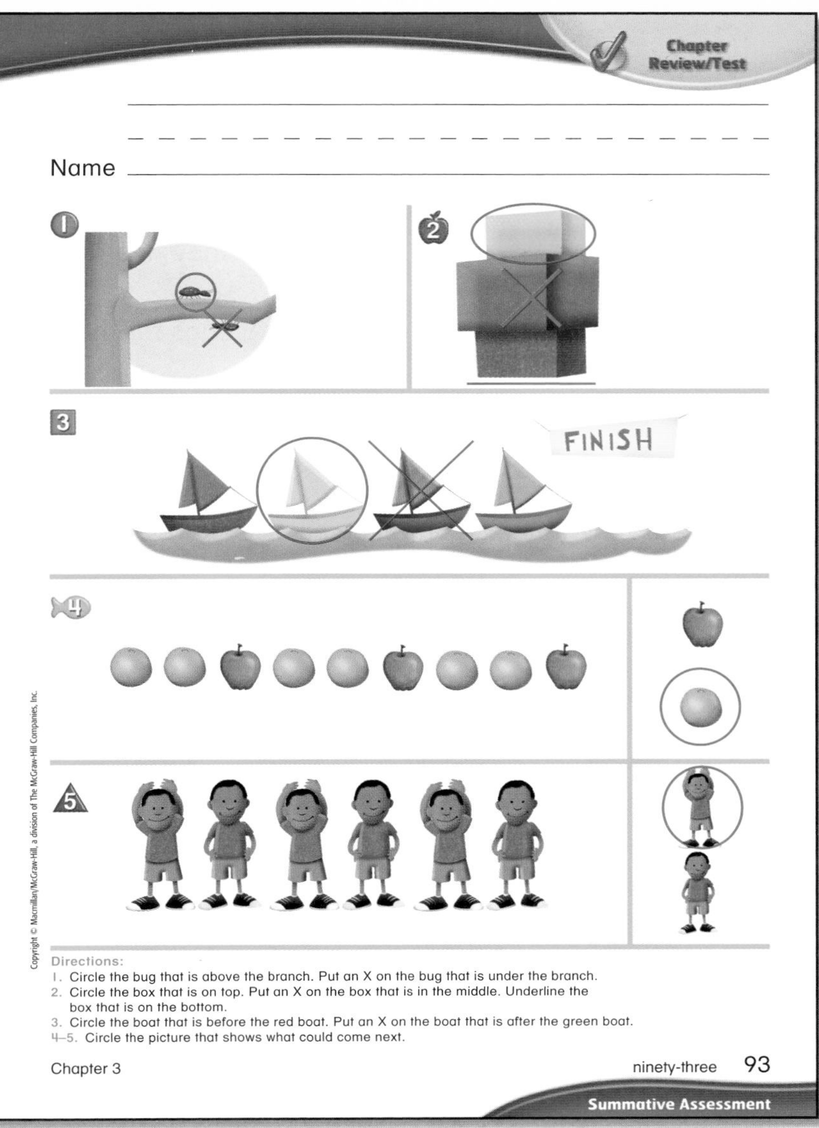

Chapter Review/Test

Name

FINISH

Directions:
1. Circle the bug that is above the branch. Put an X on the bug that is under the branch.
2. Circle the box that is on top. Put an X on the box that is in the middle. Underline the box that is on the bottom.
3. Circle the boat that is before the red boat. Put an X on the boat that is after the green boat.
4–5. Circle the picture that shows what could come next.

Chapter 3 ninety-three 93

Summative Assessment

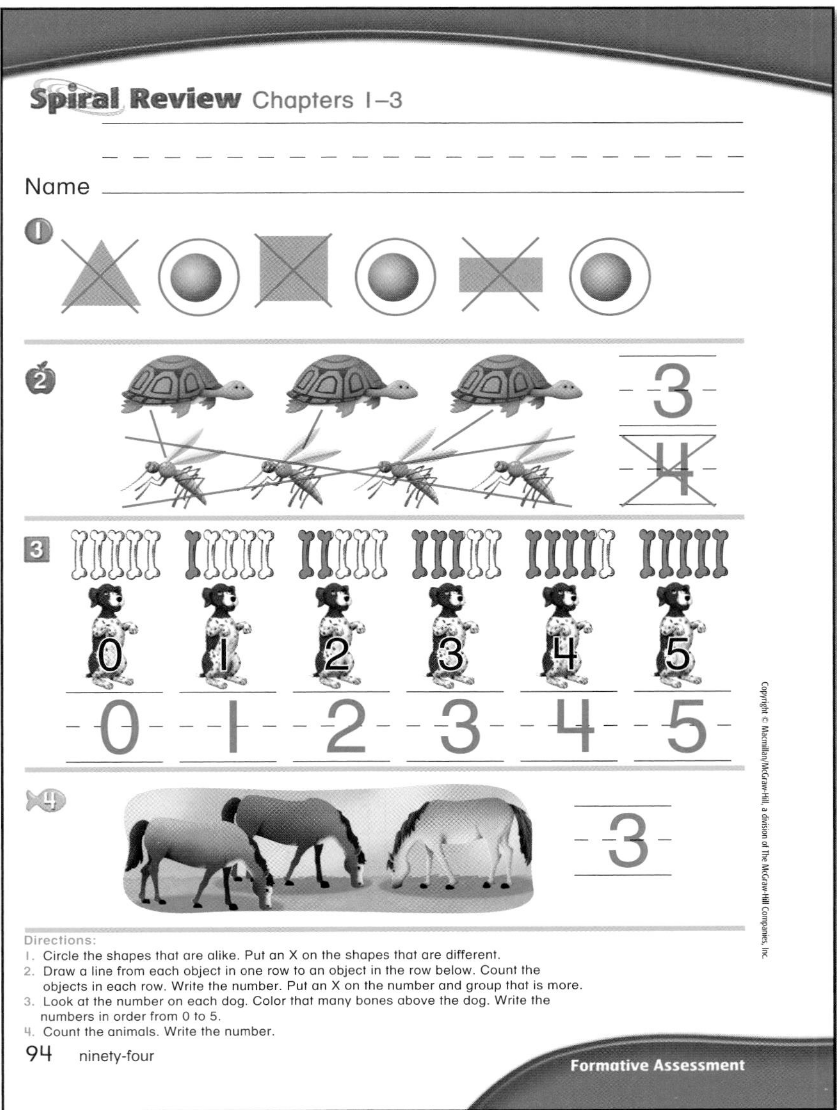

Spiral Review Chapters 1–3

Name

3

4

0 1 2 3 4 5

0 1 2 3 4 5

3

Directions:
1. Circle the shapes that are alike. Put an X on the shapes that are different.
2. Draw a line from each object in one row to an object in the row below. Count the objects in each row. Write the number. Put an X on the number and group that is more.
3. Look at the number on each dog. Color that many bones above the dog. Write the numbers in order from 0 to 5.
4. Count the animals. Write the number.

94 ninety-four

Formative Assessment

Summative Assessment

Use these alternate leveled chapter tests to differentiate assessment for the specific needs of your students.

Leveled Chapter 3 Tests			
Form	**Type**	**Level**	**CRM Pages**
1	Multiple Choice	BL	50–51
2A	Multiple Choice	OL	52–53
2C	Multiple Choice	OL	54–55
2D	Free Response	AL	56–57

BL = below/approaching grade level
OL = on grade level
AL = above/beyond grade level

Spiral Review

Reviews Chapters 1 and 2

Objective: Review and assess mastery of skills and concepts from previous chapters.

Resources for Review

Based on student results, refer to these lessons for remediation:

- **Exercise 1: Lesson 1-1** p. 17
- **Exercise 2: Lesson 2-7** p. 29
- **Exercise 3: Lesson 2-8** p. 59
- **Exercise 4: Lesson 2-2** p. 45

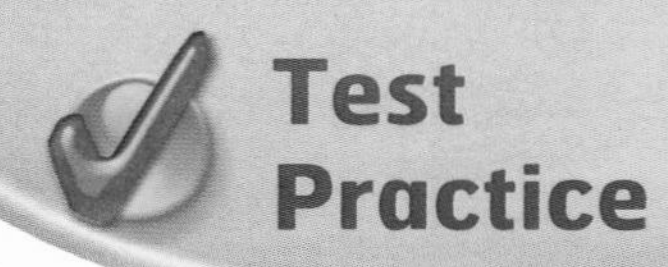

Test Practice

Chapters 1–3

Formative Assessment

- You can use Student Edition pp. 95-96 to benchmark student progress.
- Additional practice pages can be found in Chapter 3 Resource Masters.

Chapter 3 Resource Masters
Cumulative Test Practice

- Multiple Choice format (pp. 50–55)
- Free Response format (pp. 56–57)

Create additional practice worksheets or tests.

Math Online

For additional practice with the Connections, visit macmillanmh.com.

Test-Taking Tips

For the Teacher

- Be sure students have all the supplies they need for the test before they start.
- Be sure students understand the directions for the test before the test begins.

For the Student

- Tell students to write in their test booklet.
- Tell students to cross out answers they know that are wrong.
- Remind students to take their time and be sure to mark the correct answer.

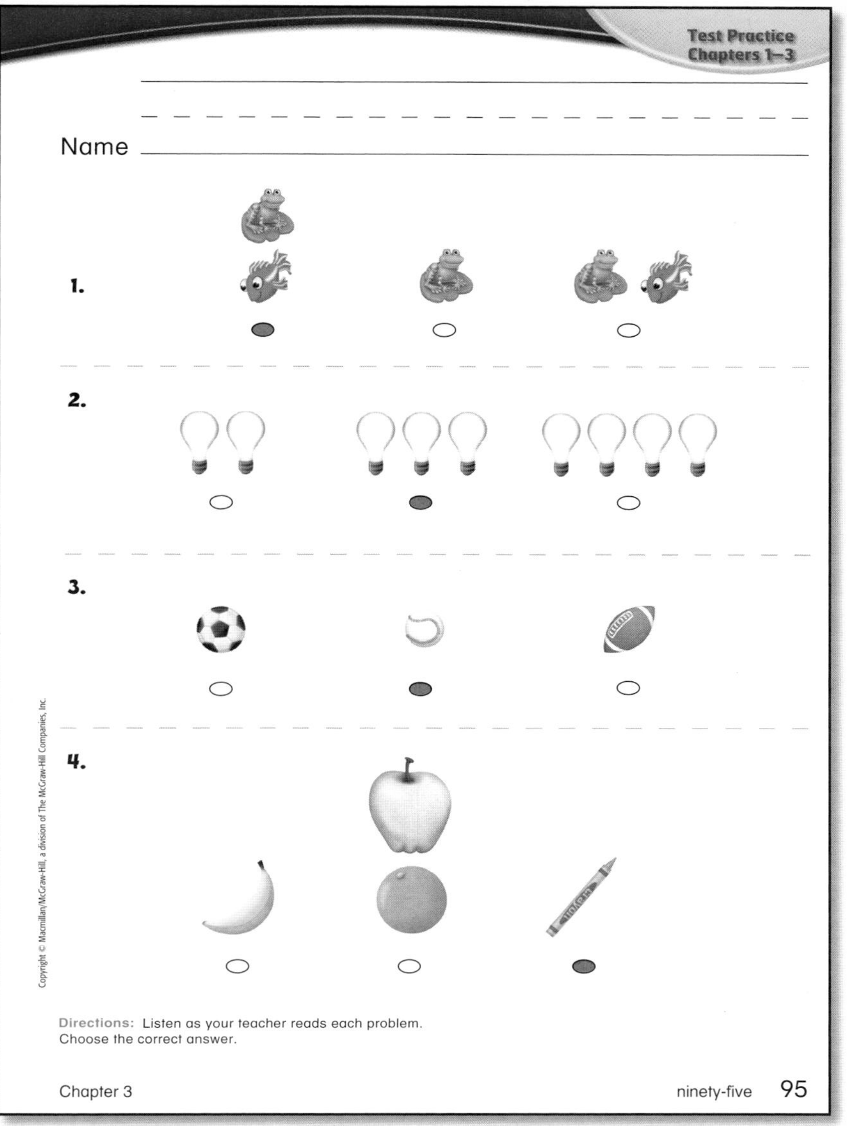
Test Practice Chapters 1–3

Name

1.

2.

3.

4.

Directions: Listen as your teacher reads each problem. Choose the correct answer.

Copyright © Macmillan/McGraw-Hill, a division of The McGraw-Hill Companies, Inc.

Chapter 3 ninety-five 95

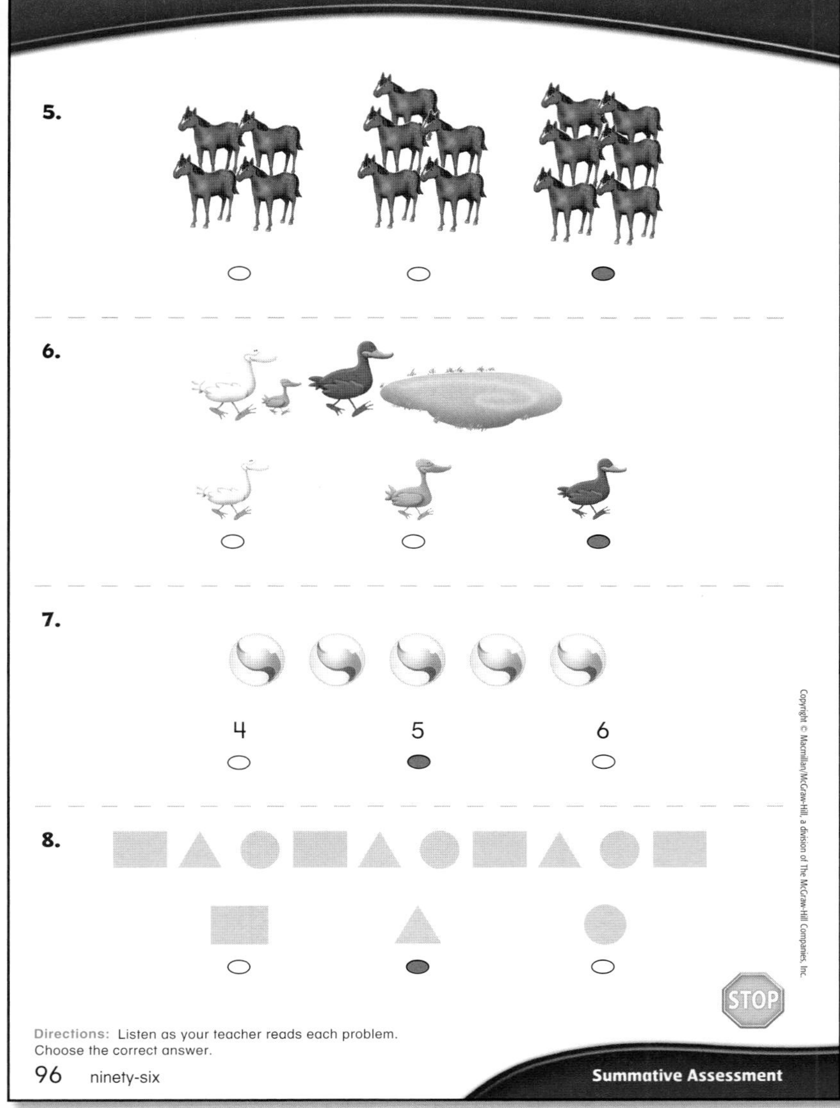
5.

6.

7.

4 5 6

8.

Directions: Listen as your teacher reads each problem. Choose the correct answer.

Copyright © Macmillan/McGraw-Hill, a division of The McGraw-Hill Companies, Inc.

96 ninety-six Summative Assessment

Test Directions for Teachers

Read the following directions to students before they begin. Then read each question followed by a pause to allow students time to work and choose an answer. The first test item can be worked as a class example.

- **Write your name at the top of the page.**
- **I am going to read each question to you. Listen carefully to the entire question before you choose an answer.**

1. Look at the frog and the fish. Mark the picture that shows the frog is above the fish.
2. Find the group that has 3 light bulbs. Mark the group that has exactly 3 light bulbs.
3. Look at the soccer ball, football, and baseball. Mark the ball that is in the middle.
4. Look at the row of objects. Find the object that does not belong. Mark the object that does not belong.

- **Turn the page over.**

5. Look at the group of horses. Mark the group that shows more than the other groups.
6. Look at the ducks in line. Mark the duck that comes before the small gray duck.
7. Look at the group of marbles. Count the number of marbles. Mark the number that shows the same number of marbles.
8. Look at the pattern of shapes. Mark the shape that could come next.

Chapter Overview

Chapter-at-a-Glance

Lesson		Math Objective	State/Local Standards
4-1	**Numbers 6 and 7** (pp. 101–102)	Name, recognize, and count the numerals 6 and 7 using concrete objects and illustrations.	
4-2	**Number 8** (pp. 103–104)	Name, recognize, and count the numeral 8 using concrete objects and illustrations.	
4-3	**Read and Write 6, 7, and 8** (pp. 105–106)	Recognize and write the numerals 6, 7, and 8.	
4-4	**Numbers 9 and 10** (pp. 109–110)	Name, recognize, and count the numerals 9 and 10 using concrete objects and illustrations.	
4-5	**Read and Write 9 and 10** (pp. 111–112)	Recognize and write the numerals 9 and 10.	
4-6	**Problem-Solving Strategy: Draw a Picture** (pp. 113–114)	Count, recognize, represent, and name numerals 6 through 10 using concrete objects and illustrations.	
4-7	**Compare Numbers to 10** (pp. 115–116)	Use one-to-one correspondence and counting to compare sets and determine which has more than, less than, or whether the sets are the same/equal.	
4-8	**Order Numbers to 10** (pp. 117–118)	Order numbers from 1 to 10 in sequence using illustrations.	
4-9	**Ordinal Numbers** (pp. 119–120)	Use ordinal numbers to describe the position of an object in a row.	

Use Numbers to 10

BIG Idea Understanding numbers to 10 and their relative values and magnitudes is of critical importance. The numbers to 10 serve as the first layer of the foundation for numeration, place value, and whole number operations.

- Numbers from six to 10 are represented concretely, pictorially, and symbolically.
- Students' understanding of each number and its value is applied as they compose, compare and order numbers.

Algebra Students prepare for algebra by relating quantities and sets to written numbers. (Lesson 4-3)

Geometry Students are introduced to basic shapes. (Lesson 4-1)

Focal Points and Connections

GK-FP1 *Number and Operations:* **Representing, comparing, and ordering whole numbers and joining and separating sets**

Children use numbers, including written numerals, to represent quantities and to solve quantitative problems, such as counting objects in a set, creating a set with a given number of objects, comparing and ordering sets or numerals by using both cardinal and ordinal meanings, and modeling simple joining and separating situations with objects. They choose, combine, and apply effective strategies for answering quantitative questions, including quickly recognizing the number in a small set, counting and producing sets of given sizes, counting the number in combined sets, and counting backward.

Skills Trace
Vertical Alignment

PreKindergarten

In PreK, students learned to:

- Count by ones to 10
- Arrange sets of concrete objects in one-to-one correspondence.
- Name "how many" are in a set of up to three (or more) objects without counting (e.g., recognizing two or three crayons in a box).

Kindergarten

During this chapter, students learn to:

- Name, recognize, and count the quantities 9 and 10.
- Represent and order a number of objects.

After this chapter, students will learn to:

- Collect information about objects in their environment.
- Name, recognize, and count a number of objects up to 30.

First Grade

In first grade, students will learn to:

- Model addition.
- Represent equivalent forms of the same number.
- Show the meaning of addition and subtraction.
- Count, read, and write whole numbers to 100.

BackMapping and Vertical Alignment McGraw-Hill's *Math Connects* program was conceived and developed with the final results in mind: student success in Algebra 1 and beyond. The authors, using the **NCTM Focal Points and Focal Connections** as their guide, developed this brand new series by back-mapping from Algebra 1 concepts, and vertically aligning the topics so that they build upon prior skills and concepts and serve as a foundation for future topics.

Math Vocabulary

The following math vocabulary words for Chapter 4 are listed in the glossary of the ***Student Edition***. You can find interactive definitions in 13 languages in the ***eGlossary*** at macmillanmh.com.

eight (p. 103) 8

ordinal numbers (p. 119)

nine (p. 109) 9

seven (p. 101) 7

six (p. 101) 6

ten (p. 109) 10

Chapter Planner

Suggested Pacing		
Instruction	Review and Assessment	TOTAL
9 days	2 days	**11 days**

Diagnostic Assessment
Are You Ready? (p. 98)

	Lesson 4-1 (Pacing: 1 day)	Lesson 4-2 (Pacing: 1 day)	Lesson 4-3 (Pacing: 1 day)
Lesson/ Objective	**Numbers 6 and 7** (pp. 101–102) **Objective:** Name, recognize, and count the numerals 6 and 7 using concrete objects and illustrations.	**Number 8** (pp. 103–104) **Objective:** Name, recognize, and count the numeral 8 using concrete objects and illustrations.	**Read and Write 6, 7, and 8** (pp. 105–106) **Objective:** Recognize and write the numerals 6, 7, and 8.
State/Local Standards			
Math Vocabulary	**six, seven**	**eight**	
Lesson Resources	**Materials** paper, crayons, paper plates, cups, spoons, forks, napkins **Manipulatives** counters, color tiles **Other Resources** CRM Leveled Worksheets (pp. 6-9); Daily Reteach; Problem of the Day	**Materials** modeling clay, pipe cleaners, workmat **Manipulatives** connecting cubes, counters **Other Resources** CRM Leveled Worksheets (pp. 10-13); Daily Reteach; Problem of the Day	**Materials** glue, colored paper, drawing paper, pencils, paper bag, chalk, crayons, buttons **Other Resources** CRM Leveled Worksheets (pp. 14-17); Daily Reteach; Problem of the Day
Technology Math Online	Math Adventures	Math Adventures	Math Adventures; Concepts in Motion
Reaching All Learners	English Learners, p. 101B ELL; Gifted and Talented, p. 101B AL; Early Finishers, p. 101B OL AL	English Learners, p. 103B ELL; Below Level, p. 103B BL; Early Finishers, p. 103B OL AL	English Learners, p. 105B ELL; Below Level, p. 103B BL; Early Finishers, p. 105B OL AL
Alternate Lesson	*Math Their Way,* p. 46	*Math Their Way,* p. 176	*Math Their Way,* p. 51

Formative Assessment
Mid-Chapter Check (p. 107)

Game Time: Surf's Up! (p. 108)

KEY

BL Below/Approaching Level; OL On Level; AL Above/Beyond Level; ELL English Learners
SE Student Edition; TE Teacher Edition; CRM Chapter 1 Resource Masters; CD-Rom
Transparency; Flip Chart; Real-World Problem Solving Library

Use Numbers to 10

	Lesson 4-4 (Pacing: 1 day)	Lesson 4-5 (Pacing: 1 day)	Lesson 4-6 (Pacing: 1 day)
Lesson/ Objective	**Numbers 9 and 10** (pp. 109–110) **Objective:** Name, recognize, and count the numerals 9 and 10 using concrete objects and illustrations.	**Read and Write 9 and 10** (pp. 111–112) **Objective:** Recognize and write the numerals 9 and 10.	**Problem-Solving Srategy: Draw a Picture** **Objective:** Count, recognize, represent, and name numerals 6 through 10 using concrete objects and illustrations.
State/Local Standards			
Math Vocabulary	**nine, ten**		
Lesson Resources	**Materials** paper, markers, paper clips **Manipulatives** connecting cubes, counters **Other Resources** CRM Leveled Worksheets (pp.18-21) Daily Reteach Problem of the Day	**Materials** paper, circle stickers, modeling clay, number cards **Other Resources** CRM Leveled Worksheets (pp. 22-25) Daily Reteach Problem of the Day	**Materials** flower sticker, paper, crayons, tape **Manipulatives** counters, color tiles **Other Resources** CRM Leveled Worksheets (pp. 26-30) Daily Reteach Problem of the Day *Numbers About Me*
Technology Math Online	Math Adventures	Math Adventures	
Reaching All Learners	English Learners, p. 109B ELL Gifted and Talented, p. 109B AL Early Finishers, p. 109B OL AL	English Learners, p. 111B ELL Below Level, p. 113B BL Early Finishers, p. 111B OL AL	English Learners, p. 113B ELL Gifted and Talented, p. 113B AL Early Finishers, p. 113B OL AL
Alternate Lesson	*Math Their Way,* p. 101	*Math Their Way,* p. 50	

Chapter Planner

	Lesson 4-7 Pacing: 1 day	Lesson 4-8 Pacing: 1 day	Lesson 4-9 Pacing: 1 day
Lesson/ Objective	**Compare Numbers to 10** (pp. 115–116) **Objective:** Use one-to-one correspondence and counting to compare sets and determine which has more than, less than, or whether the sets are the same/equal.	**Order Numbers to 10** (pp. 117–118) **Objective:** Order numbers from 1 to 10 in sequence using illustrations.	**Ordinal Numbers** (pp. 119–120) **Objective:** Use ordinal numbers to describe the position of an object in a row.
State/Local Standards			
Math Vocabulary			**ordinal numbers**
Lesson Resources	**Materials** construction paper, pencil, paper bags, small classroom objects: paper clips, beads, crayons, rubber bands, WorkMats ten-frame **Manipulatives** counters **Other Resources** CRM Leveled Worksheets (pp. 31-34) Daily Reteach Problem of the Day	**Materials** sheet of number cards, index cards, labels, glue, children cutouts, pencils, paper **Other Resources** CRM Leveled Worksheets (pp. 35-38) Daily Reteach Problem of the Day	**Materials** pictures of animals **Other Resources** CRM Leveled Worksheets (pp. 39-42) Daily Reteach Problem of the Day
Technology Math Online	Math Adventures	Math Adventures Concepts in Motion	Math Adventures Concepts in Motion
Reaching All Learners	English Learners, p.115B ELL Gifted and Talented, p. 115B AL Early Finishers, p. 115B OL AL	English Learners, p.117B ELL Below Level, p. 117B BL Early Finishers, p. 117B OL AL	English Learners, p.119B ELL Gifted and Talented, p. 119B AL Early Finishers, p. 119B OL AL
Alternate Lesson	*Math Their Way*, p. 102 *IMPACT Mathematics*: Unit B	*Math Their Way*, p. 49 *IMPACT Mathematics*: Unit B	*IMPACT Mathematics*: Unit E

Problem Solving: Science (p. 121)

Summative Assessment
- Chapter Review/Test (p. 123)
- Test Practice (p. 125)

Assessment Options

Diagnostic Assessment

- SE *Option 1:* Are You Ready? (p. 98)
- *Option 2:* Online Quiz (macmillanmh.com)
- CRM *Option 3:* Diagnostic Test (p. 44)

Formative Assessment

- TE Alternate Teaching Strategies (every lesson)
- TE Writing in Math (every lesson)
- TE Line Up (every lesson)
- SE Mid-Chapter Check (p. 107)
- CRM Mid-Chapter Test (p. 45)

Summative Assessment

- SE Chapter Review/Test (p. 123)
- SE Test Practice (p. 125)
- CRM Leveled Chapter Tests (pp. 50-57)
- CRM Cumulative Test Practice (p. 58)
- CRM Listening Assessment (p. 48)
- CRM Oral Assessment (p. 46)
- Exam*View*® Assessment Suite
- Advance Tracker

Mc Graw Hill Professional Development

Targeted professional development has been articulated throughout **McGraw-Hill's *Math Connects*** program. The **McGraw-Hill Professional Development Video Library** provides short videos that support the **NCTM Focal Points and Focal Connections**. For more information, visit macmillanmh.com

Model Lessons

Instructional Strategies

Assessment Tips

For many students, this will be their first experience with understanding the relationship between numbers and quantities.

- Come up with four or five specific objectives you want to observe during this chapter.
- Create a class checklist which includes these four or five objectives.
- As students master a specific objective, check it off.
- Add comments where appropriate.

Teacher Notes

Learning Stations
Cross-Curricular Links

Science

pair | VISUAL

Count and Sort Leaves

- Group the leaves by shape.
- Count six of one group, seven of another group, and eight of a third group.
- Write the number in each group.

Teacher Note: Have students work in pairs. Provide real or colored paper tree leaves with different shapes such as maple, oak, and beech. Be sure each student pair has three different types of leaves and from six to eight of each type of leaf. Have students group their leaves on paper.

Materials:
- art paper
- three different types of tree leaves

Art

individual | VISUAL

Drawing with Six, Seven, and Eight

- Draw a picture using six stickers.
- Draw a picture using seven stickers.
- Draw a picture using eight stickers.
- Write how many stickers.

Teacher Note: Make a booklet for each student by stapling three pieces of drawing paper together. Give each student a booklet, six to eight of three different types of stickers, and crayons. Have students draw a picture that uses six identical stickers on one page, seven identical stickers on a second page, and eight identical stickers on a third page. Students should write the number of stickers on each page.

Materials:
- stapled booklet of three pages of drawing paper
- stickers
- crayons

Reading

individual | LINGUISTIC

Write the Number

- Count the buttons.
- Write the number.

Teacher Note: Glue six buttons on a poster board. Write "_____ buttons," below the buttons. Make similar poster boards for seven through 10 buttons. Post the boards at the Learning Station. Have volunteers count the buttons aloud, then write the number. Erase or cover answers so other students can write their answers.

Materials:
- buttons
- poster board
- glue
- crayons or markers

Language Arts

pair | LINGUISTIC

Number Story

- Look at the picture.
- Say the number.
- Tell about the picture and number.
- Tell a story about the pictures.

Teacher Note: Cut out pictures of different plants and animals from magazines. Glue the pictures to poster boards. Cut out and glue or draw the numbers five through 10 on poster boards. Show a picture poster board and a number poster board side-by-side. Have students "read" a story of the plants and animals and numbers by describing the pictures and reading the numbers. Encourage students to embellish and tell any story the pictures conjure in their own words. Change the pictures and number poster boards as students take turns reading.

Materials:

- pictures of plants and animals
- pictures of numbers 5–10
- poster board
- glue

Social Studies

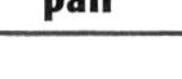

pair | LOGICAL

How Many People in a City?

- Pretend each block is one person.
- Make ten cities of different sizes.
- Line up the cities.
- Count the number of people in each city.

Teacher Note: Have students work in pairs. Students should make a city of one person, then a city of two people, then a city of three people, and so on. Have students line up their cities one in front of the other, like a staircase. Lead students to understand that each city has one more person than the city in front of it.

Materials:

- blocks

Calendar Time

How Many Days in a Week?

- Find a calendar with weeks that begin on Sunday as the first day and end on Saturday as the seventh day.
- Remember that this activity covers one week in a calendar.
- Have a student point to each numbered day and count one to seven aloud.
- Ask students how many days are in one week.
- Relate calendar dates to ordinal numbers by having students identify the first, second, third, etc. day of the month.

Teacher Note: If a calendar is not available with weeks that begin with Sunday, make one with a blank calendar page.

Introduce the Chapter

Real World: Counting Apples

- Gather students in a circle in front of you.
- Tell them a farmer needs help picking apples from a tree. Tell them the farmer needs bags of six, seven, eight, nine, and ten apples to sell at market.
- Draw a large outline of an apple tree. Draw six apples on the tree. Ask students how many apples they see. Point to each apple as students count to six.
- Add one apple to the tree. Ask students how many apples they see. Point to each apple as students count to seven.
- Repeat the activity up to ten apples.

Use the Student Page

Have students turn to p. 97. Guide students to discuss the images on the page and answer the Explore questions.

Key Vocabulary

Introduce the key vocabulary in the chapter using the routine below.

Define: After means to follow in place or time.
Example: Two is after one.
Ask: What number comes after two?

Diagnostic Assessment

- **Option 1:** ***Are You Ready for Chapter 4?***
  SE Student Edition, p. 98
- **Option 2:** ***Online Assessment Quiz***
  Math Online macmillanmh.com
- **Option 3:** ***Diagnostic Test***
  CRM Chapter 4 Resource Masters, p. 44

RTI (Response to Intervention)

Apply the Results Based on the results of the diagnostic assessment on p. 98, use the chart on the next page to address individual needs before and during the chapter.

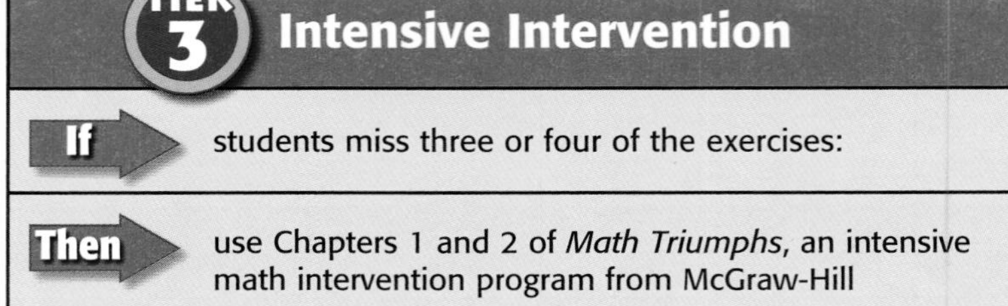

TIER 3 **Intensive Intervention**

If	students miss three or four of the exercises:
Then	use Chapters 1 and 2 of *Math Triumphs*, an intensive math intervention program from McGraw-Hill

Dinah Zike's Foldables

Help students create their own Accordion Book Foldable graphic organizer to order numbers 6–10.

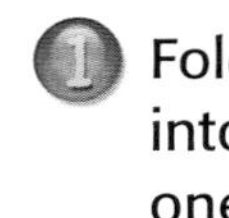

1. Fold four pieces of paper into hamburgers. Fold one side one half inch shorter than the other side.

2. Fold this tab forward over the shorter side, and then fold it back away from the shorter piece of paper.

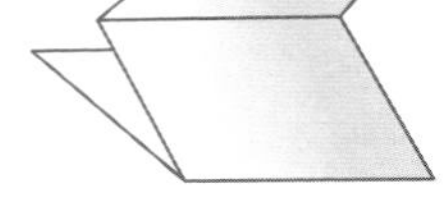

3. Glue together to form an accordion. Glue a straight edge of one section into the valley of another section.

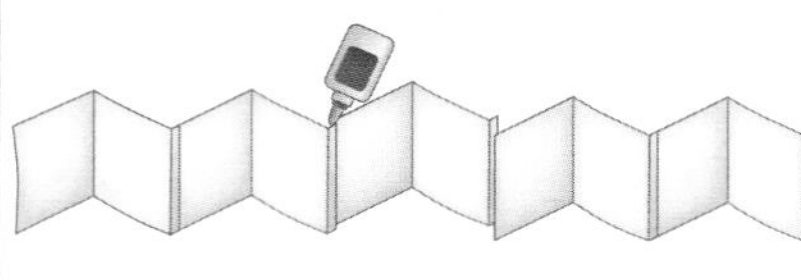

4. Write the numbers 6 and 7 on the top left side of each of the two sections.

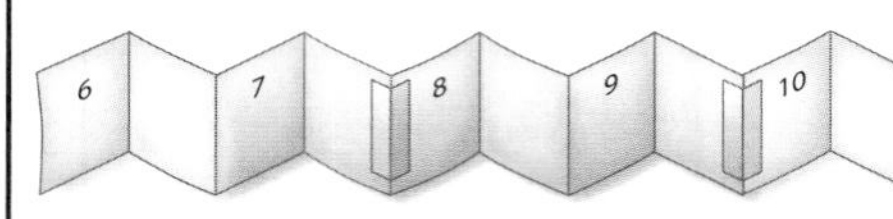

When to Use It *Lessons 4-1, 4-3, 4-5, and 4-7 (Additional instructions for using the Foldable with these lessons are found on pp. 107 and 123.)*

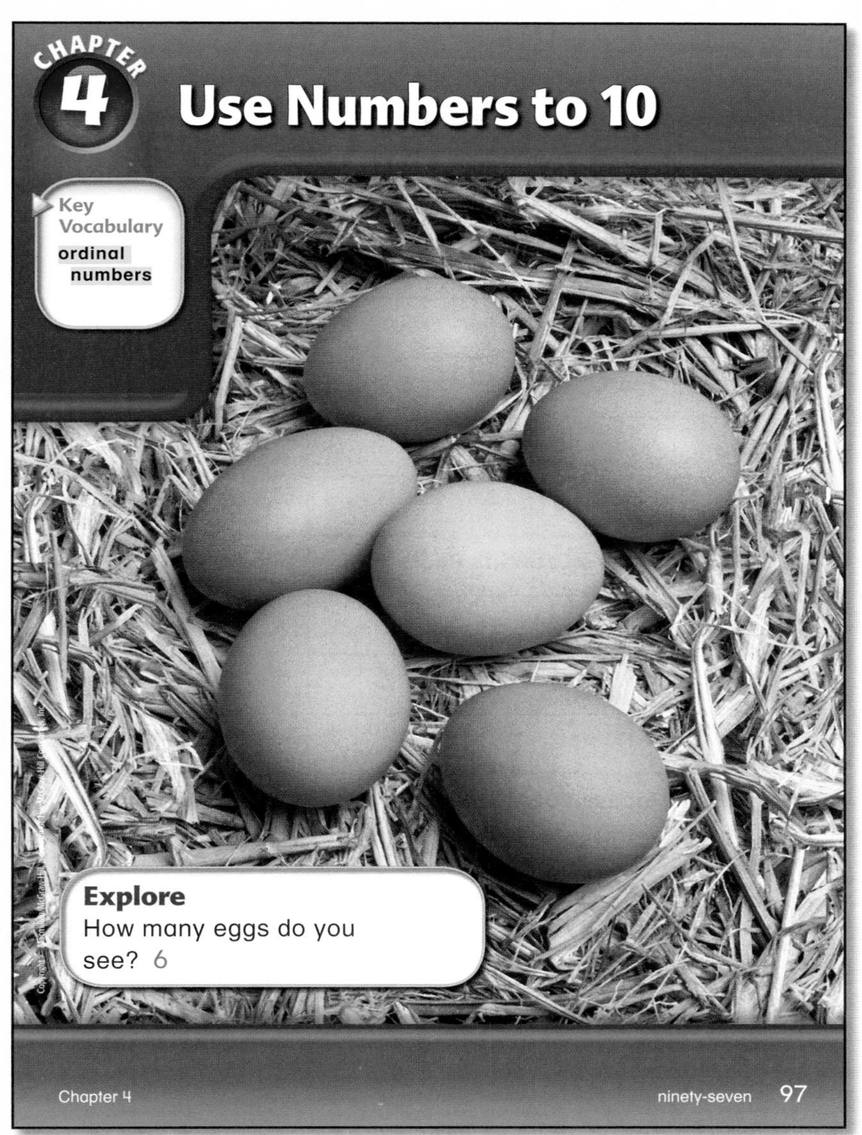

How many eggs do you see? 6

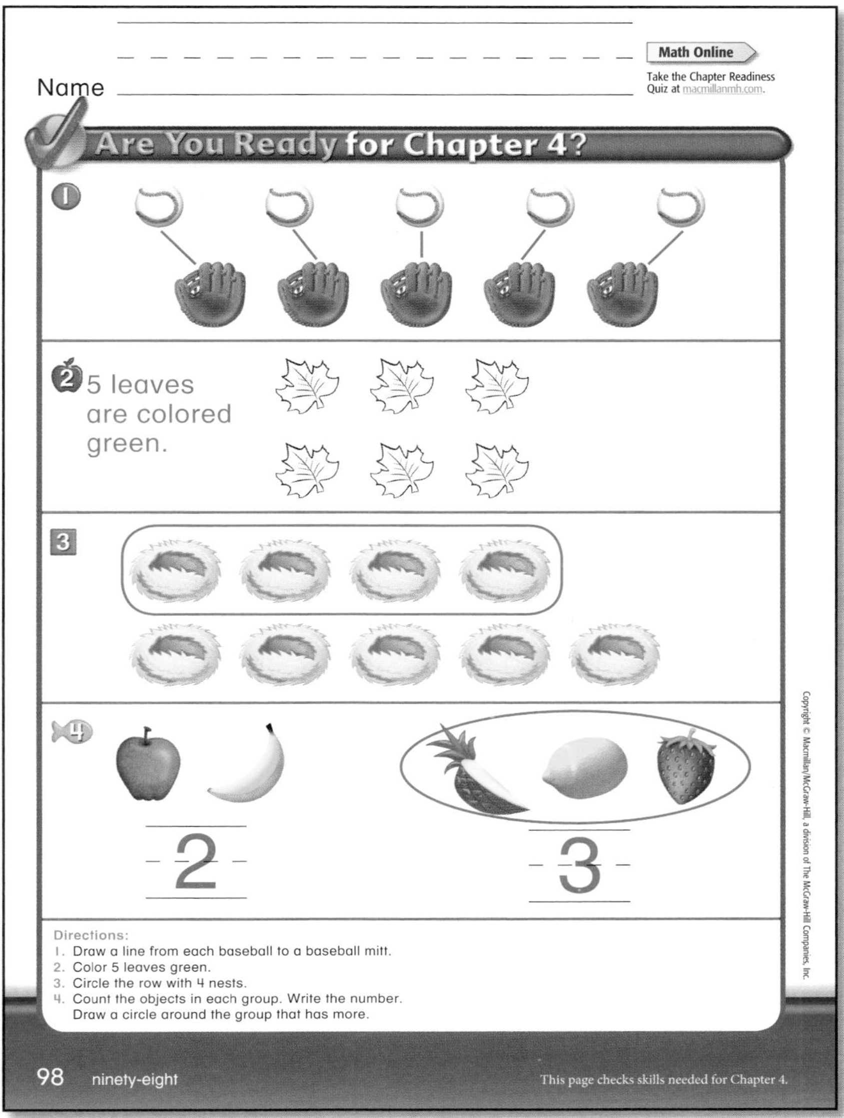

ninety-seven 97

Name
Math Online
Take the Chapter Readiness Quiz at macmillanmh.com.
Are You Ready for Chapter 4?
5 leaves are colored green.
2
3
Directions:
1. Draw a line from each baseball to a baseball mitt.
2. Color 5 leaves green.
3. Circle the row with 4 nests.
4. Count the objects in each group. Write the number. Draw a circle around the group that has more.
98 ninety-eight
This page checks skills needed for Chapter 4.

RTI (Response to Intervention)

TIER 2 Strategic Intervention below/approaching grade level	TIER 1 On-Level	Above/Beyond Level
If students miss two in: **Exercises 1–4**	**If** students miss one in: **Exercises 1–4**	**If** students miss none in: **Exercises 1–4**
Then choose a resource:	**Then** choose a resource:	**Then** choose a resource:
CRM Chapter 2 Resource Masters (Reteach Worksheets) Math Online Concepts in Motion	TE Learning Stations (pp. 97G–97H) TE Chapter Project (p. 99) CRM Game: Paper Cup Shuffle Math Adventures My Math Zone Chapter 3	TE Learning Stations (pp. 97G–97H) TE Chapter Project (p. 99) Real-World Problem Solving: *Numbers About Me* My Math Zone Chapters 3, 4 Math Online Online Game

WRITING IN ➤ MATH

Starting the Chapter
Have students use connecting cubes to make sets of six, seven, eight, nine, and 10 cubes. Have students trace the cubes. Then have students write the number representing each set of cubes on a sheet of paper.

Chapter 4 Project

My Number Book 0–10

- Ask students to make a number book of numbers zero to 10. Each number will be represented on a separate sheet of paper, so each book will be 12 pages in length (one page cover).
- To create each page for their book, students should write the number, write the word for the number, cut out and glue pictures from old magazines or glue items like Cheerios or noodles to represent the number.
- Have students design a cover for their book with the title, *My Number Book 0–10*, and put the pages of their book in order from zero to 10.
- Bind the books with binder rings, staples, or yarn and ask students to share their book with the class.

Chapter 4 Literature List

Lesson	Book Title	Author
4-1	**Hop Jump**	Ellen Stoll Walsh
4-2	**Hop Jump**	Ellen Stoll Walsh
4-3	**Hopscotch Around the World**	Mary D. Lankford
4-4	**Tea for Ten**	Lena Anderson
4-5	**Ten Black Dots**	Donald Crews
4-6	**Who's Counting?**	Nancy Tafuri
4-7	**Ten Little Ducks**	Franklin Hammond
4-8	**Anno's Counting Book**	Mitsumasa Anno
4-9	**Henry the Fourth**	Stuart J. Murphy
Any	**Ten Flashing Fireflies**	Philemon Sturges
Any	**1 Hunter**	Pat Hutchins
Any	**Mouse Count**	Ellen Stoll Walsh

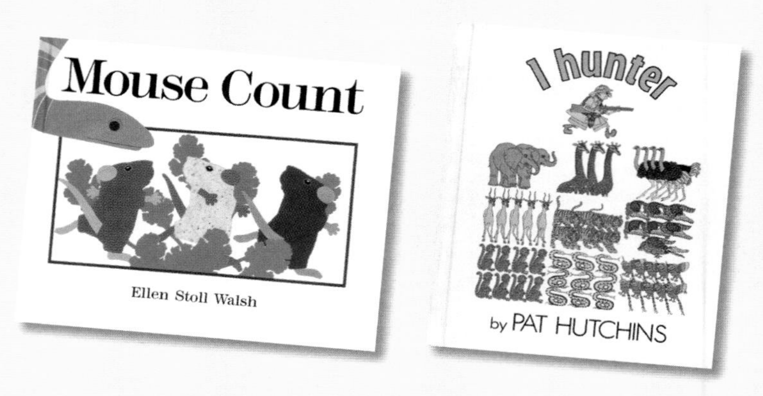

ELL National ESL Standards Alignment for Chapter 4

Lesson, Page	ESL Standard	Modality	Level
4-1, p. 101B	Goal 3, Standard 1, a	Auditory, Kinesthetic	Intermediate
4-2, p. 103B	Goal 1, Standard 2, d	Auditory, Visual	Beginning
4-3, p. 105B	Goal 1, Standard 3, k	Linguistic, Visual/Spacial	Beginning
4-4, p. 109B	Goal 1, Standard 3, i	Auditory, Kinesthetic	Beginning
4-5, p. 111B	Goal 1, Standard 2, d	Kinesthetic, Visual	Beginning
4-6, p. 113B	Goal 2, Standard 2, e	Kinesthetic	Intermediate
4-7, p. 115B	Goal 1, Standard 3, l	Kinesthetic	Intermediate
4-8, p. 117B	Goal 2, Standard 2, f	Social, Visual	Intermediate
4-9, p. 119B	Goal 2, Standard 1, f	Kinesthetic, Visual	Intermediate

The National ESL Standards can be found in the Teacher Reference Handbook.

English

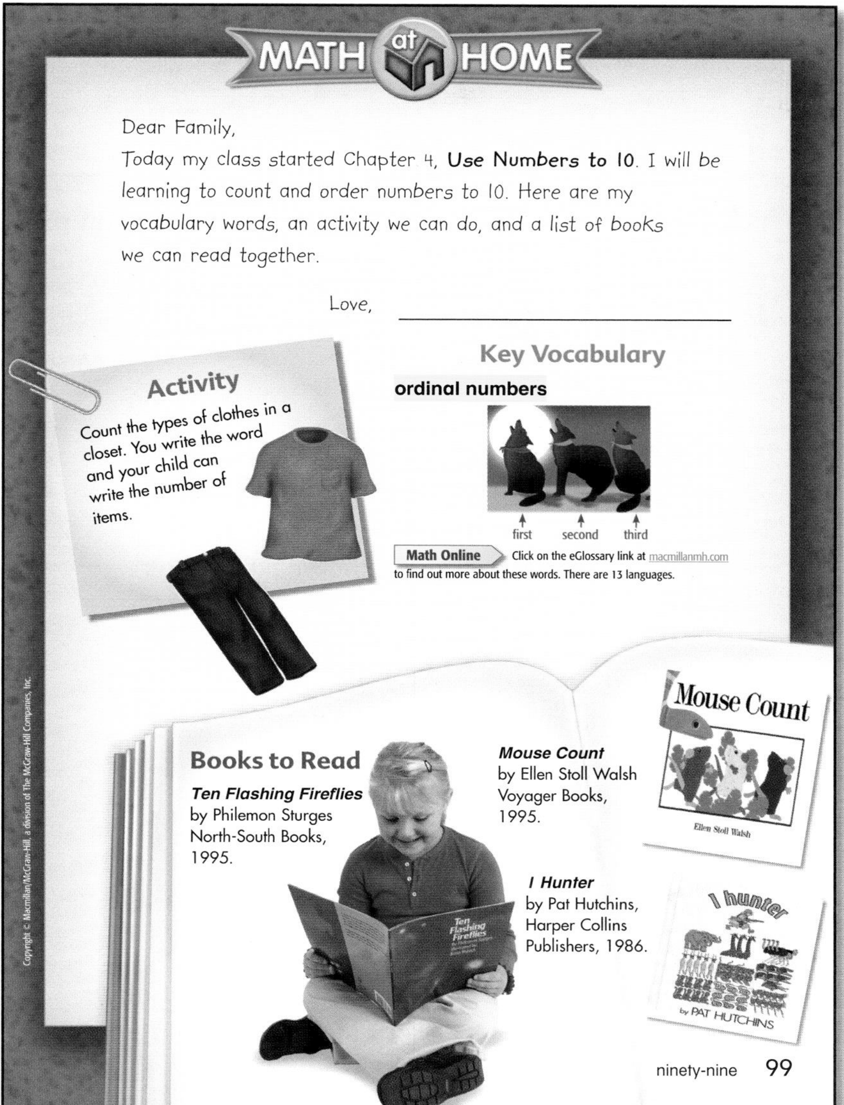

MATH at HOME

Dear Family,

Today my class started Chapter 4, **Use Numbers to 10**. I will be learning to count and order numbers to 10. Here are my vocabulary words, an activity we can do, and a list of books we can read together.

Love, ______________________

Activity

Count the types of clothes in a closet. You write the word and your child can write the number of items.

Key Vocabulary

ordinal numbers

first second third

Math Online Click on the eGlossary link at macmillanmh.com to find out more about these words. There are 13 languages.

Books to Read

Ten Flashing Fireflies
by Philemon Sturges
North-South Books, 1995.

Mouse Count
by Ellen Stoll Walsh
Voyager Books, 1995.

I Hunter
by Pat Hutchins,
Harper Collins Publishers, 1986.

ninety-nine 99

Español

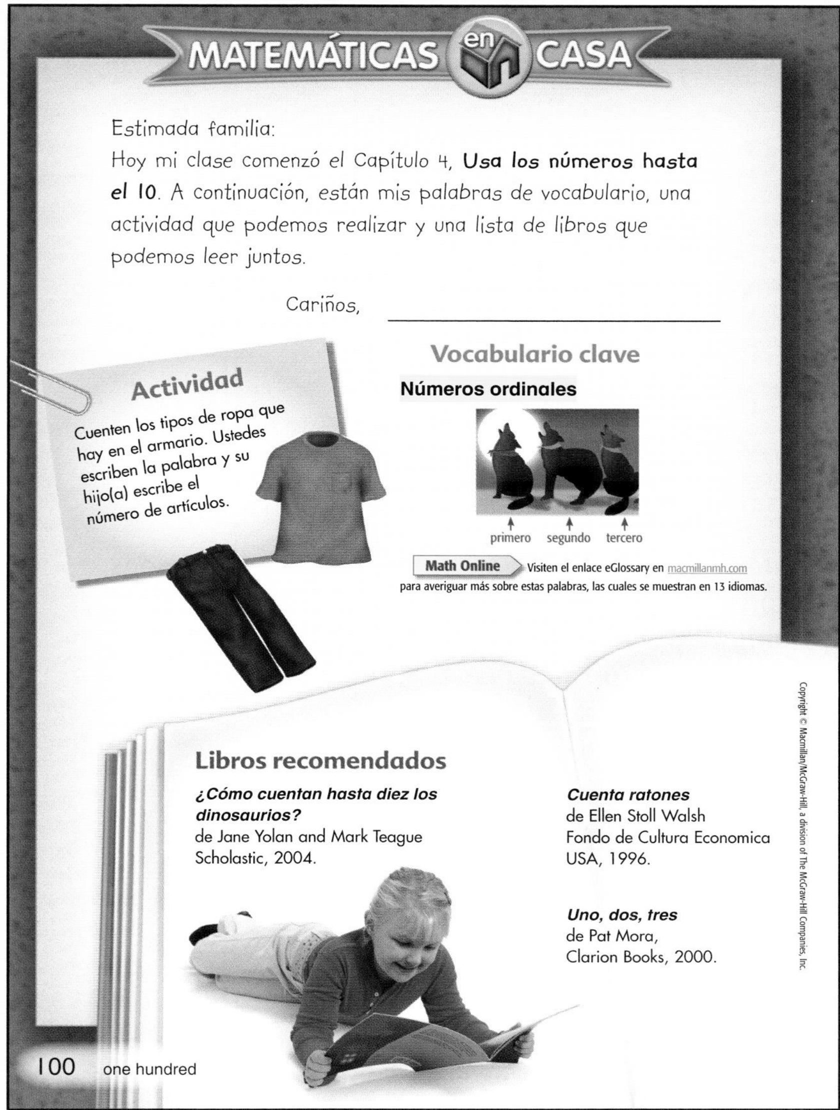

MATEMÁTICAS en CASA

Estimada familia:

Hoy mi clase comenzó el Capítulo 4, **Usa los números hasta el 10**. A continuación, están mis palabras de vocabulario, una actividad que podemos realizar y una lista de libros que podemos leer juntos.

Cariños, ______________________

Actividad

Cuenten los tipos de ropa que hay en el armario. Ustedes escriben la palabra y su hijo(a) escribe el número de artículos.

Vocabulario clave

Números ordinales

primero segundo tercero

Math Online Visiten el enlace eGlossary en macmillanmh.com para averiguar más sobre estas palabras, las cuales se muestran en 13 idiomas.

Libros recomendados

¿Cómo cuentan hasta diez los dinosaurios?
de Jane Yolan and Mark Teague
Scholastic, 2004.

Cuenta ratones
de Ellen Stoll Walsh
Fondo de Cultura Economica USA, 1996.

Uno, dos, tres
de Pat Mora,
Clarion Books, 2000.

100 one hundred

- Read the Math at Home letter on p. 99 with the class and have each student sign it.
- Send home copies of the Math at Home letter with each student.
- Use the Spanish letter on p. 100 for students with Spanish-speaking parents or guardians.

Read-Aloud Anthology

For an optional reading activity to introduce this chapter's math concepts, see the Read-Aloud Anthology on p. TR27.

LESSON 4-1

Numbers 6 and 7

Lesson Planner

Objective

Name, recognize, and count the numerals 6 and 7 using concrete objects and illustrations.

Vocabulary

six, **seven**

Resources

Materials: paper, crayons, paper plates, cups, spoons, forks, napkins
Manipulatives: counters, color tiles
Literature Connection: *Hop Jump* by Ellen Stoll Walsh
Alternate Lesson: Adapt *Cookie Dough Numerals* on page 46 of *Math Their Way* for practice naming the quantities 6 and 7.
Teacher Technology
TeacherWorks

Focus on Math Background

This lesson focuses on quantifying amounts with six and seven objects. Six is an important and meaningful number for many kindergarteners as they are, or will turn, six during the school year. Seven is less familiar. An arrangement of seven objects is not as easy to identify as a group of six or five. Students will likely count each item one-by-one in a group of seven.

Daily Routine

Use these suggestions before beginning the lesson on p. 101.

5-Minute Check

(Reviews Lesson 3-9)

1. Show an AB pattern using snowflakes and sunshines.
2. Tell students that each snowflake means the weather will be cold and that each sunshine means the weather will be hot.
3. Ask students to predict the weather for the day after the last object in the pattern.

Problem of the Day

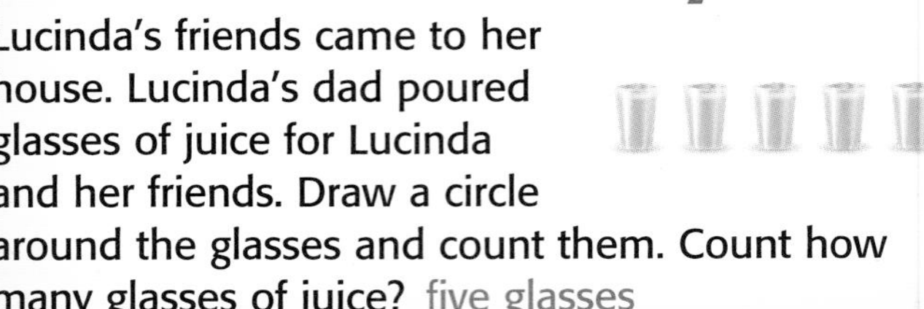

Lucinda's friends came to her house. Lucinda's dad poured glasses of juice for Lucinda and her friends. Draw a circle around the glasses and count them. Count how many glasses of juice? five glasses

LINE UP Call six students to line up. Have the class count as each student lines up. Repeat with seven students until all students are lined up.

Building Math Vocabulary

- Show the numbers 6 and 7 on the chalkboard. Print **six** and **seven**. Have students read the words aloud. Underline the letter *s* and say that both words begin with the letter *s*.
- **What other words begin with *s*?** Sample answers: shoe, sock, song, story, skate, ship
- Write six answers on the chalkboard and underline the *s*. Have students count the words as you point to them.
- Repeat using seven words that begin with *s*.

Differentiated Instruction

Small Group Options

Option 1 LINGUISTIC

Gifted and Talented AL

Materials: drawing paper, crayons

- Have students draw a picture grocery list of six apples, seven oranges, seven carrots, seven bananas, six lemons, and seven pears. Have them circle each group, and represent them with numbers one to seven in written form.
- Have students draw seven tomatoes at the end of their list, draw a box around this group, and label it with a number seven.

Option 2 AUDITORY, KINESTHETIC

English Language Learners ELL

Core Vocabulary: play, May I?, You may
Common Use Verb: may line up

Talk Math This strategy teaches numbers 6 and 7 using polite language.

- Say: "May I line up?" Answer yourself: "**You may.**"
- Repeat, prompting six students to line up. Chant: "**May I line up**? Yes
- Continue as time permits, rotating so that everyone gets a turn.

Independent Work Options

Option 1 VISUAL

Early Finishers OL AL

Materials: drawing paper, crayons, small classroom objects: chalk, paper clips, buttons

- Give a sheet of paper and a crayon to each student. Have each student find six or seven identical classroom objects, put the objects on their desk, and trace each object on the paper.
- Have students say the number of objects aloud to another student.
- Repeat twice.

Option 2

Student Technology

Math Online macmillanmh.com

Math Adventures

Option 3

Learning Station: Science (p. 97G)

Direct students to the Science Learning Station for more opportunities to explore and extend the lesson concept.

Leveled Lesson Resources

Reteach (p. 6) BL

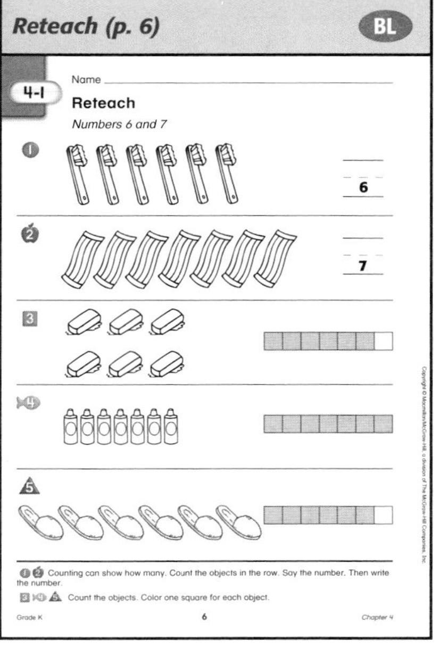
4-1 Name
Reteach
Numbers 6 and 7

1 6
2 7

1 2 Counting can show how many. Count the objects in the row. Say the number. Then write the number.
3 4 5 Count the objects. Color one square for each object.

Grade K 6 Chapter 4

Skills Practice (p. 7) OL

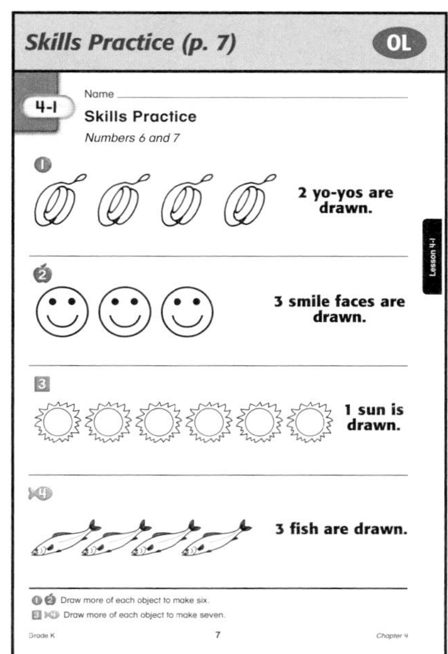
4-1 Name
Skills Practice
Numbers 6 and 7

1 2 yo-yos are drawn.
2 3 smile faces are drawn.
3 1 sun is drawn.
4 3 fish are drawn.

1 2 Draw more of each object to make six.
3 4 Draw more of each object to make seven.

Grade K 7 Chapter 4

Enrich (p. 9) AL

4-1 Name
Enrich
Apple Picking

1 6 green apples are drawn. 6
2 7 red apples are drawn. 7

1 Draw six green apples in the basket. Write the number.
2 Draw seven red apples in the basket. Write the number.

Grade K 9 Chapter 4

Homework Practice (p. 8) OL

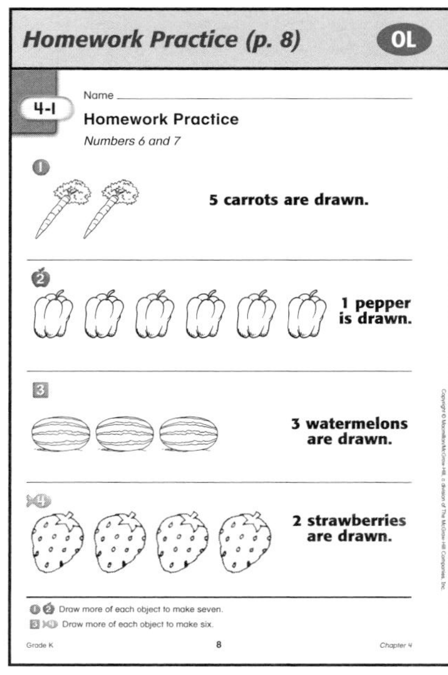
4-1 Name
Homework Practice
Numbers 6 and 7

1 5 carrots are drawn.
2 1 pepper is drawn.
3 3 watermelons are drawn.
4 2 strawberries are drawn.

1 2 Draw more of each object to make seven.
3 4 Draw more of each object to make six.

Grade K 8 Chapter 4

1 Introduce

Circle Time

Activity Choice 1 • Literature

Hop Jump by Ellen Stoll Walsh

Materials: paper, crayons, counters

- Count the frogs on pages 1–2 aloud. Write the number **six** on the chalkboard and say six aloud. Have students count six frogs aloud on pages 3–4.
- Count the frogs on pages 13–14. Write the number **seven** and say seven aloud. Have students count seven frogs aloud on pages 21–22 and 23–24.
- Give each student 13 counters and a sheet of paper. Tell them each counter represents a frog.
- Have students draw two large circles to represent ponds. Have students write the number six below one pond and the number seven below the other pond.
- Have students draw six lily pads on one pond and seven lily pads on the other pond. Have them count the frogs as they put counters on the lily pads. Ask students if the number of frogs in the ponds are the same number as, more than, or less than each other.

Activity Choice 2 • Hands-On 

Materials: paper plates, cups, spoons, forks, napkins

- Have students form a circle. Tell them a boy named Shawn will be inviting six friends to his party.
- Have groups of students count aloud and bring six plates, cups, spoons, forks, and napkins. Help students create six place settings.
- Have students count the place settings. **Do we need another place setting?** yes; Shawn's place setting Ask volunteers to create a place setting for Shawn. **How many places are set now?** seven Have students count the place settings aloud.

2 Teach

- Direct students to the top of p. 101.
- Discuss things children have and do at parties.
- Give each student color tiles.
- Have students use their fingers to count out the number of presents. Have them show the number 6.
- Have them tell the total number of presents.
- Repeat with balloons.

BL Alternate Teaching Strategy

 **If** students have trouble representing, recognizing, or counting the quantities six and seven . . .

 **Then** use one of the following reteach options.

1. CRM **Daily Reteach Worksheet** (p. 6)
2. **Count Six and Seven** Give each student a set of two-colored counters, paper, and crayons.
   - Show the 6 card and have students say *six* aloud. Have students line up six two-colored counters in a row on their desk. Then have students return their counters to the classroom pile.
   - Show the 7 card and have students say *seven* aloud. Have students line up seven two-colored counters on their desk. Then have students return their counters to the classroom pile.
   - Have students make a line of six red counters. Have them count each counter aloud. Ask them how many more counters they need to take to make seven. Have them add a red counter to the line and count off each counter.
   - Have students draw a picture of six red counters and a picture of seven red counters.

! COMMON ERROR!

Students may have difficulty counting objects twice or missing an object while counting. Have them use a pencil to mark on each object as they count it. Then have them count the number of marks.

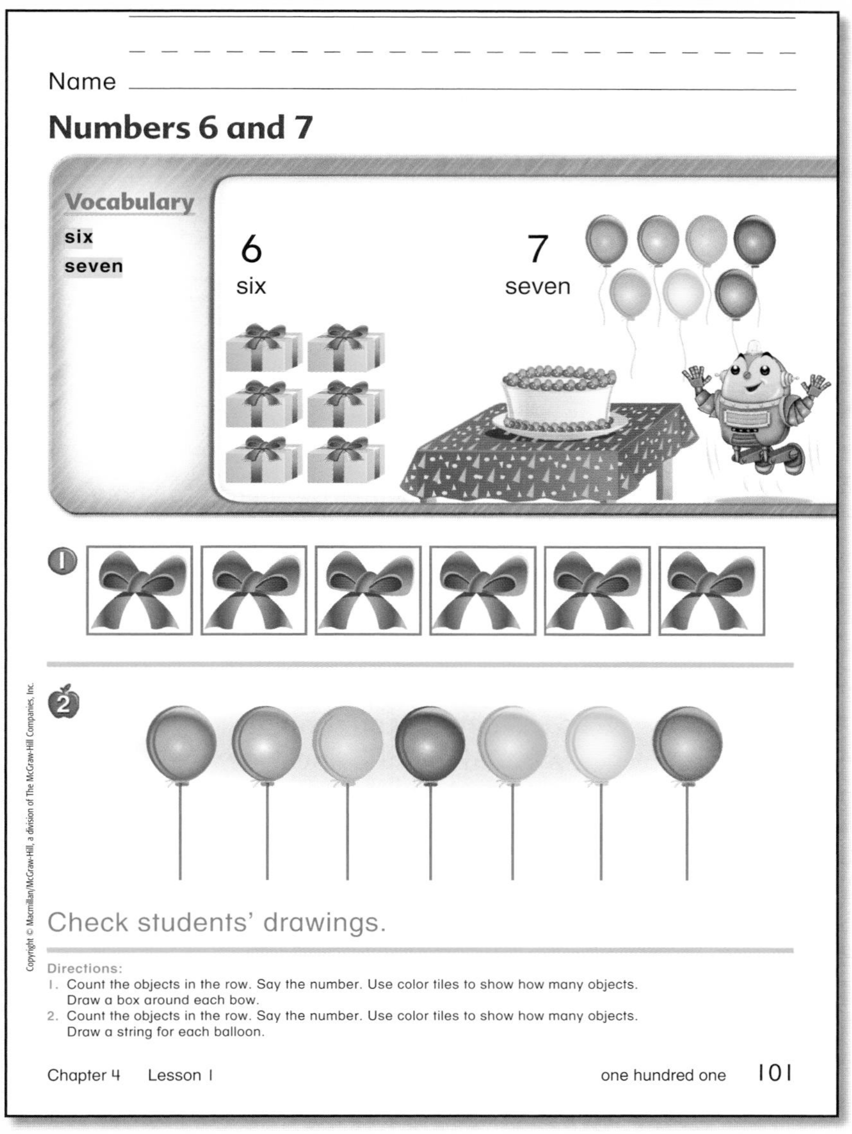

Name
Numbers 6 and 7
Vocabulary
six
seven
6
six
7
seven
Check students' drawings.
Directions:
1. Count the objects in the row. Say the number. Use color tiles to show how many objects. Draw a box around each bow.
2. Count the objects in the row. Say the number. Use color tiles to show how many objects. Draw a string for each balloon.
Chapter 4 Lesson 1
one hundred one 101

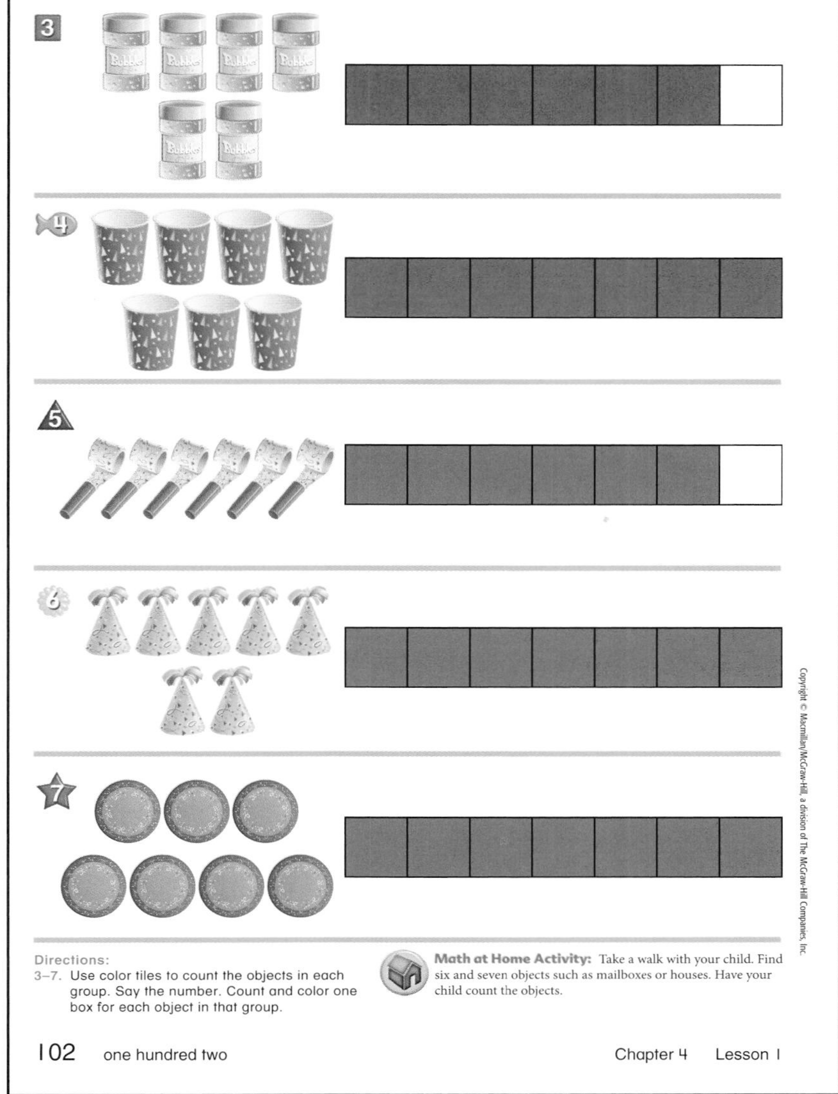

Directions:
3–7. Use color tiles to count the objects in each group. Say the number. Count and color one box for each object in that group.
Math at Home Activity: Take a walk with your child. Find six and seven objects such as mailboxes or houses. Have your child count the objects.
102 one hundred two
Chapter 4 Lesson 1

3 Practice

Guided Practice

- Direct students to the bows in Exercise 1 on p. 101. Count the bows and say the number.
- **What is missing from the six bows in the row?** presents
- Ask students to make a box (a present) around each bow. Lay one color tile on each present and count the presents together.
- Have students look at Exercise 2, count the balloons, and say the number.
- Have students lay one color tile on each balloon. Have students draw a string for each balloon and count the balloons together. Say that seven is one more than six.

Independent Practice

Have students turn to p. 102. Explain the directions and have students work independently on the exercises.

4 Assess

Formative Assessment

Draw six circles on the chalkboard. Have students count aloud.

- **How many circles are there?** six **How many more circles do we need to make seven circles?** one
- Draw another circle. Have students count aloud.
- **How much more than six is seven?** one more

Quick Check **Are students still struggling to count from one to seven?**

If Yes → Small Group Options (p. 101B)

If No → Independent Work Options (p. 101B)

CRM Skills Practice Worksheet (p. 7)

CRM Enrich Worksheet (p. 9)

LESSON 4-2

Number 8

Lesson Planner

Objective

Name, recognize, and count the numeral 8 using concrete objects and illustrations.

Vocabulary

eight

Resources

Materials: modeling clay, pipe cleaners, workmat
Manipulatives: connecting cubes, counters
Literature Connection: *Hop Jump* by Ellen Stoll Walsh
Alternate Lesson: Use *Geoboards* on page 176 of *Math Their Way* to provide practice with the quantity 8.
Teacher Technology
TeacherWorks

Focus on Math Background

This lesson focuses on the number eight. By the end of kindergarten, most students can conserve quantities to about eight. Conservation of number is a skill in which students know that an amount remains constant regardless if it is rearranged or in a different order. Representing numbers in multiple ways—by pictures, objects, or models—helps students develop conservation of number.

Daily Routine

Use these suggestions before beginning the lesson on p. 103.

5-Minute Check

(Reviews Lesson 4-1)
Have students draw a picture of objects to show the number seven. Suggest using circles, boxes, or other objects.

Problem of the Day

Give seven students each a cube and have them form a row. Have them count off. Ask a volunteer to hold a cube and join the line. How many students holding cubes are in the row now? eight

LINE UP Have the class count as eight girls line up. Repeat with eight boys. Repeat until all students are lined up.

Building Math Vocabulary

- Write the number eight and the vocabulary word **eight** on the chalkboard. Draw an octopus on the chalkboard.
- Have students count the eight legs.
- Point to the word *eight* again and say that an octopus has eight legs.
- Ask students to say the word *eight* again and to hold up that many fingers.

Differentiated Instruction

Small Group Options

Option 1 LOGICAL 

Below/Approaching Level BL

Materials: index cards, connecting cubes, counters, attribute buttons, blocks

- Write the number eight on four index cards. Give each student four cards. Have them put their cards in a row in front of them.
- Have students describe the number eight symbolically by putting eight items under each card, using different items for each card.
- Say that the number eight tells us that there are eight items. Have students count their items.

Option 2 AUDITORY, VISUAL

English Language Learners ELL

Core Vocabulary: eight, legs, spider
Common Use Verb: has/have

Hear Math This strategy teaches numbers to 8.

- Knit fingers like a spider. Move them as you sing to the tune of "Old McDonald".
- *This big **spider has eight legs:** two plus two plus four, I am really happy that he does not **have** more!*

Independent Work Options

Option 1 VISUAL

Early Finishers OL AL

Materials: drawing paper, crayons,

- Tell students to think of their favorite fruit.
- Have students draw and color eight of their favorite fruit on a sheet of paper.
- Have students trade papers and count the number of fruit.

Option 2

Student Technology

Math Online macmillanmh.com

 Math Adventures

Option 3

Learning Station: Art (p. 97G)

Direct students to the Art Learning Station for more opportunities to explore and extend the lesson concept.

Leveled Lesson Resources

Reteach (p. 10) BL

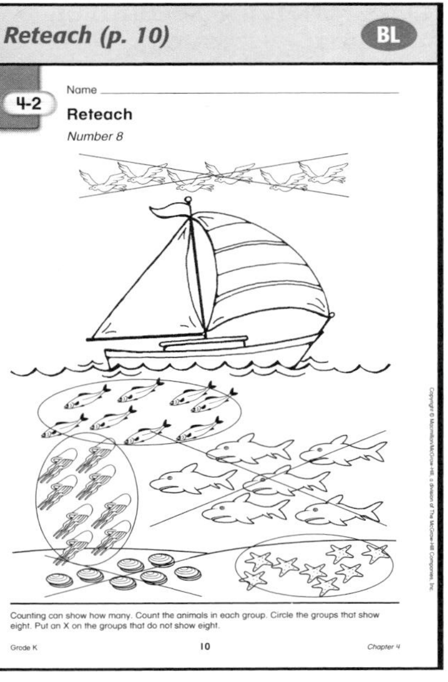

4-2 Name
Reteach
Number 8

Counting can show how many. Count the animals in each group. Circle the groups that show eight. Put an X on the groups that do not show eight.

Grade K 10 Chapter 4

Skills Practice (p. 11) OL

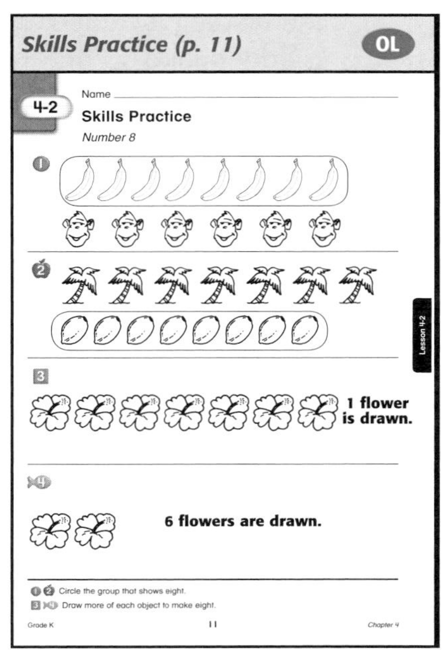

4-2 Name
Skills Practice
Number 8

1 flower is drawn.

6 flowers are drawn.

1 2 Circle the group that shows eight.
3 4 Draw more of each object to make eight.

Grade K 11 Chapter 4

Enrich (p. 13) AL

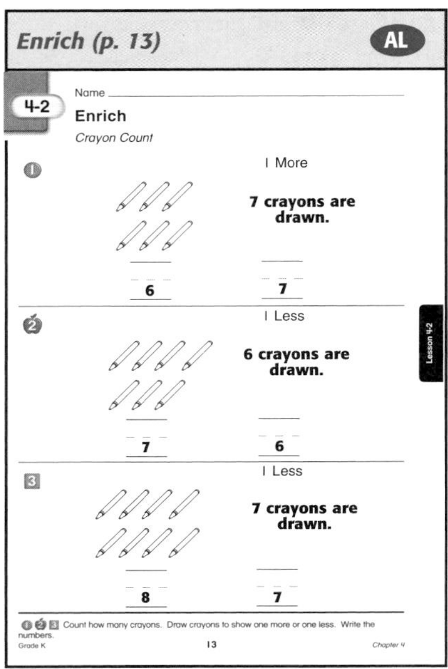

4-2 Name
Enrich
Crayon Count

1 — 1 More — 7 crayons are drawn. — 6 — 7
2 — 1 Less — 6 crayons are drawn. — 7 — 6
3 — 1 Less — 7 crayons are drawn. — 8 — 7

1 2 3 Count how many crayons. Draw crayons to show one more or one less. Write the numbers.

Grade K 13 Chapter 4

Homework Practice (p. 12) OL

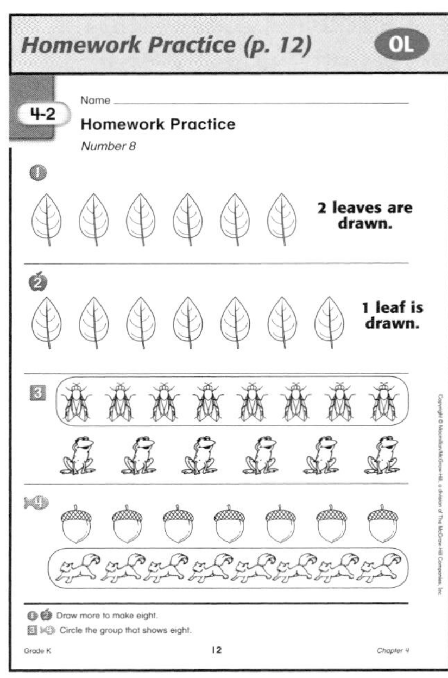

4-2 Name
Homework Practice
Number 8

2 leaves are drawn.

1 leaf is drawn.

1 2 Draw more to make eight.
3 4 Circle the group that shows eight.

Grade K 12 Chapter 4

1 Introduce

Circle Time

Activity Choice 1 • Literature

Hop Jump by Ellen Stoll Walsh

Materials: connecting cubes

- Count aloud the number of frogs on pages 26–27. Print and say the number **eight**. Have students count aloud eight frogs on pages 28–29.
- Describe the number eight symbolically by joining eight connecting cubes in a straight line.
- **How can the eight cubes be connected in a different way?** Sample answer: Connect four cubes across and four cubes down.
- Have students each create two different designs with eight cubes. Ask volunteers to share their designs.
- **Are all the designs made of eight cubes?** yes **Are all the designs the same?** no

Activity Choice 2 • Hands-On

- Have students sit in a circle and join in as you sing the "Eensy Weensy Spider" song.
- Model how to tuck in the thumb. Have students tuck in their thumbs when they make the rain motion.
- **How many fingers do you have up on a hand?** four
- Hold your hands up next to each other with thumbs tucked in. Count aloud the total number of fingers on both hands to eight.
- Have students hold their hands in the same way and count their eight fingers.
- **How many fingers do you count?** eight

2 Teach

Direct students to the top of p. 103.

- Direct students to the larger spider. Tell them that it's name is "Daddy Long Legs" and that this is also the name of a real spider.
- Have students count the legs on the larger spider using their fingers. Have them show you the number 8. Have students repeat the process for the number of shoes and sleeves on the spider.
- Direct them to the baby spiders beside the larger spider. Count with the students as they lay one cube on each baby spider.
- **How many baby spiders does this Daddy Long Legs spider have?** eight

BL Alternate Teaching Strategy

If students have trouble counting to eight . . .

Then use one of the following reteach options.

1. CRM **Daily Reteach Worksheet** (p. 10)
2. **Count to Eight** Have students play a game called "Put the Legs on the Spider".
   - Put an oval-shaped piece of clay in front of students. Say that the clay represents a spider.
   - **What is the spider missing?** legs
   - Tell students that spiders have eight legs. Say that they will now give the spider legs. Invite eight volunteers to describe the number eight symbolically by taking a pipe cleaner and pushing it into the spider to give it eight legs. After each leg is added, have students clap that leg number (one clap when the first leg is added, two claps when the second leg is added, and so on).
   - When finished, have students count aloud the number of legs the spider has.
   - **Does the spider have all its legs?** yes

COMMON ERROR!

Students may have trouble counting objects to eight. Have them touch and move each object as they count the number.

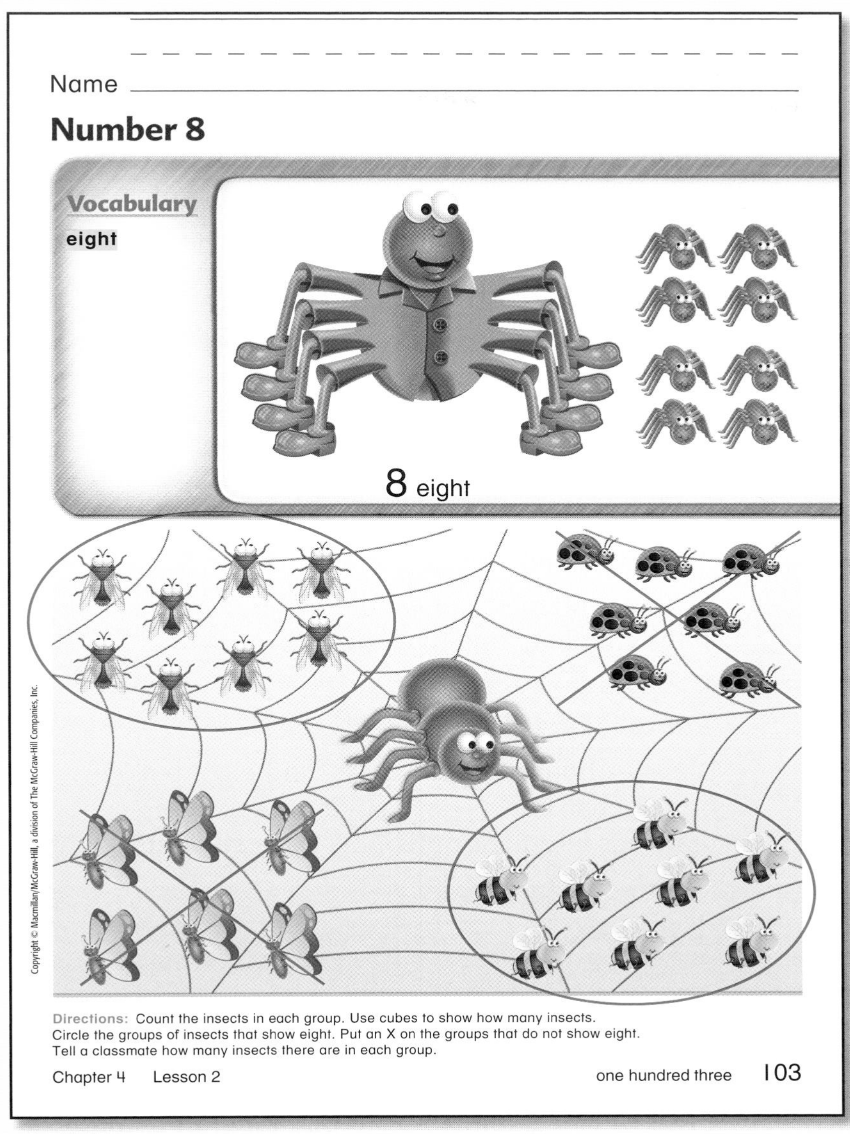
Name

Number 8

Vocabulary

eight

8 eight

Directions: Count the insects in each group. Use cubes to show how many insects. Circle the groups of insects that show eight. Put an X on the groups that do not show eight. Tell a classmate how many insects there are in each group.

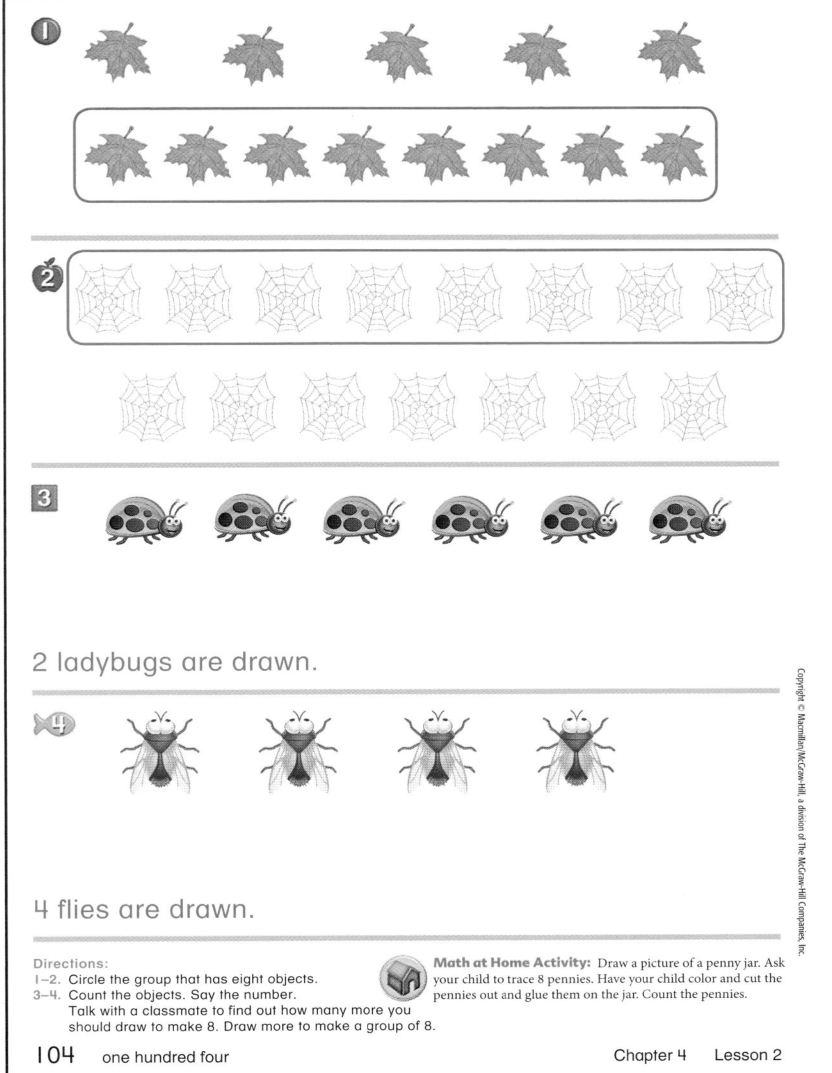
1

2

3

2 ladybugs are drawn.

4

4 flies are drawn.

Directions:
1–2. Circle the group that has eight objects.
3–4. Count the objects. Say the number. Talk with a classmate to find out how many more you should draw to make 8. Draw more to make a group of 8.

Math at Home Activity: Draw a picture of a penny jar. Ask your child to trace 8 pennies. Have your child color and cut the pennies out and glue them on the jar. Count the pennies.

3 Practice

Guided Practice

- Direct students to the bottom of p. 103.
- Tell the students that some insects got caught in the spider's web. Ask them to count each set of insects.
- Have students use cubes to show how many insects are in each group.
- Tell them to circle the sets that have eight insects in them and put an X on the groups that do not have eight insects in them.
- Have students tell a classmate how many insects are in each group.

Independent Practice

Have students turn to p. 104. Explain the directions and have students work independently on the exercises.

4 Assess

Formative Assessment

Put a row of seven and eight counters on a workmat.

- **How many counters are in each row?** seven, eight
- Add a counter to the row of seven. **Are both rows the same? Why?** Yes; both have eight.
- **How much more than seven is eight?** one more

Quick Check **Are students still struggling to count and write to eight?**

If Yes → Small Group Options (p. 103B)

If No → Independent Work Options (p. 103B)

CRM Skills Practice Worksheet (p. 11)

CRM Enrich Worksheet (p. 13)

LESSON 4-3

Read and Write 6, 7, and 8

Lesson Planner

Objective

Recognize and write the numerals 6, 7, and 8.

Review Vocabulary

six, seven, eight

Resources

Materials: drawing paper, pencils, paper bag, chalk, crayons, buttons, colored paper, glue

Literature Connection: *Hopscotch Around the World* by Mary D. Lankford

Alternate Lesson: Use *Writing Papers* on page 51 of *Math Their Way* to provide practice recognizing and writing the numerals 6, 7, and 8.

Teacher Technology

TeacherWorks • Concepts in Motion

Focus on Math Background

This lesson focuses on reading and writing numbers six, seven, and eight to describe and label matching quantities. Give students practice in writing numbers in meaningful ways, such as writing important calendar dates or phone numbers. Practice helps students make less errors, such as reversing six and seven or confusing numbers.

Daily Routine

Use these suggestions before beginning the lesson on p. 105.

5-Minute Check

(Reviews Lesson 4-2)

1. Give each student eight cubes that are connected. Have students take the cubes apart, saying aloud each cube number one to eight.
2. Have students connect the cubes, saying aloud the numbers one to eight.

Problem of the Day

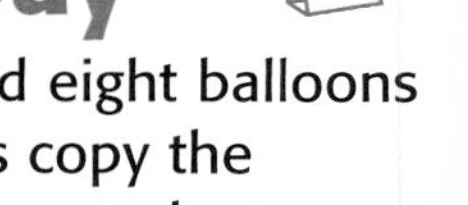

Draw six houses, seven socks, and eight balloons on the chalkboard. Have students copy the drawings into their notebook. Have students count each.

LINE UP Have students line up one-by-one, counting off one through eight. Repeat until all students are lined up. Have the first five students hold blue number cards one to five, and the next three hold red number cards six to eight.

Review Math Vocabulary

Materials: index cards, crayons or markers, classroom objects

- Distribute three index cards to each student.
- Display a group of **six**, **seven**, or **eight** identical classroom objects (e.g., six books, seven pencils, eight balls, etc.).
- Tell students to count silently the number of objects displayed.
- Have students say the number they counted.
- Repeat three times, displaying different groups of six, seven, and eight objects.

Differentiated Instruction

Small Group Options

Option 1 Below/Approaching Level BL

LINGUISTIC

Materials: art paper, crayons

- Have students write the numbers six, seven, and eight on a sheet of art paper.
- **What are some objects that you see often?** Sample answers: spoons, shoes, pants, crayons, pencils, markers, erasers, clocks
- Have students represent six, seven, and eight by drawing any of these objects to match the numbers on their paper (for example, six spoons for the number six).

Option 2 English Language Learners ELL

LINGUISTIC, VISUAL/SPATIAL

Core Vocabulary: loop, across, circle
Common Use Verb: make/makes
Write Math: This strategy uses a poem to teach how to write numbers.

- Read the poem. Demonstrate writing as students practice.
- Old Mr. Six rolls a hoop, comes right down to make a loop.
- Across the sky and down from heaven, that's the way to make a seven.
- Two circles are great, put one on top and you make an eight.

Independent Work Options

Option 1 Early Finishers OL AL

LINGUISTIC

Materials: paper; blue, red, green crayons and tiles

- Have students make a design by connecting six, seven, or eight boxes.
- Have them draw six connected boxes with a blue crayon, seven boxes with a red crayon, and eight boxes with a green crayon.

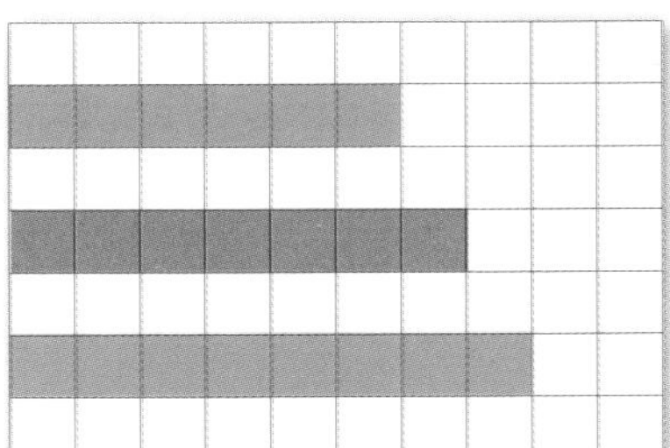

- Give students blue, red, and green tiles. Have them represent their boxes with tiles.

Option 2 Student Technology

Math Online macmillanmh.com

Math Adventures

Option 3 Learning Station: Reading (p. 97G)

Direct students to the Reading Learning Station for more opportunities to explore and extend the lesson concept.

Leveled Lesson Resources

Additional support for English Language Learners can be found in the ELL Guide (p. 83). ELL

Reteach (p. 14) BL

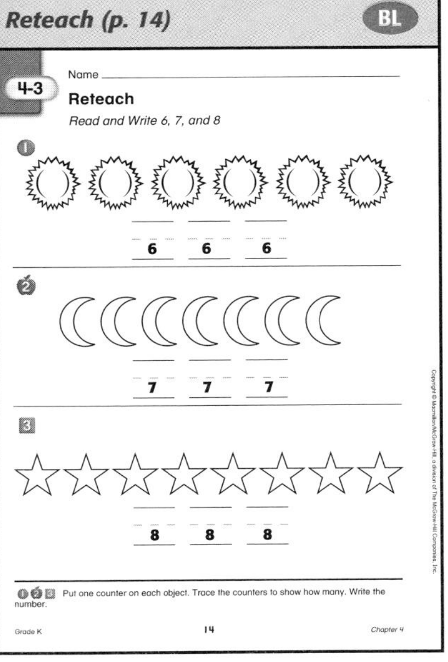

4-3 Name

Reteach

Read and Write 6, 7, and 8

6 6 6

7 7 7

8 8 8

1 2 3 Put one counter on each object. Trace the counters to show how many. Write the number.

Grade K 14 *Chapter 4*

Skills Practice (p. 15) OL

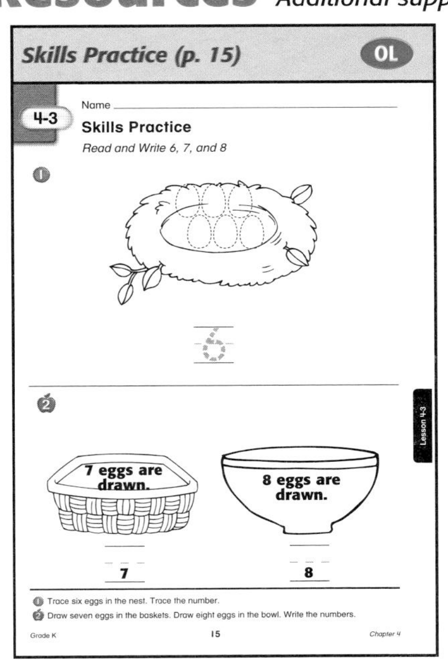

4-3 Name

Skills Practice

Read and Write 6, 7, and 8

7 eggs are drawn.

8 eggs are drawn.

7 8

1 Trace six eggs in the nest. Trace the number.
2 Draw seven eggs in the baskets. Draw eight eggs in the bowl. Write the numbers.

Grade K 15 *Chapter 4*

Enrich (p. 17) AL

4-3 Name

Enrich

Cookies in the Box

1 6 Cookies 2
2 7 Cookies 5
3 8 Cookies 3

1 2 3 Some cookies are in the box. Some are on the plate. The number shows how many cookies there are in all. Write how many cookies are in the box.

Grade K 17 *Chapter 4*

Homework Practice (p. 16) OL

4-3 Name

Homework Practice

Read and Write 6, 7, and 8

8 bones are drawn. 8

6 carrots are drawn. 6

7 balls are drawn. 7

8 eggs are drawn. 8

1 Draw eight bones in the box. Write the number.
2 Draw six carrots in the box. Write the number.
3 Draw seven balls in the box. Write the number.
4 Draw eight eggs in the box. Write the number.

Grade K 16 *Chapter 4*

1 Introduce

Circle Time

Activity Choice 1 • Literature

Hopscotch Around the World
by Mary D. Lankford

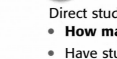

Materials: glue, colored paper, drawing paper, pencils

- On pages 9 and 35, show students the hopscotch boards.
- **How many boxes are there?** seven
  Have them count to **seven** aloud.
- On pages 25 and 31, repeat for boards containing **eight** squares. **Describe what a hopscotch board with six squares might look like.** Answers will vary. Sample answer: three squares across and three squares down Draw an example on the chalkboard and label it with numbers.
- Have students represent the numbers by gluing colored paper squares on drawing paper to show six, seven, or eight squares. Have them label each box in written form with the correct number.

Activity Choice 2 • Hands-On

Materials: paper bag, chalk, crayons, buttons

- Put into a paper bag six pieces of chalk, seven crayons, and eight buttons. Have students gather around. Have a student shake the bag, and another student put in one hand and try to guess how many objects are in the bag. Pour objects out.
- Ask volunteers to put the objects into three groups. Count with the class the objects in each group.
- **How many pieces of chalk, crayons, and buttons were in the bag?** six, seven, eight
- Refer to each group of objects beginning with six. Model writing a number six on the chalkboard. Have students write the number six in the air.
- Repeat with seven and eight.
- Give opportunities for students to write numbers six, seven, and eight.

2 Teach

Direct students to the top of p. 105.

- **How many marbles fell out of the first bag?** six
- Have students count the marbles aloud. They should count one marble at a time.
- Repeat the activity for seven marbles in the second bag and eight marbles in the third bag.

BL Alternate Teaching Strategy

If students have trouble with the names or order of numbers six, seven, or eight . . .

Then use one of the following reteach options.

1 CRM **Daily Reteach Worksheet** (p. 14)

2 **Clap the Number!** Write the numbers six, seven, and eight on the chalkboard.

- Point to the number six and say the number aloud.
- Have students say *six* aloud and then have them clap six times, counting aloud at each clap.
- Repeat for numbers seven and eight.

COMMON ERROR!

Students may have trouble keeping track of the number of marbles shown on page 105 of this lesson. Have them draw a mark for each marble as they count it.

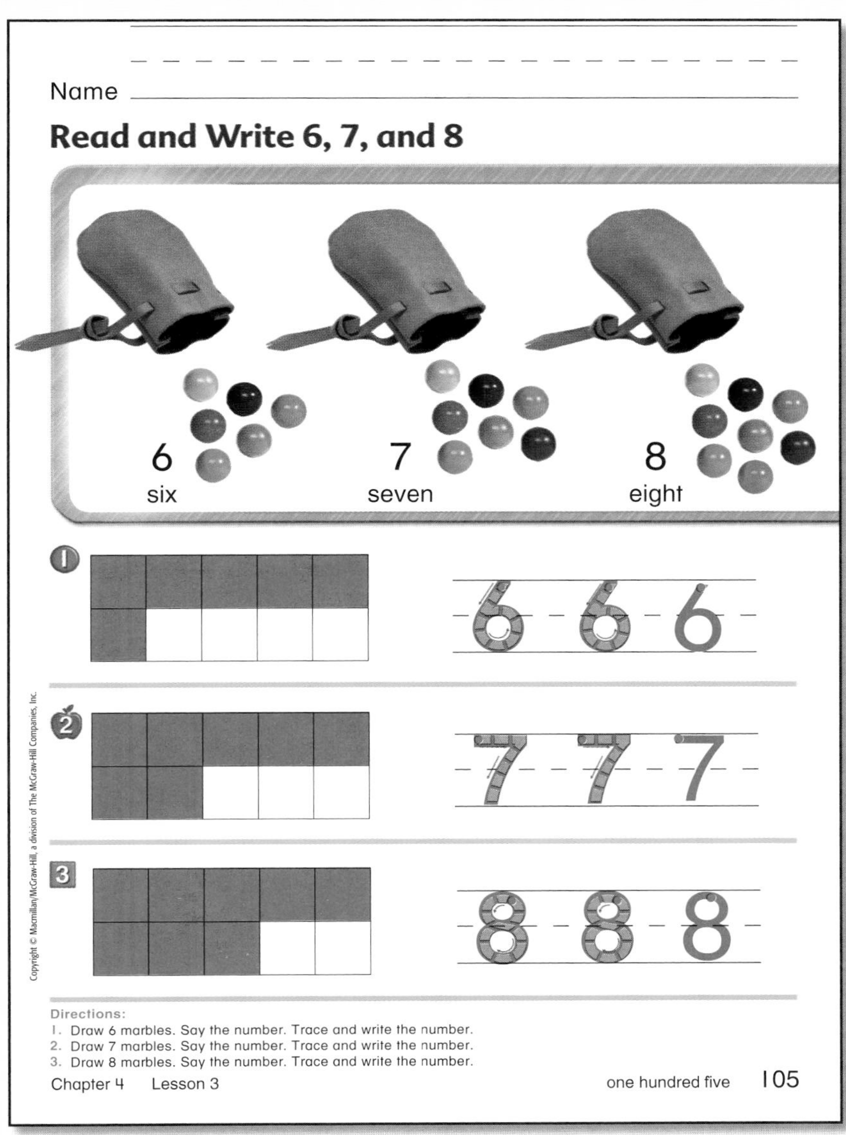

Name
Read and Write 6, 7, and 8
6
six
7
seven
8
eight
Directions:
1. Draw 6 marbles. Say the number. Trace and write the number.
2. Draw 7 marbles. Say the number. Trace and write the number.
3. Draw 8 marbles. Say the number. Trace and write the number.
Chapter 4 Lesson 3
one hundred five 105

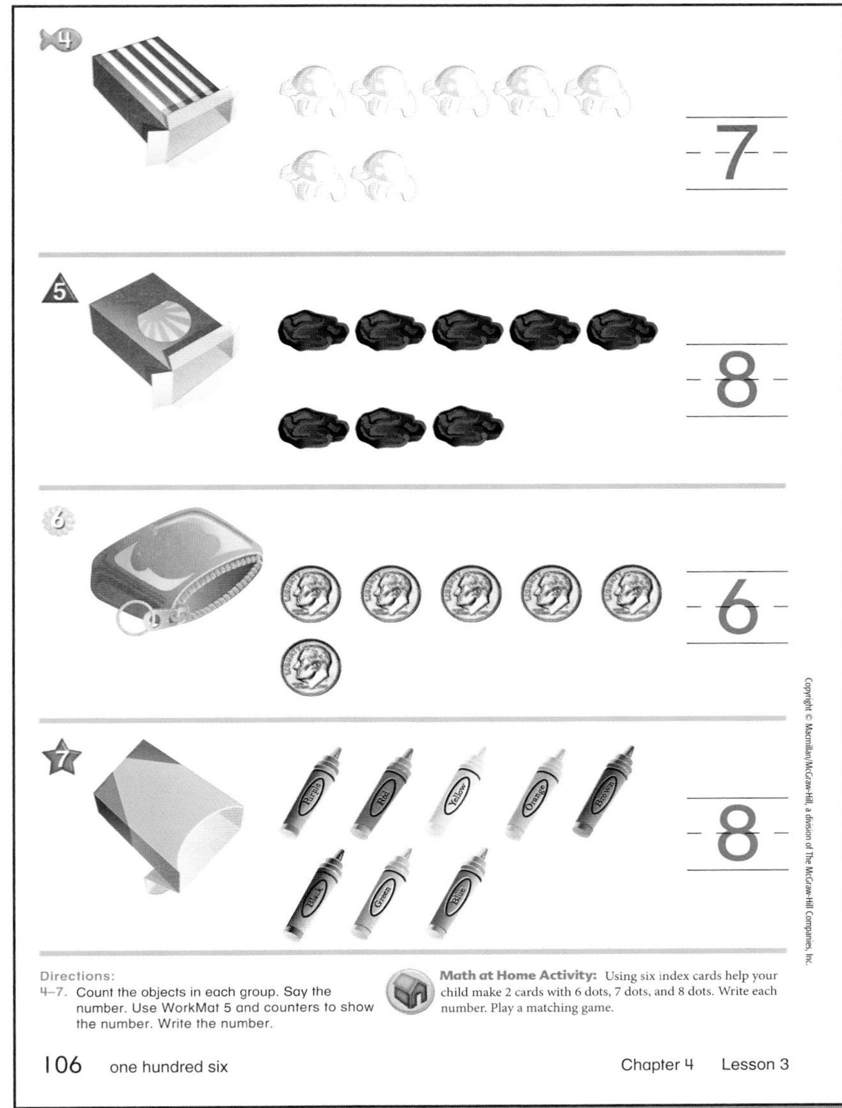

7
8
6
8
Directions:
4–7. Count the objects in each group. Say the number. Use WorkMat 5 and counters to show the number. Write the number.
Math at Home Activity: Using six index cards help your child make 2 cards with 6 dots, 7 dots, and 8 dots. Write each number. Play a matching game.
106 one hundred six
Chapter 4 Lesson 3

3 Practice

Guided Practice

Direct students to Exercise 1 on p. 105.

- Tell them that this is a ten-frame, which can be used to show how many marbles there were in the bag.
- **Are there enough boxes in the ten-frame to put each marble in its own box?** yes
- Have students draw six marbles (circles), each one in its own box. Four boxes will remain empty. Then have students say the total number of marbles in the bag.
- Have students trace and write the number six.
- Repeat the activity for Exercises 2 and 3.

Independent Practice

Have students turn to p. 106. Explain the directions. Have students work independently on the exercises.

4 Assess

Formative Assessment

- Draw five apples on the chalkboard. **How many more apples should I draw to show six apples?** one
- Draw another apple. Have students write on a sheet of paper the number of apples that are on the chalkboard.
- Repeat for seven and then eight apples.

Quick Check **Are students still struggling to recognize and write six, seven, and eight?**

If Yes → Small Group Options (p. 105B)

If No → Independent Work Options (p. 105B)

 Skills Practice Worksheet (p. 15)

CRM Enrich Worksheet (p. 17)

Mid-Chapter Check

Lessons 4-1 to 4-3

Formative Assessment

Use the Mid-Chapter Check to assess students' progress in the first half of the chapter.

ExamView Assessment Suite Customize and create multiple versions of your Mid-Chapter Check and their answer keys.

FOLDABLES Dinah Zike's Foldables

Use these lesson suggestions for incorporating the Foldables during the chapter.

Lesson 4-1 Make and glue together two sections of the Foldable Number Line. Write the numbers six and seven on the top left side of each of the two sections and have students find and place pictures on the appropriate sections to illustrate each of the numbers. Students can use magazines, catalogs, or advertisements to find pictures or the illustrations can come from worksheets or original student artwork.

Lesson 4-3 Make and glue another section to the number line. Write the number eight on the top left side of the section and have students find and place pictures on this section to illustrate the number.

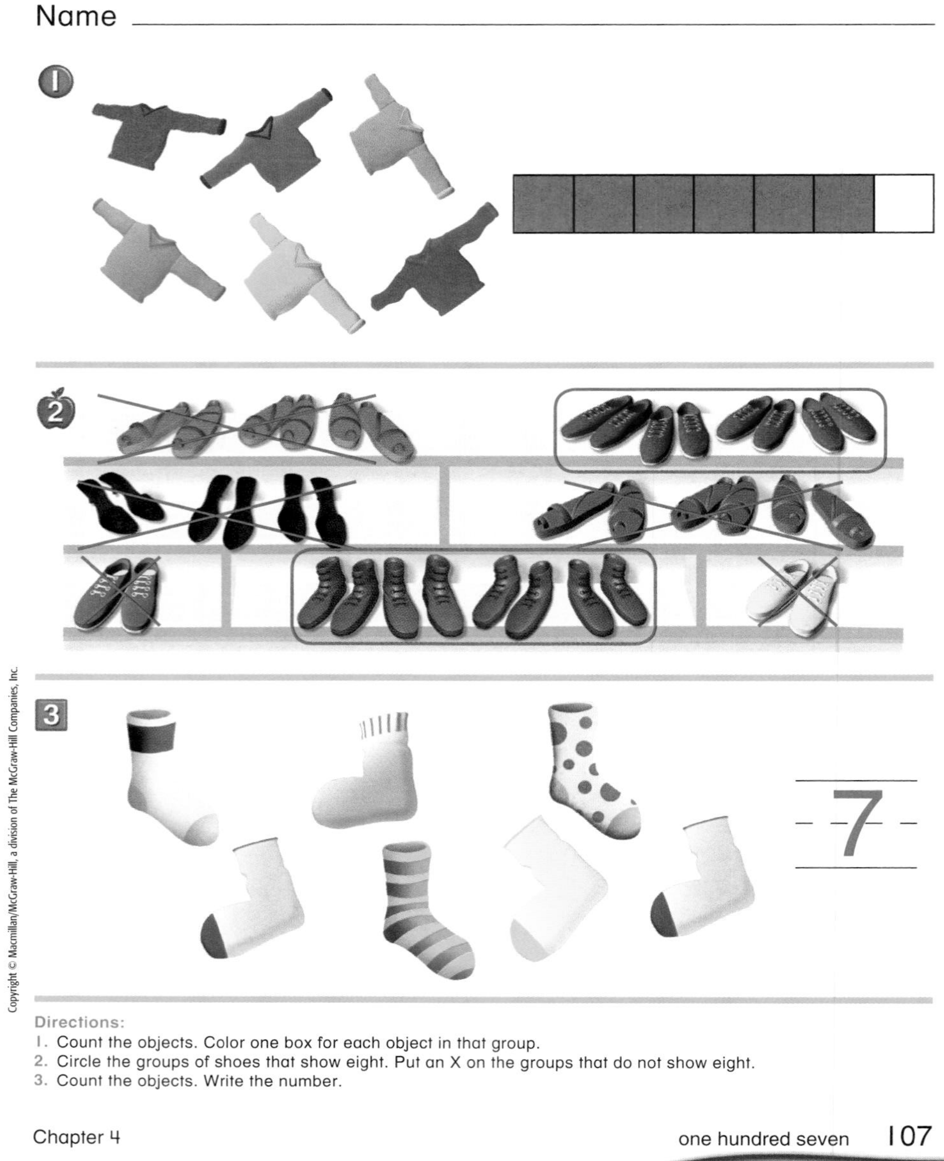

Mid-Chapter Check Lessons 1-3

Name

1

2

3 7

Directions:
1. Count the objects. Color one box for each object in that group.
2. Circle the groups of shoes that show eight. Put an X on the groups that do not show eight.
3. Count the objects. Write the number.

Copyright © Macmillan/McGraw-Hill, a division of The McGraw-Hill Companies, Inc.

Chapter 4 one hundred seven 107

Data-Driven Decision Making

Based on the results of the Mid-Chapter Check, use the following resources to review concepts that continue to give students problems.

Exercises	State / Local Standards	What's the Math?	Error Analysis	Resources for Review
1 Lesson 4-1		Understand the relationship between numbers and quantities. Name, recognize, and count number of objects up to 7.	Does not count correctly. Does not color correct number of boxes.	CRM Chapter 4 Resource Master (Reteach Worksheets) Math Online Concepts in Motion Math Adventures
2 Lesson 4-2		Understand the relationship between numbers and quantities. Name, recognize, and count number of objects up to 8.	Counts the number of shoes in a set incorrectly. Does not follow directions or circles wrong sets or X's wrong sets.	
3 Lesson 4-3		Understand the relationship between numbers and quantities. Recognize and write the number of objects up to 8.	Does not count accurately. Writes the wrong number.	

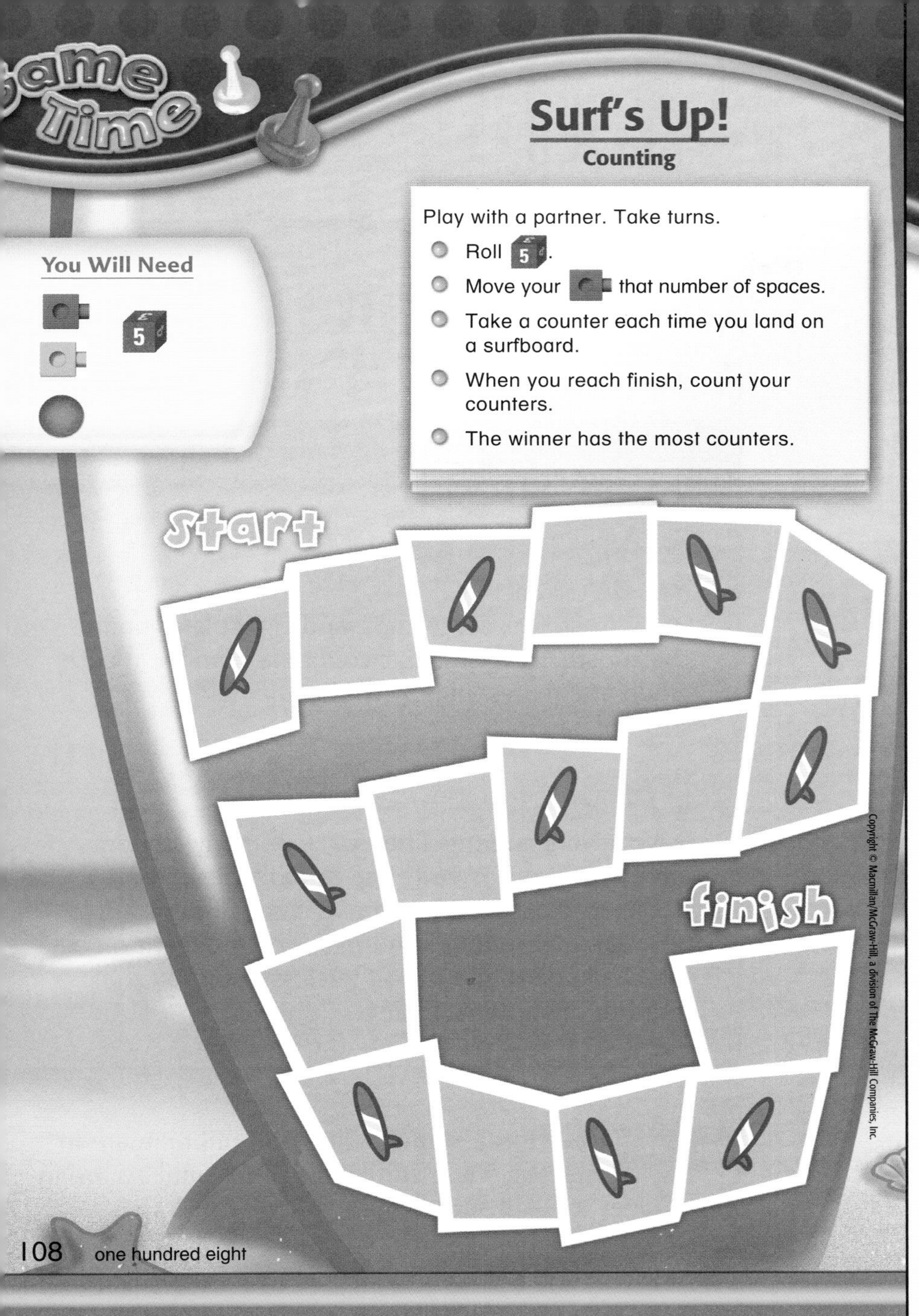
Surf's Up!
Counting
You Will Need
5
Play with a partner. Take turns.
Roll 5.
Move your that number of spaces.
Take a counter each time you land on a surfboard.
When you reach finish, count your counters.
The winner has the most counters.
Start
finish
108 one hundred eight
Copyright © Macmillan/McGraw-Hill, a division of The McGraw-Hill Companies, Inc.

Surf's Up!

Math Concept:
Counting

Materials: crayons
Manipulatives: 0–5 number cube, different color connecting cubes, counters

Introduce the game on p. 108 to your students in pairs, or at a learning workstation to review concepts introduced in this chapter.

Instructions

Each student uses a different color connecting cube as a game piece to move around the game board.

- Students roll the number cube, then move their game piece that number of squares along the board.
- If students land on a space with a surfboard, they take a counter.
- When students reach Finish, they count their counters.
- Student with more counters wins.

Extend the Game

Play the game again, this time having 10 counters to start. Each time a student lands on a surf board, the student loses a counter. When students reach Finish, they count their counters. Students with less counters wins.

Differentiated Practice

Use these leveling suggestions to differentiate the game for all learners.

Level	Assignment
BL Below/Approaching Level	Have students use counters to count out the number shown on the number cube. Have them touch each counter as they move their game piece one space.
OL On Level	Have students play the game with the rules as written.
AL Above/Beyond Level	Have students design a more complex and larger game board and play the game by rolling two number cubes, adding the two numbers, and moving their game piece that number of spaces.

LESSON 4-4 Numbers 9 and 10

Lesson Planner

Objective

Name, recognize, and count the numerals 9 and 10 using concrete objects and illustrations.

Vocabulary

nine, **ten**

Resources

Materials: paper, markers, paper clips
Manipulatives: connecting cubes, counters
Literature Connection: *Tea for Ten* by Lena Anderson
Alternate Lesson: Use *The Piggy Bank Game* on page 101 of *Math Their Way* to provide practice for the quantities 9 and 10.
Teacher Technology
TeacherWorks

Focus on Math Background

This lesson completes students' work quantifying numbers through nine. The number ten is also a focus in this lesson. As students gain confidence with numbers zero to 10, they will develop strategies to keep track of counts to 100. Students also need a solid understanding of ten for future work with place value concepts, such as grouping quantities into units of tens and ones.

Daily Routine

Use these suggestions before beginning the lesson on p. 109.

5-Minute Check

(Reviews Lesson 4-3)
Draw six straws, seven cups, and eight plates on the chalkboard. Have students count the number in each group and represent it by writing the number on a sheet of paper.

Problem of the Day

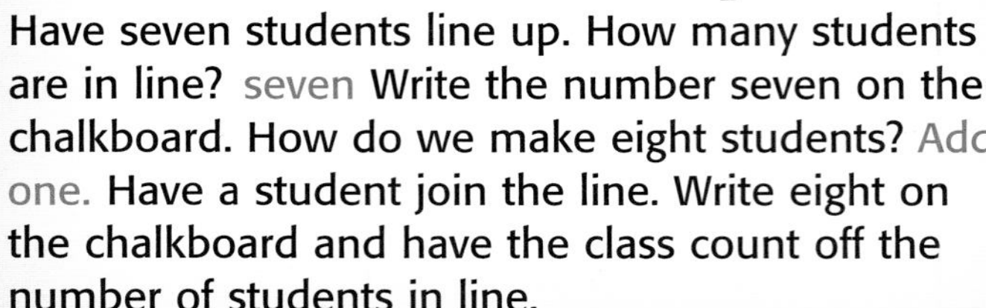

Have seven students line up. How many students are in line? seven Write the number seven on the chalkboard. How do we make eight students? Add one. Have a student join the line. Write eight on the chalkboard and have the class count off the number of students in line.

LINE UP Have three students line up until nine are in line. Have two students line up until 10 are in line. Repeat until all students are in line.

Building Math Vocabulary

Materials: construction paper, tape, bag

- Cut out **ten** different colored circles. Tape them around the room.
- Ask **nine** volunteers to find a hidden circle. Have them drop the circles into a bag as the class counts aloud.
- **How many circles are in the bag?** nine
- **How many more circles are needed to make 10?** one
- Have a volunteer find the last circle and drop it into the bag.
- **How many circles are in the bag?** 10 circles
- Pour the circles out and count them aloud with students.

Differentiated Instruction

Small Group Options

Option 1 Gifted and Talented AL

SOCIAL, SPATIAL

Materials: beach objects cut from magazines: balls, buckets, shovels, umbrellas, towels, craft paper for a mural, glue

- Put out a pile of beach objects.
- Assign students a beach object and the number of objects to be found: nine or 10.
- Have students glue their objects to a class mural.
- Have volunteers count out to ten while pointing at the mural.

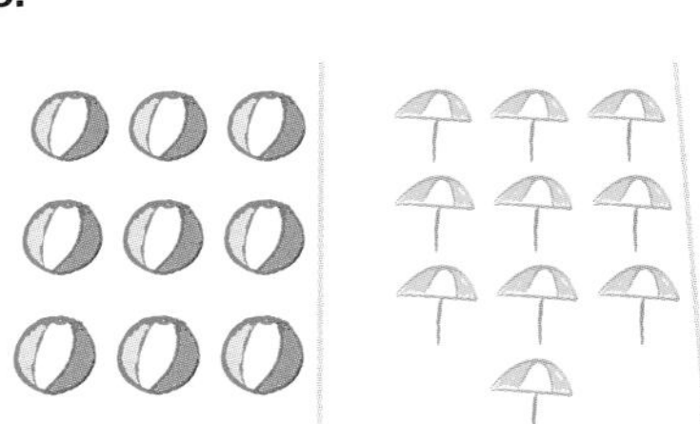

Option 2 English Language Learners ELL

AUDITORY, KINESTHETIC

Core Vocabulary: in all, kids, join the fun
Common Use Verb: comes
Talk Math This strategy uses music to explore numbers 9 and 10.

- With eight children in a circle, sing to the tune of "The Farmer in the Dell". Repeat for nine and 10.
- *There are eight kids in all. (2x) One comes to join the fun, there are nine kids in all.*

Independent Work Options

Option 1 Early Finishers OL AL

VISUAL

Materials: paper, pencils

- Have students count their fingers and thumbs, beginning with either thumb, from one to 10.
- Have students trace both hands, with fingers and thumbs separated, on paper.
- Have students count their fingers and thumbs on paper, beginning with either thumb, from one to 10.

Option 2 Student Technology

Math Online macmillanmh.com

Math Adventures

Option 3 Learning Station: Reading (p. 97G)

Direct students to the Reading Learning Station for more opportunities to explore and extend the lesson concept.

Leveled Lesson Resources

Additional support for English Language Learners can be found in the ELL Guide (p. 39). ELL

Reteach (p. 18) BL

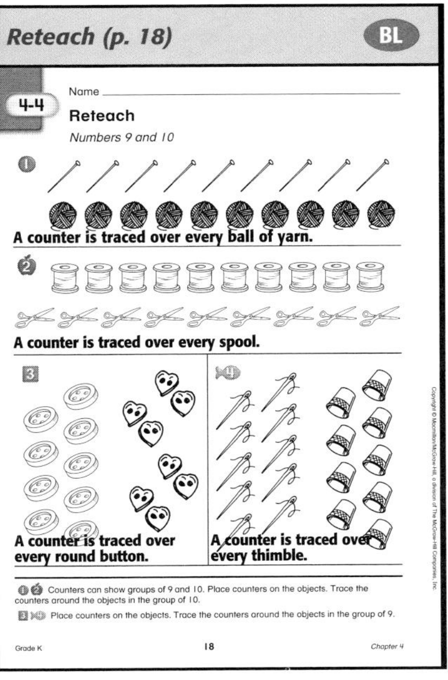
4-4 Reteach
Numbers 9 and 10

A counter is traced over every ball of yarn.

A counter is traced over every spool.

A counter is traced over every round button.

A counter is traced over every thimble.

1–2 Counters can show groups of 9 and 10. Place counters on the objects. Trace the counters around the objects in the group of 10.
3–4 Place counters on the objects. Trace the counters around the objects in the group of 9.

Grade K 18 Chapter 4

Skills Practice (p. 19) OL

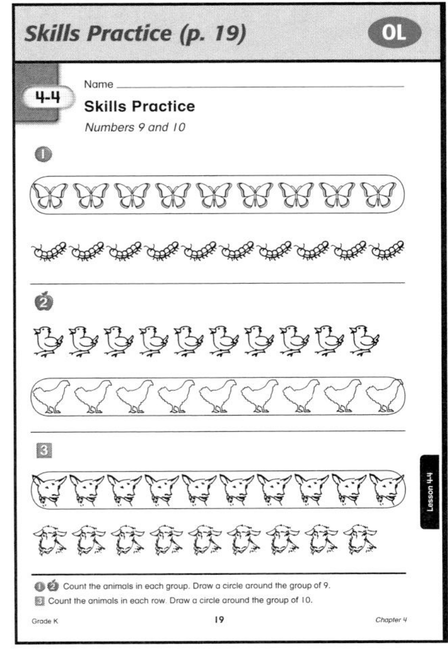
4-4 Skills Practice
Numbers 9 and 10

1–2 Count the animals in each group. Draw a circle around the group of 9.
3 Count the animals in each row. Draw a circle around the group of 10.

Grade K 19 Chapter 4

Enrich (p. 21) AL

4-4 Enrich
Froggy Fun

Start with the frog that is closest to the finish line. Write the order that the frogs will finish.

Grade K 21 Chapter 4

Homework Practice (p. 20) OL

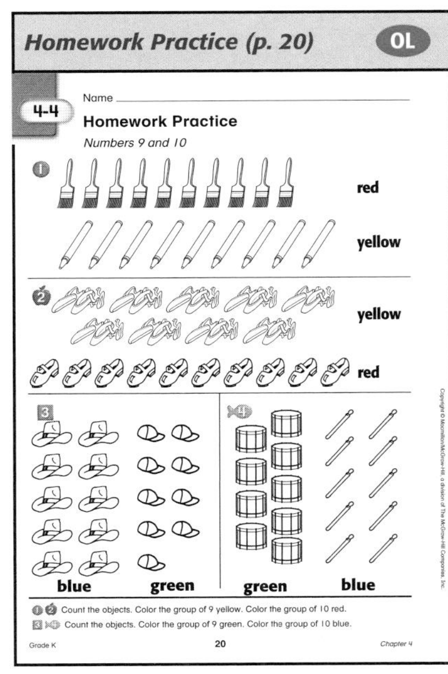
4-4 Homework Practice
Numbers 9 and 10

red
yellow
yellow
red
blue green green blue

1–2 Count the objects. Color the group of 9 yellow. Color the group of 10 red.
3–4 Count the objects. Color the group of 9 green. Color the group of 10 blue.

Grade K 20 Chapter 4

1 Introduce

Circle Time

Activity Choice 1 • Literature

Tea for Ten by Lena Anderson

Materials: paper, markers

- On pages 19–20, have students count **nine** guests, nine teacups, and nine saucers.
- On pages 21–24, have students count **ten** guests at the table and ten guests leaving through the door.
- Give students paper and markers. Have them draw two large circles. Tell students that the two circles are two tables. Have them draw teacups and saucers for nine guests on one table, then draw teacups and saucers for 10 guests on the other table.
- Have students form a circle. Ask volunteers to hold up their pictures. Have other volunteers point and say which table is set for nine and which table is set for 10.

Activity Choice 2 • Hands-On 

Materials: connecting cubes

- Give each student a set of eight connected connecting cubes and two individual cubes.
- **How many cubes are connected together?** eight
- Have students add one cube to the eight connected cubes.
- **How many cubes are connected now?** nine
- Have students count the cubes aloud.
- Have students add one cube to the nine connected cubes.
- **How many cubes are connected now?** 10 cubes
- Have students count the cubes aloud.
- Have students explore the classroom to find nine and 10 objects and to share their finding with another student.

2 Teach

Direct students to the top of p. 109. Identify the animal.

- Have students count the birds on the higher line using their fingers. Have them show the number 9 on their fingers. Have students flap their arms nine times like a bird flying. Have students count each arm flap aloud.
- Count the birds on the lower line together. Have students show counting using their fingers. Have them show the number 10. Say that 10 is one more than nine. Have students flap their arms 10 times like a bird flying. Have students count each arm flap aloud.

BL Alternate Teaching Strategy

If students have trouble naming, recognizing, and counting the quantities nine and 10 . . .

Then use one of the following reteach options.

1. CRM **Daily Reteach Worksheet** (p. 18)
2. **Seeing Nine and Ten** Put nine counters in a bubble container.
   - Pour out the nine counters. Invite students to pretend that these counters are bubbles.
   - Ask a student to count them. Tell students that nine is one more than eight. Lay them on the floor for all to see.
   - Ask students what nine sounds like. Have students clap nine times, one time for each counter.
   - Ask students what nine looks like. Have students jump nine times, one time for each counter.
   - Show the bubble container with 10 counters. Follow the same procedure as for nine. Tell students that 10 is one more than nine.

COMMON ERROR!

Students may have trouble recognizing the order of the one and zero in the number 10. Show three 10s with number cards for one and zero. Mix up the cards. Have students make 10s with the cards.

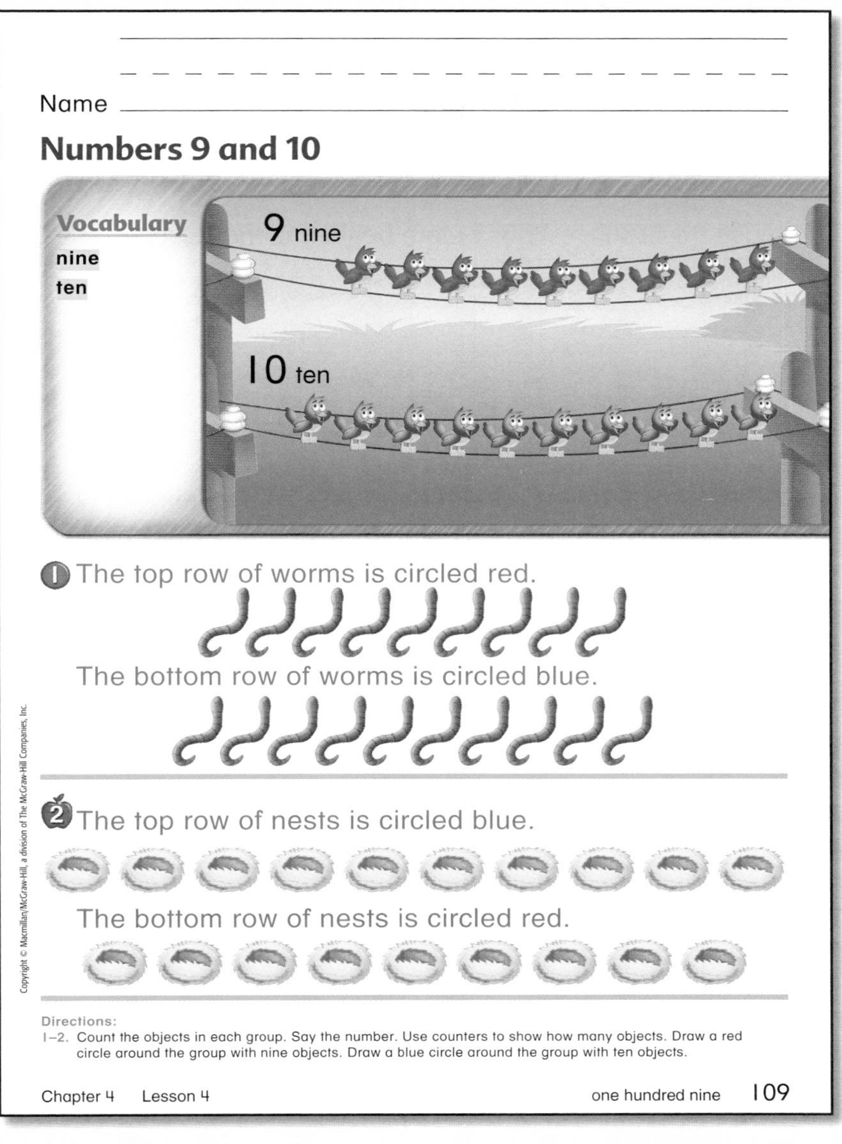

Name
Numbers 9 and 10
Vocabulary
nine
ten
9 nine
10 ten
The top row of worms is circled red.
The bottom row of worms is circled blue.
The top row of nests is circled blue.
The bottom row of nests is circled red.
Directions:
1–2. Count the objects in each group. Say the number. Use counters to show how many objects. Draw a red circle around the group with nine objects. Draw a blue circle around the group with ten objects.
Chapter 4 Lesson 4
one hundred nine 109

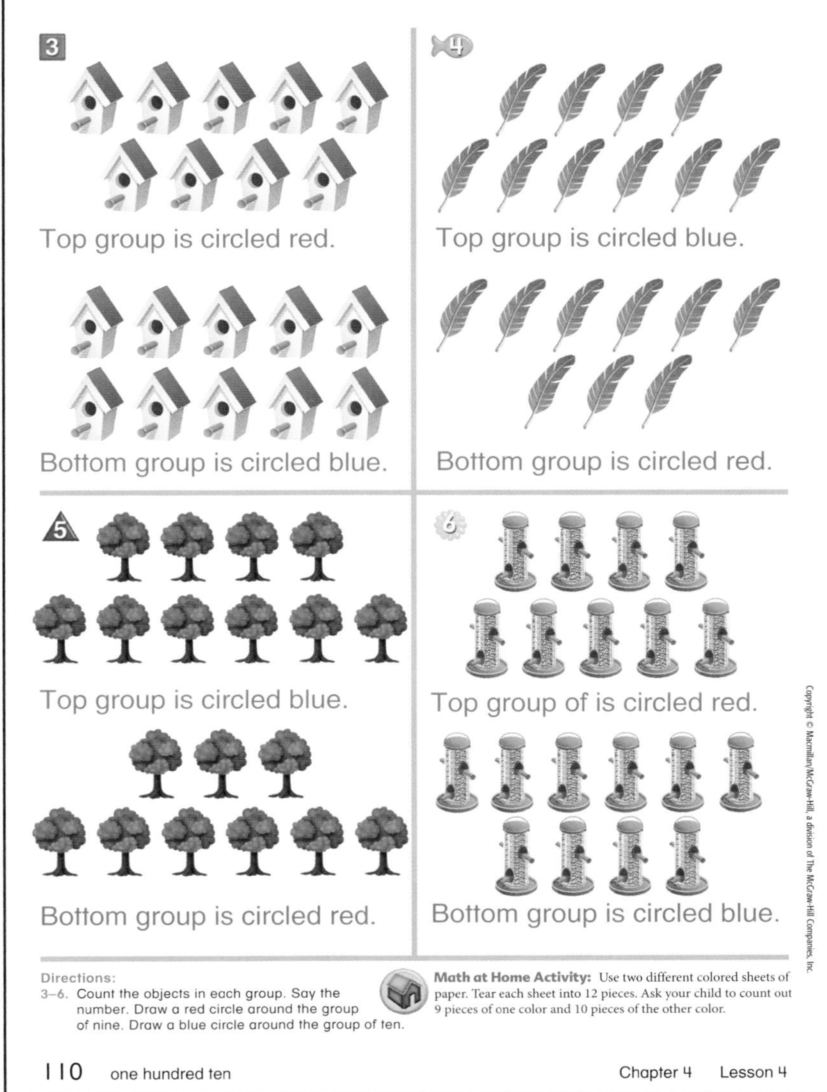

Top group is circled red.
Bottom group is circled blue.
Top group is circled blue.
Bottom group is circled red.
Top group is circled blue.
Bottom group is circled red.
Top group of is circled red.
Bottom group is circled blue.
Directions:
3–6. Count the objects in each group. Say the number. Draw a red circle around the group of nine. Draw a blue circle around the group of ten.
Math at Home Activity: Use two different colored sheets of paper. Tear each sheet into 12 pieces. Ask your child to count out 9 pieces of one color and 10 pieces of the other color.
110 one hundred ten
Chapter 4 Lesson 4

3 Practice

Guided Practice

- Direct students to Exercise 1 on p. 109. Have students use counters to show nine and 10.
- Have students count and say how many worms are in each group.
- **How many worms are in the top group? How many worms are in the group below them?** nine; ten
- Have students circle the group with nine red, and then circles the group with 10 blue.
- Repeat for the birds' nests.

Independent Practice

Have students turn to p. 110. Explain the directions. Have students work independently on the exercises.

4 Assess

Formative Assessment

- Give nine paper clips to each student. Have students count the clips. **How many clips are there?** nine
- **How many more clips do you need to have 10?** one more
- Give students one more clip and have them count each clip to 10.

Quick Check **Are students still having trouble naming, recognizing, or counting 10?**

If Yes → Small Group Options (p. 109B)

If No → Independent Work Options (p. 109B)

CRM Skills Practice Worksheet (p. 19)

CRM Enrich Worksheet (p. 21)

LESSON 4-5 Read and Write 9 and 10

Lesson Planner

Objective

Recognize and write the numerals 9 and 10.

Review Vocabulary

nine, **ten**

Resources

Materials: paper, circle stickers, modeling clay, number cards
Literature Connection: *Ten Black Dots* by Donald Crews
Alternate Lesson: Adapt *The Number Line Templates* on page 50 of *Math Their Way* for practice in recognition and writing the numbers 9 and 10.
Teacher Technology
TeacherWorks

Focus on Math Background

By the end of this lesson, which focuses on writing and reading numbers eight, nine, and 10, students will have had all the initial practice they need to write any number in our number system. Students will come to recognize that all multi-digit numbers are made up of an arrangement of any one of the basic digits zero to nine. Understanding that our number system is based on patterns is the hallmark of algebra.

Daily Routine

Use these suggestions before beginning the lesson on p. 111.

5-Minute Check

(Reviews Lesson 4-4)
Have students make nine balls of modeling clay and count the balls aloud. How many balls are needed to make 10 balls? one more Have students make another ball and count the 10 balls aloud.

Problem of the Day

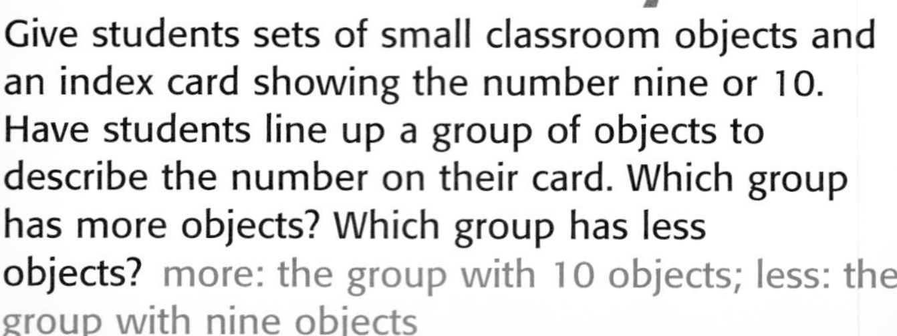

Give students sets of small classroom objects and an index card showing the number nine or 10. Have students line up a group of objects to describe the number on their card. Which group has more objects? Which group has less objects? more: the group with 10 objects; less: the group with nine objects

LINE UP Hold up a card with a number nine written on it. Ask students to tell what number is written, and then line up by hopping nine times to get to the line. Have students count their hops aloud. Repeat with the number 10, having each student take ten baby steps to get to the line. Repeat until all students are lined up.

Review Math Vocabulary

Materials: classroom objects, number cards 9 and 10, index cards, pencils

- Have students work in groups of three or four.
- Hold up a number card for **nine** or **ten** and have students read the number aloud.
- Have each group gather and display that number of identical classroom objects.
- Have groups count the objects aloud and then write the number on an index card, displaying it in front of their objects.
- Repeat the activity for nine or 10.

Differentiated Instruction

Small Group Options

Option 1 Below/Approaching Level BL

SPATIAL

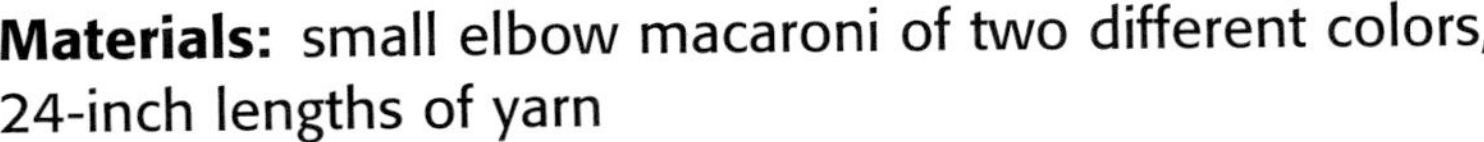

Materials: small elbow macaroni of two different colors, 24-inch lengths of yarn

- Have students count out nine pieces of macaroni of one color and 10 pieces of macaroni of another color.
- Help students string their macaroni onto the yarn, tying the ends to make necklaces that symbolically describe nine and 10.

Option 2 English Language Learners ELL

KINESTHETIC, VISUAL

Core Vocabulary: in, out, hand

Common Use Verb: circle

Write Math This strategy uses motion and music to teach writing nine and ten.

- In a circle, demonstrate in and out by singing the following to the tune of the "Hokey Pokey".
- "Make a circle, then a line, that's the way to make a nine" and "one ***hands*** up and out ***circles*** again, it takes two ***hands*** to make a ten".

Independent Work Options

Option 1 Early Finishers OL AL

VISUAL

Materials: uncooked lima beans, bowls, art paper, crayons

- Give students two bowls and 19 beans.
- Have students count out nine beans to place in the first bowl and 10 beans to place in the second bowl.
- Give students art paper and crayons. Have them symbolically describe the numbers by drawing the two bowls and labeling one bowl 9 and the other bowl 10.
- Have students draw and color the number of beans in each bowl that matches the label. Then have them count their beans to check the number.

Option 2 Student Technology

Math Online macmillanmh.com

Math Adventures

Option 3 Learning Station: Social Studies (p. 97H)

Direct students to the Social Studies Learning Station for more opportunities to explore and extend the lesson concept.

Leveled Lesson Resources

Reteach (p. 22) BL

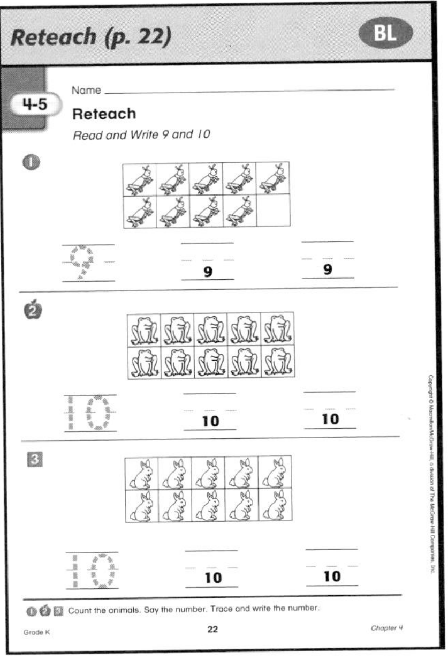

4-5 Name

Reteach

Read and Write 9 and 10

9 9 9

10 10 10

10 10 10

Count the animals. Say the number. Trace and write the number.

Grade K 22 Chapter 4

Skills Practice (p. 23) OL

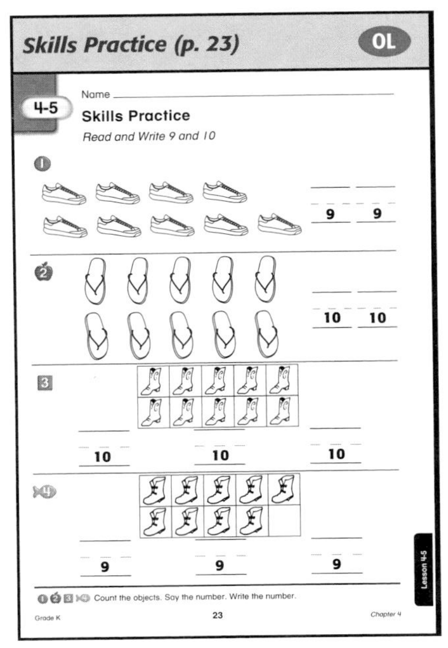

4-5 Name

Skills Practice

Read and Write 9 and 10

9 9

10 10

10 10 10

9 9 9

Count the objects. Say the number. Write the number.

Grade K 23 Chapter 4

Enrich (p. 25) AL

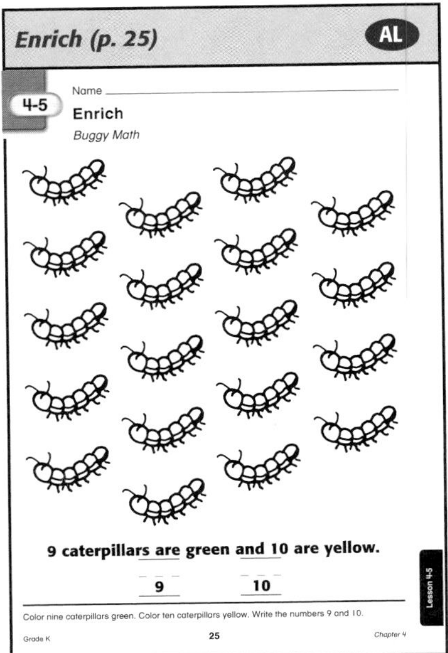

4-5 Name

Enrich

Buggy Math

9 caterpillars are green and 10 are yellow.

9 10

Color nine caterpillars green. Color ten caterpillars yellow. Write the numbers 9 and 10.

Grade K 25 Chapter 4

Homework Practice (p. 24) OL

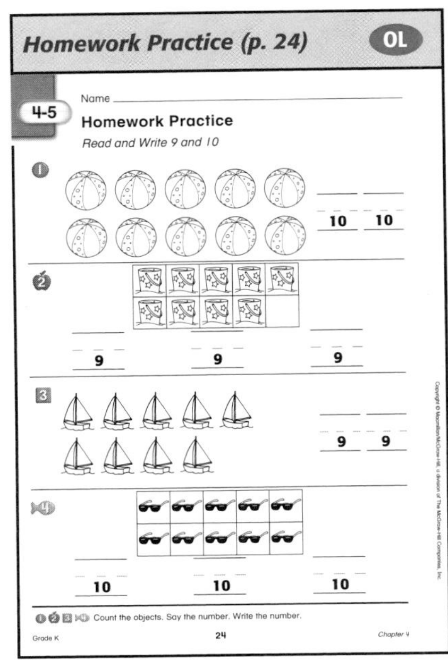

4-5 Name

Homework Practice

Read and Write 9 and 10

10 10

9 9 9

9 9

10 10 10

Count the objects. Say the number. Write the number.

Grade K 24 Chapter 4

1 Introduce

Circle Time

Activity Choice 1 • Literature

Ten Black Dots by Donald Crews

Materials: paper, circle stickers

- On pages 18–19, have students count aloud the number of soldiers. Write the number **nine** on the chalkboard. Have students count nine pennies in the piggy bank on the following page. Write the number nine on the chalkboard.
- On pages 22–23, have students verbally describe the numbers by counting the balloons. Write the number **ten** on the chalkboard. Have students count 10 balloons on the following page. Write the number 10 on the chalkboard.
- Give each student two sheets of paper and 19 circle stickers. Have them label one paper 9 and the other paper 10.
- Have students attach the correct number of circles to each paper.

Activity Choice 2 • Hands-On

Materials: modeling clay

- Give students a large piece of modeling clay. Have them divide the clay into three equal pieces and then roll out each piece into a long, thin log.
- Have students use one log to shape into the number nine. Have them use the two remaining logs to shape into the number 10.
- Write numbers nine and 10 on the chalkboard. Ask if their number nine and number 10 look like yours, and if not, model numbers nine and 10 with clay.
- Have them make their number nine into nine small balls and put the balls in a row. Tell them to remove the balls one-by-one, counting each ball.
- **How many balls do you have?** nine
- Repeat with 10.

2 Teach

- Direct students to the top of p. 111.
- **How many hats do you see?** nine
- **How many pairs of binoculars do you see?** 10 pairs
- Have students pantomime putting a hat on their head nine times. Then, have students pantomime bringing binoculars up to their eyes 10 times.

BL Alternate Teaching Strategy

If students have trouble counting from one to 10 . . .

Then use one of the following reteach options.

1 CRM **Daily Reteach Worksheet** (p. 22)

2 **Count to Nine and Ten** Ask 10 volunteers to stand up.

- Have sitting students count the volunteers by clapping 10 times.
- Have different groups of nine or 10 students stand up and the sitting students count by stomping, tapping on their desk, or holding up a pencil.

COMMON ERROR!

Students may have difficulty aligning the one and the zero when writing the number ten. Have them practice writing the number by tracing over dashed lines of 10s.

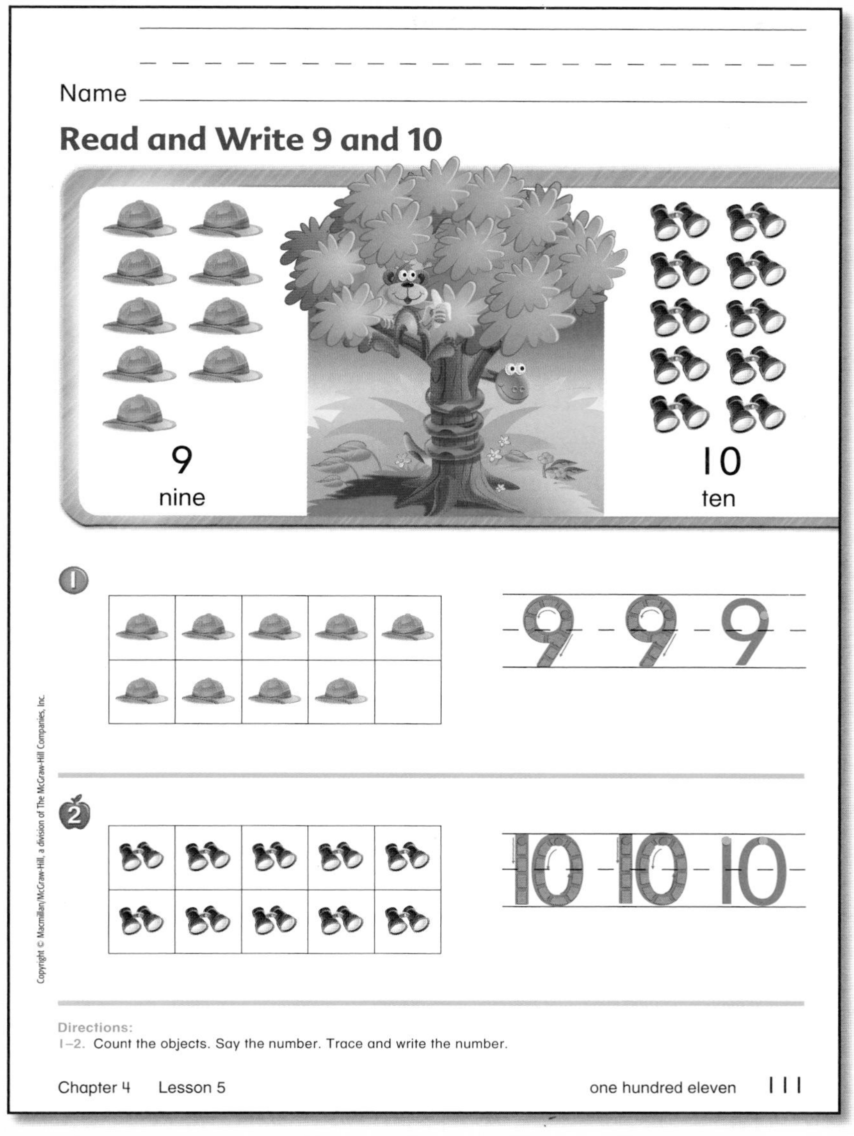

Name
Read and Write 9 and 10
9
nine
10
ten
9 9 9
10 10 10
Directions:
1–2. Count the objects. Say the number. Trace and write the number.
Chapter 4 Lesson 5 one hundred eleven 111

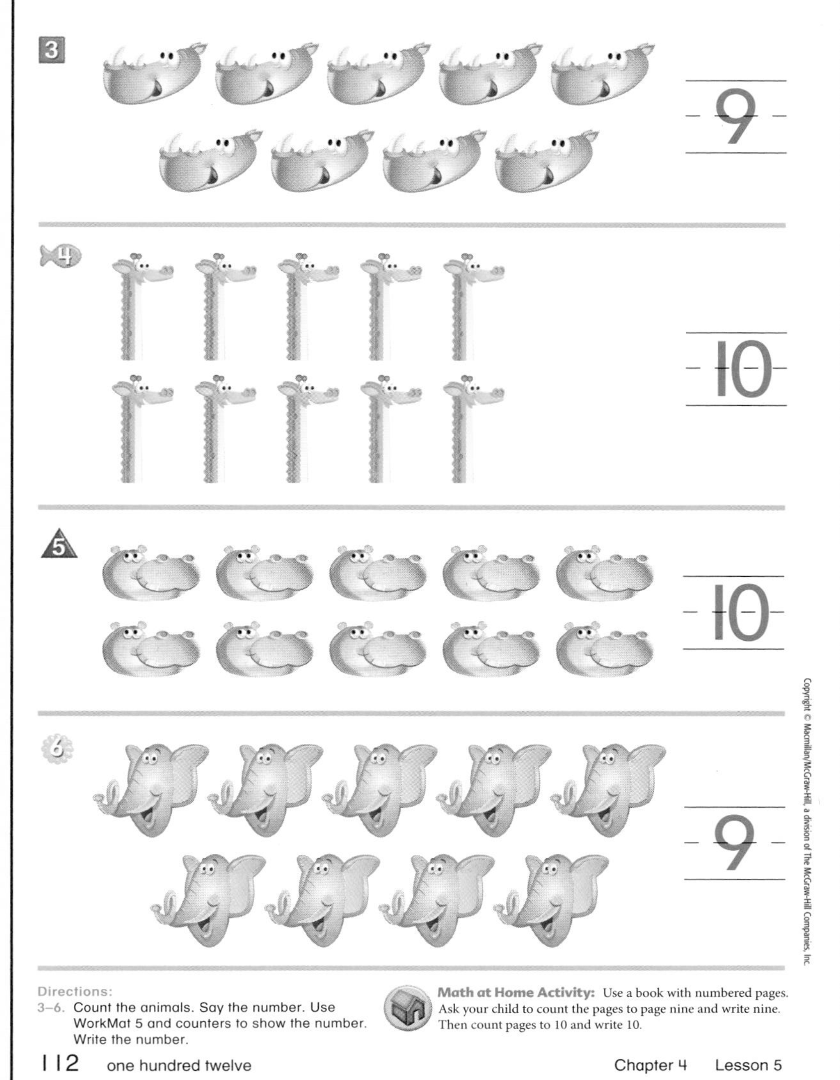

9
10
10
9
Directions:
3–6. Count the animals. Say the number. Use WorkMat 5 and counters to show the number. Write the number.
Math at Home Activity: Use a book with numbered pages. Ask your child to count the pages to page nine and write nine. Then count pages to 10 and write 10.
112 one hundred twelve Chapter 4 Lesson 5

3 Practice

Guided Practice

- Direct students to p. 111.
- Tell them to count the number of hats. Have students trace and write the number.
- **What number did you write?** nine
- Tell students to count the number of binoculars. Have students trace and write the number.
- **What number did you write?** 10

Independent Practice

Have students turn to p. 112. Explain the directions. Have students work independently on the exercises.

4 Assess

Formative Assessment

- Show a card with the number nine on it. Have students say and write the number. Repeat for number 10.
- **How many more is 10 than nine?** one

Quick Check **Are students having trouble aligning the one and the zero when writing the number 10?**

If Yes → Small Group Options (p. 111B)

If No → Independent Work Options (p. 111B)

CRM Skills Practice Worksheet (p. 23)

CRM Enrich Worksheet (p. 25)

Problem-Solving Strategy
Draw a Picture

Lesson Planner

Objective

Count, recognize, represent, and name numerals 6 through 10 using concrete objects and illustrations.

Resources

Materials: flower sticker, paper, crayons, tape
Manipulatives: counters
Literature Connection: *Who's Counting?* by Nancy Tafuri
Teacher Technology
TeacherWorks

Real-World Problem Solving Library
Math and Science: *Numbers About Me*
Use these leveled readers to reinforce and extend problem-solving skills and strategies.

Leveled for:
- OL On Level
- ELL Sheltered English
- SP Spanish

For additional support, see the Real-World Problem Solving Teacher Guide.

On-level title is available in classroom Big Book.

Daily Routine

Use these suggestions before beginning the lesson on p. 113.

5-Minute Check

(Reviews Lesson 4-5)
Show students a picture of nine objects. Have them count the objects and then write the number nine. Repeat for the number 10.

Problem of the Day

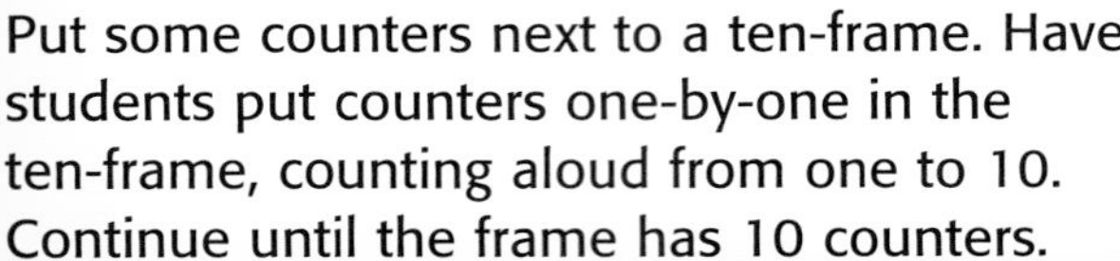

Put some counters next to a ten-frame. Have students put counters one-by-one in the ten-frame, counting aloud from one to 10. Continue until the frame has 10 counters.

LINE UP Give pictures of three different animals to students randomly. Have students with the same animal pictures line up. Have other students count how many of each animal is in line.

Differentiated Instruction

Small Group Options

Option 1 Gifted and Talented AL

VISUAL, KINESTHETIC

Materials: 10 index cards numbered 1–10, 5 index cards with a phrase and visual: draw birds, draw trees, draw balls, draw suns, draw children

- Have students work in pairs. Have one student pick a card from each set. The partner then does what the cards say, such as "draw three trees".
- Have the other students guess the drawing.

Option 2 English Language Learners ELL

KINESTHETIC

Materials: index cards, counters, pocket chart labeled 1–10
Core Vocabulary: where, should, counters
Common Use Verb: draw/drew

Hear Math This strategy teaches drawing pictures to solve problems.

- Demonstrate drawing 3 counters on the index card. Prompt students to repeat.
- Say: "I **drew** three. **Where should** it go?".

Independent Work Options

Option 1 Early Finishers OL AL

VISUAL

Materials: small classroom objects (such as crayons, pencils, paper clips, rubber bands)

- Tell students that you are thinking of a number between six and 10. Have each student guess the number, then symbolically describe the number by drawing that number of classroom objects.
- Tell students what number you were thinking of. Write the number on the chalkboard. Count students' objects as a class to see who guessed correctly.
- Repeat for six, seven, eight, nine, and 10.

Option 2 Student Technology

Option 3 Learning Station: Art (p. 97G)

Direct students to the Art Learning Station for more opportunities to explore and extend the lesson concept.

Leveled Lesson Resources

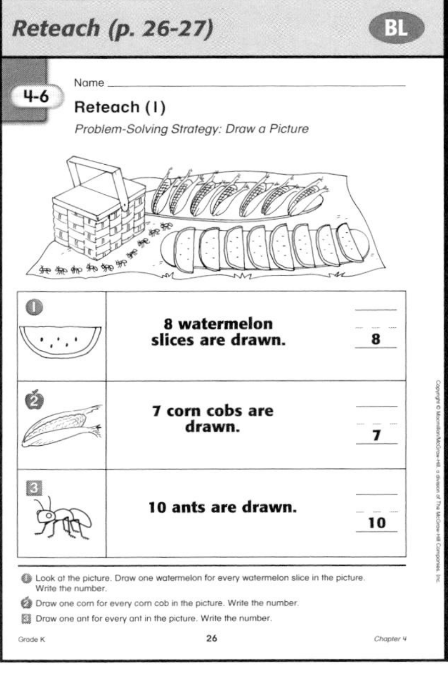

Reteach (p. 26-27) BL

4-6 Name ______
Reteach (1)
Problem-Solving Strategy: Draw a Picture

1	8 watermelon slices are drawn.	8
2	7 corn cobs are drawn.	7
3	10 ants are drawn.	10

1 Look at the picture. Draw one watermelon for every watermelon slice in the picture. Write the number.
2 Draw one corn for every corn cob in the picture. Write the number.
3 Draw one ant for every ant in the picture. Write the number.

Grade K 26 Chapter 4

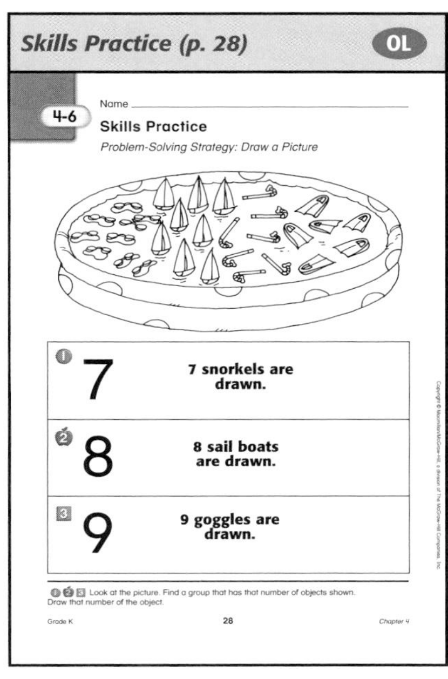

Skills Practice (p. 28) OL

4-6 Name ______
Skills Practice
Problem-Solving Strategy: Draw a Picture

1	7	7 snorkels are drawn.
2	8	8 sail boats are drawn.
3	9	9 goggles are drawn.

1 2 3 Look at the picture. Find a group that has that number of objects shown. Draw that number of the object.

Grade K 28 Chapter 4

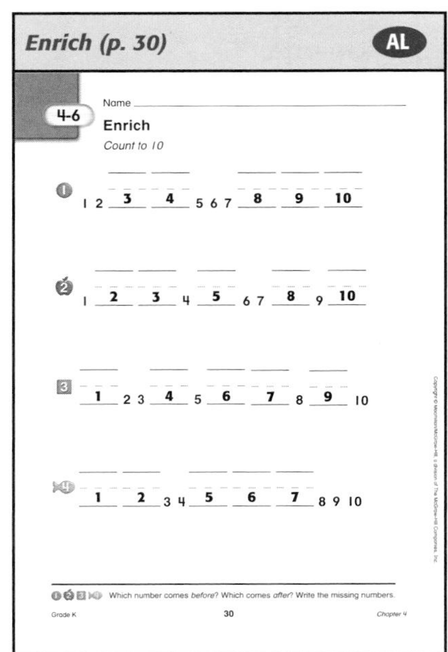

Enrich (p. 30) AL

4-6 Name ______
Enrich
Count to 10

1. 1 2 **3** **4** 5 6 7 **8** **9** **10**
2. 1 **2** **3** 4 **5** 6 7 **8** 9 **10**
3. **1** 2 3 **4** 5 **6** **7** 8 **9** 10
4. **1** **2** 3 4 **5** **6** **7** 8 9 10

1 2 3 4 Which number comes *before*? Which comes *after*? Write the missing numbers.

Grade K 30 Chapter 4

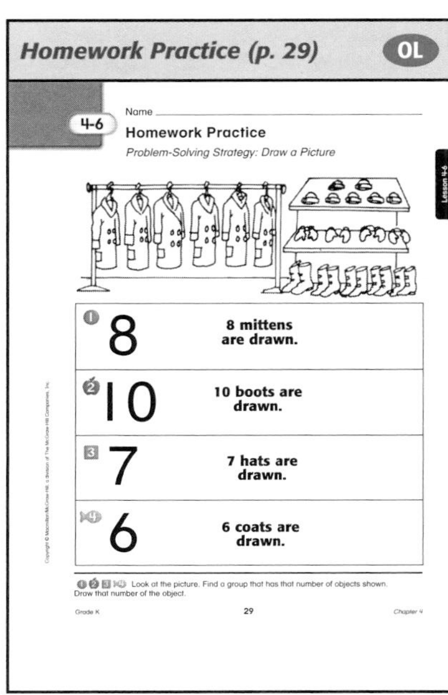

Homework Practice (p. 29) OL

4-6 Name ______
Homework Practice
Problem-Solving Strategy: Draw a Picture

Lesson 4-6

1	8	8 mittens are drawn.
2	10	10 boots are drawn.
3	7	7 hats are drawn.
4	6	6 coats are drawn.

1 2 3 4 Look at the picture. Find a group that has that number of objects shown. Draw that number of the object.

Grade K 29 Chapter 4

1 Introduce

Circle Time

Activity Choice 1 • Literature

Who's Counting? by Nancy Tafuri

Materials: flower sticker, crayons

- Read aloud the text on the back cover to introduce the story.
- Read the story aloud, counting the objects and finding the puppy in each picture. Note the part of the story where students can always find "our puppy" by the flower he picked.
- Have students draw ten puppies. Have them mark one puppy with a flower.
- Have students identify each other's puppy by finding the flower and saying that puppy's number.

Activity Choice 2 • Hands-On

Materials: paper, crayons, tape

- Divide students into small groups. Give each group paper and crayons. Tell students to decorate the paper to make a party hat. Help students decorate, then make party hats by curling the paper into a cone and taping it to keep the cone shape.
- Have each group make a different number of party hats, from six to 10.
- Have each group count the number of party hats they made and tell how many friends will be at their party.
- Ask one volunteer from each group to write the number of party hats for their group.
- Tell the students that by drawing party hats it was easier to tell how many people would be at the party.

2 Teach

Drawing a picture helps students to solve problems through visual cues. The use of student drawings helps students to see the problem concretely. Working with drawings allows students to count and see number quantities.

Understand Review what students know and what they need to find for each problem.

Plan Have students discuss their strategy for solving the problems.

Solve Guide students to draw a picture to solve the problem. By drawing a picture students will be able to identify how many of each object are at the circus.

Check Have students look back at the problem to be sure that the answers fit what they already know about the problem. Discuss with students that mathematical statements can be true or false. Students need to check to make sure their answers are true statements.

BL Alternate Teaching Strategy

If students have trouble identifying the numeral represented by an object . . .

Then use one of the following reteach options.

1.  **Daily Reteach Worksheet** (p. 26-27)
2. **Count the Animals** Have students use counters to represent each animal in each group.
   - Students then count the counters and the animals.
   - If students still have difficulty, have them put a counter on each animal in each animal group and then count.

! COMMON ERROR!

Students may skip or repeat number names when learning to count. Have students touch each picture when counting.

Name

Problem-Solving Strategy

Draw a Picture

How many are at the circus?

1 8 bananas are drawn 8

2 9 hats are drawn 9

Directions:
1–2. Look at the picture. Find a group of objects that has the number shown. Draw those objects.

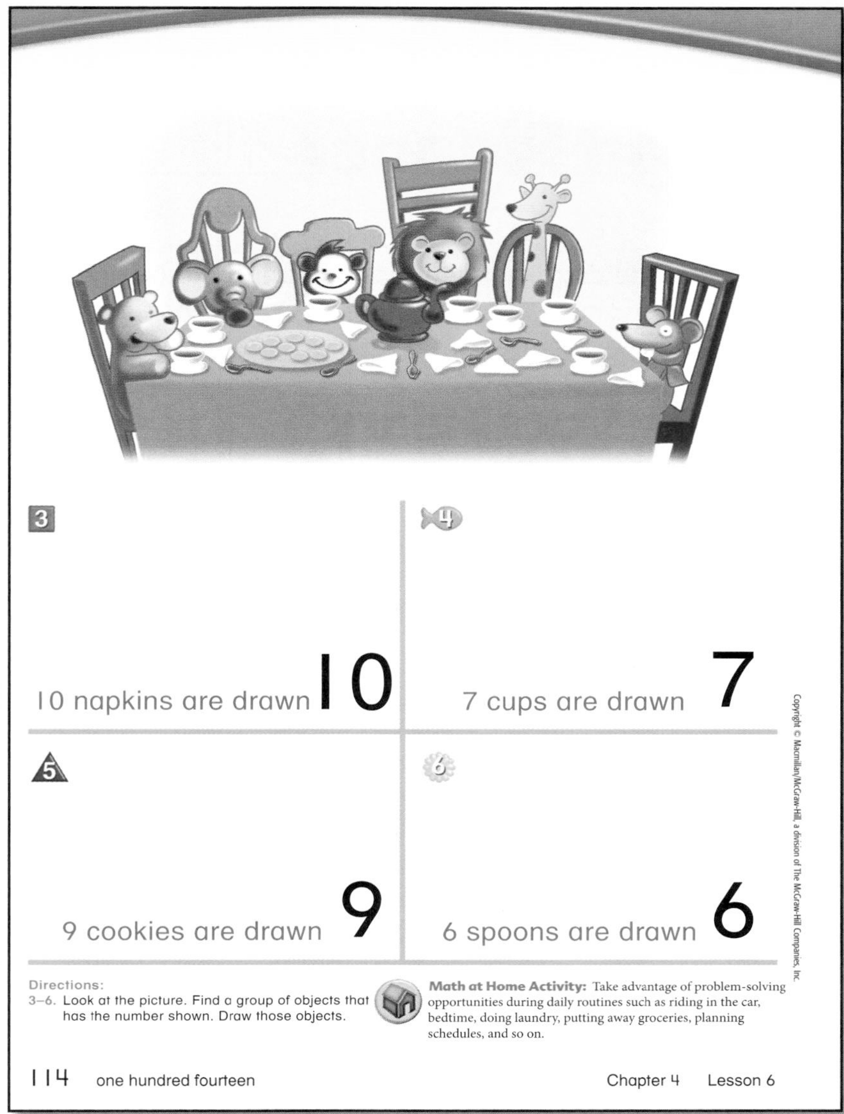

3 10 napkins are drawn 10

4 7 cups are drawn 7

5 9 cookies are drawn 9

6 6 spoons are drawn 6

Directions:
3–6. Look at the picture. Find a group of objects that has the number shown. Draw those objects.

Math at Home Activity: Take advantage of problem-solving opportunities during daily routines such as riding in the car, bedtime, doing laundry, putting away groceries, planning schedules, and so on.

3 Practice

Guided Practice

- Direct students to p. 113. Make sure students understand the problem and count objects to determine the number of animals or circus objects in each group.
- Have students identify each number; find a set of objects that has that number in the picture; then draw those objects in each box.

Independent Practice

- Have students turn to p. 114. Explain the directions. Have students work independently on the exercises.

4 Assess

Formative Assessment

- Distribute color tiles to each student.
- Direct students to the circus picture on p. 113.
- Have students draw a picture to show how many seals are at the circus. Have students draw two more seals and tell how many seals there are in all.

Quick Check **Are students still struggling to count and write numbers six through 10?**

If Yes → Small Group Options (p. 113B)

If No → Independent Work Options (p. 113B)

CRM Skills Practice Worksheet (p. 28)

CRM Enrich Worksheet (p. 30)

LESSON 4-7

Compare Numbers to 10

Lesson Planner

Objective

Use one-to-one correspondence and counting to compare sets and determine which has more than, less than, or whether the sets are the same/equal.

Review Vocabulary

ten

Resources

Materials: construction paper, pencil, paper bags, small classroom objects: paper clips, beads, crayons, rubber bands, Workmat5: Ten-Frame
Manipulatives: counters
Literature Connection: *Ten Little Ducks by Franklin Hammond*
Alternate Lesson: Adapt *Spill the Beans* on page 102 of *Math Their Way* to provide one-to-one correspondence and counting practice with numbers 1 through 10.
Use *IMPACT Mathematics*: Unit B to provide practice with comparing numbers.
Teacher Technology
TeacherWorks

Focus on Math Background

This lesson focuses on comparing numbers to 10. When students have in-depth understanding of number relationships to 10, they can compare any numbers in the number system.

Daily Routine

Use these suggestions before beginning the lesson on p. 115.

5-Minute Check

(Reviews Lesson 4-6)
Have students show nine books and write the number nine next to them. Have them show 10 color tiles and write 10 next to them.

Problem of the Day

Show four cube trains: train A has two squares, trains B and C have three, and train D has four. How many cubes are in each stack? two, three, four Which trains have the same number of cubes? B and C

Have a row of six and a row of 10 students line up. **Which line has more? Which line has less?** 10, six Have another row of six students line up. **Are two lines the same? Why?** Yes; two lines have six students.

Review Math Vocabulary

Materials: number dot cards (6–10)
Write *more, less,* and *the same* on the chalkboard. Point to the words as you do the following activity.

- Show dot cards for seven and nine.
- **What are the numbers?** seven and nine
- **What number is less?** seven
- Show dot cards for six and **ten.**
- **What are the numbers?** six and 10
- **What number is more?** 10
- Show two dot cards with four dots each for eight. **Are these numbers the same/equal? Why?** Yes; there are the same number of dots on both cards.

Differentiated Instruction

Small Group Options

Option 1 Gifted and Talented AL

LOGICAL/VISUAL

Materials: connecting cubes, 3 bowls

- Place a different number of cubes in each bowl, with each bowl containing ten or fewer cubes.
- Have students count the number of cubes in each bowl.
- Have students tell which bowl has more cubes and which has less cubes in it.

Option 2 English Language Learners ELL

KINESTHETIC

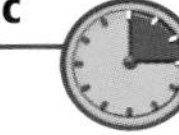

Materials: counters
Core Vocabulary: no, now we know, has more
Common Use Verb: know/do not know

See Math This strategy helps students compare numbers to 10.

- Write "no" and "know" on the board. Explain the difference between the two words.
- Put a few counters in each hand. Say: "Do I **know** which hand has more? No, I **do not know**".
- Model solution with counters. Say: "**Now we know** which hand **has more**".

Independent Work Options

Option 1 Early Finishers OL AL

VISUAL

Materials: two sets of number cards, cubes

- Have student partners place the pile of number cards face down on a table.
- Have each student draw a number card from the pile.
- Have students say the number and count that many cubes.
- Have students compare amounts of cubes and numbers to determine which number is more than, less than, or if the numbers are the same.

Option 2 Student Technology

Math Adventures

Option 3 Learning Station: Science (p. 97G)

Direct students to the Science Learning Station for more opportunities to explore and extend the lesson concept.

Leveled Lesson Resources

Reteach (p. 31) BL

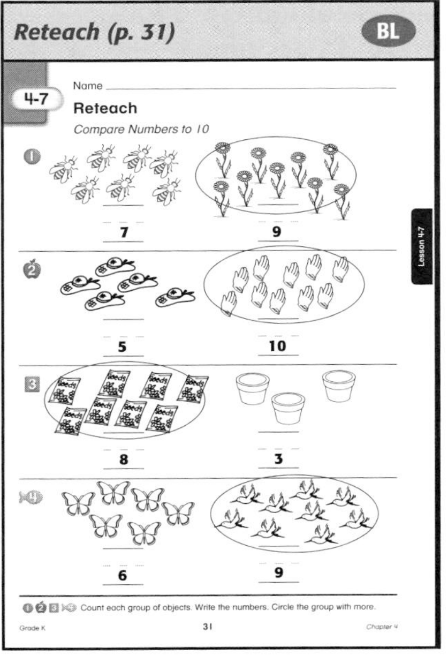

4-7 Name
Reteach
Compare Numbers to 10

1. 7 9
2. 5 10
3. 8 3
4. 6 9

Count each group of objects. Write the numbers. Circle the group with more.

Grade K 31 Chapter 4

Skills Practice (p.32) OL

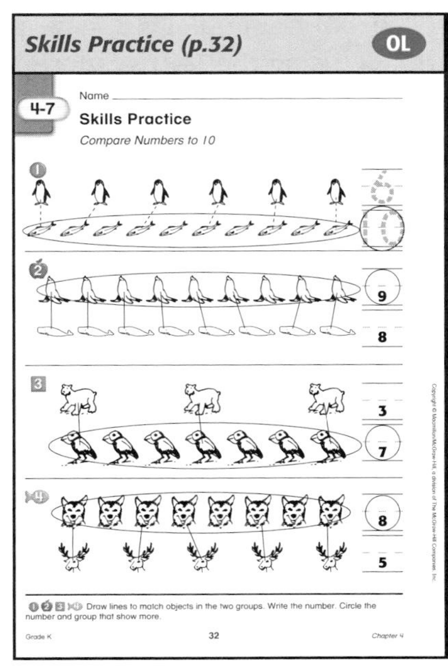

4-7 Name
Skills Practice
Compare Numbers to 10

1. 6 10
2. 9 8
3. 3 7
4. 8 5

Draw lines to match objects in the two groups. Write the number. Circle the number and group that show more.

Grade K 32 Chapter 4

Enrich (p. 34) AL

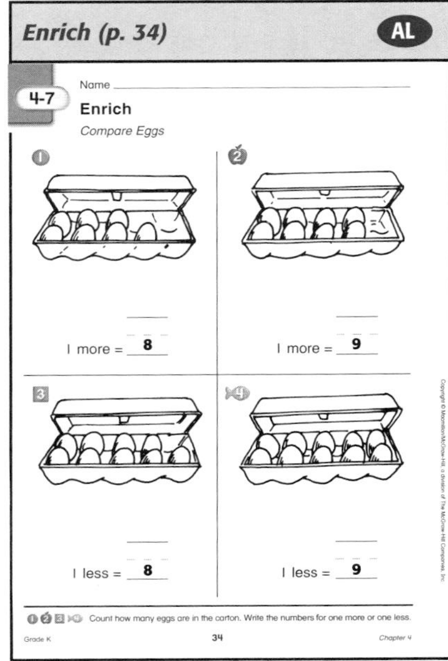

4-7 Name
Enrich
Compare Eggs

1. 1 more = 8
2. 1 more = 9
3. 1 less = 8
4. 1 less = 9

Count how many eggs are in the carton. Write the numbers for one more or one less.

Grade K 34 Chapter 4

Homework Practice (p. 33) OL

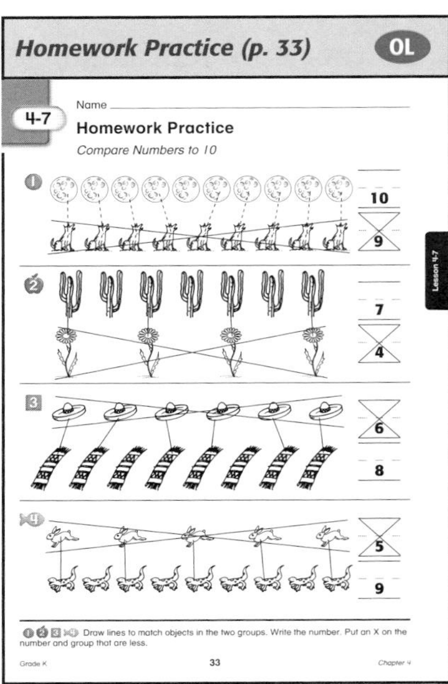

4-7 Name
Homework Practice
Compare Numbers to 10

1. 10 9
2. 7 4
3. 6 8
4. 5 9

Draw lines to match objects in the two groups. Write the number. Put an X on the number and group that are less.

Grade K 33 Chapter 4

1 Introduce

Circle Time

Activity Choice 1 • Literature

At the Edge of the Woods: A Counting Book
by Cynthia Cotten

Materials: construction paper, pencil

- Read the story aloud. Have students count the animals in each picture.
- Ask students comparative questions such as whether there are more lilies or lizards (page with number 4) or whether there are less (or more) yellow flowers or purple flowers (page with number 5).
- Write the numbers one to ten on construction paper. Form 10 groups of students and give each group a piece of paper with a number. Have each group choose an animal and describe their number symbolically by drawing pictures of the animal.

Activity Choice 2 • Hands-On 

Materials: paper bags, small classroom objects: paper clips, beads, crayons, rubber bands

Put small classroom objects into paper bags for each student. Each bag should contain an even number of objects up to 10. Fold the tops of the bags down.

- Give each student a bag. Pair off students and have them take all the objects out of their bags.
- **How many objects are in your bags? Does your partner have more than you? Does your partner have less than you? Does your partner have the same number of objects?** Sample answers: eight; no; yes; no
- Have the student with more objects give the partner an object.
- **How many objects do you have now? Does your partner have the same number of objects?** Sample answers: nine; yes

2 Teach

- Direct students to the top of p. 115.
- Discuss more than at the top of the page by asking the students to trace the lines to match the fish. Compare the groups and discuss.
- **What do you notice about the groups of fish?** One group has more than the other.
- **What do you notice about the lines that are matched to the fish in each group?** Sample answer: They all match except one.
- Trace each line. Count the red and blue fish with the students. Ask them to write the number of fish in each group below each column. Compare numbers. Circle the number and group that has more objects than the other.
- Discuss less than with green and yellow birds following the same procedure above. Put an X on the number and group that has less objects than the other group.
- Discuss same number as with brown and tan hamsters following the same procedure above. Put a box around both groups that have the same number of objects.

BL Alternate Teaching Strategy

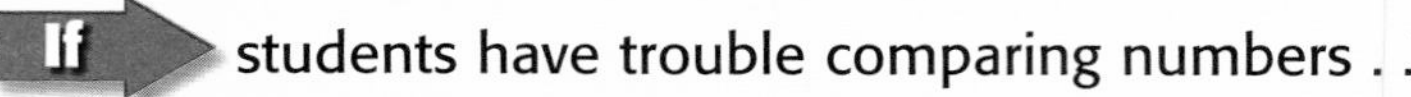

If students have trouble comparing numbers . . .

Then use one of the following reteach options.

1  **Daily Reteach Worksheet** (p. 31)

2 **Workmat 5 Practice** Provide students with manipulatives to help them count on a ten-frame workmat.

- Have students make rows with different numbers of manipulatives from one to 10.
- After making at least four rows with different numbers of manipulatives, have students compare the rows, using the terms "more than" and "less than".
- Have students make a row that has the same number of manipulatives as one original row.

COMMON ERROR!

Students may be confused by lines from objects that cannot be connected to a corresponding object. Have them circle each picture in each line so they can see the numbers that represent each object.

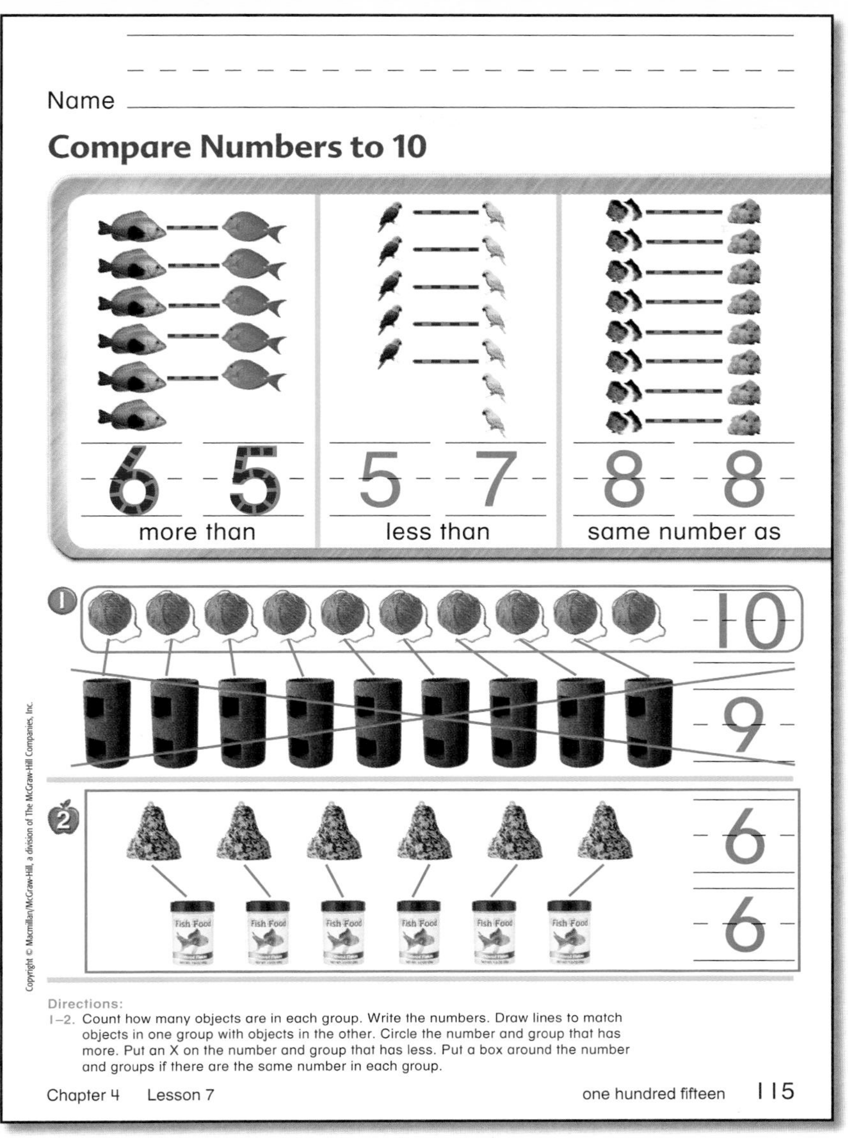

Name
Compare Numbers to 10
6 5
more than
5 7
less than
8 8
same number as
10
9
6
6
Directions:
1–2. Count how many objects are in each group. Write the numbers. Draw lines to match objects in one group with objects in the other. Circle the number and group that has more. Put an X on the number and group that has less. Put a box around the number and groups if there are the same number in each group.
Chapter 4 Lesson 7
one hundred fifteen 115

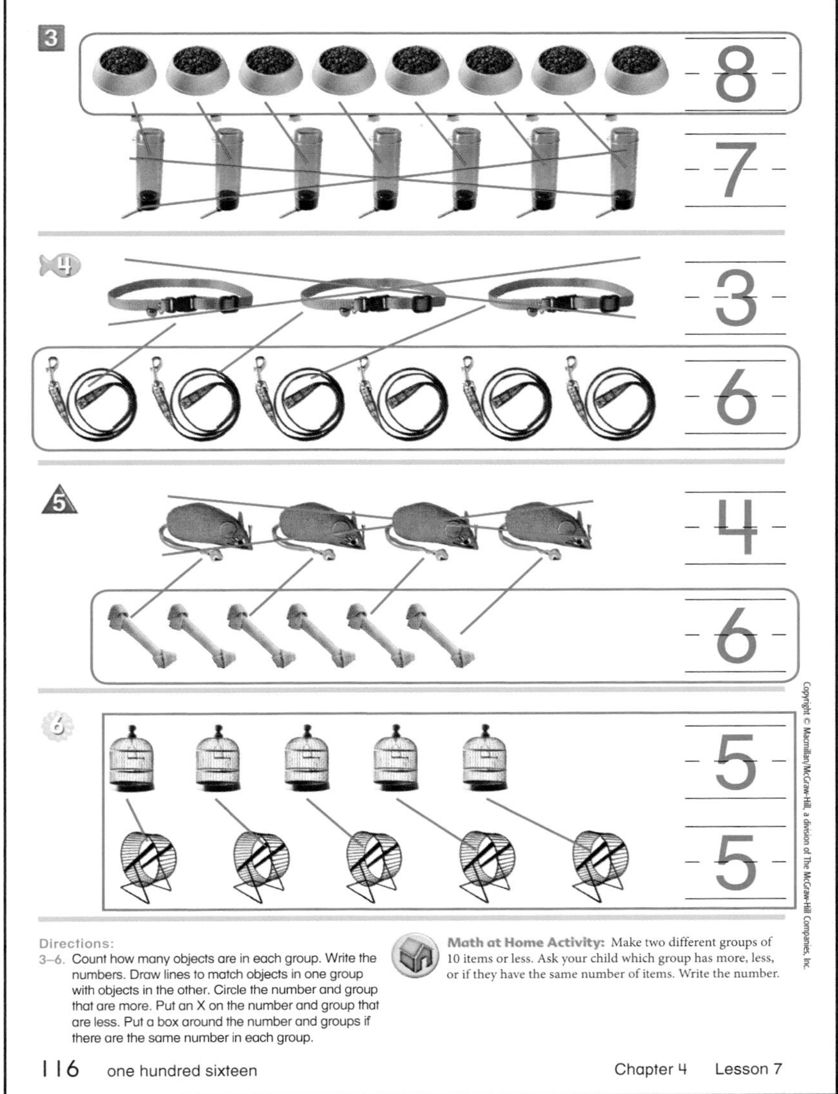

8
7
3
6
4
6
5
5
Directions:
3–6. Count how many objects are in each group. Write the numbers. Draw lines to match objects in one group with objects in the other. Circle the number and group that are more. Put an X on the number and group that are less. Put a box around the number and groups if there are the same number in each group.
Math at Home Activity: Make two different groups of 10 items or less. Ask your child which group has more, less, or if they have the same number of items. Write the number.
116 one hundred sixteen
Chapter 4 Lesson 7

3 Practice

Guided Practice

- Direct students to Exercise 1 on p. 115. Have students count aloud the number of objects in each row and write the number on the line. Have students compare the number of objects in each row using more than, less than, the same or equal.
- Have students draw lines to match objects and circle the number and group with more, cross out the number and group with less, and put a box around the numbers and groups that are the same or equal.
- Repeat for Exercise 2.

Independent Practice

Have students turn to p. 116. Explain the directions. Have students work independently on the exercises.

4 Assess

Formative Assessment

- Show students a row of eight stars and a row of six moons.
- Have students tell how many in each row, write the numbers and tell which number is more than, less than, or if they are the same number.

Quick Check **Are students still having trouble comparing numbers to 10?**

If Yes → Small Group Options (p. 115B)

If No → Independent Work Options (p. 115B)

 Skills Practice Worksheet (p. 32)

CRM Enrich Worksheet (p. 34)

LESSON 4-8

Order Numbers to 10

Lesson Planner

Objective

Order numbers from 1 to 10 in sequence using illustrations.

Review Vocabulary

before, after

Resources

Materials: master sheet of number cards, paper, scissors, index cards, labels, glue, children cut-outs, pencils

Literature Connection: *Anno's Counting Book* by Mitsumasa Anno

Alternate Lesson: Adapt *Dot to Dots* on page 49 of *Math Their Way* to provide practice with ordering numbers 0 to 10 in sequence.
Use *IMPACT Mathematics*: Unit B to provide practice with ordering numbers.

Teacher Technology
TeacherWorks • Concepts in Motion

Focus on Math Background

In this lesson students will apply their knowledge about patterns and relationships to order numbers to 10. Through experiences with changing patterns, students can begin to generalize how 10 is one more than nine, and nine is one more than eight. Working with patterns helps students predict what number comes next in numerical sequences.

Daily Routine

Use these suggestions before beginning the lesson on p. 117.

5-Minute Check

(Reviews Lesson 4-7)
Show a bowl with eight cubes and a bowl with 5 cubes. Which bowl has more cubes? eight Which bowl has less cubes? five Remove three cubes from the bowl of eight cubes. Is the number of cubes in both bowls the same number? Why? Yes; both have five.

Problem of the Day

Write the numbers 1 to 5 in any order on the chalkboard. Have students write the numbers in order. Check students' work

LINE UP Give 10 students a card with a number from one to 10 on it. Have students line up in order from one to 10. Repeat.

Review Math Vocabulary

Write the numbers one to 10 horizontally across the chalkboard. Put a square around the number five.

- **What number comes just before five?** four
- Invite a volunteer to circle four.
- **What number comes just after five?** six
- Invite another volunteer to circle six.
- **What number is between four and six?** five
- Invite another volunteer to circle five.
- Repeat the activity with the other numbers.

Differentiated Instruction

Small Group Options

Option 1 Gifted and Talented AL

LOGICAL, KINESTHETIC

Materials: connecting cubes, small pieces of tape, pencils

- Divide students into small groups. Give each group of students 11 cubes and 11 pieces of tape.
- Have students symbolically describe the number by using tape to label each cube zero to 10.
- Have students mix up the cubes so they are not in order and then connect the cubes in order from zero to 10.

Option 2 English Language Learners ELL

SOCIAL, VISUAL

Core Vocabulary: sit by, name, is by

Common Use Verb: read

Do Math This strategy builds ordering experience while reinforcing English sentence structure.

- Put an "is by" card between two students name tags.
- Say: "(name) **is by** (name)" as you point out each word.
- Have students move seats as you read new sentences. Repeat.

Independent Work Options

Option 1 Early Finishers OL AL

VISUAL

Materials: number cards 0–10

- Give each student number cards.
- Have them turn each card face up in numerical order and count out from zero to 10.
- Shuffle cards and order them from 10 to zero.

Option 2 Student Technology

Math Online macmillanmh.com

Math Adventures

Option 3 Learning Station: Language Arts (p. 97H)

Direct students to the Language Arts Learning Station for more opportunities to explore and extend the lesson concept.

Leveled Lesson Resources

Additional support for English Language Learners can be found in the ELL Guide (p. 41). ELL

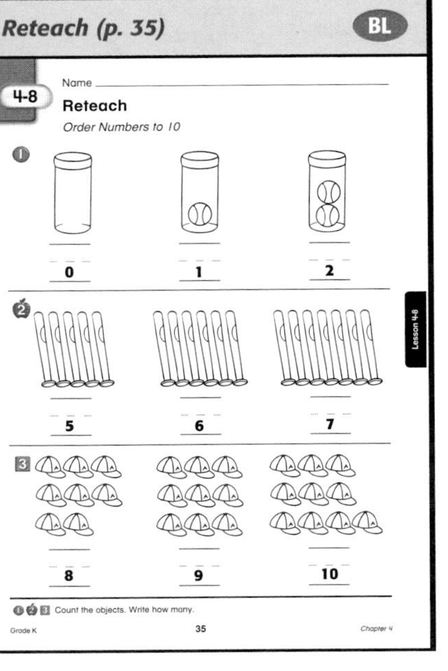
Reteach (p. 35) BL

4-8 Name

Reteach

Order Numbers to 10

1. 0, 1, 2
2. 5, 6, 7
3. 8, 9, 10

Count the objects. Write how many.

Grade K 35 *Chapter 4*

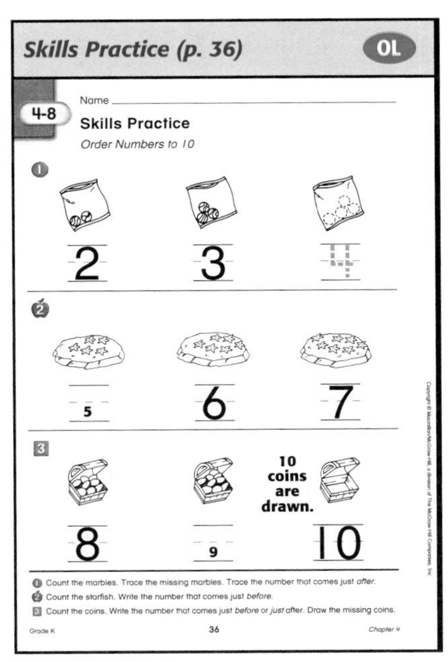
Skills Practice (p. 36) OL

4-8 Name

Skills Practice

Order Numbers to 10

1. 2, 3, 4
2. 5, 6, 7
3. 8, 9, 10 — 10 coins are drawn.

1. Count the marbles. Trace the missing marbles. Trace the number that comes just *after*.
2. Count the starfish. Write the number that comes just *before*.
3. Count the coins. Write the number that comes just *before* or *just* after. Draw the missing coins.

Grade K 36 *Chapter 4*

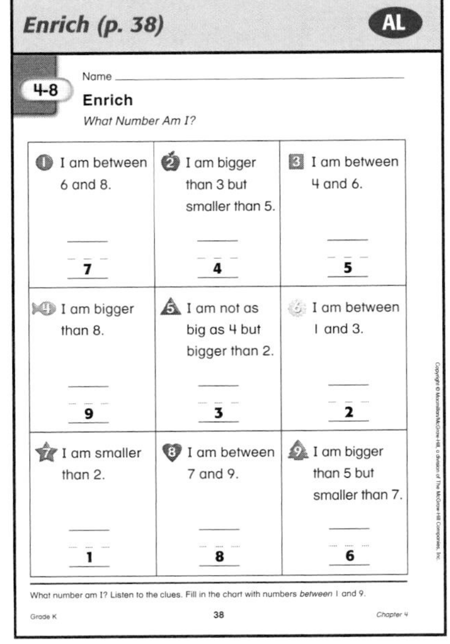
Enrich (p. 38) AL

4-8 Name

Enrich

What Number Am I?

1. I am between 6 and 8. 7	2. I am bigger than 3 but smaller than 5. 4	3. I am between 4 and 6. 5
4. I am bigger than 8. 9	5. I am not as big as 4 but bigger than 2. 3	6. I am between 1 and 3. 2
7. I am smaller than 2. 1	8. I am between 7 and 9. 8	9. I am bigger than 5 but smaller than 7. 6

What number am I? Listen to the clues. Fill in the chart with numbers *between* 1 and 9.

Grade K 38 *Chapter 4*

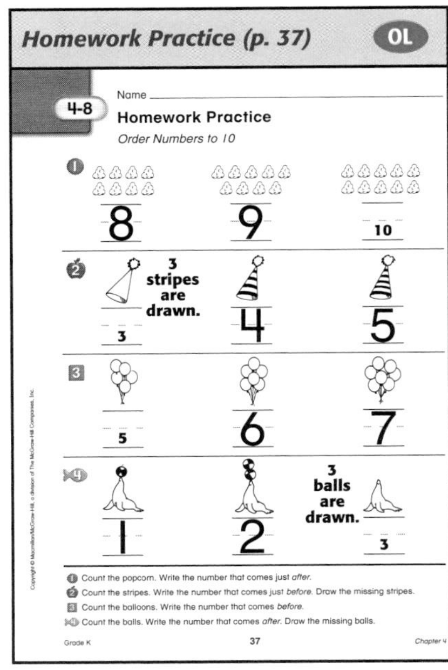
Homework Practice (p. 37) OL

4-8 Name

Homework Practice

Order Numbers to 10

1. 8, 9, 10
2. 3, 4, 5 — 3 stripes are drawn.
3. 5, 6, 7
4. 1, 2, 3 — 3 balls are drawn.

1. Count the popcorn. Write the number that comes just *after*.
2. Count the stripes. Write the number that comes just *before*. Draw the missing stripes.
3. Count the balloons. Write the number that comes *before*.
4. Count the balls. Write the number that comes *after*. Draw the missing balls.

Grade K 37 *Chapter 4*

1 Introduce

Circle Time

Activity Choice 1 • Literature

Anno's Counting Book
by Mitsumasa Anno

Materials: number cards 1–10, poster showing numbers zero to 10 written in order

- Have students count the numbers on the poster in order while each number is pointed to.
- Open *Anno's Counting Book* to a page that shows a picture of any objects between zero and 10. Have students count the objects, say the number, find the same number card, and match it to the same number on the poster.
- Draw the objects on the poster above the corresponding number.
- Have students point to that number on the poster and tell what numbers come **before** and **after** it.
- Choose other pages in the book and have students do the same until all numbers have been matched.

Activity Choice 2 • Hands-On

Materials: index cards

- Write the numbers zero to 10 in order on the chalkboard. Have students look at the numbers. Tell them that you will give clues about what numbers come before and after, then have them guess the number.
- Have students go to the chalkboard one at a time with an index card. Have all other students close their eyes while the student at the chalkboard uses the index card to cover one of the numbers.
- Have the rest of the class open their eyes and identify the "missing" number.
- Repeat this game with partners, covering two numbers at one time.

2 Teach

- Direct students to the top of p. 117.
- **How many fence posts are shown?** 11 posts
- Have students count the number of butterflies on each fence post, and say the number aloud, including zero butterflies.
- **How can you tell that the numbers go in order from smallest to largest?** Sample answer: Each fence post has one more butterfly than the one before it.
- Have students point to the post with five butterflies and count the butterflies.
- **What number comes before five?** four
- Have students point to the post with seven butterflies and count the butterflies.
- **What number comes after seven?** eight
- Have the students get into groups of 10 or less students.
- Give each group number cards from 1-10.
- Have students mix up the cards and make sure all of the numbers are face down.
- Ask students to each select a number card and order the numbers backwards from 10-1. Have students repeat activity if time permits.

BL Alternate Teaching Strategy

If students have trouble understanding numerical order . . .

Then use one of the following reteach options.

1 CRM **Daily Reteach Worksheet** (p. 35)

2 **Ordering Practice** Place labels with numbers one to 10 out of order around a table, one at each chair.
- Glue number labels, one to 10, on 10 pictures of children from magazines.
- Have students match the numbered picture with the corresponding place setting.
- Have them count the number of children at the table.

COMMON ERROR!

Students may skip or repeat number names when learning to count. Have them move each picture to a different place when counting objects.

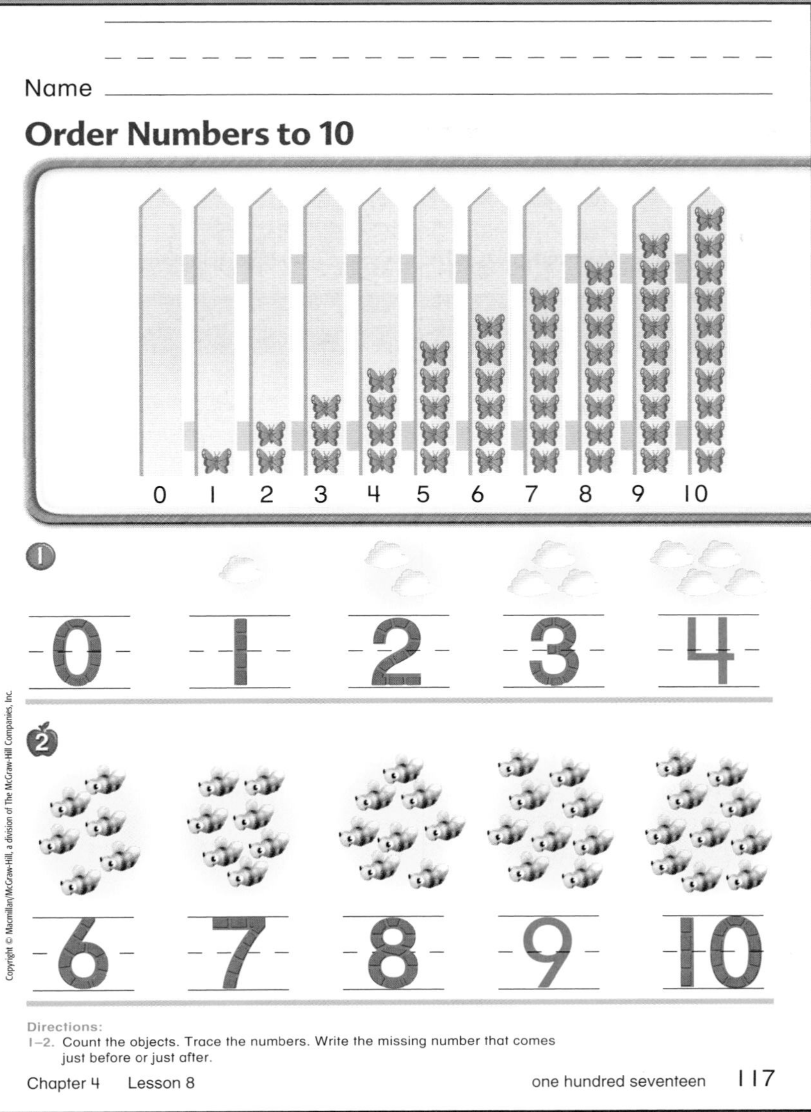

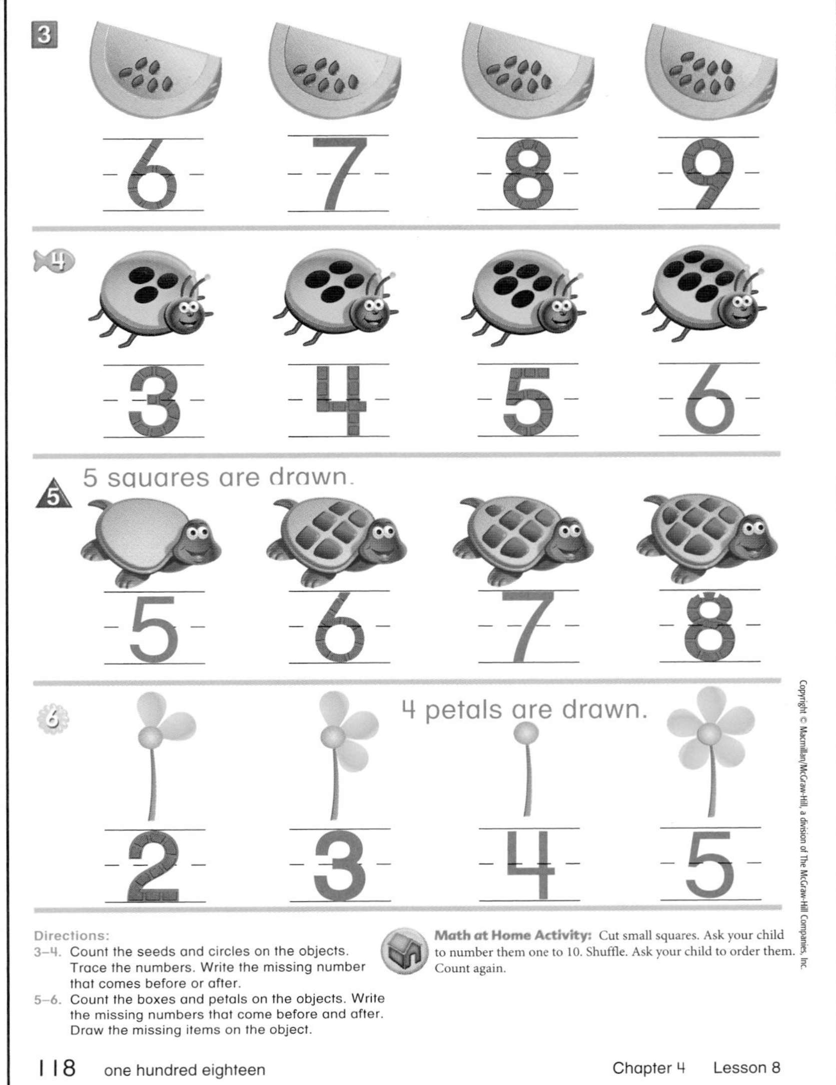

3 Practice

Guided Practice

- Direct students to Exercise 1. Tell students that they are going to do some detective work to find missing numbers. Explain that they will get to count and to figure out which number it is.
- Begin with the number 0, say the number, and trace it below it. Ask them which number is missing. Assist them in writing the number four.
- In Exercise 2, begin by counting the bees, saying the numbers, tracing the numbers, and determining which number is missing.

Independent Practice

Have students turn to p. 118. Explain the directions. Have students work independently on the exercises.

4 Assess

Formative Assessment

- Have students write the numbers zero to 10, one number to an index card.
- Have students mix up the cards.
- Then have students put the cards in numerical order.

Quick Check **Are students still struggling with numerical order?**

If Yes → Small Group Options (p. 117B)

If No → Independent Work Options (p. 117B)

CRM Skills Practice Worksheet (p. 36)

CRM Enrich Worksheet (p. 38)

LESSON 4-9

Ordinal Numbers

Lesson Planner

Objective

Use ordinal numbers to describe the position of an object in a row.

Vocabulary

ordinal numbers

Resources

Materials: pictures of animals
Literature Connection: *Henry the Fourth* by Stuart J. Murphy
Alternate Lesson: Use *IMPACT Mathematics*: Unit E to provide practice with ordinal numbers.
Teacher Technology
TeacherWorks • Concepts in Motion

Daily Routine

Use these suggestions before beginning the lesson on p. 119.

5-Minute Check

(Reviews Lesson 4-8)
Make a set of 1–10 index cards and a set with 1–10 dots. Have students pair a set of dots with a number set, then order the number cards 1–10. Point to a number. Ask what number is before and after.

Problem of the Day

Write the numbers 6,7,_,9,10 on the chalkboard. Have students fill in the missing number.

As students line up in groups of 10, ask who is first in line, who is third in line, and so on.

Building Math Vocabulary

- Teach the finger play, *5 Little Pumpkins* to introduce the term **ordinal numbers**.

  Five little pumpkins sitting on a gate,
  The first one said, "Oh, it's getting late."
  The second one said, "Owls are in the air!"
  The third one said, "I don't care."
  The fourth one said, "I'm ready for fun!"
  The fifth one said, "Let's run."
  WOOO went the wind and out went the light,
  And five little pumpkins rolled from sight.

- Have students wiggle their thumb for *first* and wiggle the correct finger to show which pumpkin is talking. Ask which pumpkin said what.

Differentiated Instruction

Small Group Options

Option 1 Gifted and Talented AL

LOGICAL

Materials: paper, pencil

- Have students in pairs with sheets of paper.
- Direct the pairs of students to describe the school day by drawing what happens first, second, third, etc.
- The students should label pictures first, second, third, etc.
- Have students compare their pictures with other students to see if they have the same images, events, or activities.

Option 2 English Language Learners ELL

KINESTHETIC, LOGICAL

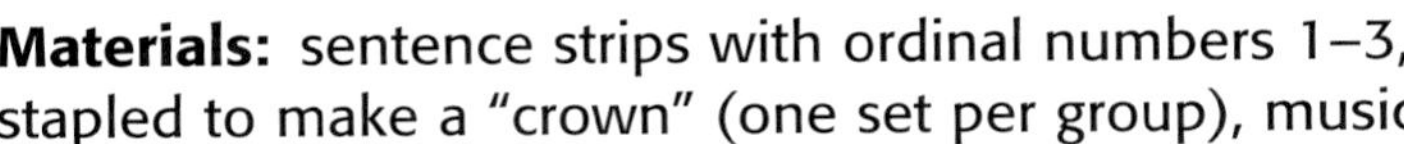

Materials: sentence strips with ordinal numbers 1–3, stapled to make a "crown" (one set per group), music

Core Vocabulary: first, second, third

Common Use Verb: march

See Math This strategy helps student integrate different ways to sequence.

- Have students follow a set order: "**First clap**, **second** stomp, **third** jump." Repeat.
- Show and read crowns. Say: "This person is **first/second/third**." Have these students select the right "crown" to show their placement. When they are in order, say: "**March** in order until the music stops."
- Repeat changing crowns with new students as time permits.

Independent Work Options

Option 1 Early Finishers AL OL

LINGUISTIC

Materials: crayons, drawing paper

- Have students draw a line of 10 cats.
- Tell them to make the third cat in line the biggest.
- Have students form pairs and exchange pictures. Have a partner identify the sixth cat in line. Have the other partner identify the second cat in line.

Option 2 Student Technology

Math Online macmillanmh.com

Math Adventures

Option 3 Learning Station: Social Studies (p. 97H)

Direct students to the Social Studies Learning Station for opportunities to explore and extend the lesson concept.

Leveled Lesson Resources

Reteach (p. 39) BL

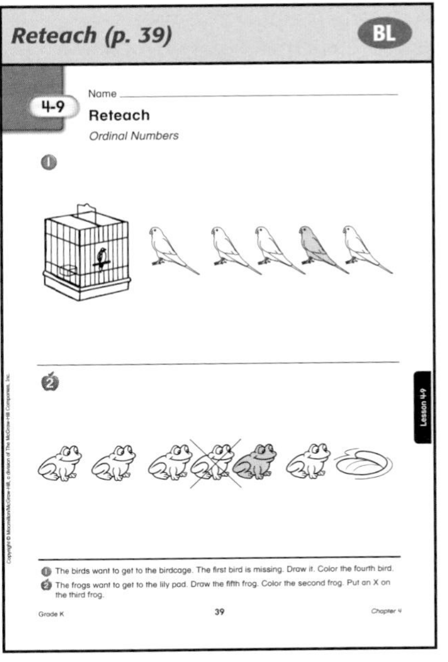

4-9 Name
Reteach
Ordinal Numbers

1. The birds want to get to the birdcage. The first bird is missing. Draw it. Color the fourth bird.
2. The frogs want to get to the lily pad. Draw the fifth frog. Color the second frog. Put an X on the third frog.

Grade K 39 Chapter 4

Skills Practice (p. 40) OL

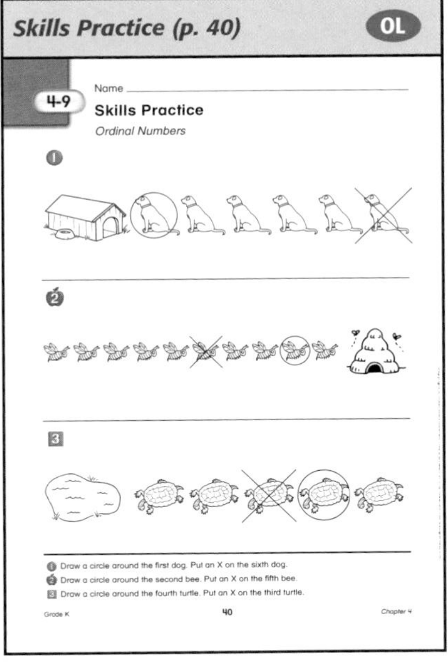

4-9 Name
Skills Practice
Ordinal Numbers

1. Draw a circle around the first dog. Put an X on the sixth dog.
2. Draw a circle around the second bee. Put an X on the fifth bee.
3. Draw a circle around the fourth turtle. Put an X on the third turtle.

Grade K 40 Chapter 4

Enrich (p. 42) AL

4-9 Name
Enrich
Order Them

You do some things every day. They happen in order. Look at the pictures. Circle what you do first in the day. Put an X on what you do second. Color what you do third.

Grade K 42 Chapter 4

Homework Practice (p. 41) OL

4-9 Name
Homework Practice
Ordinal Numbers

1. Draw a circle around the seventh cat. Put an X on the second cat.
2. Draw a circle around the eighth squirrel. Put an X on the fourth squirrel.
3. Draw a circle around the fifth ant. Put an X on the tenth ant.

Grade K 41 Chapter 4

1 Introduce

Circle Time

Activity Choice 1 • Literature

Henry the Fourth
by Stuart J. Murphy

- On pages 6–7, ask students to identify which dog (by color) is first, second, third, and fourth.
- Ask four students to arrange themselves in a straight line, and ask the remaining students to identify who is third, first, fourth, or second.
- Make a line of eight students and ask students to identify positions for first through eighth.
- Repeat with other students in the line.
- Extend the activity by having students form a line of 10 students (or unique objects). Ask students to identify who is in each position. (Do not do them in order.)

Activity Choice 2 • Hands-On

- Ask 10 volunteers to line up facing the same direction.
- Explain that the student at the front of the line is number one or is in the first position. Name the remaining positions.
- Have the row of volunteers face the opposite direction. Discuss their new ordinal positions.
- Explain that most **ordinal number** names have a number word in them, such as *sixth* has six in it. Count to six to find the sixth position in a line.
- Discuss first, second, and third. Count to find the positions.
- Have the class identify all positions.
- Repeat the activity with new volunteers. Give directions, such as having the seventh student sit on the floor.

2 Teach

Direct students to the top of p. 119.

- Ask a volunteer to describe the scene at the top of the page.
- **Point to the student who is first in line.**
- **Point to the student who is fifth in line.**
- Continue pointing to and identifying the children in the remaining ordinal positions.

BL Alternate Teaching Strategy

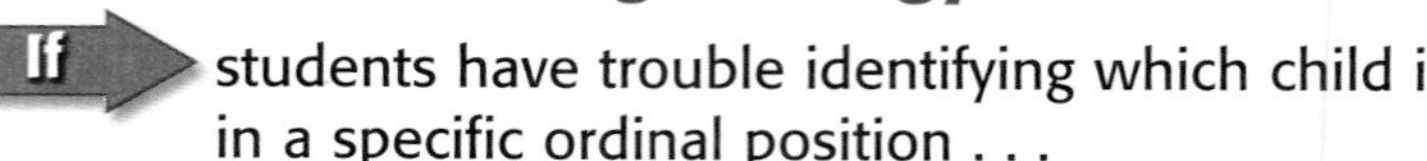

If students have trouble identifying which child is in a specific ordinal position . . .

Then use one of these reteach options.

1 CRM **Daily Reteach Worksheet** (p. 39)

2 **Listen and Count** Have students write numbers 1–10 under the line of children.

- Remind them to listen for the number word at the beginning of each number.
- Have students count aloud to find the child in a specific position, such as the third position.

COMMON ERROR!

Students may not identify the first position or beginning of a line. Tell them to look at the way the animals are facing. The animal in the first position is the beginning of the line.

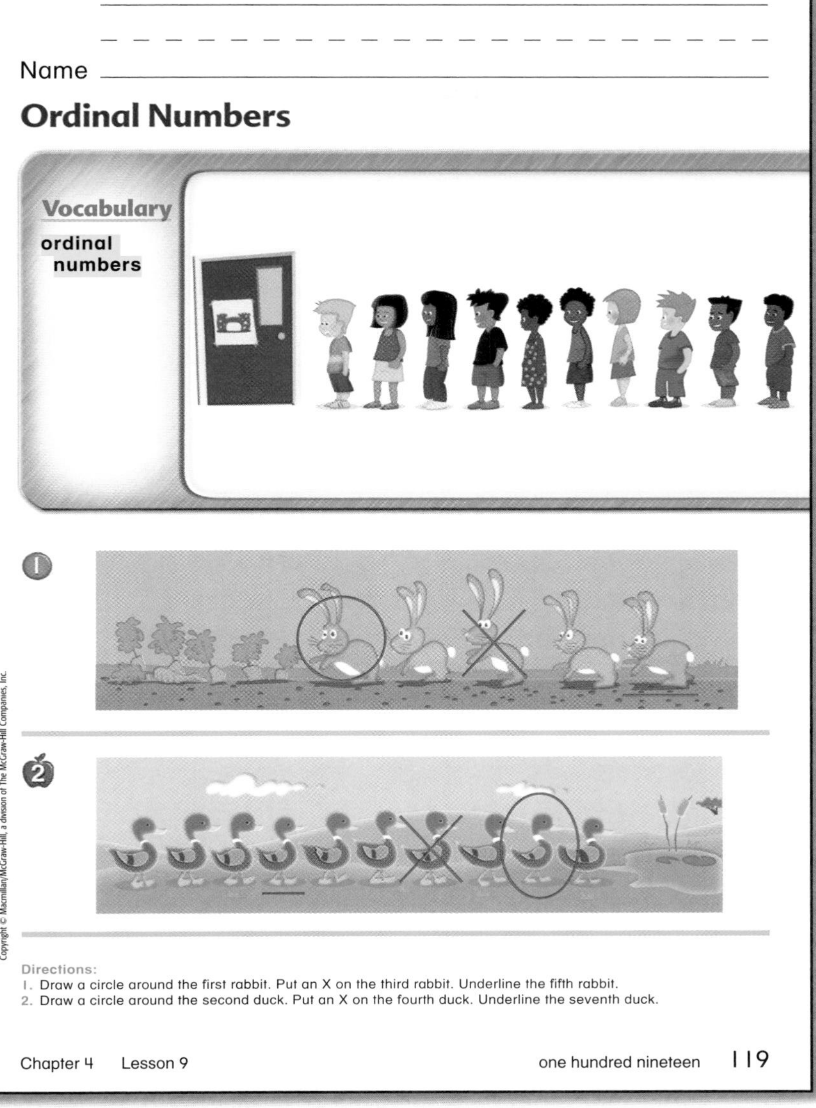

Name

Ordinal Numbers

Vocabulary

ordinal numbers

1

2

Directions:
1. Draw a circle around the first rabbit. Put an X on the third rabbit. Underline the fifth rabbit.
2. Draw a circle around the second duck. Put an X on the fourth duck. Underline the seventh duck.

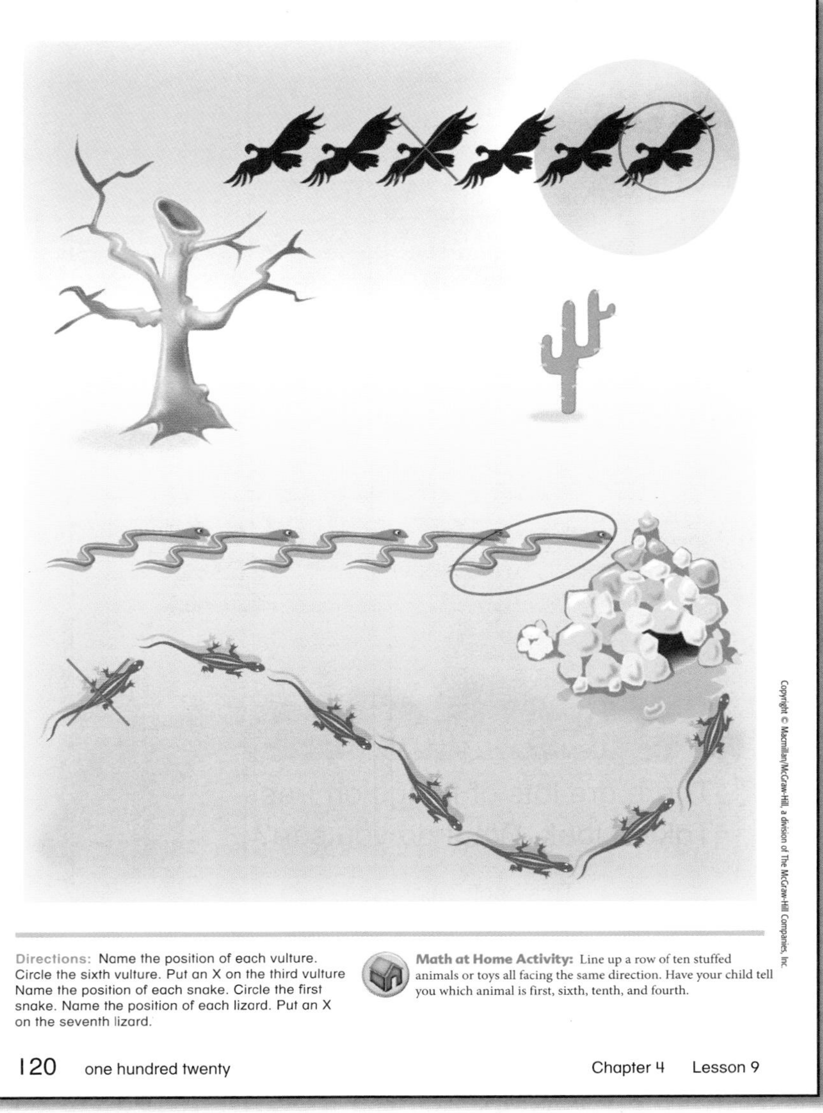

Directions: Name the position of each vulture. Circle the sixth vulture. Put an X on the third vulture Name the position of each snake. Circle the first snake. Name the position of each lizard. Put an X on the seventh lizard.

Math at Home Activity: Line up a row of ten stuffed animals or toys all facing the same direction. Have your child tell you which animal is first, sixth, tenth, and fourth.

3 Practice

Guided Practice

- Direct students to p. 119.
- Ask a volunteer to identify the scene in Exercise 1. **Where are the rabbits going?** the carrot patch
- Have students circle the first rabbit. Have them put an X on the third rabbit. Have them underline the fifth rabbit.
- Ask a volunteer to identify the animals in Exercise 2. **Where are the ducks going?** to the pond
- Tell students to circle the second duck. Have them put an X on the fourth duck. Have students underline the seventh duck.

Independent Practice

Have students turn to p. 120 and work independently on the exercises.

4 Assess

Formative Assessment

- Show a picture of 10 animals in a line.
- Ask students to identify animals in specific ordinal positions.

Quick Check **Are students still struggling to identify the ordinal positions in a sequence?**

If Yes → Small Group Options (p. 119B)

If No → Independent Work Options (p. 119B)

CRM Skills Practice Worksheet (p. 40)

CRM Enrich Worksheet (p. 42)

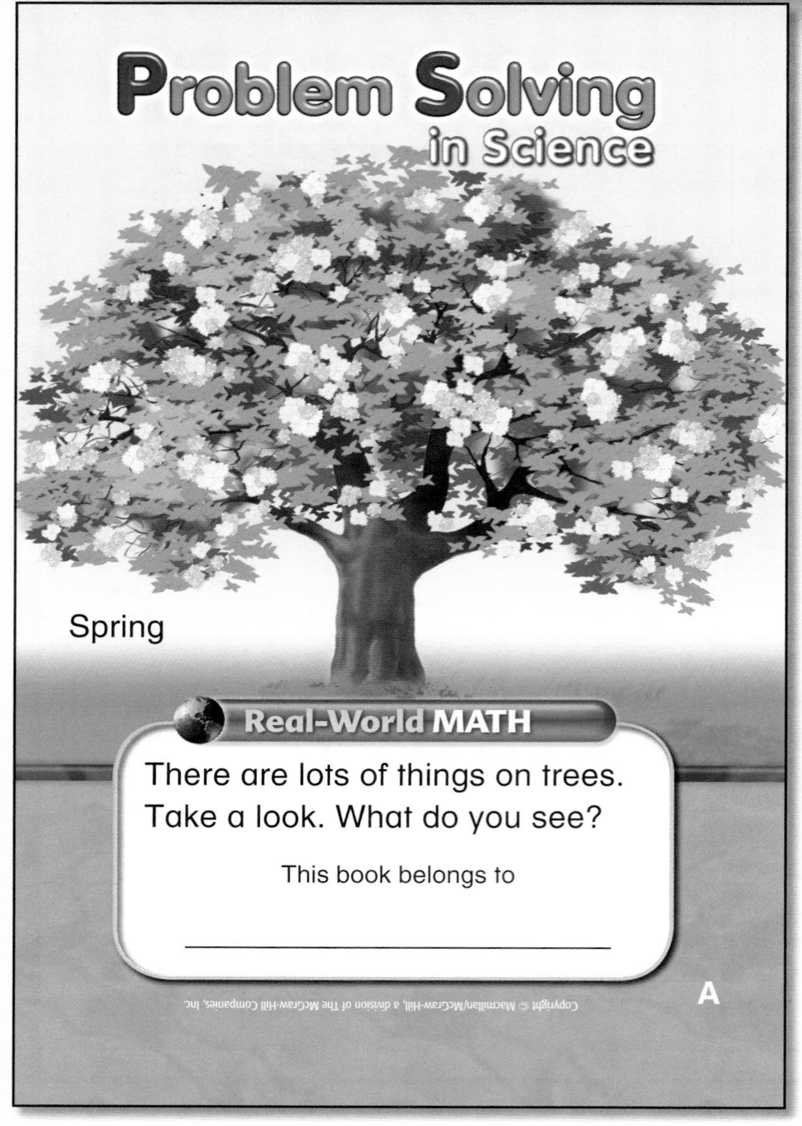

Problem Solving
in Science
Spring
Real-World MATH
There are lots of things on trees.
Take a look. What do you see?
This book belongs to
A
Copyright © Macmillan/McGraw-Hill, a division of The McGraw-Hill Companies, Inc.

Apples are on the tree.
Summer
How many apples do you see?
I see ______ apples.
B
Copyright © Macmillan/McGraw-Hill, a division of The McGraw-Hill Companies, Inc.

Lesson Planner

Objective

Use illustrations to count objects.

National Standards

Students learn about changes in an environment.

Activate Prior Knowledge

Before you turn students' attention to the pages, discuss with them things they have noticed about trees.

- **What do some trees have growing on their branches in the summer?** leaves, fruits, needles, cones
- **What are some animals you may see in a tree?** birds, squirrels, raccoons, opossum, bats

Birds are in the tree.
Autumn
How many birds do you see?
I see ______ birds.
C

Nests are in a tree.
Winter
How many nests do you see?
I see ______ nests.
D
FOLD DOWN

Create the Book

Guide students to create their book.

- Have them fold the page in half.
- Ask them to write their name on page A.
- Explain that page A is the front cover and page D is the back cover. If necessary, have them practice flipping through the book in order.
- Guide them in reading the information and word problems on each of the pages.

Use the Student Pages

Have students work individually or in pairs to solve the word problems on pages B–D.

Page B Have students point to and touch each apple in the picture as they count.

Page C Have students use counters to count each bird as they point to and touch the picture.

Page D Have students use counters to count each nest as they point to and touch the picture.

WRITING IN MATH Have students draw one more apple on the tree, then write the number of apples.

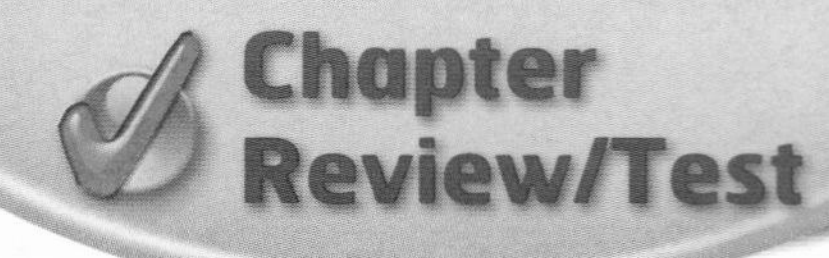

Dinah Zike's Foldables

Use these lesson suggestions for incorporating the Foldables during the chapter.

Lesson 4-5 Make and glue two more sections to the Foldable number line. Write the numbers nine and 10 on the top left side of each of the two sections and have students find and place pictures on the appropriate sections to illustrate each of the numbers.

Lesson 4-7 Use the display cases made in chapter one to compare sets of six, seven, eight, nine, or 10 objects. Determine which sets have *more, less*, or *the same* number of objects.

My Number Book 1–10

Lead a discussion on the results of the completed chapter project with the class.

Vocabulary Review

Review chapter vocabulary using one of the following options.

- **Visual Vocabulary Cards** (2 and 4)
- **eGlossary** at macmillanmh.com

Data-Driven Decision Making

Based on the results of the Chapter/Review Test, use the following to review concepts that continue to present students with problems.

Exercises	State/Local Standards	What's the Math?	Error Analysis	Resources for Review
1 Lesson 4-1		Understand relationship between numbers and quantities. Count, name, and recognize numbers up to 7.	Does not count number of objects correctly.	CRM Chapter 4 Resource Masters (Reteach Worksheets) Math Online Concepts in Motion Math Adventures
2 Lesson 4-3		Understand relationship between numbers and quantities. Recognize and write numbers up to 8.	Does not count number of objects correctly. Writes wrong numbers down.	
3 Lesson 4-4		Understand relationship between numbers and quantities. Count, name, and recognize numbers up to 10.	Does not draw lines correctly. Writes wrong numbers. Circles wrong number and group.	
4 Lesson 4-8		Understand relationship between numbers and quantities. Count, write, and draw objects up to 10.	Does not count correctly. Writes wrong number. Does not draw correct number of drum sticks.	

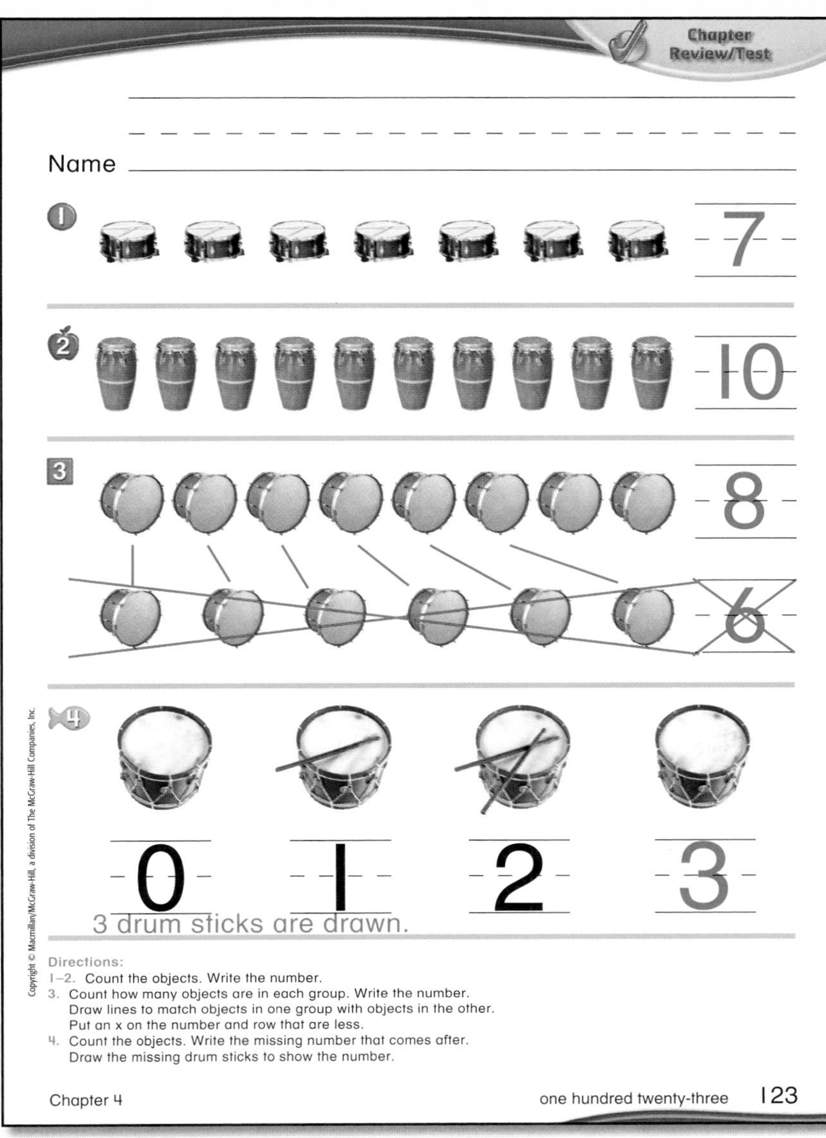

Chapter Review/Test
Name
7
10
8
6
0
1
2
3
3 drum sticks are drawn.
Directions:
1–2. Count the objects. Write the number.
3. Count how many objects are in each group. Write the number. Draw lines to match objects in one group with objects in the other. Put an x on the number and row that are less.
4. Count the objects. Write the missing number that comes after. Draw the missing drum sticks to show the number.
Chapter 4
one hundred twenty-three
123

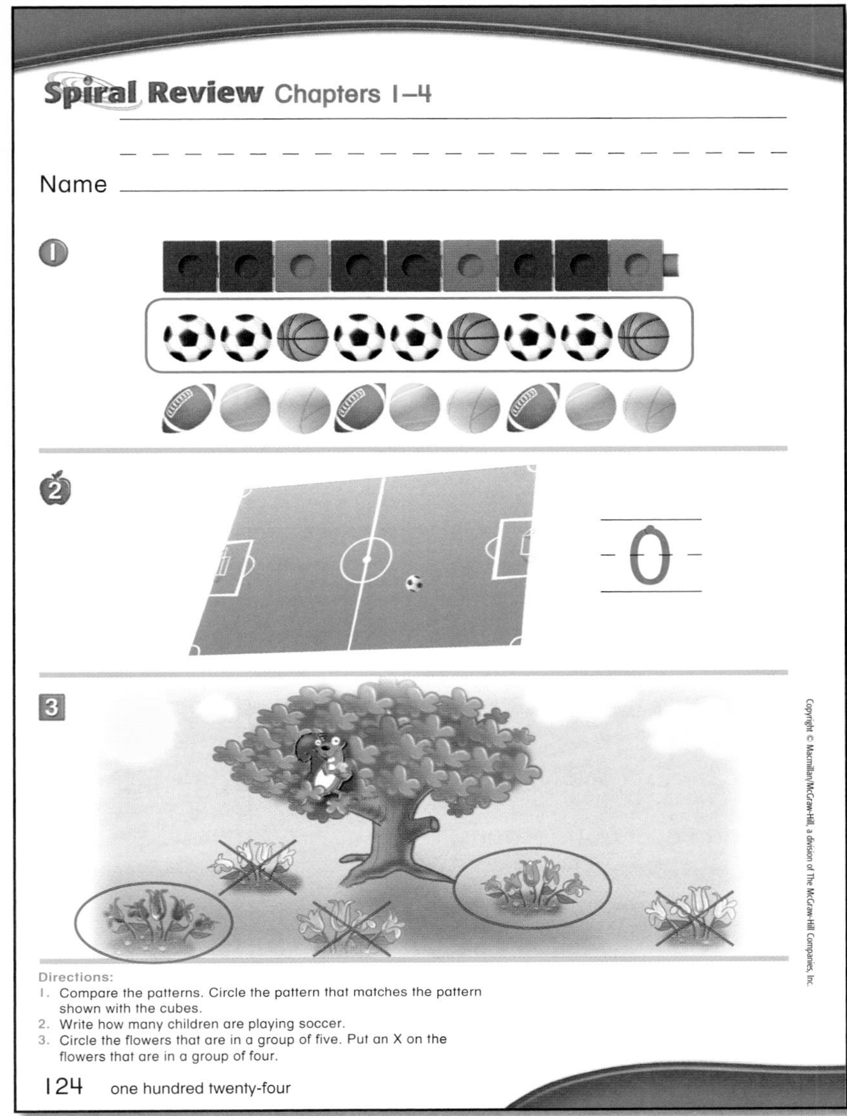

Spiral Review Chapters 1–4
Name
0
Directions:
1. Compare the patterns. Circle the pattern that matches the pattern shown with the cubes.
2. Write how many children are playing soccer.
3. Circle the flowers that are in a group of five. Put an X on the flowers that are in a group of four.
124
one hundred twenty-four

Summative Assessment

Use these alternate leveled chapter tests to differentiate assessment for the specific needs of your students.

Leveled Chapter 4 Tests			
Form	Type	Level	CRM Pages
1	Multiple Choice	BL	50–51
2A	Multiple Choice	OL	52–53
2C	Multiple Choice	OL	54–55
2D	Free Response	AL	56–57

BL = below/approaching grade level
OL = on grade level
AL = above/beyond grade level

Spiral Review

Reviews Chapters 1 to 4

Objective: Review and assess mastery of skills and concepts from previous chapters.

Resources for Review

Based on student results, refer to these lessons for remediation.

- **Exercise 1: Lesson 3-5** (p. 81)
- **Exercise 2: Lesson 2-6** (p. 55)
- **Exercise 3: Lesson 2-3** (p. 47)

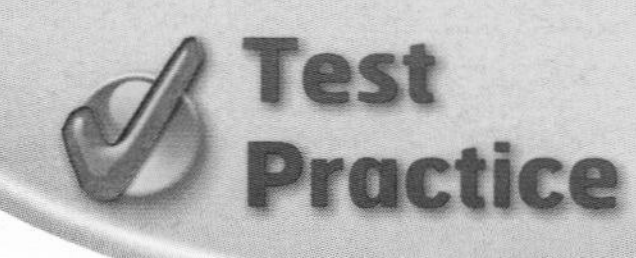

Chapters 1–3

Formative Assessment

- You can use Student Edition pp. 125-126 to benchmark student progress.
- Additional practice pages can be found in Chapter 4 Resource Masters.

CRM **Chapter 4 Resource Masters**
Cumulative Test Practice

- Multiple Choice format (pp. 50–55)
- Free Response format (pp. 56–57)

ExamView Assessment Suite Create additional practice worksheets or tests.

Math Online For additional practice with the NCTM Focal Points and Focal Connections, visit macmillanmh.com.

Test-Taking Tips

For the Teacher

- It may be helpful to remind students how to count from 1–10 by telling them to picture all the toes on their feet, then count each toe silently.
- Explain that different types of test questions will take different amounts of time to complete.
- Before starting a test, check for student understanding of the test questions.

For the Student

- Encourage students to skip questions they are unsure of, then come back to them after finishing the other questions.
- Remind students to mark questions they have not answered so they are easy to find.

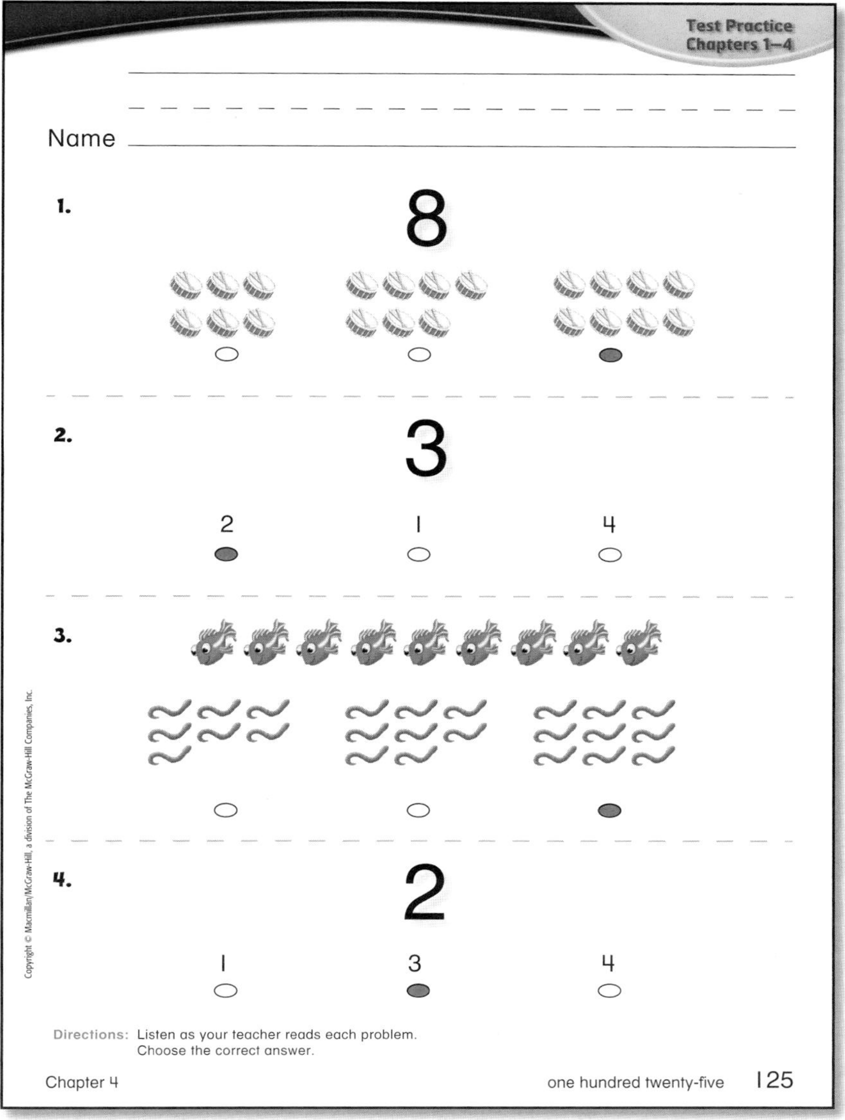

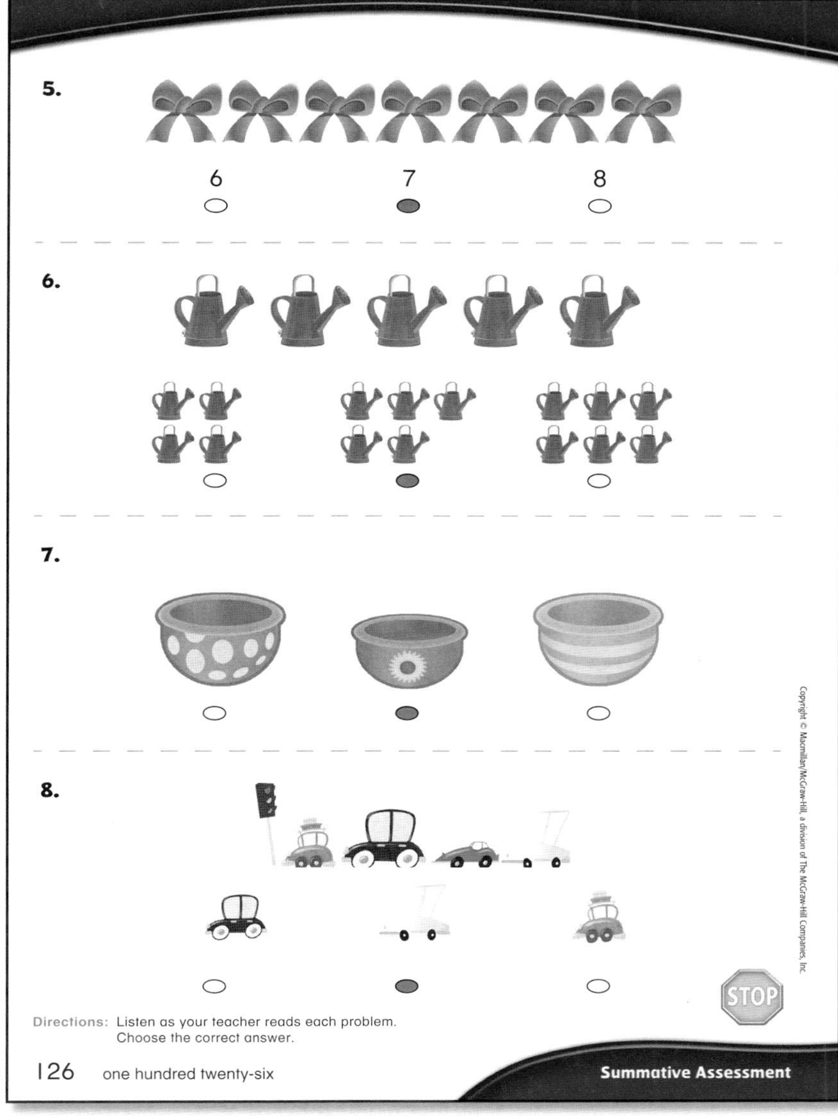

Test Directions for Teachers

Read the following directions to students before they begin. Then read each question followed by a pause to allow students time to work and choose an answer. The first test item can be worked as a class example.

- **Write your name at the top of the page.**
- **I am going to read each question to you. Listen carefully to the entire question before you choose an answer.**

1. Look at the number. Find the picture that shows the same number of objects. Mark the picture that shows the same number of objects.
2. Find the number that is one less than the number shown. Mark the number that is one less than the number shown.
3. Count the fish. Find the set that has the same number of worms as there are fish. Mark the set that has the same number of worms as there are fish.
4. Find the number that is one more than the number shown. Mark the number that is one more than the number shown.

- Turn the page over.

5. Count the bows. Find the number that shows how many bows. Mark the number that shows how many bows.
6. Count the row of watering cans. Find the set of watering cans that shows the same number. Mark the set that shows the same number of watering cans.
7. Find the bowl in the group that is different. Mark the bowl that is different.
8. Look at the cars. Mark the car that is fourth in line.

Chapter Overview

Chapter-at-a-Glance

In Chapter 5, the emphasis is on collecting and graphing information and using that information to compare numbers and solve problems.

Lesson		Math Objective	State/Local Standards
5-1	**Collect and Record Data** (pp. 131–132)	Collect data from a picture and record data on a graph.	
5-2	**Real Graphs** (pp. 133–134)	Make and read a concrete graph or real graph.	
5-3	**Problem-Solving Strategy: Look for a Pattern** (pp. 135–136)	Collect data from a picture, record data on a graph, and make and read a concrete graph or real graph.	
5-4	**Picture Graphs** (pp. 139–140)	Make and read picture graphs.	
5-5	**Make a Graph** (pp. 141–142)	Collect and organize data in a picture graph to answer questions.	

Construct and Use Graphs

BIG Idea Chapter 5 has a direct correlation to Chapter 1, in which students learned to identify and sort objects by attributes. Sorting comes into play when students record their data on graphs.

Algebra Students prepare for algebra through realizing that if they record information accurately they can discover patterns. (Lessons 5-2 and 5-3)

Geometry Students prepare for geometry through observing shapes, sorting them, classifying them, and then recording that information on a graph. (Lessons 5-1, 5-2, 5-3, 5-4, 5-5)

Measurement Students prepare for measurement through observing the size of objects, as well as through recording data on a grid. (Lessons 5-1, 5-2, 5-3, 5-4, 5-5)

GK-FP4C *Data Analysis:* Children sort objects and use one or more attributes to solve problems. For example, they might sort solids that roll easily from those that do not. Or they might collect data and use counting to answer such questions as, "What is our favorite snack?" They re-sort objects by using new attributes (e.g., after sorting solids according to which ones roll, they might re-sort the solids according to which ones stack easily).

Skills Trace

Vertical Alignment

PreKindergarten

In PreK, students learned to:

- Sort objects into groups by an attribute and begins to explain how the grouping was done.
- Participate in creating and using real and pictorial graphs.

Kindergarten

During this chapter, students learn to:

- Collect information about objects and events in their environment.
- Pose information questions; collect data; and record the results using objects, pictures, and picture graphs.

After this chapter, students will learn to:

- Understand the relationship between numbers and quantities (i.e., that a set of objects has the same number of objects in different situations regardless of its position or arrangement).
- Count, recognize, represent, name, and order a number of objects (beyond 20).

First Grade

In first grade, students will learn to:

- Organize, represent, and compare data by category on simple graphs and charts.
- Represent and compare data (e.g., largest, smallest, most often, least often) by using pictures, bar graphs, tally charts, and picture graphs.

BackMapping and Vertical Alignment **McGraw-Hill's *Math Connects*** program was conceived and developed with the final results in mind: student success in Algebra 1 and beyond. The authors, using the **NCTM Focal Points and Focal Connections** as their guide, developed this brand new series by back-mapping from Algebra 1 concepts, and vertically aligning the topics so that they build upon prior skills and concepts and serve as a foundation for future topics.

Math Vocabulary

The following math vocabulary words for Chapter 5 are listed in the glossary of the ***Student Edition.*** You can find interactive definitions in 13 languages in the ***eGlossary*** at macmillanmh.com.

data (p. 131)

Favorite Foods	
Food	Votes
	HHT
	|||
	HHT |||

graph a way to present data collected; also a type of chart; **Example:** a bar graph (p. 131)

picture graph (p. 139)

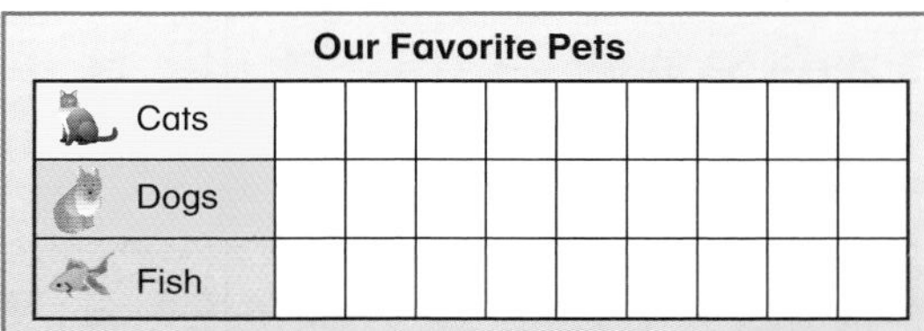

picture graph

real graph graph using real objects (p. 133)

survey (p. 141)

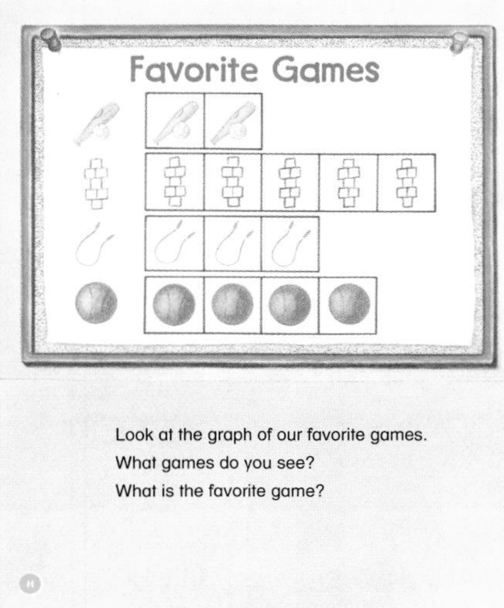

survey

Visual Vocabulary Cards

Use Visual Vocabulary Cards 12, 31, 33, and 43 to introduce and reinforce the vocabulary in this chapter. (The Define/Example/Ask routine is printed on the back of each card.)

Chapter Planner

Suggested Pacing		
Instruction	Review and Assessment	TOTAL
5 days	2 days	**7 days**

Diagnostic Assessment
Are You Ready? (p. 128)

	Lesson 5-1 (Pacing: 1 day)	Lesson 5-2 (Pacing: 1 day)	Lesson 5-3 (Pacing: 1 day)
Lesson/ Objective	**Collect and Record Data** (pp. 131–132) **Objective:** Collect data from a picture and record data on a graph.	**Real Graphs** (pp. 133–134) **Objective:** Make and read a concrete graph or real graph.	**Problem-Solving Strategy** **Look for a Pattern** (pp. 135–136) **Objective:** Collect data from a picture, record data on a graph, and make and read a concrete graph or real graph.
State/Local Standards			
Math Vocabulary	**data, graph**	**real graph**	
Lesson Resources	**Materials** graph paper, chart paper, graph mat **Manipulatives** attribute buttons, color tiles **Other Resources** CRM Leveled Worksheets (pp. 6–9) Daily Reteach Problem of the Day	**Materials** graph paper, chart paper, pencil, paper, crayons, glue, paper clips **Manipulatives** connecting cubes, color tiles **Other Resources** CRM Leveled Worksheets (pp. 10–13) Daily Reteach Problem of the Day	**Materials** classroom objects, crayons, pencils **Manipulatives** connecting cubes, pattern blocks **Other Resources** CRM Leveled Worksheets (pp. 14–18) Daily Reteach Problem of the Day *Our Country*
Technology Math Online	Math Adventures	Math Adventures Concepts in Motion	
Reaching All Learners	English Learners, p. 131B ELL Gifted and Talented, p. 131B AL Early Finishers, p. 131B OL AL	English Learners, p. 133B ELL Gifted and Talented, p. 133B AL Early Finishers, p. 133B OL AL	English Learners, p. 135B ELL Gifted and Talented, p. 135B AL Early Finishers, p. 135B OL AL
Alternate Lesson	*Math Their Way,* p. 156 *IMPACT Mathematics:* Unit H	*IMPACT Mathematics:* Unit H	

Formative Assessment
Mid-Chapter Check (p. 137)

Game Time: Boat Building (p. 138)

KEY

BL Below/Approaching Level · OL On Level · AL Above/Beyond Level · ELL English Learners
SE Student Edition · TE Teacher Edition · CRM Chapter 5 Resource Masters · CD-Rom
Transparency · Flip Chart · Real-World Problem Solving Library

	Lesson 5-4 (Pacing: 1 day)	Lesson 5-5 (Pacing: 1 day)
Lesson/ Objective	**Picture Graphs** (pp. 139–140) **Objective:** Make and read picture graphs.	**Make a Graph** (pp. 141–142) **Objective:** Collect and organize data in a picture graph to answer questions.
State/Local Standards		
Math Vocabulary	**picture graph**	**survey**
Lesson Resources	**Materials** crayons, graph paper, glue, chart paper, magazine pictures, poster-board, tape **Other Resources** CRM Leveled Worksheets (pp. 19–22) Daily Reteach	**Materials** graph paper, markers, paper, crayons, scissors, glue **Other Resources** CRM Leveled Worksheets (pp. 23–26) Daily Reteach
Technology Math Online	Math Adventures Concepts in Motion	Math Adventures
Reaching All Learners	English Learners, p. 139B ELL Below Level, p. 139B BL Early Finishers, p. 139B OL AL	English Learners, p. 141B ELL Below Level, p. 141B BL Early Finishers, p. 141B OL AL
Alternate Lesson	*Math Their Way,* p. 148 *IMPACT Mathematics:* Unit H	*Math Their Way,* p. 149 *IMPACT Mathematics:* Unit H

Problem Solving in Social Studies (p. 143)

Summative Assessment
- Chapter Review/Test (p. 145)
- Test Practice (p. 147)

Chapter Planner

Assessment Options

Diagnostic Assessment

- SE *Option 1:* Are You Ready? (p. 128)
- *Option 2:* Online Quiz (macmillanmh.com)
- CRM *Option 3:* Diagnostic Test (p. 28)

Formative Assessment

- TE Alternate Teaching Strategies (every lesson)
- TE Writing in Math (every lesson)
- TE Line Up (every lesson)
- SE Mid-Chapter Check (p. 137)
- CRM Mid-Chapter Test (p. 29)

Summative Assessment

- SE Chapter Review/Test (p. 145)
- SE Test Practice (p. 147)
- CRM Leveled Chapter Tests (pp. 34–41)
- CRM Cumulative Test Practice (p. 42–43)
- CRM Listening Assessment (p. 32–33)
- CRM Oral Assessment (p. 30–31)
- Exam*View*® Assessment Suite
- Advance Tracker

McGraw-Hill Professional Development

Targeted professional development has been articulated throughout **McGraw-Hill's *Math* Connects** program. The **McGraw-Hill Professional Development Video Library** provides short videos that support the **NCTM Focal Points and Focal Connections.** For more information, visit macmillanmh.com.

Model Lessons

Instructional Strategies

What the Research Says . . .

Phyllis and David Whitin, professors of elementary education at Wayne State University in Detroit, describe an engaging kindergarten episode in which the students go through all of the processes for gathering, organizing, displaying, and interpreting data. At the conclusion of this article, the authors list six implications for conducting data analysis with young children:

1. Tie graphing experiences to rich social contexts in the classroom.
2. Use multiple forms of representation for the same set of data.
3. Frame discussions of data using open-ended questions.
4. Interpret a graph; then, invite children to create a title for it.
5. Provide opportunities for children to revisit data after a class discussion.
6. Materials themselves do not teach mathematics. (Whitin & Whitin, 2003, p. 28).

Whitin, P., & D. Whitin. "Developing Mathematical Understanding Along the Yellow Brick Road." In *Spotlight on Young Children and Math*, edited by D. Koraleck. Washington, D.C.: National Association for the Education of Young Children, 2003: 25–28.

Teacher Notes

Learning Stations

Cross-Curricular Links

Language Arts

small group | SPATIAL

Juice Graph

- Listen to the story.
- Say what juice you like best.
- Put your cup on the graph.

Teacher Note: Read What Do You Like? *aloud. Make a real graph. Write A for apple, O for orange, or G for grape juice on the bottom of real drinking cups. Include a simple drawing of an apple, orange, or grape on the bottom of the glass to go along with the letter. Have students say their favorite juice, turn the cup over, and put it on the graph in the appropriate column.*

Materials:

- *What Do You Like?* by Michael Grejniec
- cups
- crayons
- graph paper

Art

small group | SPATIAL

Fur, Fins, or Feathers Graph

- Draw a pet with fur, fins, or feathers.
- Cut out your picture.
- Tape your picture to the graph.

Teacher Note: Make a picture graph with three columns: one column has a cat and dog, one column has two to three assorted colorful fish, and one column has two pet birds. Have students say and draw what type of pet they would rather have, one with fur, fins, or feathers. Have students tape their drawing in the column on the graph. Discuss results with the class.

Materials:

- drawing paper
- crayons
- graph paper
- tape

Health

individual | KINESTHETIC

Jump Charts

- Listen to the story.
- Jump as far as you can.
- Talk about the graph.

Teacher Note: Read aloud If You Hopped Like a Frog *by David Schwartz. Have students take turns jumping. Use a piece of yarn to measure the distance each student jumped. Label the yarns with the student's name. Have students tape their yarn to the board or butcher block paper in a column labeled with their name. All pieces of yarn must line up at the top of the graph. Students can tell who jumped farthest by finding the longest piece of yarn. Have students say who jumped the farthest and how they know.*

Materials:

- yarn
- crayon or marker
- board or butcher block paper
- tape
- *If You Hopped Like A Frog* by David M. Schwartz

Technology

small group | VISUAL

Creating Graphs

- Choose the Graphing button.
- Use data to make your own graph.

Teacher Note: Provide information such as: graph title, number of objects to be graphed, and questions to be answered. For example, you might have students say the number of different types of pets students have. Tell students to create the graph from the information provided and answer the questions using the graph. Direct students to use the graph they created to justify their answers.

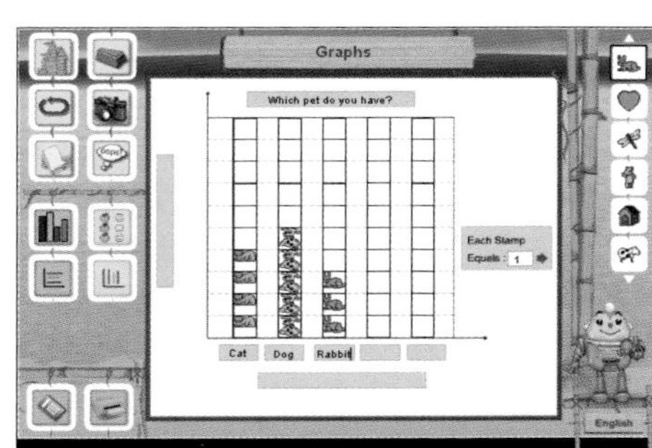

Materials:

- Math Tool Chest: Graphing Tool

Science

pair | LOGICAL

Books and Graphs

- Draw the animal on your card.
- Listen to the story.
- Put your picture on the graph.

Teacher Note: Make a picture graph with columns for each animal in the book. Print an animal name from the book at the top of index cards. Give a card to each student. Have them draw a picture of the animal on their card, then tape it to the graph while you read the story aloud. Have students tell how the graph gives the same information as the book but in a different way.

Materials:

- index card
- crayons
- *Rooster's Off to See the World* by Eric Carle
- tape

Calendar Time

Days of the Week by Letters Graph

- Show a week on a calendar, starting with Sunday.
- Say and write the days of the week on the chalkboard.
- Make a picture graph with four columns. Label the columns 6, 7, 8, 9.
- Have students count the letters in each of the seven days and put an X for the total number of letters for each day in the appropriate column.
- Ask what day of the week has more letters and what day of the week has less letters.

Introduce the Chapter

 Real World: Graph Favorite Fruits

- Tell students they are going to learn to gather data, record the information, and then use the data to solve problems.
- Tell students you want to gather information about the kind of fruit they like best. Write *Bananas, Apples,* and *Grapes* as headings on the chalkboard. Write students' names under their favorite fruit.
- **Which row has the most?** Sample answer: grapes
- **Which fruit is most popular?** Sample answer: grapes

Use the Student Page

Have students turn to p. 127. Guide students to discuss the images on the page and answer the Explore questions.

Key Vocabulary

Introduce the key vocabulary in the chapter using the routine below.

Define: A graph that has different pictures to show information collected is a picture graph.
Example: If you draw pictures of animals in a graph, you can find how many pets everyone in the class has.
Ask: What other information can be put in a picture graph?

Diagnostic Assessment

- **Option 1:** ***Are You Ready for Chapter 5?***
  SE Student Edition, p. 128
- **Option 2:** ***Online Assessment Quiz***
  Math Online macmillanmh.com
- **Option 3:** ***Diagnostic Test***
  CRM Chapter 5 Resource Masters, p. 28

RTI (Response to Intervention)

Apply the Results Based on the results of the diagnostic assessment on student p. 128, use the chart on the next page to address individual needs before and during the chapter.

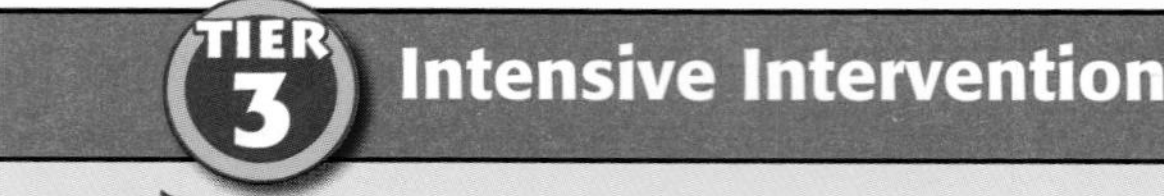

TIER 3	Intensive Intervention
 If	students miss three or four of the exercises:
Then	use Chapter 8 of *Math Triumphs*, an intensive math intervention program from McGraw-Hill

Dinah Zike's Foldables

Guide students to create a Folded Graph Foldable to organize data and create graphs.

1. Fold the 30 × 30 sheet of bulletin board paper in half three times to form eighths. Do the same folds on the opposite axis to form an 8 × 8 grid.

2. Trace along the fold lines with a crayon. Fold the grid back to show the number of columns needed to record the data collected by students. For example, if students collected three objects for the picture graph, you would fold back three columns.

3. Use Post-It Notes or clear tape to label the picture graph columns or rows.

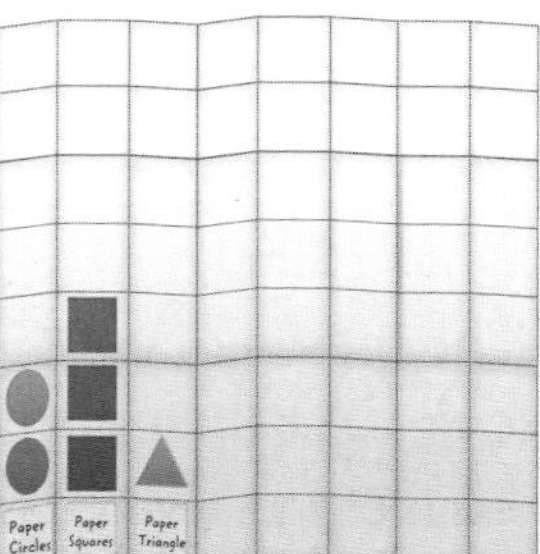

4. Place the objects collected by students on the graph to form a three-dimensional graph that shows the collected data.

When to Use It *Additional instructions for using the Foldable with these lessons are found on pp. 137 and 145.*

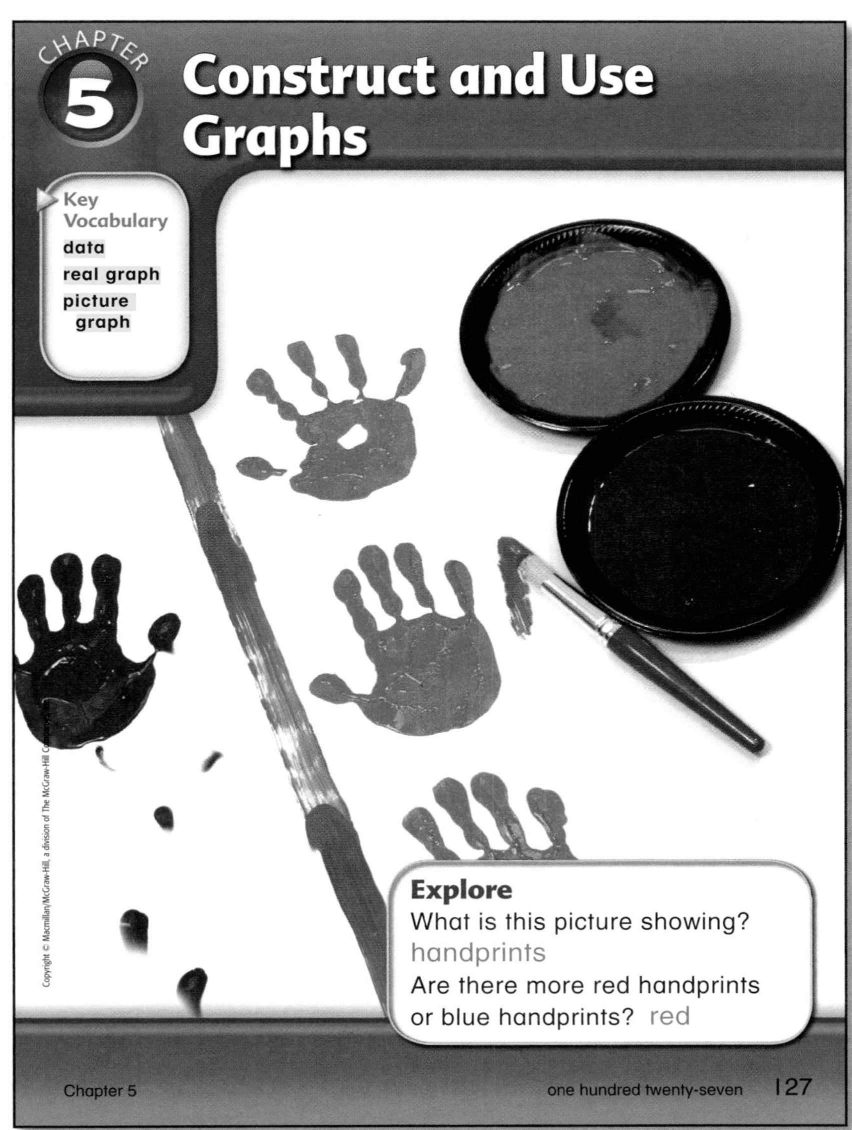

What is this picture showing?
handprints
Are there more red handprints or blue handprints? red

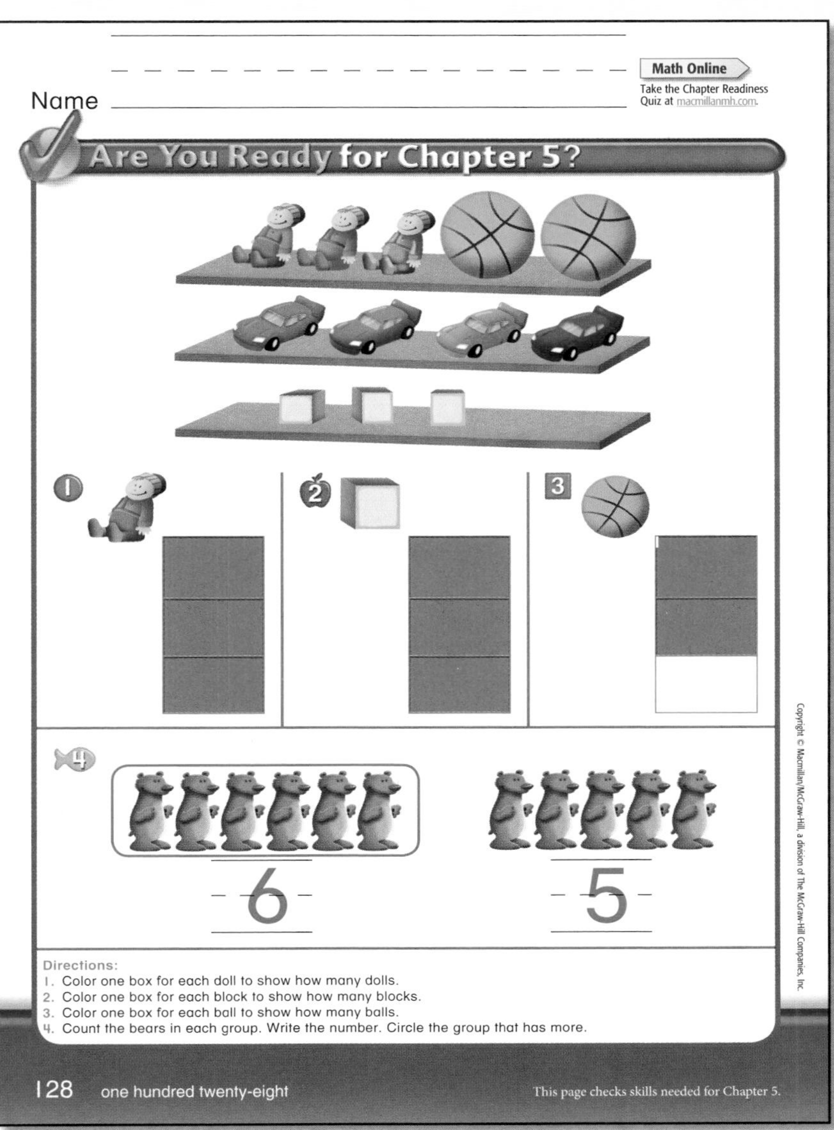

Name
Math Online
Take the Chapter Readiness Quiz at macmillanmh.com.
Are You Ready for Chapter 5?
6
5
Directions:
1. Color one box for each doll to show how many dolls.
2. Color one box for each block to show how many blocks.
3. Color one box for each ball to show how many balls.
4. Count the bears in each group. Write the number. Circle the group that has more.
128 one hundred twenty-eight
This page checks skills needed for Chapter 5.

RTI (Response to Intervention)

TIER 2 Strategic Intervention below/approaching grade level	TIER 1 On-Level	Above/Beyond Level
If students miss two in: **Exercises 1–4**	**If** students miss one in: **Exercises 1–4**	**If** students miss none in: **Exercises 1–4**
Then Choose a resource:	**Then** Choose a resource:	**Then** Choose a resource:
TE Chapter 2 Resource Masters (Reteach Worksheets) Math Online Concepts in Motion	TE Learning Stations (pp. 127G–127H) TE Chapter Project (p. 129) CRM Game: Crayon Grab My Math Zone Chapter 4 Math Adventures	TE Learning Stations (pp. 127G–127H) TE Chapter Project (pp. 129) Real-World Problem Solving: *Our Country* My Math Zone Chapters 3 and 4 Math Online Game

WRITING IN ▶ MATH

Starting the Chapter
Ask students to fold a sheet of paper in half. Have them draw a hamburger on one side and a hot dog on the other.

Ask students which they like better, hamburgers or hot dogs. Track their answers by using tally marks on the chalkboard while students track on their papers.

Chapter 5 Project

Graph Favorite Things

- Ask the class to name their favorite number from zero to five, and write the results on the chalkboard.
- Provide each student with paper and crayons or markers of various colors, and have each student work independently on making a graph about favorite numbers.
- Students can then graph favorite books, favorite foods, favorite television shows, kind and number of pets, and bed times.
- Have students use the graphs they created to answer questions.

Chapter 5 Literature List

Lesson	Book Title	Author
5-1	From One to One Hundred	Teri Sloat
5-2	The Very Hungry Caterpillar	Eric Carle
5-3	One, Two, One Pair!	Bruce McMillan
5-4	Rooster's Off to See the World	Eric Carle
5-5	Let's Count	Tana Hoban
Any	Tiger Math: Learning to Graph from a Baby Tiger	Ann Whitehead Nagda and Cindy Bickel
Any	The Best Vacation Ever	Stuart J. Murphy
Any	Anno's Flea Market	Mitsumasa Anno

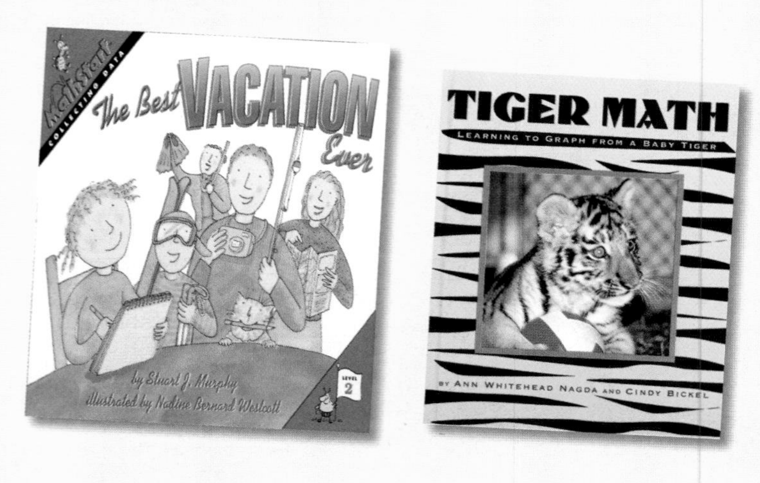

ELL National ESL Standards Alignment for Chapter 5

Lesson, Page	ESL Standard	Modality	Level
5-1, p. 131B	Goal 1, Standard 2, d	Visual, Auditory	Beginning
5-2, p. 133B	Goal 1, Standard 2, d	Visual, Auditory	Beginning
5-3, p. 135B	Goal 2, Standard 1, s	Logical	Advanced
5-4, p. 139B	Goal 2, Standard 1, h	Visual/Social	Intermediate
5-5, p. 141B	Goal 2, Standard 3, h	Auditory, Kinesthetic	Intermediate

The National ESL Standards can be found in the Teacher Reference Handbook.

English

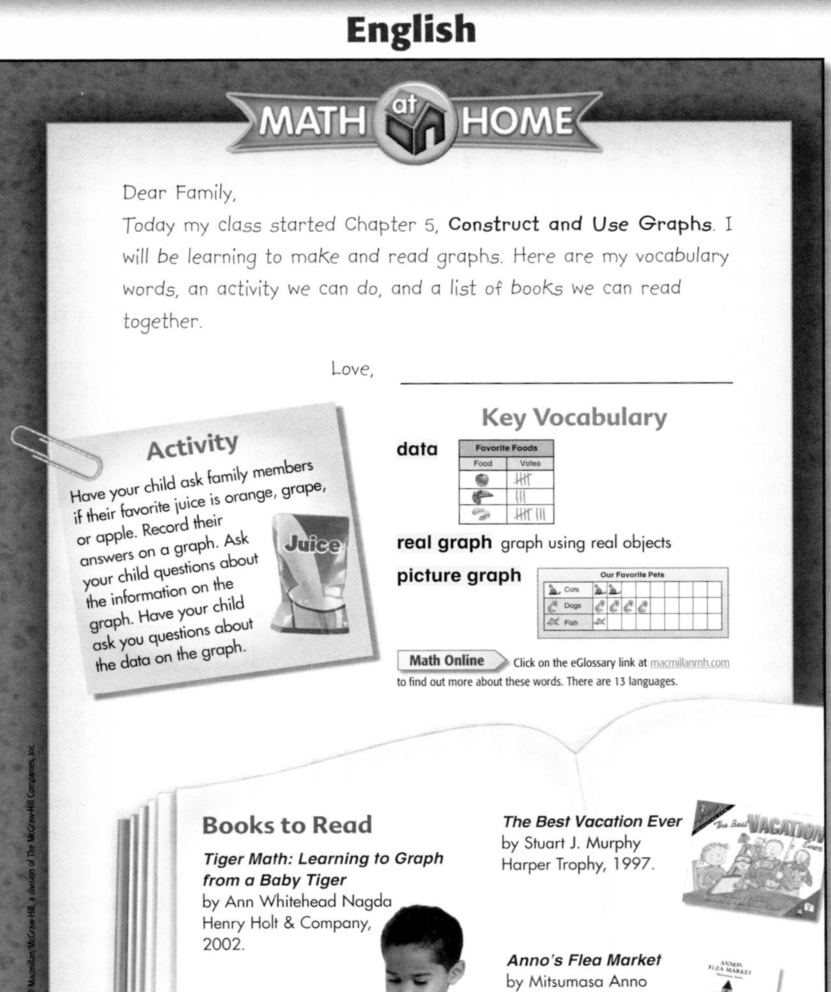

MATH at HOME

Dear Family,

Today my class started Chapter 5, **Construct and Use Graphs**. I will be learning to make and read graphs. Here are my vocabulary words, an activity we can do, and a list of books we can read together.

Love, ____________________

Activity

Have your child ask family members if their favorite juice is orange, grape, or apple. Record their answers on a graph. Ask your child questions about the information on the graph. Have your child ask you questions about the data on the graph.

Key Vocabulary

data

Favorite Foods	
Food	Votes

real graph graph using real objects

picture graph

Our Favorite Pets: Cats, Dogs, Fish

Math Online Click on the eGlossary link at macmillanmh.com to find out more about these words. There are 13 languages.

Books to Read

Tiger Math: Learning to Graph from a Baby Tiger
by Ann Whitehead Nagda
Henry Holt & Company, 2002.

The Best Vacation Ever
by Stuart J. Murphy
Harper Trophy, 1997.

Anno's Flea Market
by Mitsumasa Anno
Penguin Group Incorporated, 1984.

one hundred twenty-nine 129

Español

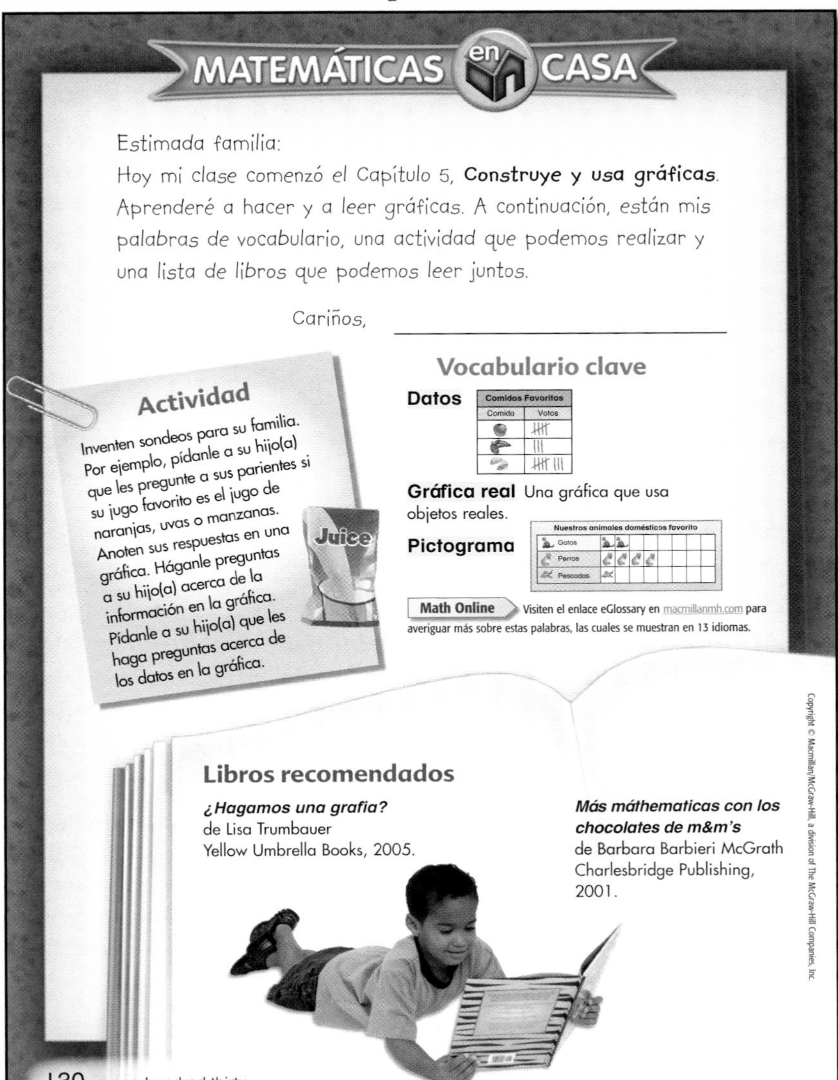

MATEMÁTICAS en CASA

Estimada familia:

Hoy mi clase comenzó el Capítulo 5, **Construye y usa gráficas**. Aprenderé a hacer y a leer gráficas. A continuación, están mis palabras de vocabulario, una actividad que podemos realizar y una lista de libros que podemos leer juntos.

Cariños, ____________________

Actividad

Inventen sondeos para su familia. Por ejemplo, pídanle a su hijo(a) que les pregunte a sus parientes si su jugo favorito es el jugo de naranjas, uvas o manzanas. Anoten sus respuestas en una gráfica. Háganle preguntas a su hijo(a) acerca de la información en la gráfica. Pídanle a su hijo(a) que les haga preguntas acerca de los datos en la gráfica.

Vocabulario clave

Datos

Comidas Favoritas	
Comida	Votos

Gráfica real Una gráfica que usa objetos reales.

Pictograma

Nuestros animales domésticos favorito: Gatos, Perros, Pescados

Math Online Visiten el enlace eGlossary en macmillanmh.com para averiguar más sobre estas palabras, las cuales se muestran en 13 idiomas.

Libros recomendados

¿Hagamos una grafia?
de Lisa Trumbauer
Yellow Umbrella Books, 2005.

Más máthematicas con los chocolates de m&m's
de Barbara Barbieri McGrath
Charlesbridge Publishing, 2001.

130 one hundred thirty

- Read the Math at Home letter on p. 129 with the class and have each student sign it.
- Send home copies of the Math at Home letter with each student.
- Use the Spanish letter on p. 130 for students with Spanish-speaking parents or guardians.

Read-Aloud Anthology

For an optional reading activity to introduce this chapter's math concepts, see the Read-Aloud Anthology on p. TR28.

LESSON 5-1

Collect and Record Data

Lesson Planner

Objective

Collect data from a picture and record data on a graph.

Vocabulary

data, graph

Resources

Materials: graph paper, chart paper, graph mat
Manipulatives: attribute buttons, color tiles
Literature Connection: *From One to One Hundred* by Teri Sloat
Alternate Lesson: Use *When is Your Birthday* graphing on page 156 of *Math Their Way* to provide practice on collecting and recording data.
Use *IMPACT Mathematics:* Unit H to provide practice with graphing.
Teacher Technology
TeacherWorks

Focus on Math Background

This lesson focuses on observation skills needed to describe and identify details and attributes of data. Help students consider only the parts of the data that answer the targeted question *(the whole)*.

For example, kindergarteners can be easily distracted when grouping coins: "*shiny/dirty*" or "*large/small*." Use the feature of greatest interest to focus them. Kindergartners are usually drawn to concrete attributes such as appearance and usage. Also, help students think of questions and responses about data for which they have knowledge and vocabulary.

Daily Routine

Use these suggestions before beginning the lesson on p. 131.

5-Minute Check

(Reviews Lesson 4-9)
Show students a row of three green squares and three yellow circles, arranged in an AB pattern with a square in the first position. If the green square is first, then what color and figure is second? Third? Fifth? yellow circle; green square; green square

Problem of the Day

Have students stand in a line. Have each student identify his or her ordinal position. Have students turn around and say their new ordinal positions.

LINE UP Have students with straight hair form a line on a graph mat. Have students with curly or wavy hair form another line to make a real graph.

Building Math Vocabulary

- Make a **graph** showing an image of winter and an image of summer.
- Have students stand if they like winter better than summer. Draw a snowflake on the graph for every student who likes winter better.
- Repeat the activity for summer, drawing a sun for each student who likes summer best.
- **Does winter or summer have the most?** Sample answer: summer
- **What is a math word for information?** data
- **Where do we put data?** in a graph

Visual Vocabulary Cards

Use Visual Vocabulary Card 12 to reinforce the vocabulary introduced in this lesson. (The Define/Example/Ask routine is printed on the back of each card.)

Differentiated Instruction

Small Group Options

Option 1 Gifted and Talented AL

LOGICAL

Materials: paper, crayons, pencils

- Have students draw what the weather is like for five days, using a sun, raindrop, cloud, and snowflake.
- After data is collected, have students construct a picture graph.
- Have students compare their graph to a local forecast.

Monday					
Tuesday					
Wednesday					
Thursday					
Friday					

Option 2 English Language Learners

AUDITORY, VISUAL

Materials: label, large grid with sky blue on top and sea blue on the bottom, toy or paper boat

Core Vocabulary: across, row, along

Common Use Verb: move

Hear Math This strategy uses music to activate understanding of vocabulary and graphs.

- Show the grid. Pantomime how to move across a row as you sing the following (to "Row Row Row Your Boat").

  Move move move your boat, move along the row
  Across, across, across, across, move along the row.

Independent Work Options

Option 1 Early Finishers OL AL

LINGUISTIC

Materials: baskets, attribute blocks of different colors, classroom graphing mats

- Give each student a basket containing attribute blocks.
- Have students sort the blocks by color.
- Ask students to guess what color has the most.
- Have students construct a graph using a graphing mat to check their guess.

Option 2 Student Technology

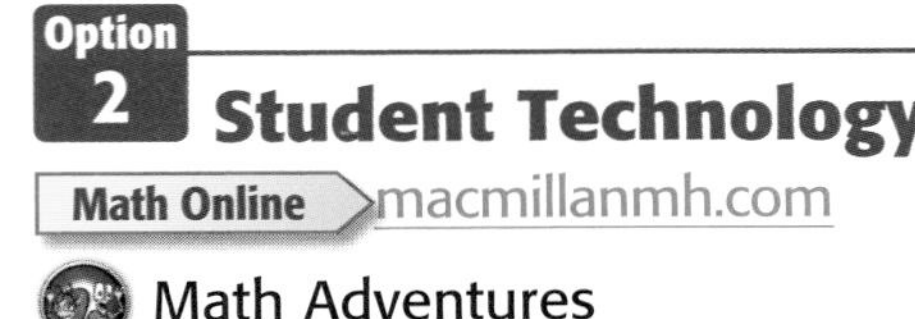

Option 3 Learning Stations: Health (p. 127G)

Direct students to the Health Learning Station for more opportunities to explore and extend the lesson concept.

Leveled Lesson Resources

Reteach (p. 6) BL

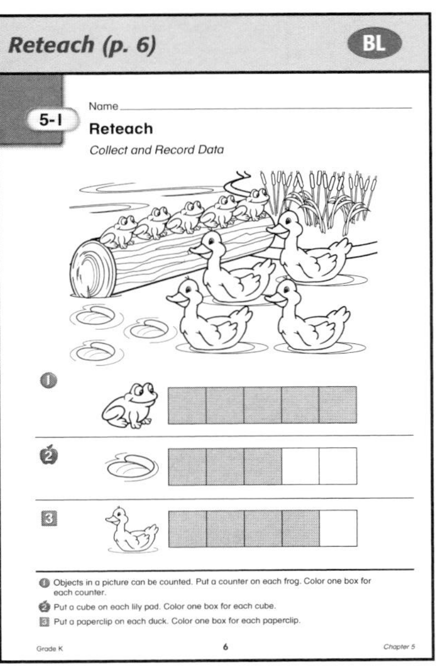
5-1 Name
Reteach
Collect and Record Data

1. Objects in a picture can be counted. Put a counter on each frog. Color one box for each counter.
2. Put a cube on each lily pad. Color one box for each cube.
3. Put a paperclip on each duck. Color one box for each paperclip.

Grade K 6 Chapter 5

Skills Practice (p. 7) OL

5-1 Name
Skills Practice
Collect and Record Data

1. 5
2. 3
3. 4

1. Talk about the picture. Count the flowers. Write the number.
2. Count the trees. Write the number.
3. Count the birds. Write the number.

Grade K 7 Chapter 5

Enrich (p. 9) AL

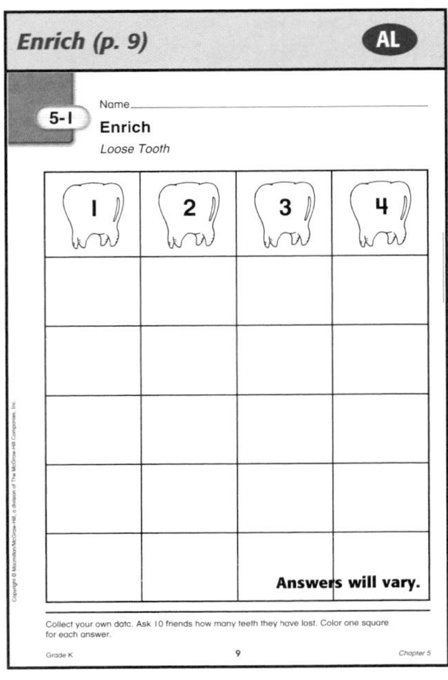
5-1 Name
Enrich
Loose Tooth

1	2	3	4
		Answers will vary.	

Collect your own data. Ask 10 friends how many teeth they have lost. Color one square for each answer.

Grade K 9 Chapter 5

Homework Practice (p. 8) OL

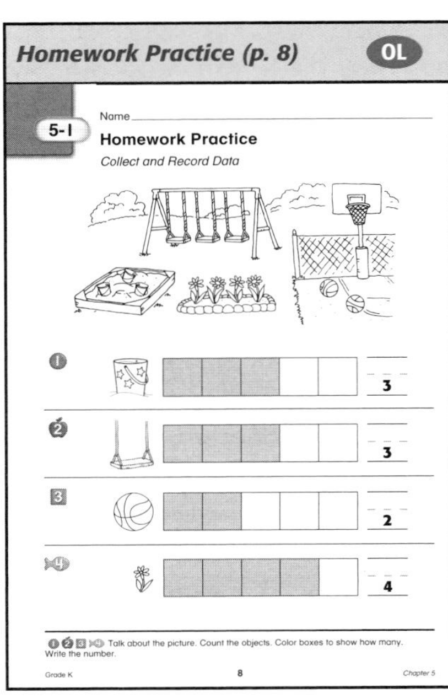
5-1 Name
Homework Practice
Collect and Record Data

1. 3
2. 3
3. 2
4. 4

1 2 3 4 Talk about the picture. Count the objects. Color boxes to show how many. Write the number.

Grade K 8 Chapter 5

1 Introduce

Activity Choice 1 • Literature

FROM ONE TO ONE HUNDRED

From One to One Hundred
by Teri Sloat
Materials: chart paper or chalkboard

- Read aloud the first page of the story. **How many different pictures of one thing do you see?** Sample answers: one crown, one princess
- Draw each object on a chart or chalkboard to represent how many pictures of one thing there are.
- Repeat with the next pages up to the number ten finding and drawing how many groups.
- Ask students which number has more pictures.
- Have students collect **data** about real objects in the classroom such as number of pencils, boxes of crayons, or erasers, up to ten.
- Tell students to draw simple pictures of each object to represent how many they found.
- Ask students which object has less.

Activity Choice 2 • Hands-On 

Materials: graph mat, six blue triangle attribute buttons, four green triangle buttons

- Say that we can look around our room to find information and that we can record this information, or data, by making **graphs**.
- Put out the attribute buttons. Tell students that they will construct a graph using paper and the attribute buttons.
- Have a volunteer sort the buttons. Have a volunteer place the buttons on the graph.
- Ask how many buttons of each color are on the graph.
- Repeat that graphs are a way to show information and that information can be called data.

2 Teach

- Direct students to the top of p. 131.
- **How many different objects appear on the table?** eight
- Count the total number together.

BL Alternate Teaching Strategy

If students have trouble understanding how to graph data . . .

Then use one of the following reteach options.

1 CRM **Daily Reteach Worksheet** (p. 6)

2 **Graphing Data** Show a model of a graph mat.

- Ask students a question that would lend itself to graphing, such as what is their favorite movie or book character.
- Have students show their opinions by standing on the graph mat.

COMMON ERROR!

Students may lose track of information when collecting data to graph. Limit the scope of the graph by asking a small number of students for information or by using only a few manipulatives.

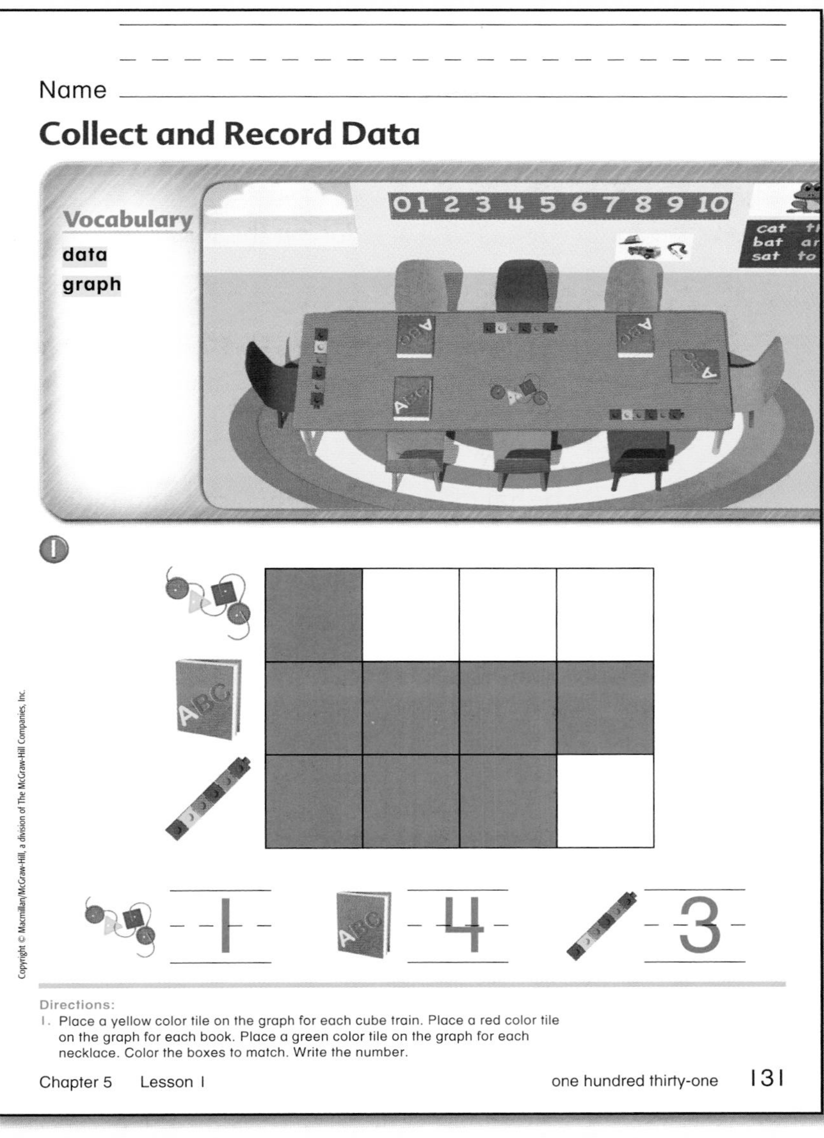

Name

Collect and Record Data

Vocabulary
data
graph

1

1 4 3

Directions:
1. Place a yellow color tile on the graph for each cube train. Place a red color tile on the graph for each book. Place a green color tile on the graph for each necklace. Color the boxes to match. Write the number.

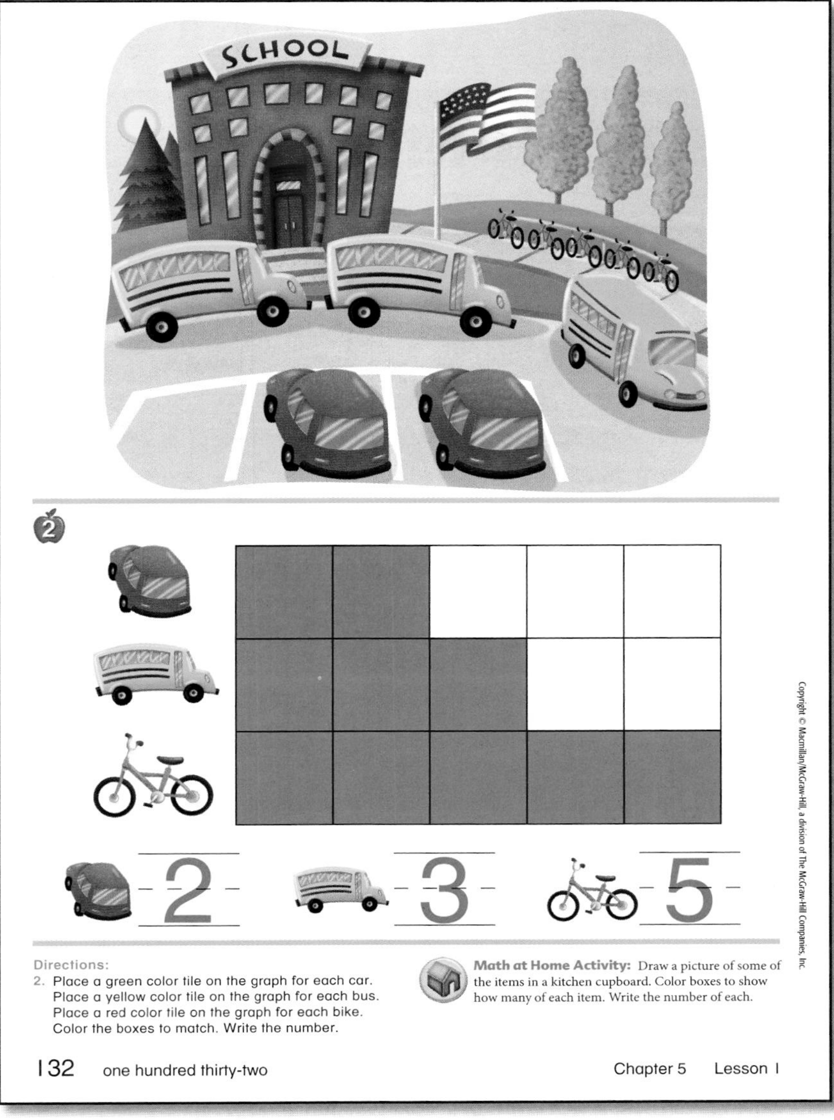

2

2 3 5

Directions:
2. Place a green color tile on the graph for each car. Place a yellow color tile on the graph for each bus. Place a red color tile on the graph for each bike. Color the boxes to match. Write the number.

Math at Home Activity: Draw a picture of some of the items in a kitchen cupboard. Color boxes to show how many of each item. Write the number of each.

3 Practice

Guided Practice

- Point out the table of objects on p. 131.
- Place a yellow color tile on the graph for each cube train, a red tile for each book, and a green tile for each necklace.
- Have students hold up the same number of fingers as each object is counted, then write the number in the spaces next to each object.
- Say that we can use the graph in Exercise 1 to keep track of the number of objects. Have students color the same number of boxes as the number of button necklaces.
- **How many boxes did you color?** one
- Repeat for the book and cube train.

Independent Practice

Have students turn to p. 132. Explain the directions. Have students work independently on the exercise.

Assess

Formative Assessment

- **Why do we make graphs?** to record information
- **What is another name for information?** data
- Show a graph using real objects. Ask which row has more objects.

Quick Check **Are students still struggling to graph data?**

If Yes → Small Group Options (p. 131B)

If No → Independent Work Options (p. 131B)

CRM Skills Practice Worksheet (p. 7)

CRM Enrich Worksheet (p. 9)

LESSON 5-2

Real Graphs

Lesson Planner

Objective

Make and read a concrete graph or real graph.

Vocabulary

real graph

Resources

Materials: graph paper, chart paper, pencil, paper, crayons, glue, paper clips
Manipulatives: connecting cubes, color tiles
Literature Connection: *The Very Hungry Caterpillar* by Eric Carle
Alternative Lesson: Use *IMPACT Mathematics:* Unit H to provide practice with graphing.
Teacher Technology
TeacherWorks • Concepts in Motion

Focus on Math Background

In this lesson, students will use bar-type graphs to make comparisons between two sets of data. Using numerical reasoning, students will decide what of two sets has more and what has less. They will also learn how to fill in a bar-type graph starting from bottom to top so that the size difference between the two amounts is apparent.

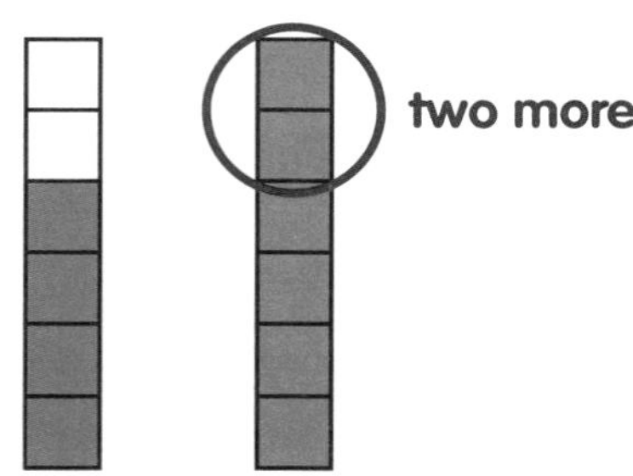

Most kindergarteners cannot yet answer, "*How many more?*" Finding a difference is easier if the question is stated to help them see how to make the two sets the same, for example "*How many more* green squares do we need to *match the* blue squares?"

Daily Routine

Use these suggestions before beginning the lesson on p. 133.

5-Minute Check

(Reviews Lesson 5-1)
Make a graph that shows two colors: red and blue. Tell students to put an X under the color they like best.

Problem of the Day

1. Why do we use a graph? to show data/information
2. How could a graph help us find out if this class has more boys or girls? compare data

LINE UP Ask students to line up if they like raisins. Ask students to line up in a second line if they do not like raisins. Ask which line has the most. Have volunteers count the numbers in each line.

Building Math Vocabulary

Materials: bags, pennies, crayon, floor graph

- Invite four students to stand. Give each student a bag of pennies. Say that we will make a **real graph** to show who has the most pennies.
- Write the students' names on a floor graph. One at a time ask students to put their pennies on the graph. Have volunteers count the pennies to find out who has the most.

Visual Vocabulary Cards

Use Visual Vocabulary Card 33 to reinforce the vocabulary introduced in this lesson. (The Define/Example/Ask routine is printed on the back of each card.)

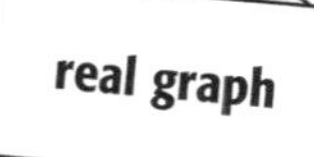

Differentiated Instruction

Small Group Options

Option 1 Gifted and Talented AL

LOGICAL

Materials: graph paper, with one-inch squares paper clips (different sizes)

- Give groups of students graph paper and a cup containing paper clips of different sizes.
- Tell them to construct a real graph by laying out the paper clips in columns by size.
- Have them count each column and use information to find what size has the most and the least.

Option 2 English Language Learners ELL

VISUAL/AUDITORY

Core Vocabulary: column, up, down
Common Use Verb: go

See Math This strategy shows vocabulary with music.

- Pantomime moving up and down along a grid column. Sing to "Twinkle Twinkle Little Star."

Up and **down** the **columns go**
They don't *move across* like *rows*.
They **go** like the bird can fly,
Up and **down** into the sky.

Independent Work Options

Option 1 Early Finishers OL AL

LINGUISTIC

Materials: bowl, attribute buttons of assorted colors

- Give each pair a bowl filled with ten attribute buttons. Have each student work with a partner.
- Have one student take a handful of buttons. Have the other student sort the attribute buttons by color.
- Have each pair construct a real graph with the attribute buttons. Have pairs report their findings.
- Have students take turns filling the bowls, sorting, and graphing.

Option 2 Student Technology

Math Online macmillanmh.com

 Math Adventures

Option 3 Learning Station: Language Arts (p. 127G)

Direct students to the Language Arts Learning Station for more opportunities to explore and extend the lesson concept.

Leveled Lesson Resources

Reteach (p. 10) BL

5-2 Name
Reteach
Real Graphs

Answers will vary.

Spread a handful of connecting cubes on the picture. Move each cube to the graph. Put it in the correct row by color. Circle the group with less objects.

Grade K 10 *Chapter 5*

Skills Practice (p. 11) OL

5-2 Name
Skills Practice
Real Graphs

Answers will vary.

Spread a handful of yellow and green tiles on the plates. Move each tile to the graph. Put it in the correct row (yellow with corn; green with beans.) Circle the group with more objects.

Grade K 11 *Chapter 5*

Enrich (p. 13) AL

5-2 Name
Enrich
Shoe Count

Answers will vary.

What kind of shoes are you wearing? Do they have laces, velcro, or buckles? Ask 10 friends. Color one square for each answer.

Grade K 13 *Chapter 5*

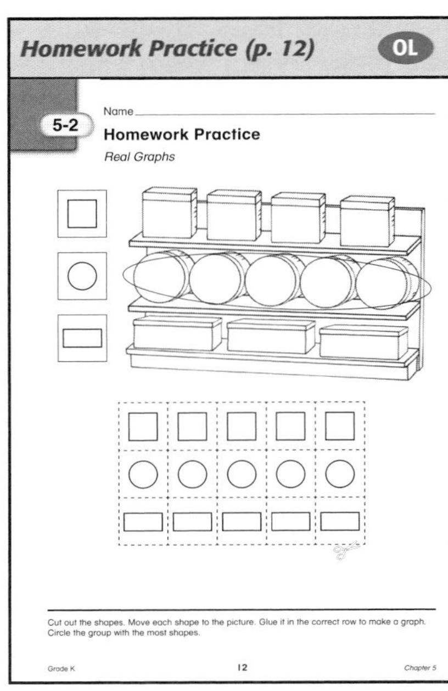

Homework Practice (p. 12) OL

5-2 Name
Homework Practice
Real Graphs

Cut out the shapes. Move each shape to the picture. Glue it in the correct row to make a graph. Circle the group with the most shapes.

Grade K 12 *Chapter 5*

1 Introduce

Circle Time

Activity Choice 1 • Literature

The Very Hungry Caterpillar
by Eric Carle
Materials: chart paper, pencil, paper, crayons, glue

- Explain that a **real graph** is a graph using real objects.
- Read the book aloud. Have students draw and cut out a picture of each food the caterpillar ate.
- Create a graph labeling it with days of the week. Place the objects on it.
- Ask students which day has the least pieces of food. Ask which days have more food than Wednesday.
- Post the chart in the Math Center.

Activity Choice 2 • Hands-On

Materials: connecting cubes, graph paper

- Tell students that we ask questions to find out information. One way to record this information, or data, is by making graphs.
- Have students use connecting cubes to make a real graph.
- First, students should sort the connecting cubes by colors.
- Next, students should put the connecting cubes by color on a graph. Have them use a different row for each color of connecting cubes.

2 Teach

- Direct students to p. 133.
- Have students take a handful of red and blue tiles.
- Have them use the tiles on the easel on the page to create a picture.

BL Alternate Teaching Strategy

If students have trouble understanding real graphs . . .

Then use one of the following reteach options.

1 CRM **Daily Reteach Worksheet** (p. 10)

2 **Sort and Graph!** Provide students with real objects found in the classroom, such as crayons, pencils, or paper clips.

- Have students sort the objects by one attribute.
- When students are sure of sorting, show them a model of a graph.
- Help them construct a graph using their information.

COMMON ERROR!

Students may record information too fast and put inaccurate data on the graph, affecting the accuracy of their answers. Remind students to take time to be accurate.

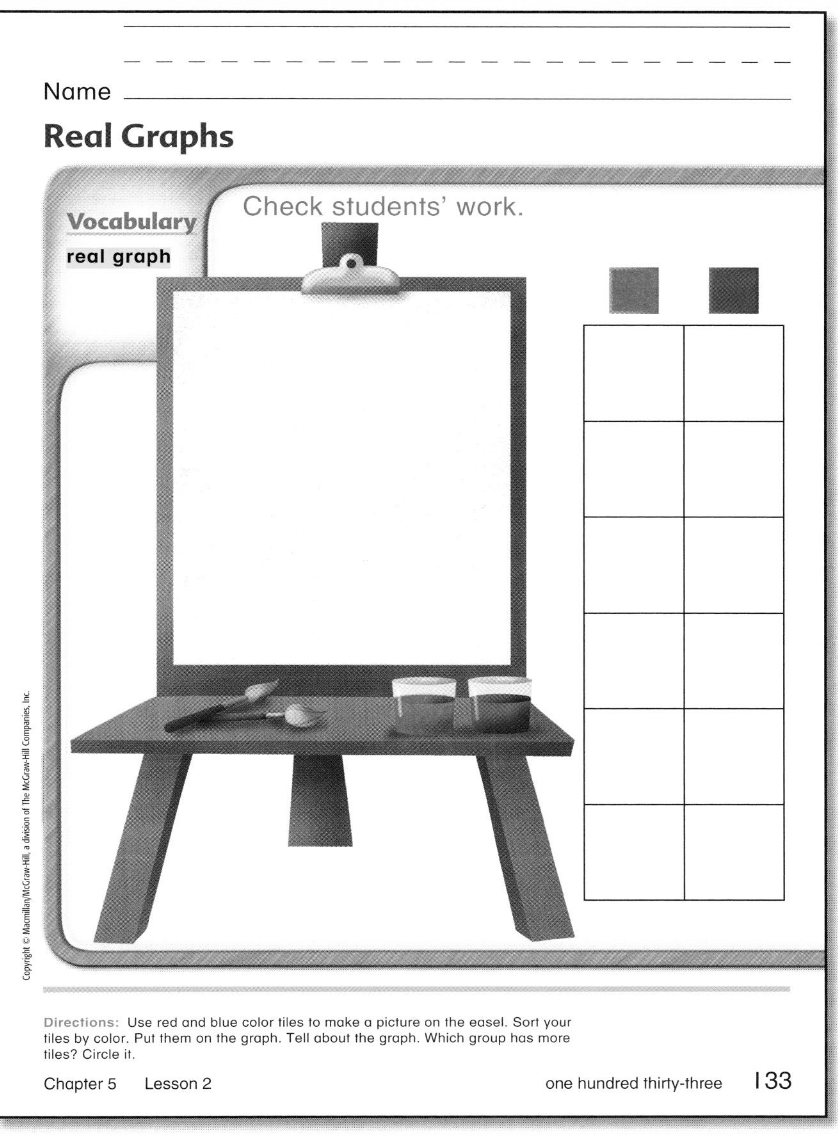

Name

Real Graphs

Vocabulary
real graph

Check students' work.

Directions: Use red and blue color tiles to make a picture on the easel. Sort your tiles by color. Put them on the graph. Tell about the graph. Which group has more tiles? Circle it.

Check students' work.

Directions: Use yellow and green color tiles to make a picture on the chalkboard. Sort your tiles by color. Put them on the graph. Tell about the graph. Which group has less tiles? Circle it.

Math at Home Activity: Toss nine pennies. Sort heads and tails. Graph results as shown above. Tell which has more and which has less.

3 Practice

Guided Practice

- Tell students they are going to find how many tiles they used to create their pictures.
- Direct students' attention to the two vertical columns on p. 133, one column showing a red tile and the other showing a blue tile.
- Have students sort the tiles by color and place each tile on the graph below the matching color.
- Discuss what the graph shows. Ask questions to relate data in the graph.
- Ask students to circle the group with more tiles.

Independent Practice

Have students turn to p. 134. Explain the directions. Have students work independently on the exercise.

4 Assess

Formative Assessment

Have students discuss what they know about real graphs.

- **Why do we call it a real graph?** Sample answer: We use real objects on the graph.
- **What can we learn from looking at a real graph?** Sample answer: object that has the most or least, what's the favorite

Quick Check **Are students still struggling to make and interpret real graphs?**

If Yes → Small Group Options (p. 133B)

If No → Independent Work Options (p. 133B)

CRM Skills Practice Worksheet (p. 11)

CRM Enrich Worksheet (p. 13)

LESSON 5-3

Problem-Solving Strategy

Look for a Pattern

Lesson Planner

Objective

Collect data from a picture, record data on a graph, and make and read a concrete graph or real graph.

Resources

Materials: classroom objects, crayons, pencils
Manipulatives: connecting cubes, pattern blocks
Literature Connection: *One, Two, One Pair!* by Bruce McMillan
Teacher Technology
TeacherWorks
Real-World Problem Solving Library
Math and Social Studies: *Our Country*
Use these leveled books to reinforce and extend problem-solving skills and strategies.
Leveled for:
- OL On Level
- ELL Sheltered English
- SP Spanish

For additional support,see the Real-World Problem Solving Teacher Guide.

On-level title is available in classroom Big Book.

Daily Routine

Use these suggestions before beginning the lesson on p. 135.

5-Minute Check

(Reviews Lesson 5-2)
Have students choose a connecting cube of their favorite color, then connect cubes of the same color to make trains. How can we use this information to find out which color our class likes the most? Find the tallest train.

Problem of the Day

1. Why do we use a graph? to show data/information
2. How could a graph help us find out if the class has more boys or girls? compare data
3. Create a graph to show if there are more boys or girls.

LINE UP Say a pattern. Say it three times. Point to a student to continue the pattern, ask them to line up, and point to another student to continue the pattern until all students have lined up.

Differentiated Instruction

Small Group Options

Option 1 — LINGUISTIC, SOCIAL

Gifted and Talented AL

Materials: paper, pencil, crayons

- Have students form small groups. Each group should look at the school menu and choose three lunch items.
- After choosing the lunch items, the group should decide how they will record their data: with pictures, check marks, or Xs. Have groups ask their classmates their favorite item from the three lunch items.
- Have groups make a graph using their information, total the results, and share any patterns they see.

Option 2 — LOGICAL

English Language Learners ELL

Materials: wall graph, groups of classroom items
Core Vocabulary: comes next, what, pattern
Common Use Verb: cross off

Write Math This strategy helps students identify a pattern.

- Group items around a circle, in an AB format.
- Count the number of items and cross off the same number of squares on the graph. Repeat with the next group.
- Ask: "What's next?" Discuss.

Independent Work Options

Option 1 — LOGICAL

Early Finishers OL AL

Materials: graph paper with one inch squares cut into 1 × 10 and 2 × 10 strips, crayons

- Show how to color a repeating pattern. Begin by coloring the box in the bottom left corner on graph paper with one color, then coloring the box to the right with a second color. Repeat.
- Have students make their own two-color repeating pattern on graph paper using the paper strips and two colors of crayons.
- Ask students to share their pattern with the class.

Option 2

Student Technology

Math Online macmillanmh.com

Option 3

Learning Stations: Art (p. 127G)

Direct students to the Art Learning Station for opportunities to explore and extend the lesson concept.

Leveled Lesson Resources

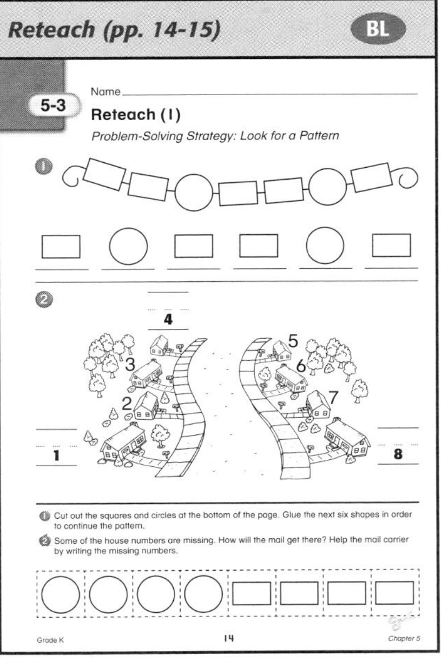

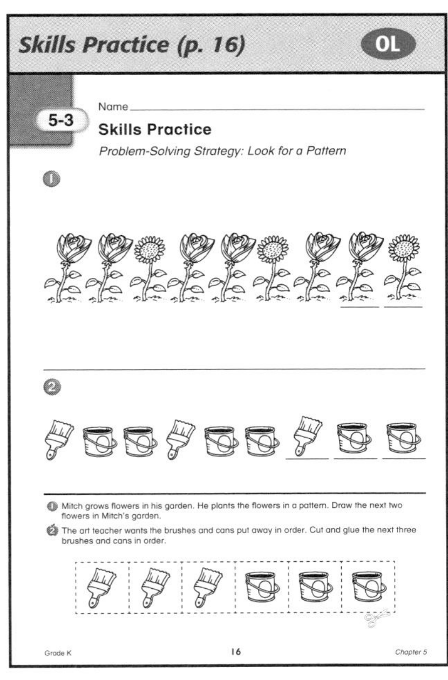

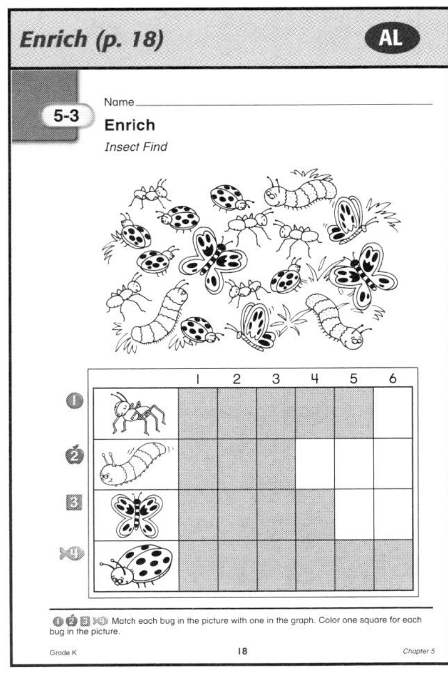

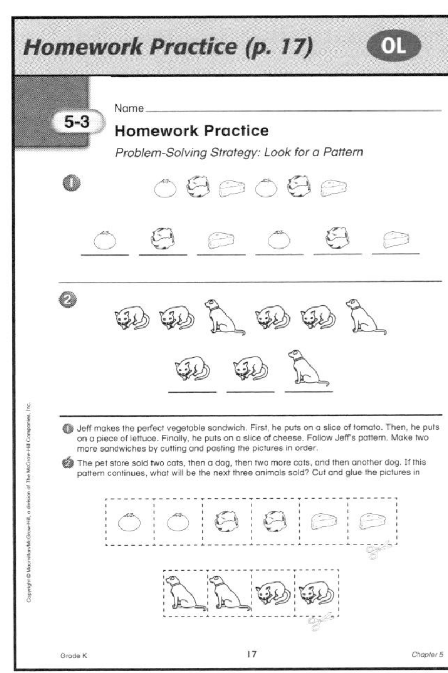

1 Introduce

Circle Time

Activity Choice 1 • Literature

One, Two, One Pair!
by Bruce McMillan

- Have students get a partner.
- Read the book stressing that to be a pair, items must be alike.
- Place an assortment of objects on tables in front of students. Instruct them to create pairs of objects. Take turns sharing by saying, "I have a pair of ____ because they both_____."
- Then challenge them to create pairs using pattern blocks.
- Challenge each child to find a pair of something on their partner (shoes, eyes, etc.).
- Repeat pairs as pattern units.

Activity Choice 2 • Hands-On

Materials: blue, red, and yellow crayons

- Gather students in a circle and tell them they are going to help you make a special line of crayons.
- Set down a line of crayons in the following order: blue, red, yellow, blue, red, yellow, blue, red, yellow, blue. Review the order of colors.
- **Which color crayon could come next after blue?** red
- **Which color is after red?** yellow
- **What is the pattern you see?** blue, red, yellow
- Ask volunteers to help you extend the pattern.
- Have students help you create other patterns using different colored crayons.

2 Teach

Understand Review what students know and what they need to find for each problem.

Plan Have students discuss their strategy for solving the problems.

Solve Guide students to look for a pattern in order to solve the problems. Have students identify and describe the pattern shown in the graph. Help students to identify the color pattern as well as the number pattern. (blue, red, blue, red, blue, red/ 2, 3, 2, 3, 2, 3)

Check Have students look back at the problem to be sure that the answers fit what they already know about the problem.

BL Alternate Teaching Strategy

If students have trouble finding a pattern in graphs . . .

Then use one of these reteach options.

1 CRM **Daily Reteach Worksheet** (pp. 14-15)

2 **Pattern Trains** Give students a handful of connecting cubes in two colors. Ask students to make a cube train of alternating colors.

- **What color is your first cube?** Sample answer: blue
- **What color is your next cube?** Sample answer: green
- **What color cube is after green?** Sample answer: blue
- **What color pattern did you make?** Sample answer: blue, green, blue
- Give students connecting cubes of a third color. Ask students to make a pattern using three colors of connecting cubes. Have students share their patterns.

COMMON ERROR!

Some students may have difficulty understanding where a pattern starts. Direct them to where the pattern begins to repeat and to look to the start of the pattern to tell what comes next.

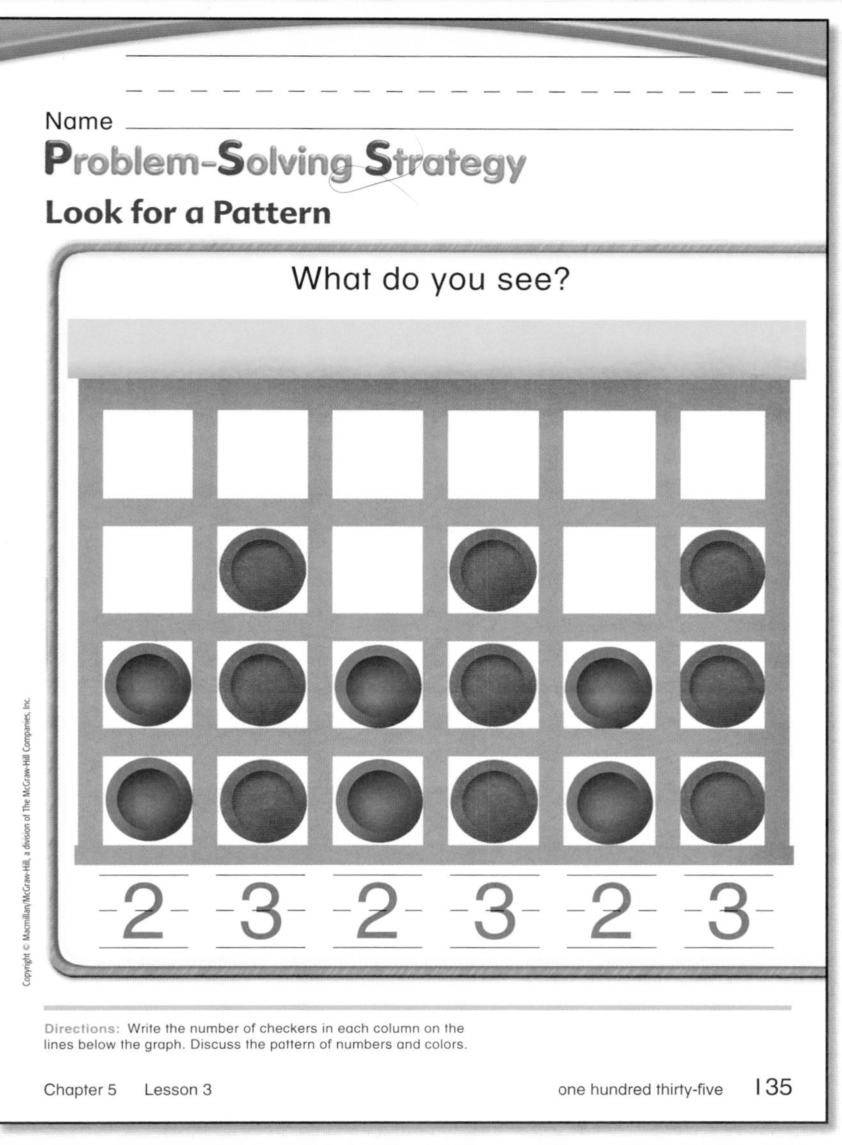

Name
Problem-Solving Strategy
Look for a Pattern
What do you see?
2 3 2 3 2 3
Copyright © Macmillan/McGraw-Hill, a division of The McGraw-Hill Companies, Inc.
Directions: Write the number of checkers in each column on the lines below the graph. Discuss the pattern of numbers and colors.
Chapter 5 Lesson 3 one hundred thirty-five 135

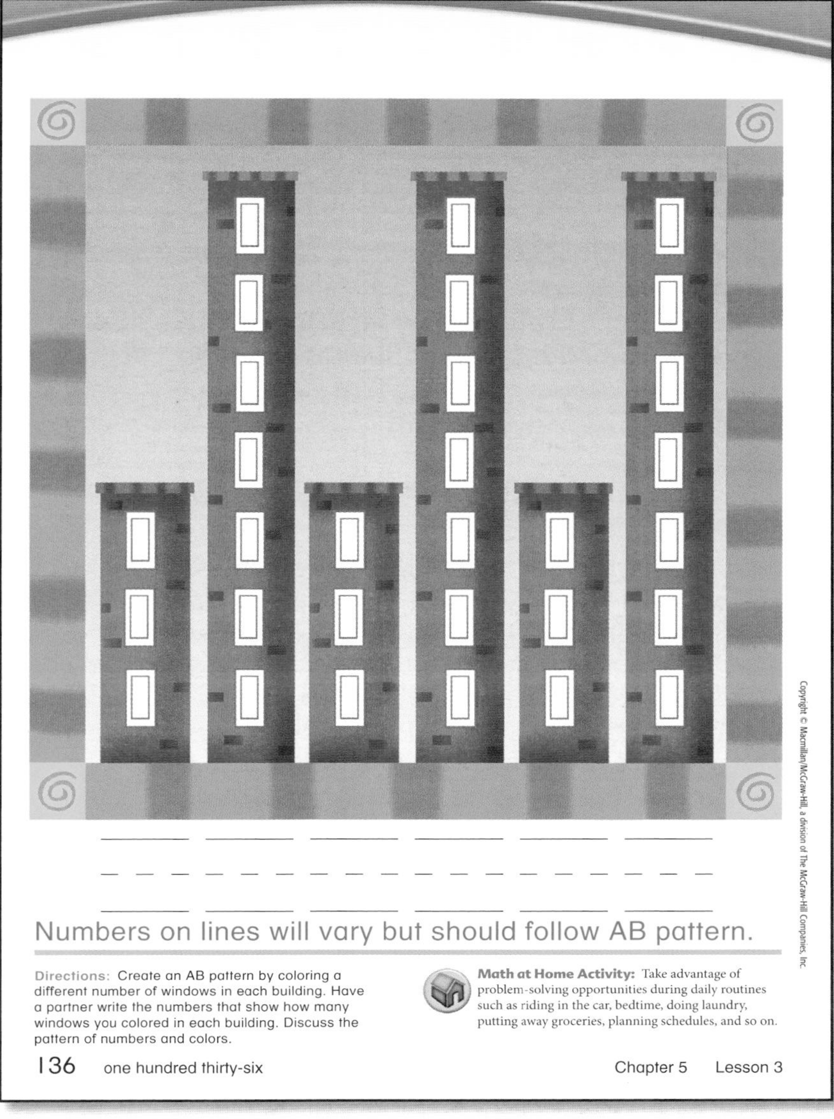

Numbers on lines will vary but should follow AB pattern.
Directions: Create an AB pattern by coloring a different number of windows in each building. Have a partner write the numbers that show how many windows you colored in each building. Discuss the pattern of numbers and colors.
Math at Home Activity: Take advantage of problem-solving opportunities during daily routines such as riding in the car, bedtime, doing laundry, putting away groceries, planning schedules, and so on.
136 one hundred thirty-six Chapter 5 Lesson 3
Copyright © Macmillan/McGraw-Hill, a division of The McGraw-Hill Companies, Inc.

3 Practice

Guided Practice

- Direct the students' attention to p. 135.
- **What do you notice about the data?** It is in a pattern: 2, 3, 2, 3, 2, 3.
- **What color checkers will be in the next column?** blue **How do you know?** Blue comes after red in the pattern.
- Help students write the number of checkers.

Independent Practice

- Have students work with a partner on the exercise on p. 136.
- **How would you use materials to show the patterns another way? What other approach strategy could be used?** Sample answers: AB patterns could be made with colors or shapes.

4 Assess

Formative Assessment

- Direct students to p. 136.
- **What other pattern do you see in the picture of the buildings?** They are small, big, small, big, small, big.

Quick Check **Are students still struggling with patterns in graphing?**

If Yes → Small Group Options (p. 135B)

If No → Independent Work Options (p. 135B)

 Skills Practice Worksheet (p. 16)

CRM Enrich Worksheet (p. 18)

Mid-Chapter Check

Lessons 5-1 to 5-3

Formative Assessment

Use the Mid-Chapter Check to assess student's progress in the first half of the chapter.

ExamView Assessment Suite Customize and create multiple versions of your Mid-Chapter Check and the test answer keys.

FOLDABLES® Dinah Zike's Foldables

If students have not completed their Foldables, guide them to create and fill in the appropriate information using the instructions on p. 127.

You may choose to use the Foldable to help students review the concepts presented in this chapter and as a tool for studying for the Mid-Chapter Check.

Name

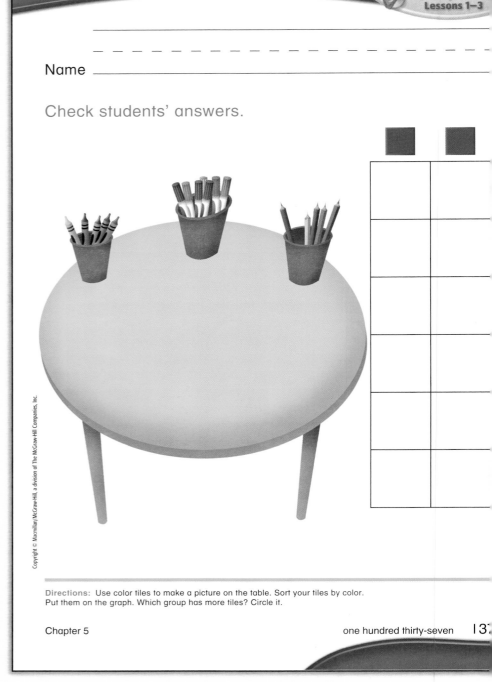

Check students' answers.

Directions: Use color tiles to make a picture on the table. Sort your tiles by color. Put them on the graph. Which group has more tiles? Circle it.

Data-Driven Decision Making

Based on the results of the Mid-Chapter Check, use the following resources to review concepts that continue to give students problems.

Exercises	State/Local Standards	What's the Math?	Error Analysis	Resources for Review
1 Lesson 5-2		Collect information about objects in the environment and record the results.	Does not sort tiles by color. Does not circle group that has more tiles.	CRM Chapter 5 Resource Masters (Reteach Worksheets) Math Online Concepts in Motion Math Adventures

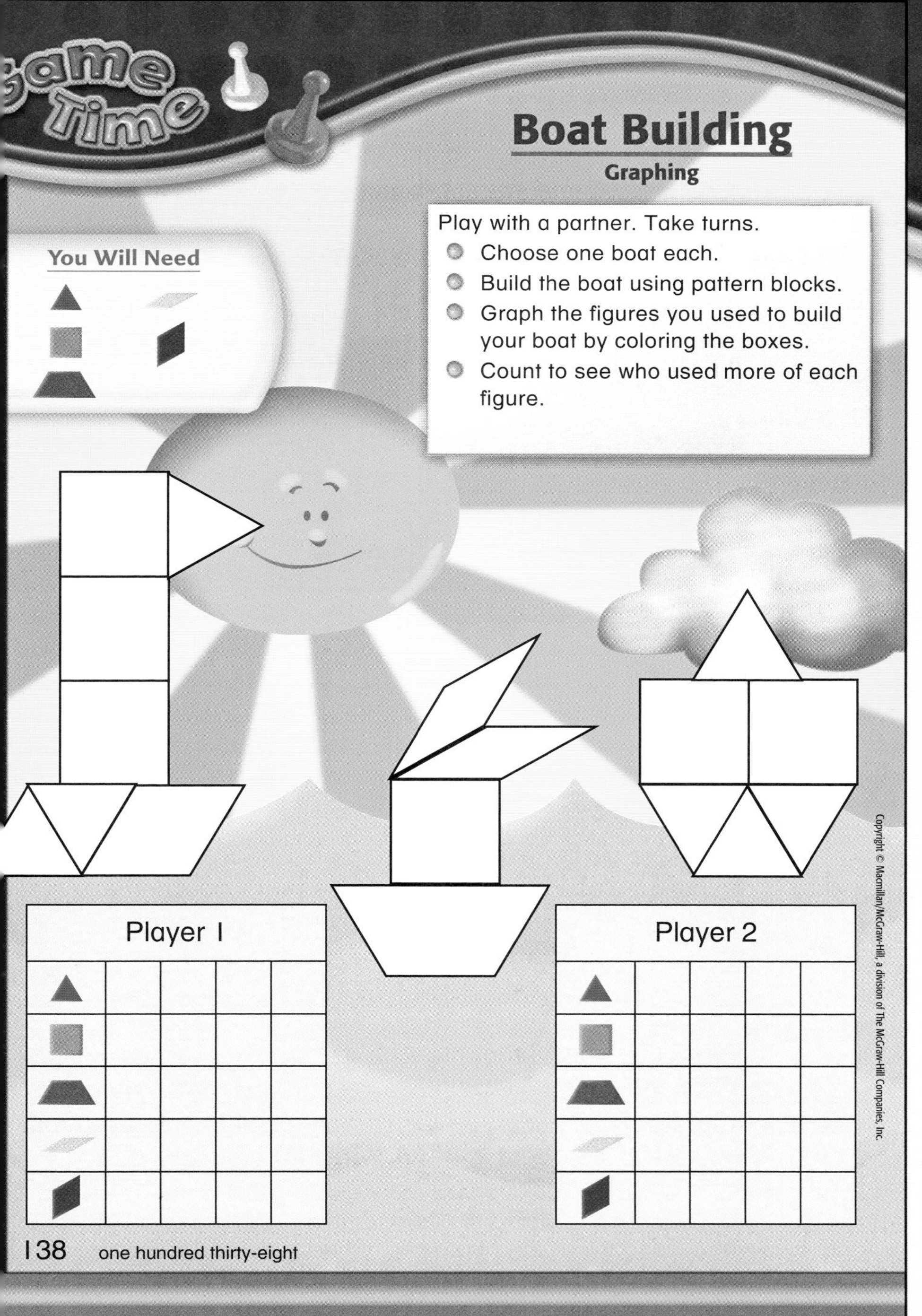

Game Time

Boat Building

Graphing

You Will Need

Play with a partner. Take turns.

- Choose one boat each.
- Build the boat using pattern blocks.
- Graph the figures you used to build your boat by coloring the boxes.
- Count to see who used more of each figure.

Player 1

Player 2

Differentiated Practice

Use these leveled suggestions to differentiate the game for all learners.

Level	Assignment
BL Below/Approaching Level	Have students sort the pattern blocks before they graph them.
OL On Level	Have students play the game with the rules as written.
AL Above/Beyond Level	Students write the total number of each shape of pattern blocks under the graph.

Boat Building

Math Concept: Graphing

Materials: crayons

Manipulatives: triangle, square, small parallelogram, parallelogram, and trapezoid pattern blocks

Introduce the game on p. 138 to your students to play as a class, in small groups, or at a learning workstation to review concepts introduced in this chapter.

Instructions

- Have students work with a partner and choose a boat to build.
- Have students build their boat using pattern blocks.
- Ask students to graph the number of triangles, squares, trapezoids, and parallelograms they used by coloring in the appropriate number of squares for each figure.
- Ask students to compare their graphs to see who used more of each figure.

Extend the Game

Have students create their own pattern block boat and graph the blocks used to make their new boat.

LESSON 5-4 Picture Graphs

Lesson Planner

Objective
Make and read a picture graph.

Vocabulary
picture graph

Resources
Materials: crayons, graph paper, glue, chart paper, magazine pictures, poster board, tape

Literature Connection: *Rooster's Off to See the World* by Eric Carle

Alternate Lesson: Use *Practice Graphs Comparing Two Groups* on page 148 of *Math Their Way* to provide practice with picture graphs.
Use *IMPACT Mathematics:* Unit H to provide practice with graphing.

Teacher Technology
TeacherWorks • Concepts in Motion

Focus on Math Background

This lesson introduces picture graphs. A picture graph shows information made up of individual pictures, each representing a quantifiable piece of the data set. In this lesson, students will gather information representing the data with pictures. Eventually, they will see how displaying information with symbols and pictures, versus with actual objects, is more manageable for storing, remembering, and referencing data.

Daily Routine

Use these suggestions before beginning the lesson on p. 139.

5-Minute Check
(Reviews Lesson 5-3)
Ask students if they are the oldest, middle, or youngest child in their family. Graph the data. Have students look for a pattern to determine what kind of child the class has the most of.

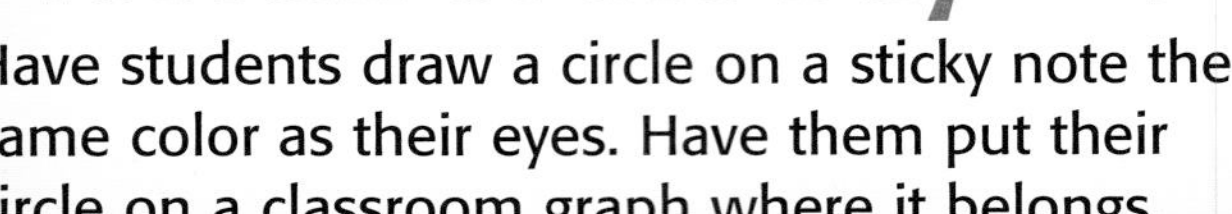

Problem of the Day
Have students draw a circle on a sticky note the same color as their eyes. Have them put their circle on a classroom graph where it belongs.

LINE UP Have students who get to school *by car* make one line, *by bus* a second line, and *by walking* a third line. Make a graph using pictures of buses, cars, and walkers. Let students hold pictures in their lines.

Building Math Vocabulary
Materials: basket, small metal and nonmetal objects, magnet, sticky notes, crayons, floor graph

- Put metal and nonmetal objects into a basket.
- **When we make a picture graph, what are we doing?** making a graph using pictures
- Tell students they will make a **picture graph** to show whether an object is made of metal or not. Explain that metal is attracted to magnets.
- Take an object from the basket. Use the magnet to find out if the object is made of metal or not. Have students put their picture of the object where it belongs on the class graph.

Visual Vocabulary Cards
Use Visual Vocabulary Card 31 to reinforce the vocabulary introduced in this lesson. (The Define/Example/Ask routine is printed on the back of each card.)

Differentiated Instruction

Small Group Options

Option 1 VISUAL

Below/Approaching Level BL

Materials: 2″ × 2″ squares of construction paper of assorted colors, pencils, graph paper

- Give each group of students 20 squares of paper.
- Have groups make three lines of squares, each line having a different number of squares from one to ten.
- Have them write the number of squares for each line on graph paper.

Option 2 VISUAL, SOCIAL

English Language Learners ELL

Materials: labels, children's drawings of a person on an index card

Core Vocabulary: pictures, These are my/your family

Common Use Verb: put

See Math This strategy practices sorting picture graphs.

- Display a picture of yourself and your family members.
- Say: "These are **pictures** of **my family**."
- Sort and arrange by gender. Say: "These are **pictures** of the boys/girls."
- Say: "Draw **pictures** of your **family**."

Independent Work Options

Option 1 LINGUISTIC

Early Finishers OL AL

Materials: crayons, paper, graph paper

- Have students draw a blue shirt or dress, red shirt or dress, and green shirt or dress on a graph for each shirt or dress of that color worn by a student in the class.
- Have students answer questions about what color shirt or dress is most and least common in class today.

Option 2

Student Technology

Math Online macmillanmh.com

Math Adventures

Option 3

Learning Stations: Science (p. 127H)

Direct students to the Science Learning Station for more opportunities to explore and extend the lesson concept.

Leveled Lesson Resources

Reteach (p. 19) BL

Skills Practice (p. 20) OL

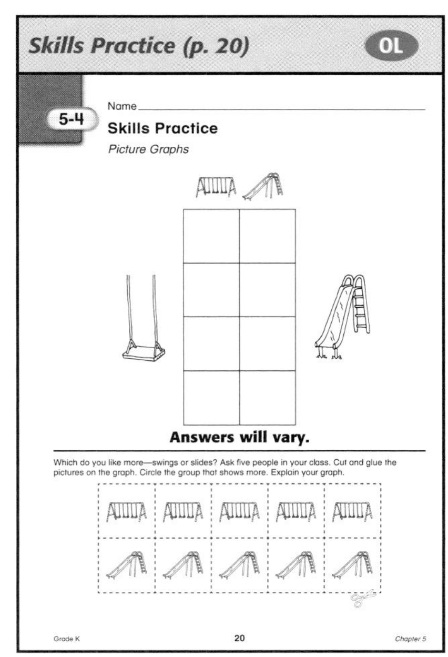

Enrich (p. 22) AL

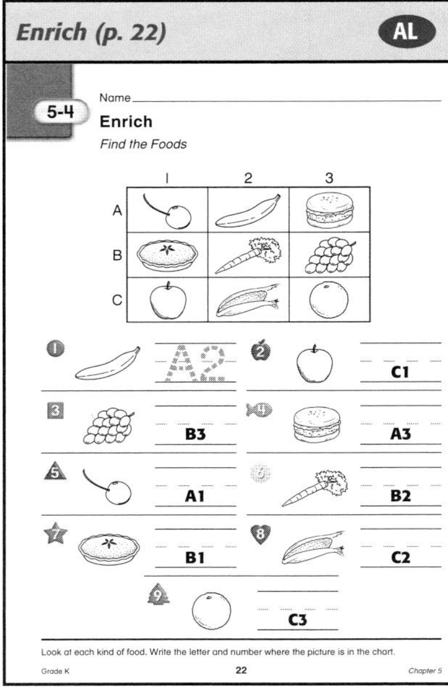

Homework Practice (p. 21) OL

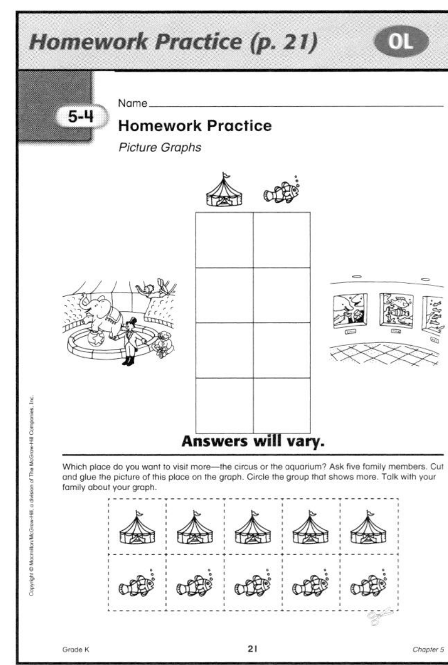

1 Introduce

Circle Time

Activity Choice 1 • Literature

Rooster's Off to See the World by Eric Carle

- Explain that a **picture graph** is a graph that uses pictures to show data.
- Read the story and show the picture graph as it changes on each page (pictures in the top right corner of each page).
- Have each child draw one of the 15 pictures.
- Create a class picture graph of the animals that went on the trip by gluing their pictures on chart paper.

Activity Choice 2 • Hands-On

Materials: poster board, pictures of hot food and cold food, tape

- Have students construct a graph using pictures of real items such as hamburgers and juice bars.
- Begin the graph by making two columns, *Hot Foods* and *Cold Foods*, on poster board.
- Have students go to the poster one at a time and attach their picture of the food they like best under the correct column. Then ask what foods, hot or cold, have the most pictures.

2 Teach

Materials: crayons, pictures of kittens, and puppies

- Direct students to p. 139.
- **What animals are shown?** kitten, puppy
- Review the meaning of data, graph, and picture graph.
- Tell students that they will be constructing a picture graph, and that they will need to ask other students a question to collect data for the graph.
- Discuss the squares of the cats and dogs. Tell students to cut out the squares and use their classmates responses to answer the question.

BL Alternate Teaching Strategy

If students have trouble with picture graphs . . .

Then use one of the following reteach options.

1. CRM **Daily Reteach Worksheet** (p. 19)
2. **Make a Picture Graph!** Tell students that they are going to make a picture graph of favorite insects.
   - Ask what their favorite insect is.
   - Show how to make two columns, label the columns, then draw pictures to represent their favorite insects.
   - Ask how many more or less there are of their favorite insects.

! COMMON ERROR!

Students may count incorrectly, resulting in an incorrect number of pictures on their graphs. Remind students to touch each picture as they count.

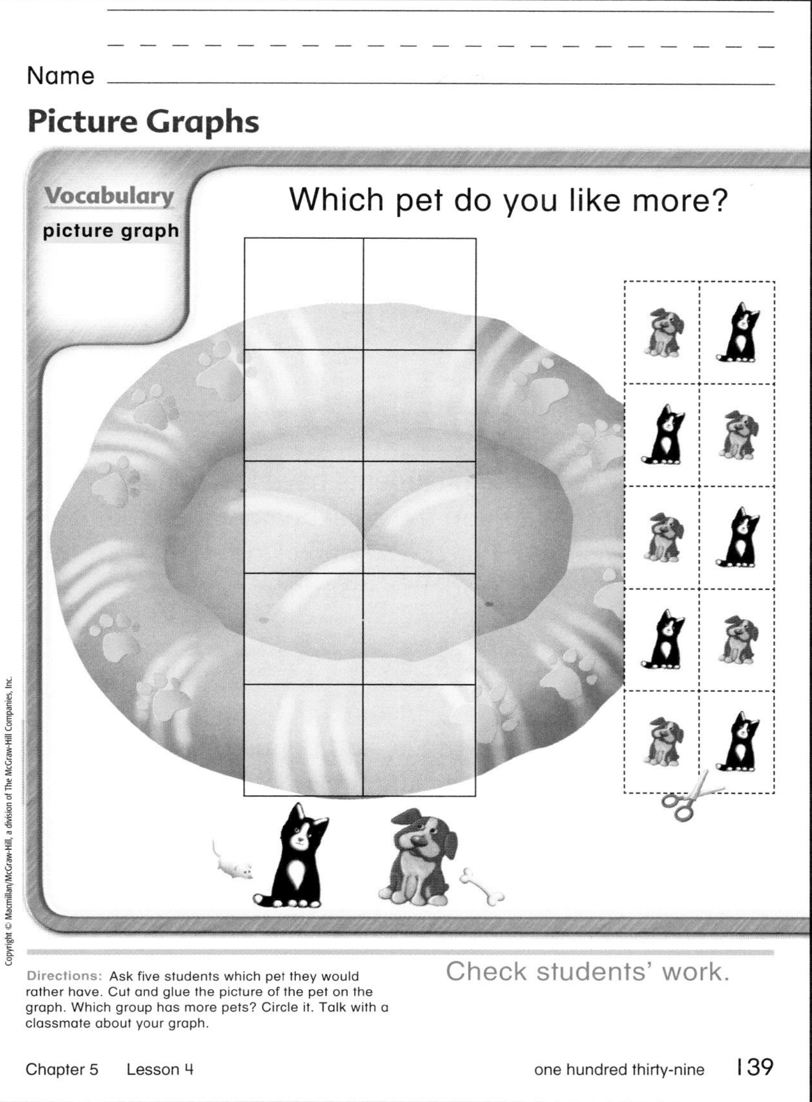

Name

Picture Graphs

Vocabulary
picture graph

Which pet do you like more?

Directions: Ask five students which pet they would rather have. Cut and glue the picture of the pet on the graph. Which group has more pets? Circle it. Talk with a classmate about your graph.

Check students' work.

Copyright © Macmillan/McGraw-Hill, a division of The McGraw-Hill Companies, Inc.

Chapter 5 Lesson 4 one hundred thirty-nine 139

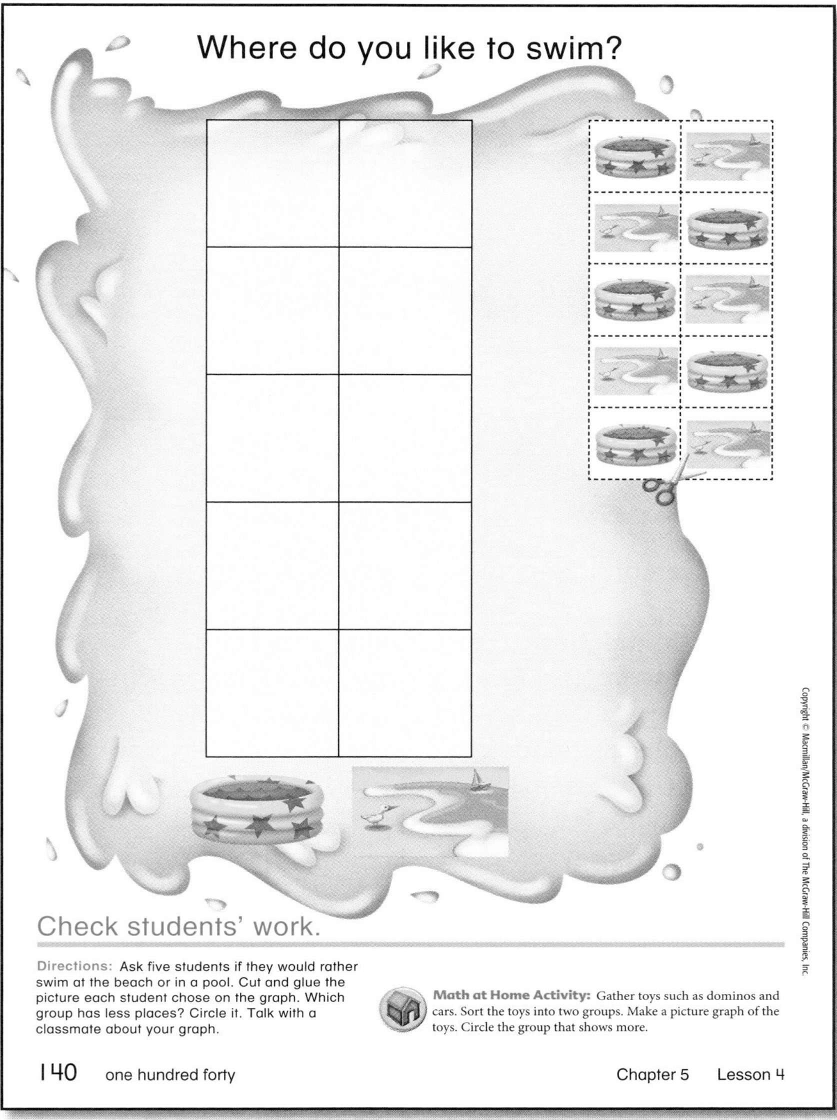

Where do you like to swim?

Check students' work.

Directions: Ask five students if they would rather swim at the beach or in a pool. Cut and glue the picture each student chose on the graph. Which group has less places? Circle it. Talk with a classmate about your graph.

Math at Home Activity: Gather toys such as dominos and cars. Sort the toys into two groups. Make a picture graph of the toys. Circle the group that shows more.

Copyright © Macmillan/McGraw-Hill, a division of The McGraw-Hill Companies, Inc.

140 one hundred forty Chapter 5 Lesson 4

3 Practice

Guided Practice

- Direct students to p. 139.
- Have students ask five other classmates which animal, the cat or dog, they like more.
- Direct the student to glue the classmates' choices in the graph. Direct them to start at the bottom square, then glue any additional pictures above it.
- Talk about the data after it is graphed. Ask which animal is liked more. Have students circle that group of animals.

Independent Practice

Have students turn to p. 140. Explain the directions. Have students work on the exercise and then share their results with a partner. Have them tell from the partner's graph which place the students would rather swim.

4 Assess

Formative Assessment

- **What is the difference between picture graphs and real graphs?** A picture graph is a graph that uses pictures to show data. A real graph is a graph that uses real objects to show data.
- Show a picture graph. Have students tell which data shows more and which shows less.

Quick Check **Are students still struggling to make picture graphs?**

If Yes → Small Group Options (p. 139B)

If No → Independent Work Options (p. 139B)

CRM Skills Practice Worksheet (p. 20)

CRM Enrich Worksheet (p. 22)

LESSON 5-5

Make a Graph

Lesson Planner

Objective

Collect and organize data in a picture graph to answer questions.

Vocabulary

survey

Resources

Materials: graph paper, markers, paper, crayons, scissors, glue

Literature Connection: *Let's Count* by Tana Hoban

Alternate Lesson: Use *Practice Graphs Comparing Three Groups* on page 149 of *Math Their Way* to provide practice collecting and organizing data.
Use *IMPACT Mathematics:* Unit H to provide practice with graphing.

Teacher Technology

TeacherWorks

Focus on Math Background

This lesson teaches students mathematical skills to formulate and respond to questions. For example, students will conduct a survey to find which set classmates like. First, they are guided through the process of conducting a survey. Then, they display the data in a picture graph while being prompted to ask questions that emphasize quantitative relationships, such as, "How many more or less are in this category?" Students are also exposed to questions that help them make inferences about data, such as, "What is the most common way to come to school?"

Daily Routine

Use these suggestions before beginning the lesson on p. 141.

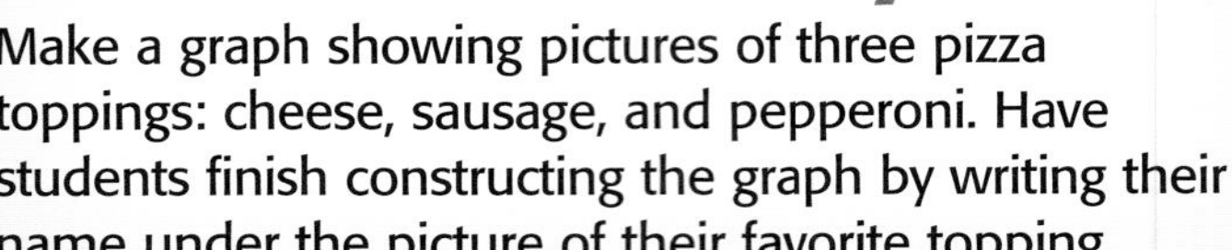

5-Minute Check

(Reviews Lesson 5-4)

Ask how many teeth students have lost. Make a five-column graph on the chalkboard with headings 0, 1, 2, 3, and 4. Put check marks under the correct column for each student's response.

Problem of the Day

Make a graph showing pictures of three pizza toppings: cheese, sausage, and pepperoni. Have students finish constructing the graph by writing their name under the picture of their favorite topping.

LINE UP Have students wearing tennis shoes make one line and students without tennis shoes make a second line. Graph the data using check marks.

Building Math Vocabulary

- **How can we learn more about someone?** Ask questions. **What is it called when we ask questions to learn more about someone?** survey
- **What are possible questions for a survey?** Sample answers: What food do you like? What is your favorite movie? What pets do you have?
- **What information could we find out about our classmates and show on a graph?** Sample answers: age, favorite color, favorite book
- Ask a volunteer to take a **survey** of the class, using one of the suggestions.

Visual Vocabulary Cards

Use Visual Vocabulary Card 43 to reinforce the vocabulary introduced in this lesson. The Define/Example/Ask routine is printed on the back of each card.)

Differentiated Instruction

Small Group Options

Option 1 Below/Approaching Level BL

VISUAL

Materials: pictures of vehicles such as cars, trucks, vans

- Post pictures of vehicles. Have small groups tell what vehicles they have at their home.
- Have them write an X for each vehicle classmates have at home by that particular picture.
- Help them construct a picture graph representing the group totals for each of the three vehicles.

Option 2 English Language Learners ELL

AUDITORY, KINESTHETIC

Materials: pictures from Lesson 5-4, cards, pocket graph
Core Vocabulary: brother/sister, father/mother, uncle/aunt
Common Use Verb: label

Do Math This strategy uses background knowledge to make a graph.

- Say: Graphs need labels to sort the information. Draw a picture of your parents. Say: "These are my parents."
- Post your picture above the parent label in the pocket chart. Repeat with brother(s)/sister(s).

Independent Work Options

Option 1 Early Finishers OL AL

LINGUISTIC

Materials: drawing paper, crayons, tape

- Ask students to survey their classmates' favorite vegetables: corn, potatoes, or green beans.
- Have students construct a real graph with three columns. Have them draw a picture of each vegetable for each column, then place a color tile in the appropriate column for each response.
- Ask students what vegetable is the favorite and how they know.

Option 2 Student Technology

Math Online macmillanmh.com

Math Adventures

Option 3 Learning Stations: Technology (p. 127H)

Direct students to the Technology Learning Station for more opportunities to explore and extend the lesson concept.

Leveled Lesson Resources

Additional support for English Language Learners can be found in the ELL Guide (p. 135). ELL

Reteach (p. 23) BL

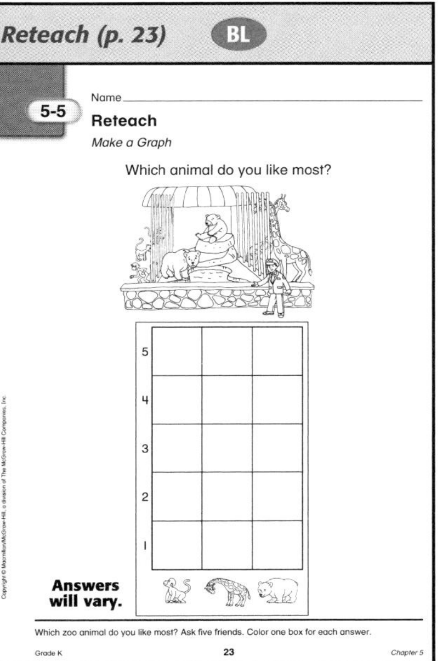

5-5 Name
Reteach
Make a Graph

Which animal do you like most?

Answers will vary.

Which zoo animal do you like most? Ask five friends. Color one box for each answer.

Grade K 23 *Chapter 5*

Skills Practice (p. 24) OL

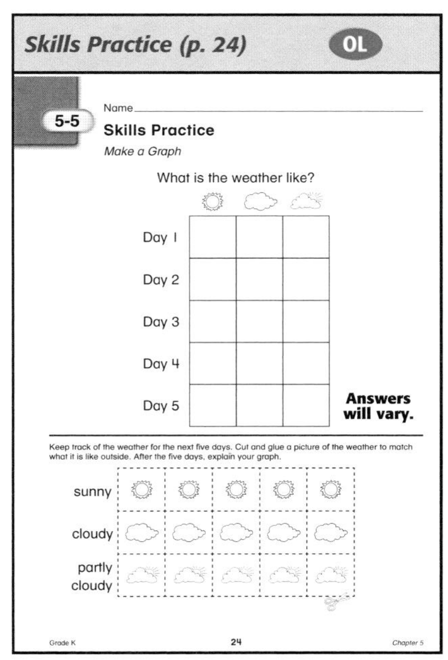

5-5 Name
Skills Practice
Make a Graph

What is the weather like?

Day 1
Day 2
Day 3
Day 4
Day 5

Answers will vary.

Keep track of the weather for the next five days. Cut and glue a picture of the weather to match what it is like outside. After the five days, explain your graph.

sunny
cloudy
partly cloudy

Grade K 24 *Chapter 5*

Enrich (p. 26) AL

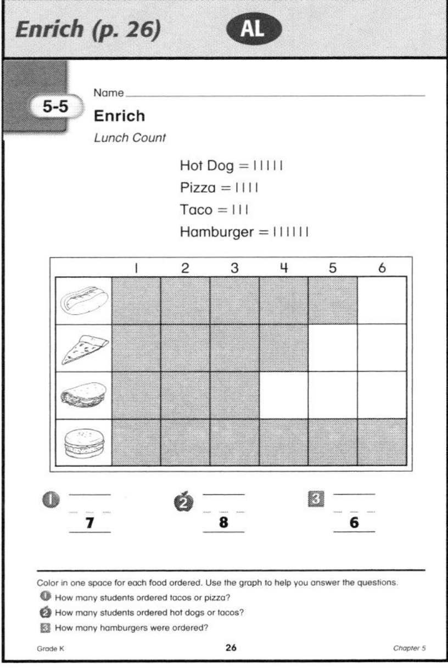

5-5 Name
Enrich
Lunch Count

Hot Dog = IIIII
Pizza = IIII
Taco = III
Hamburger = IIIIII

1 2 3 4 5 6

1. 7
2. 8
3. 6

Color in one space for each food ordered. Use the graph to help you answer the questions.
1. How many students ordered tacos or pizza?
2. How many students ordered hot dogs or tacos?
3. How many hamburgers were ordered?

Grade K 26 *Chapter 5*

Homework Practice (p. 25) OL

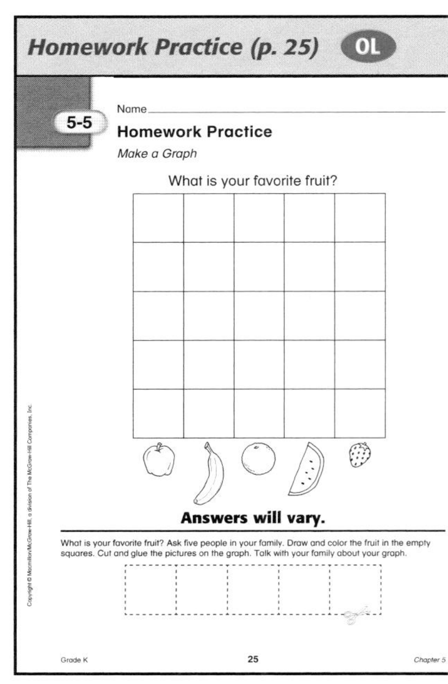

5-5 Name
Homework Practice
Make a Graph

What is your favorite fruit?

Answers will vary.

What is your favorite fruit? Ask five people in your family. Draw and color the fruit in the empty squares. Cut and glue the pictures on the graph. Talk with your family about your graph.

Grade K 25 *Chapter 5*

1 Introduce

Circle Time

Activity Choice 1 • Literature

Let's Count by Tana Hoban

- Tell students a **survey** is when people ask other people questions and record their answers to make a graph.
- Read the book aloud. Take a class survey by asking what page was their favorite.
- Have students draw their favorite picture from the book.
- Have them construct a class graph with the pictures by sorting by page, then gluing each picture onto a graph. Ask what the graph shows and how they know what picture was the class favorite.

Activity Choice 2 • Hands-On

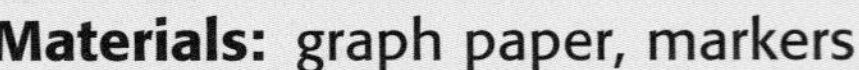

Materials: graph paper, markers

- Remind students that graphs are a way to show information and that we can find out many things when we look at a graph.
- **What are some of the things we can find out when we look at a graph?** Sample answer: how many more
- Tell students that one way to collect the data is by taking a survey, or to ask people questions and write their answers on a graph.
- Ask students what they like best: egg salad, tuna fish, or peanut butter.
- Have students record the responses and make a graph.
- **How did I get the information for this graph?** by taking a survey

2 Teach

- Direct students to p. 141.
- **How many crayons are shown?** five **What are all of the crayon colors shown?** red, green, yellow, blue, orange
- Tell students that they will be constructing a graph, and that they will need to ask other students a question to collect data.
- Explain that you are going to take a survey to find out something about the favorite colors of the students in this class.
- Talk about the squares of the crayons. Tell students to cut out the squares.

BL Alternate Teaching Strategy

If students have trouble understanding how to make a graph . . .

Then use one of the following reteach options.

1. CRM **Daily Reteach Worksheet** (p. 23)
2. **Graphing Books** Tell students that they are going to take a survey and construct a graph of favorite books.
   - Display and line up the books that were read in Lessons 5-1 to 5-4.
   - Have students show their favorite book by clapping.
   - Ask volunteers what the favorite book is and how they know.
   - Have students line up next to their favorite book. Ask volunteers to say what the favorite book is.

COMMON ERROR!

Students may have difficulty tracking on a graph. Have them use a ruler or a piece of paper as a marker to guide them when reading from a graph.

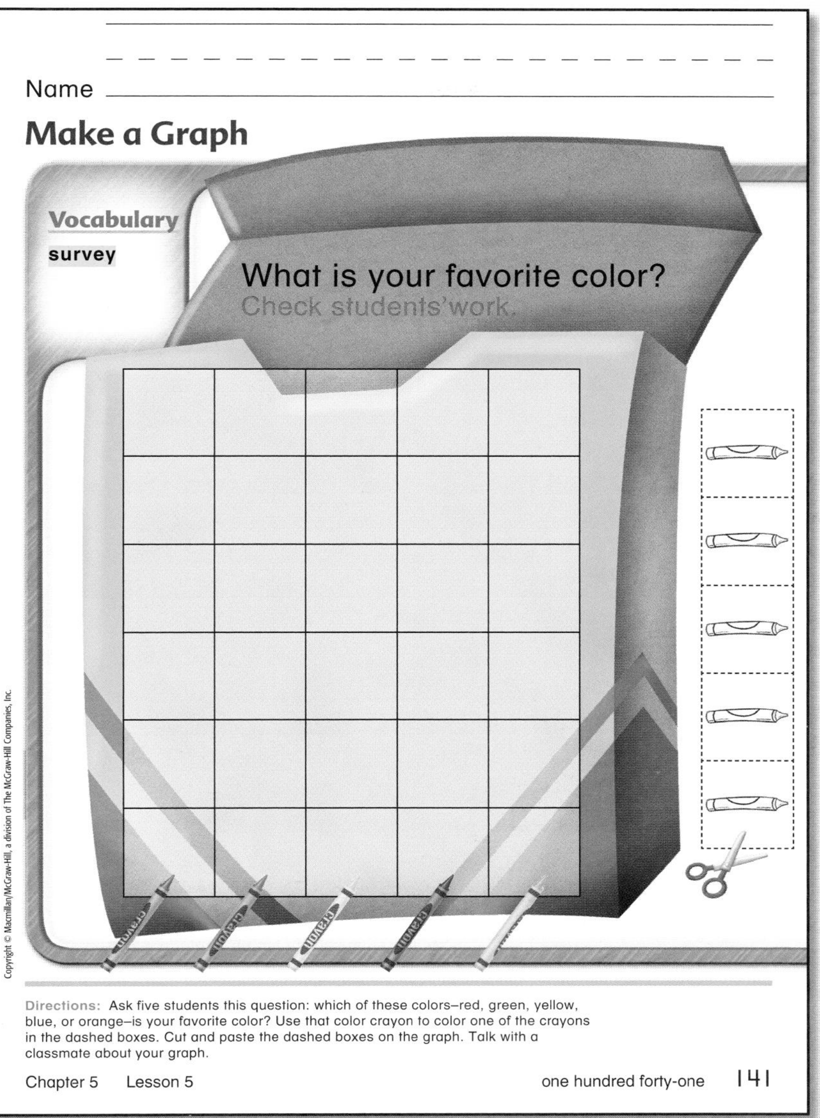

Name
Make a Graph
Vocabulary
survey
What is your favorite color?
Check students' work.
Directions: Ask five students this question: which of these colors–red, green, yellow, blue, or orange–is your favorite color? Use that color crayon to color one of the crayons in the dashed boxes. Cut and paste the dashed boxes on the graph. Talk with a classmate about your graph.
Chapter 5 Lesson 5
one hundred forty-one 141

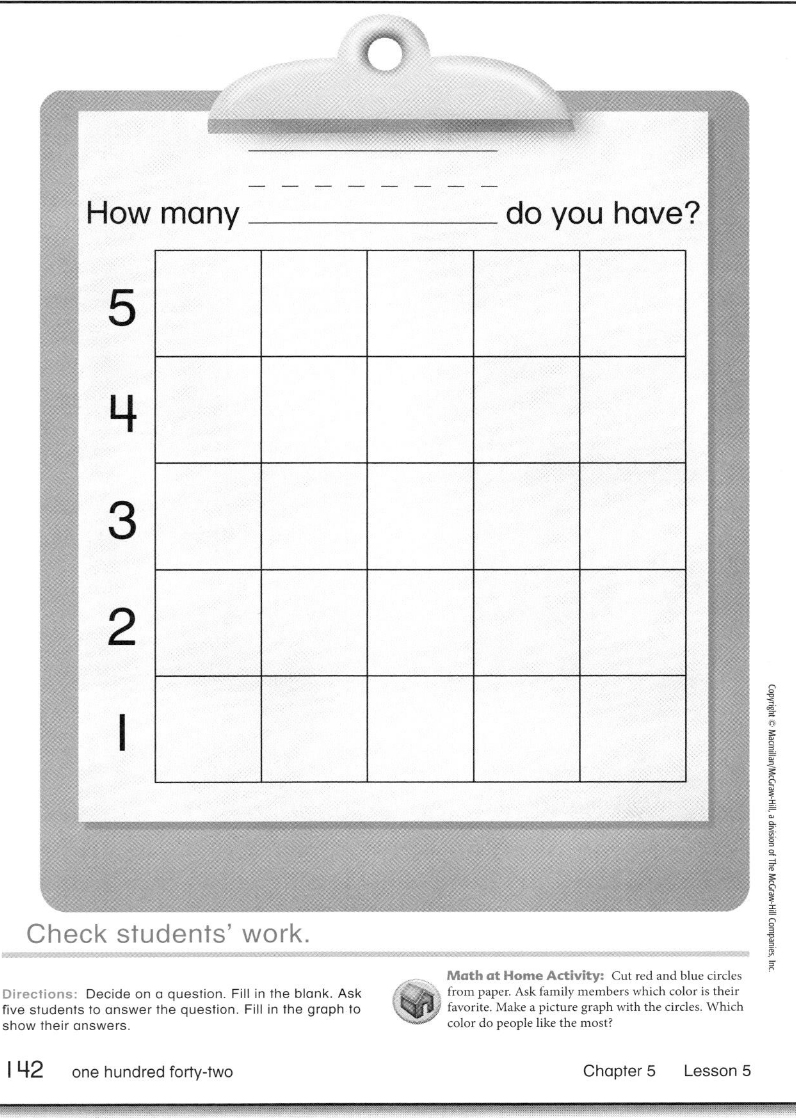

How many ______ do you have?
5
4
3
2
1
Check students' work.
Directions: Decide on a question. Fill in the blank. Ask five students to answer the question. Fill in the graph to show their answers.
Math at Home Activity: Cut red and blue circles from paper. Ask family members which color is their favorite. Make a picture graph with the circles. Which color do people like the most?
142 one hundred forty-two
Chapter 5 Lesson 5

3 Practice

Guided Practice

- Direct students to p. 141.
- Have students ask five other classmates which color is their favorite: red, green, yellow, orange, or blue.
- Have students glue the classmates' favorite colors on the graph. Direct them to start at the bottom square, then glue any additional pictures above it.
- Talk about the data after it is graphed. Discuss most favorite and least favorite color. Have students share their graph with a partner and compare results.

Independent Practice

Have students turn to p. 142. Explain the directions. Have students work on the exercise and then compare results with a partner.

4 Assess

Formative Assessment

- **What things can we learn when we read a graph?** Sample answers: how many, favorite things
- **What things can we learn when we take a survey?** Sample answers: opinions of people, favorite things
- Have students give an example of a survey question.

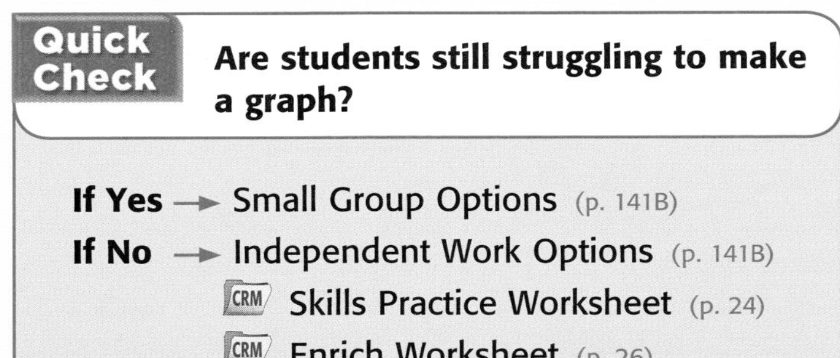

Quick Check **Are students still struggling to make a graph?**

If Yes → Small Group Options (p. 141B)

If No → Independent Work Options (p. 141B)

CRM Skills Practice Worksheet (p. 24)

CRM Enrich Worksheet (p. 26)

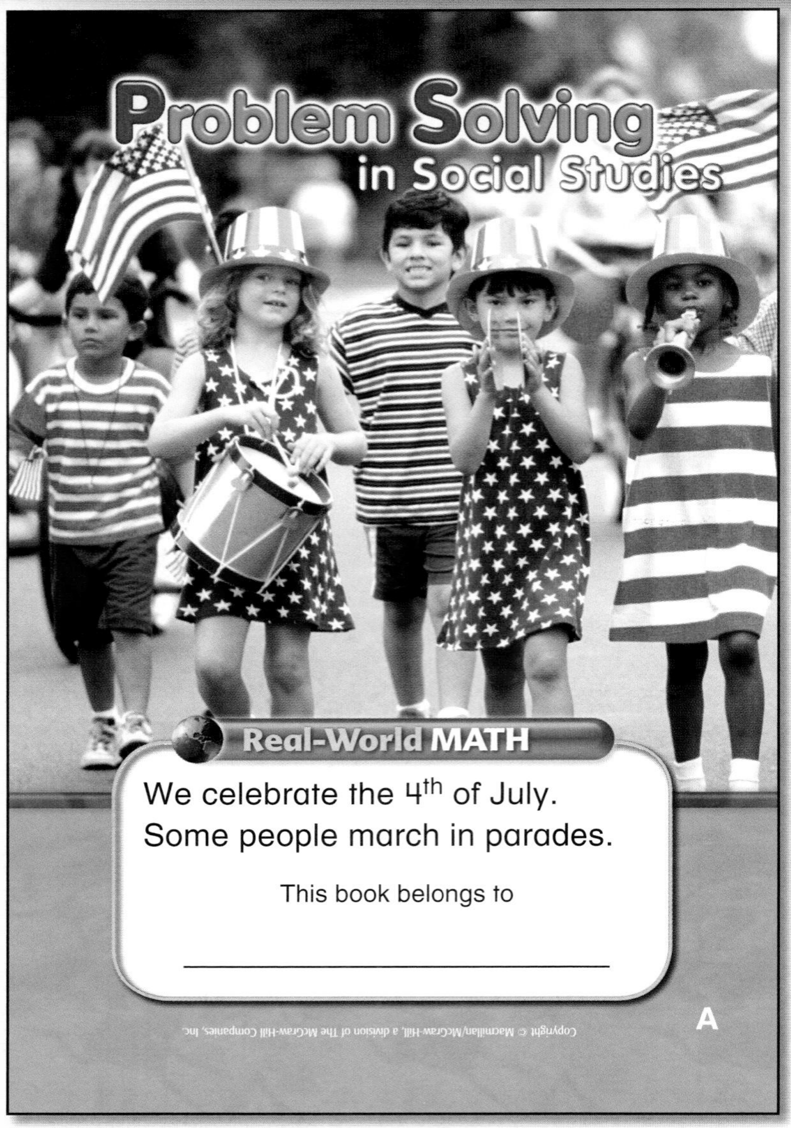

Problem Solving
in Social Studies
Real-World MATH
We celebrate the 4th of July.
Some people march in parades.
This book belongs to
A

Some people have picnics.

Lesson Planner

Objective

Use graphs to solve problems.

National Standard 

Students learn how culture and experience influence people's perceptions of places and regions.

Activate Prior Knowledge

Before you turn students' attention to the pages, discuss the Fourth of July and how students celebrate the holiday.

- Share with students that we celebrate the Fourth of July to honor and remind us of our freedom.
- **What things do you do to celebrate the Fourth of July?** Sample answers: I go to the parade; I watch the fireworks; I go to a barbeque or party.
- **Who do you spend the Fourth of July with?** Sample answer: my family and my friends
- **What colors do you see during this holiday?** red, white, and blue
- **What do you see displayed outside of many houses and stores?** the American flag

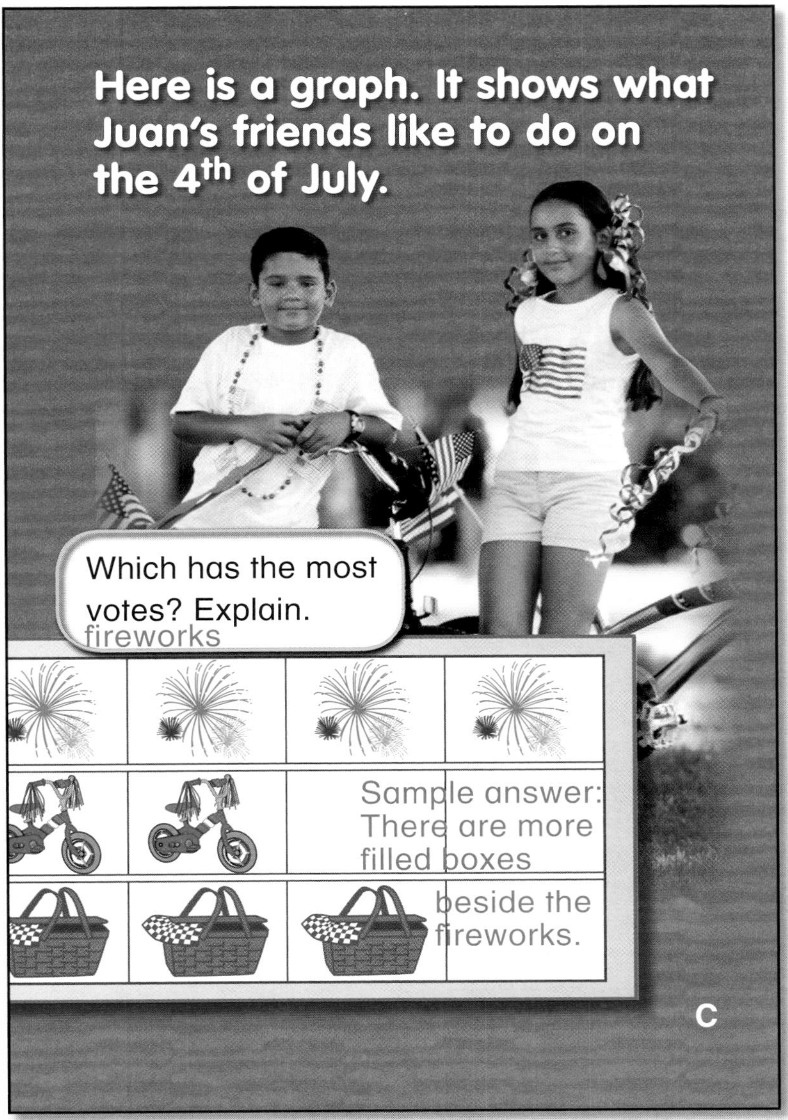

Here is a graph. It shows what Juan's friends like to do on the 4th of July.
Which has the most votes? Explain.
fireworks
Sample answer: There are more filled boxes beside the fireworks.
C

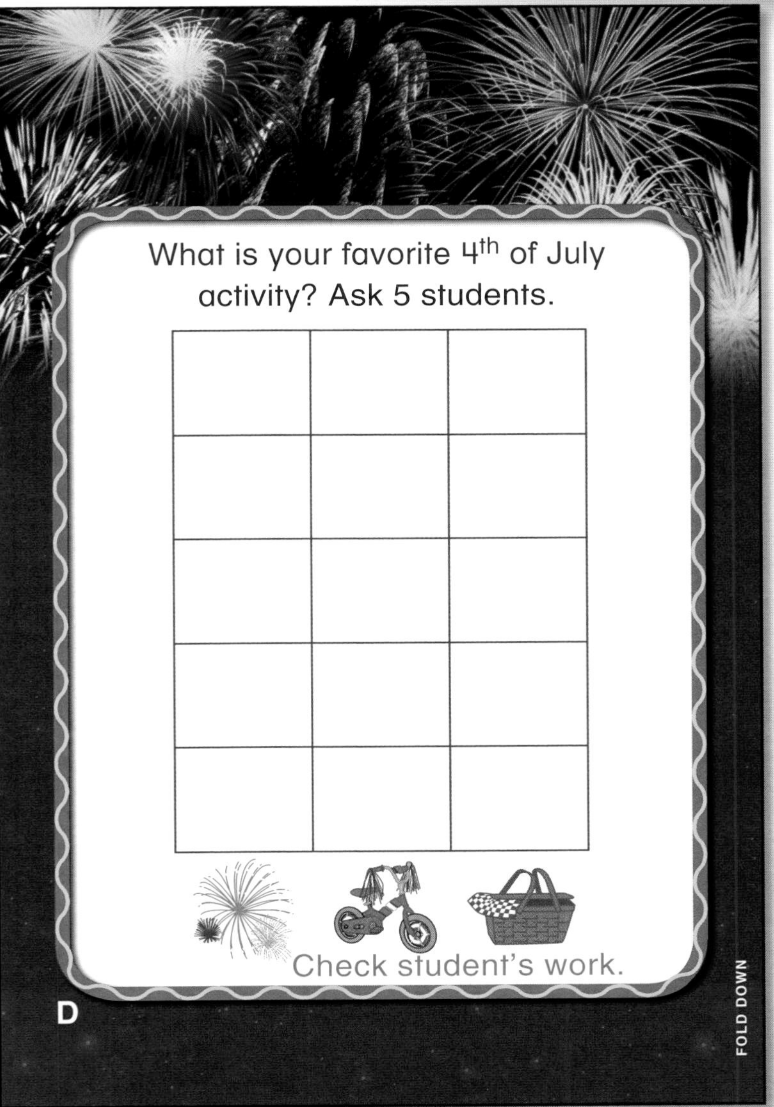

What is your favorite 4th of July activity? Ask 5 students.
Check student's work.
D
FOLD DOWN

Create the Book

Guide students to create their book.

- Have them fold the page in half.
- Ask them to write their name on page A.
- Explain that page A is the front cover and page D is the back cover. If necessary, have them practice flipping through the book in order.
- Guide them in reading the information and word problems on each of the pages.

Use the Student Pages

Page B Have students discuss other examples of food and items that would be at a Fourth of July cook out.

Page C Discuss the activities Juan's friends like to do on the Fourth of July. Ask students to circle the activity that was done most often.

Page D Discuss the ways to celebrate the Fourth of July that are shown at the bottom of the picture graph. Ask students to take a survey and see which ways most students in the class celebrate. Compare the graph students made with the one on page C.

WRITING IN MATH Have students draw a picture of the 4th of July. Have them dictate a sentence to you to write under their picture.

Chapter Review/Test

FOLDABLES® Dinah Zike's Foldables

If students have not completed their Foldables, guide them to create and fill in the appropriate information using the instructions on p. 127.

You may choose to use the Foldable to help students review the concepts presented in this chapter and as a tool for studying for the Chapter Review/Test.

Chapter 5 Project

Graph Favorite Things

Lead a discussion on the results of the completed chapter project with the class.

Vocabulary Review

Review chapter vocabulary using one of the following options.

- **Visual Vocabulary Cards** (12, 31, 33, 43)
- **eGlossary** at macmillanmh.com

Data-Driven Decision Making

Based on the results of the Chapter Review/Test, use the following to review concepts that continue to present students with problems.

Exercises	State/Local Standards	What's the Math?	Error Analysis	Resources for Review
1 Lesson 5-1		Collect information about objects and events in their environment. Record results.	Colors wrong numbers of boxes in rows. Does not count correctly. Writes wrong number. Circles or crosses out wrong objects.	CRM Chapter 5 Resource Masters (Reteach Worksheets) Math Online Concepts in Motion Math Adventures

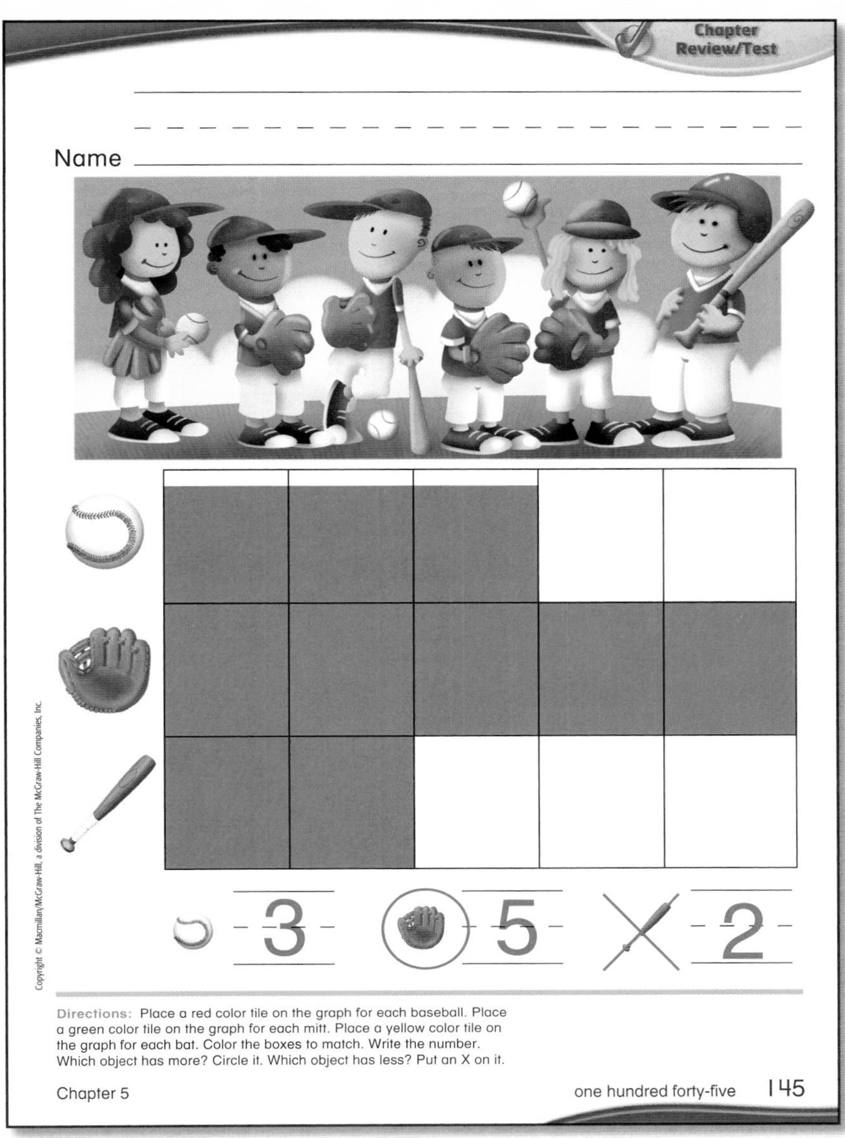
Chapter Review/Test

Name

3 5 2

Directions: Place a red color tile on the graph for each baseball. Place a green color tile on the graph for each mitt. Place a yellow color tile on the graph for each bat. Color the boxes to match. Write the number. Which object has more? Circle it. Which object has less? Put an X on it.

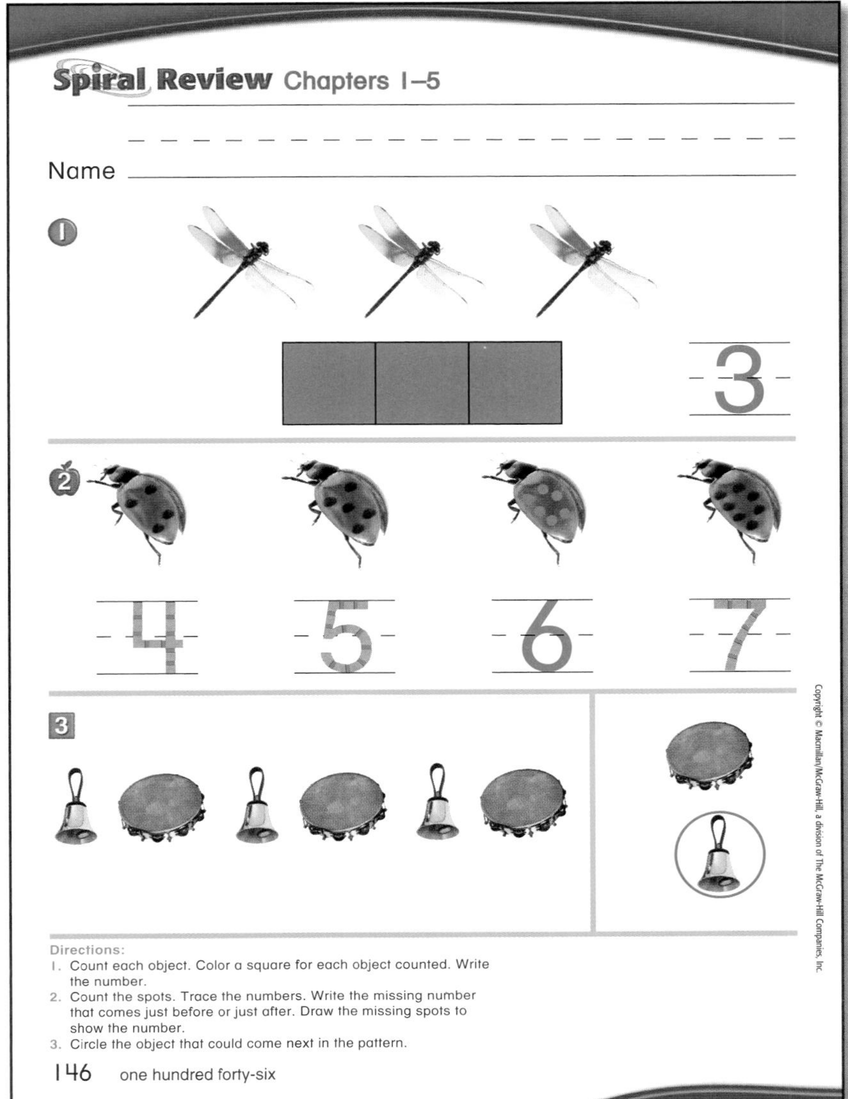
Spiral Review Chapters 1–5

Name

1 3

2 4 5 6 7

3

Directions:
1. Count each object. Color a square for each object counted. Write the number.
2. Count the spots. Trace the numbers. Write the missing number that comes just before or just after. Draw the missing spots to show the number.
3. Circle the object that could come next in the pattern.

Summative Assessment

Use these alternate leveled chapter tests to differentiate assessment for the specific needs of your students.

Leveled Chapter 5 Tests			
Form	**Type**	**Level**	**CRM Pages**
1	Multiple Choice	BL	34–35
2A	Multiple Choice	OL	36–37
2C	Multiple Choice	OL	38–39
2D	Free Response	AL	40–41

BL = below/approaching grade level
OL = on grade level
AL = above/beyond grade level

Spiral Review

Reviews Chapters 1 to 5

Objective: Review and assess mastery of skills and concepts from previous chapters.

Resources for Review

Based on student results, refer to these lessons for remediation:

- **Exercise 1: Lesson 2-1** (p. 43)
- **Exercise 2: Lesson 4-8** (p. 117)
- **Exercise 3: Lesson 3-7** (p. 85)

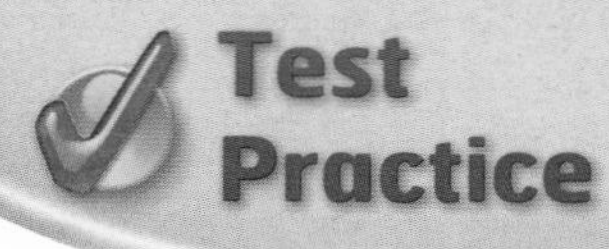

Chapters 1–5

Formative Assessment

- You can use Student Edition pp. 147-148 to benchmark student progress.
- Additional practice pages can be found in Chapter 5 Resource Masters.

CRM **Chapter 5 Resource Masters**
Cumulative Test Practice

- Multiple Choice format (pp. 34–39)
- Free Response format (pp. 40–41)

ExamView Assessment Suite Create additional practice worksheets or tests.

Math Online For additional practice with the NCTM Focal Points and Focal Connections, visit macmillanmh.com.

Test-Taking Tips

For the Teacher

- It may be helpful to create symbols for directions (words such as circle, box, color, trace, and so on).
- Before starting a test, look at examples of how the questions are to be completed.

For the Student

- Tell students that different types of test questions will take different amounts of time to complete.
- Encourage students to make a good guess for an answer if time is running out and they are stuck on a question.
- Encourage students to use as much of the test time as they need.

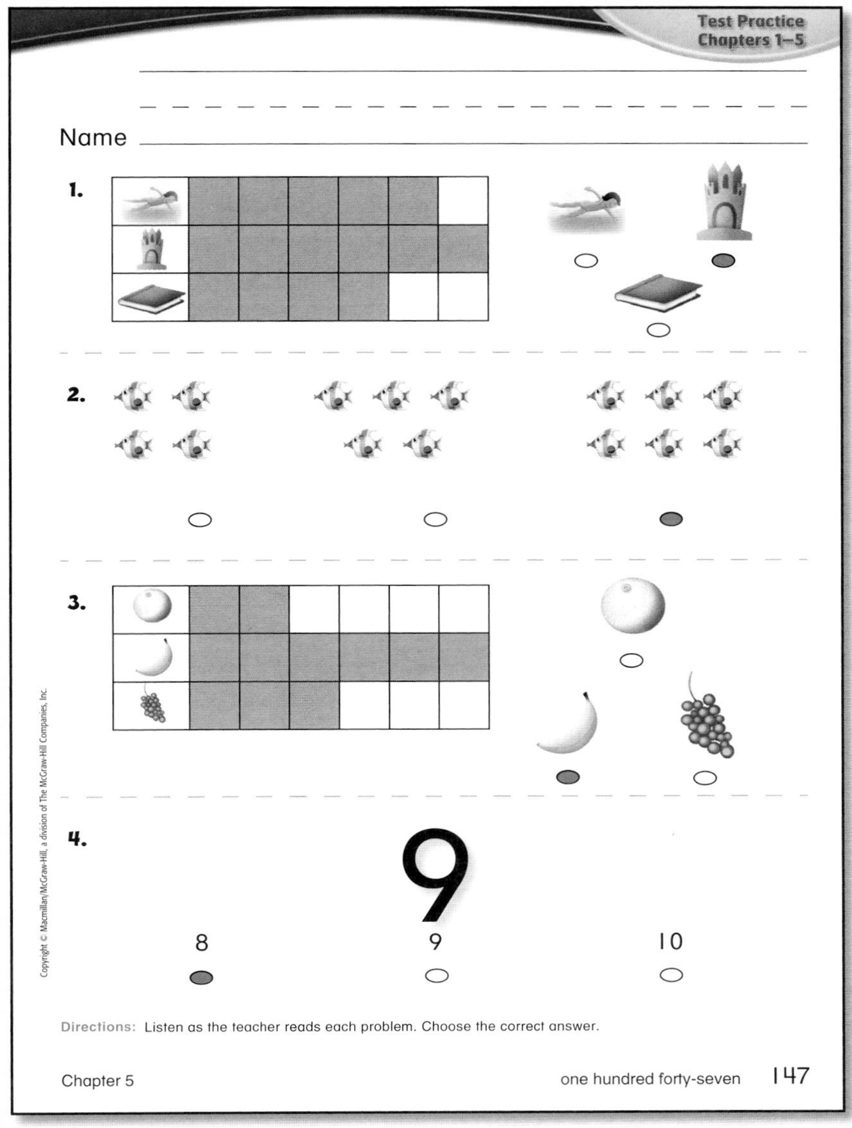

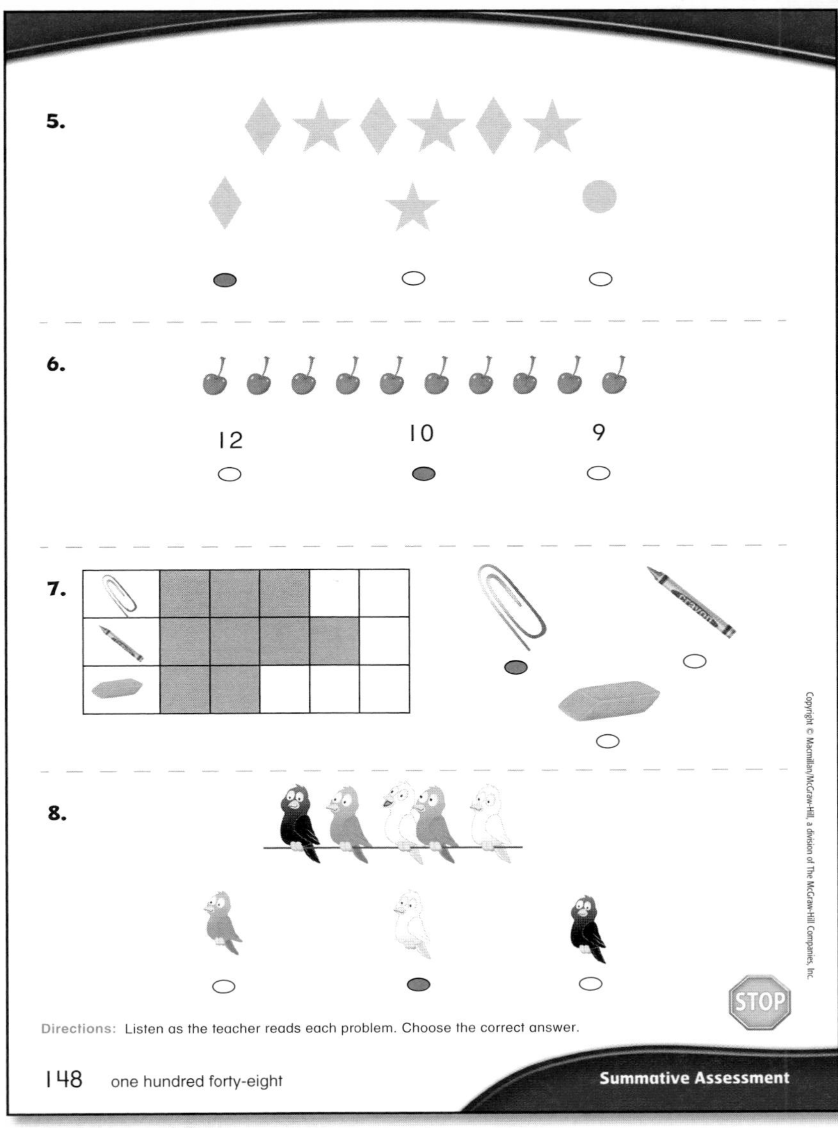

Test Directions for Teachers

Read the following directions to students before they begin. Then read each question followed by a pause to allow students time to work and choose an answer. The first test item can be worked as a class example.

- **Write your name at the top of the page.**
- **I am going to read each question to you. Listen carefully to the entire question before you choose an answer.**

1. Look at the graph. Which fun thing do six children like to do? Find and mark the picture that shows what six children like to do at the beach.

2. Look at the group of fish. Mark the group of fish that shows more than the other groups.

3. Look at the graph. Find the fruit that most people like. Mark the fruit that most people like.

4. Look at the number. Find the number that comes before this number. Mark the number that comes before this number.

- **Turn the page over.**

5. Look at the pattern of shapes. Mark the shape that could come next.

6. Look at the row of cherries. Count the number of cherries. Mark the number that shows exactly the number of cherries.

7. Look at the graph. Find the object that there are three of. Mark the object that there are three of.

8. Look at the birds sitting on the wire. The black bird is first. Mark the bird that is fifth.

Chapter Overview

Chapter-at-a-Glance

In Chapter 6, students learn to name, recognize, count, and write the numbers 11–20.

Lesson		Math Objective	State/Local Standards
6-1	**Numbers 11 and 12** (pp. 153–154)	Name, recognize, count, and write the numerals 11 and 12 using concrete objects and illustrations.	
6-2	**Numbers 13, 14, and 15** (pp. 155–156)	Name, recognize, count, and write the numerals 13, 14, and 15 using concrete objects and illustrations.	
6-3	**Numbers 16 and 17** (pp. 157–158)	Name, recognize, count, and write the numerals 16 and 17.	
6-4	**Problem-Solving Strategy: Look for a Pattern** (pp. 161–162)	Name, recognize, represent, and count the numerals 11–17 using illustrations.	
6-5	**Numbers 18, 19, and 20** (pp. 163–164)	Name, recognize, count, and write the numerals 18, 19, and 20 using concrete objects and illustrations.	
6-6	**Compare Numbers to 20** (pp. 165–166)	Count to compare groups to 20 and determine which has more, less, or are the groups the same.	
6-7	**Order Numbers to 20** (pp. 167–168)	Order numbers from 1 to 20 in sequence using a number line.	

Use Numbers to 20

BIG Idea Recognizing the relationships between quantities and applying understanding about numbers in difficult situations will help students make sense of the various ways that numbers are used.

- Students build on their understanding of numbers to 10 as they explore numbers to 20.
- Students will engage in multiple representational approaches, including composing, modeling, drawing, and writing numbers to 20.
- Students deepen their understanding of the relative magnitude of numbers as they compare and order amounts through 20.

Algebra Students prepare for Algebra by using number lines to order numbers to 20. Ordering numbers to 20 focuses on finding patterns, such as repeating the basic 0 through nine-digit sequence on a number line. Finding patterns is a hallmark of algebraic reasoning. Lesson 6-7

GK-FP1 *Number and Operations:* **Representing, comparing, and ordering whole numbers and joining and separating sets**

Children use numbers, including written numerals, to represent quantities and to solve quantitative problems, such as counting objects in a set, creating a set with a given number of objects, comparing and ordering sets or numerals by using both cardinal and ordinal meanings, and modeling simple joining and separating situations with objects. They choose, combine, and apply effective strategies for answering quantitative questions, including quickly recognizing the number in a small set, counting and producing sets of given sizes, counting the number in combined sets, and counting backward.

Skills Trace
Vertical Alignment

PreKindergarten

In Pre-K, students learned to:
- Count by ones to 10.
- Begin to name "how many" are in a group of up to 10 objects by counting.

Kindergarten

During this chapter, students learn to:
- Count, recognize, represent, write, and name numbers to 20.
- Compare and order numbers to 20.

After this chapter, students will learn to:
- Count, recognize, represent, and name numbers to 30.
- Explore addition concepts.
- Explore subtraction concepts.

First Grade

In first grade, students will learn to:
- Count, read, and write whole numbers to 100.
- Compare and order whole numbers to 100.

Backmapping and Vertical Alignment **McGraw-Hill's *Math Connects*** program was conceived and developed with the final results in mind: student success in Algebra 1 and beyond. The authors, using the **NCTM Focal Points and Focal Connections** as their guide, developed this brand new series by back-mapping from Algebra 1 concepts, and vertically aligning the topics so that they build upon prior skills and concepts and serve as a foundation for future topics.

Math Vocabulary

The following math vocabulary words for Chapter 6 are listed in the glossary of the ***Student Edition***. You can find interactive definitions in 13 languages in the ***eGlossary*** at macmillanmh.com.

eleven (p. 153)

twelve (p. 153)

thirteen (p. 155)

fourteen (p. 155)

fifteen (p. 155)

sixteen (p. 157)

seventeen (p. 157)

eighteen (p. 163)

nineteen (p. 163)

twenty (p. 163)

Chapter Planner

Suggested Pacing		
Instruction	**Review and Assessment**	**TOTAL**
7 days	2 days	**9 days**

Diagnostic Assessment
Are You Ready? (p. 150)

	Lesson 6-1 Pacing: 1 day	**Lesson 6-2** Pacing: 1 day	**Lesson 6-3** Pacing: 1 day
Lesson/ Objective	**Numbers 11 and 12** (pp. 153–154) **Objective:** Name, recognize, count, and write the numerals 11 and 12 using concrete objects and illustrations.	**Numbers 13, 14, and 15** (pp. 155–156) **Objective:** Name, recognize, count, and write the numerals 13, 14, and 15 using concrete objects and illustrations.	**Numbers 16 and 17** (pp. 157–158) **Objective:** Name, recognize, count, and write the numerals 16 and 17.
State/Local Standards			
Math Vocabulary	**eleven**, **twelve**	**thirteen**, **fourteen**, **fifteen**	**sixteen**, **seventeen**
Lesson Resources	**Materials** chart paper, crayons, 12 envelopes, basket, WorkMat 5: Ten-Frame, number cards 11 and 12 **Manipulatives** connecting cubes, counters **Other Resources** CRM Leveled Worksheets (pp. 6–9) Daily Reteach Problem of the Day	**Materials** chart paper, crayons, paper cups, WorkMat 5: Ten-Frame **Manipulatives** geometric solids, connecting cubes, two-colored counters **Other Resources** CRM Leveled Worksheets (pp. 10–13) Daily Reteach Problem of the Day	**Materials** drum, number cards 15, 16, 17, WorkMat 5: Ten-Frame, chart, string **Manipulatives** geometric solids, counters, attribute buttons **Other Resources** CRM Leveled Worksheets (pp. 14–17) Daily Reteach Problem of the Day
Technology Math Online	Math Adventures	Math Adventures	Math Adventures
Reaching All Learners	English Learners, p. 153B ELL Below Level, p. 153B BL Early Finishers, p. 153B OL AL	English Learners, p. 155B ELL Gifted and Talented, p. 155B AL Early Finishers, p. 155B OL AL	English Learners, p. 157B ELL Gifted and Talented, p. 157B AL Early Finishers, p. 157B OL AL
Alternate Lesson	*Math Their Way,* p. 175	*Math Their Way,* p. 47	*Math Their Way*, pp. 96–97

Formative Assessment
Mid-Chapter Check (p. 159)

Game Time: Leap Frog! (p. 160)

KEY

- BL Below/Approaching Level
- OL On Level
- AL Above/Beyond Level
- ELL English Learners
- SE Student Edition
- TE Teacher Edition
- CRM Chapter 8 Resource Masters
- CD-Rom
- Transparency
- Flip Chart
- Real-World Problem Solving Library

	Lesson 6-4 (Pacing: 1 day)	Lesson 6-5 (Pacing: 1 day)	Lesson 6-6 (Pacing: 1 day)
Lesson/ Objective	Problem-Solving Strategy **Look for a Pattern** (pp. 161–162) **Objective:** Name, recognize, represent, and count the numerals 11–17 using illustrations.	**Numbers 18, 19, and 20** (pp. 163–164) **Objective:** Name, recognize, count, and write the numerals 18, 19, and 20 using concrete objects and illustrations.	**Compare Numbers to 20** (pp. 165–166) **Objective:** Count to compare to 20 and determine which has more, less, or are the groups the same.
State/Local Standards			
Math Vocabulary		**eighteen**, **nineteen**, **twenty**	
Lesson Resources	**Materials** string, paper clips, paper, pencils **Manipulatives** connecting cubes, attribute buttons **Other Resources** CRM Leveled Worksheets (pp. 18–22) Daily Reteach Problem of the Day *At the Grocery Store*	**Materials** picture of an 18-wheel truck, paper, WorkMat 5: Ten-Frame, crayons, number cards 18, 19, 20 **Manipulatives** counters, connecting cubes **Other Resources** CRM Leveled Worksheets (pp. 23–26) Daily Reteach Problem of the Day	**Materials** paper, crayons, paper bags, classroom objects such as crayons, paper clips, beads, clothespins, number cards 0-20 **Manipulatives** connecting cubes, pattern blocks **Other Resources** CRM Leveled Worksheets (pp. 27–30) Daily Reteach Problem of the Day
Technology Math Online		Math Song Track 3 Math Adventures Concepts in Motion	Math Song Track 3 Math Adventures Concepts in Motion
Reaching All Learners	English Learners, p. 161B ELL Below Level, p. 161B BL Early Finishers, p. 161B OL AL	English Learners, p. 163B ELL Below Level, p. 163B BL Early Finishers, p. 163B OL AL	English Learners, p. 165B ELL Below Level, p. 165B BL Early Finishers, p. 165B OL AL
Alternate Lesson		*Math Their Way*, p. 48	*Math Their Way*, p. 177 *IMPACT Mathematics*: Unit C

Chapter Planner

Lesson 6-7

Pacing: 1 day

Lesson/ Objective	**Order Numbers to 20** (pp. 167–168) **Objective:** Order numbers from 1 to 20 in sequence using a number line.
State/Local Standards	
Math Vocabulary	
Lesson Resources	**Materials** number cards 0–20 **Other Resources** CRM Leveled Worksheets (pp. 31–34) Daily Reteach Problem of the Day
Technology Math Online	Math Song Track 3 Math Adventures
Reaching All Learners	English Learners, p. 167B ELL Below Level, p. 167B BL Early Finishers, p. 167B OL AL
Alternate Lesson	*Math Their Way*, p. 49 *IMPACT Mathematics*: Unit C

Problem Solving in Social Studies (p. 169)

Summative Assessment
- Chapter Review/Test (p. 171)
- Test Practice (p. 173)

Assessment Options

Diagnostic Assessment

- SE *Option 1:* Are You Ready? (p. 150)
- *Option 2:* Online Quiz (macmillanmh.com)
- CRM *Option 3:* Diagnostic Test (p. 36)

Formative Assessment

- TE Alternate Teaching Strategies (every lesson)
- TE Writing in Math (every lesson)
- TE Line Up (every lesson)
- SE Mid-Chapter Check (p. 159)
- CRM Mid-Chapter Test (p. 37)

Summative Assessment

- SE Chapter/Review Test (p. 171)
- SE Test Practice (p. 173)
- CRM Leveled Chapter Tests (pp. 42–49)
- CRM Cumulative Test Practice (p. 50-51)
- CRM Listening Assessment (p. 40-41)
- CRM Oral Assessment (p. 38-39)
- Exam*View*® Assessment Suite
- Advance Tracker

Professional Development

Targeted professional development has been articulated throughout the **McGraw-Hill's *Math Connects*** program. The **McGraw-Hill Professional Development Video Library** provides short videos that support the **NCTM Focal Points and Focal Connections**. For more information, visit macmillanmh.com.

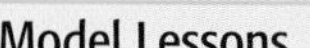

Model Lessons

Instructional Strategies

Assessment Tips

Counting, ordering, and comparing numbers to 20 are important prerequisite skills that are necessary for learning addition and subtraction concepts.

- Use a clipboard that has a list of the students' names and the concepts you want to assess.
- As students count, order, and compare numbers, write down your observations on the clipboard.
- These observations should help you plan next steps with the students.
- Make sure you record the date of the observation so you can begin to see progress over time.

Teacher Notes

Learning Stations

Cross-Curricular Links

Reading

 pair | SPATIAL 

Out of Order

- Mix up the cards.
- Put the cards in order.
- Have your partner check your work.
- Mix up the cards again.
- Have your partner put the cards in order.
- Check your partner's work.

Teacher Note: Before the activity, write a set of number cards from 1 to 20 and give to each student. Have students work in pairs. If possible, have an older student from an upper grade come in to check the students' work.

Materials:

- index cards labeled 1–20

Science

individual | SPATIAL

Nature Numbers

- Say the number. Collect that many objects.
- Line up 10. Then line up the rest.
- Write how many objects you lined up.
- Pick a new card. Do the activity again.

Teacher Note: Collect a large number of nature objects. Write a set of number cards 11–20 for each student. Give a number card, pencil, and paper to each student. Put the objects out.

Materials:

- number cards 11–20
- small nature objects: leaves, rocks, nuts, seeds

Music

individual | LOGICAL

Take Note

- Start with number one.
- Connect the dots.
- Go in order. Do not lift your crayon until you reach dot 20.

Teacher Note: On a blank sheet of paper, draw a musical triangle using 20 dots. Number each dot from one to 20. Order the numbers following the pattern that a student would use to connect the dots with a line. Copy the picture so that each student has one.

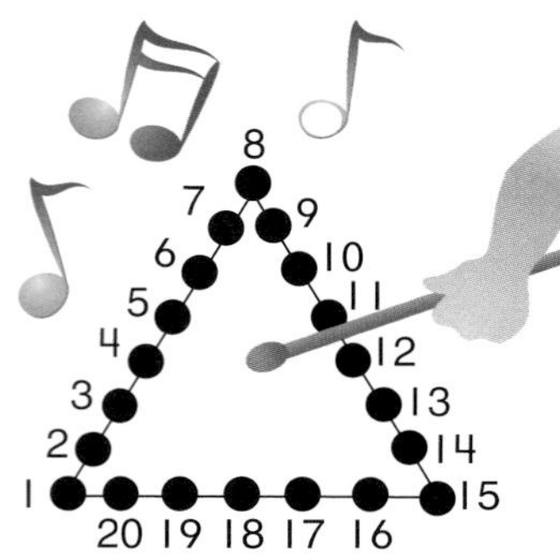

Materials:

- dot-to-dot (of musical triangle)
- crayons

Art

Number Squares

- Count out a number of paper squares between 11 and 20.
- Write that number on the construction paper.
- Trace the number with a glue stick.
- Glue that many squares on the number.

Teacher Note: Cut 20 squares for each student. Make sure they write the number large enough to glue on all of the squares. Give each student construction paper, a pencil, and a glue stick. Help students space squares evenly on the glue.

Materials:

- 20 small squares of colored paper
- construction paper
- pencils
- glue sticks

Language Arts

Bag It

- Count the objects in your bag. Put them on a ten-frame.
- Turn the bag over. Say the number.
- Is the number the same?
- Write the number.

Teacher Note: Write a number from 11–20 on a bag for each student. Put that number of pattern blocks in each bag. Give each student a filled bag, a ten-frame, and crayons. Be sure the bag number and number of objects are the same.

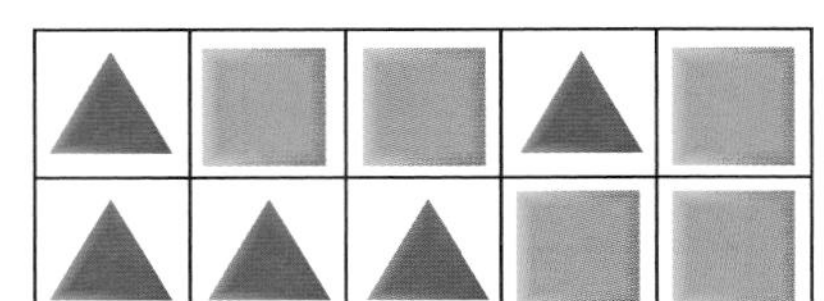

Materials:

- crayons
- Workmat 5: Ten-Frame
- pattern blocks
- 10 bags, bottoms labeled 11–20 with that many pattern blocks placed inside the bag

Calendar Time

Missing Days

- Get a blank calendar.
- Fill in the numbers for the days. Leave out two numbers between 10 and 20.
- Exchange calendars with your partner.
- Write in the missing numbers. Have your partner write in the missing numbers.
- Check each other's work.
- Count the days from one to 20.

Teacher Note: Write the name of the current month on the calendars. Help students write the numbers for the days of the month one to 20. Draw an example of a calendar page on the chalkboard—with days one to 20 numbered—so that students can copy it. Be sure students leave out two numbers between days 10 and 20. Have students work in pairs.

Sunday	Monday	Tuesday	Wednesday	Thursday	Friday	Saturday
	1	2	3	4	5	6
7	8	9	10	11		13
14	15	16	17	18		20

January

Introduce the Chapter

Real World: Patterns

Share with students that there will be times that they need to count more than 10.

- Start counting the number of students in the classroom. Have the students count with you.
- When you get to 10, stop and ask if that is everyone.
- **How many more students are in the class?** Sample answer: eight
- Tell students that this is one example of why they need to know numbers that come after 10.

Use the Student Page

Have students turn to p. 149. Have students discuss the images on the page and answer the Explore question.

Key Vocabulary

Introduce the key vocabulary in the chapter using the routine below.

Define: The number 20 is made of two tens.
Example: I have 20 cubes or two groups of ten.
Ask: What other things could you have 20 of?

Diagnostic Assessment

Check for students' prerequisite skills before beginning the chapter.

- **Option 1:** ***Are You Ready for Chapter 6?***

  SE Student Edition, p. 150

- **Option 2:** ***Online Quiz***

  Math Online macmillanmh.com

- **Option 3:** ***Diagnostic Test***

  CRM Chapter 6 Resource Masters, p. 36

RTI (Response to Intervention)

Apply the Results Based on the results of the diagnostic assessment on p. 150, use the chart on the next page to address individual needs before and during the chapter.

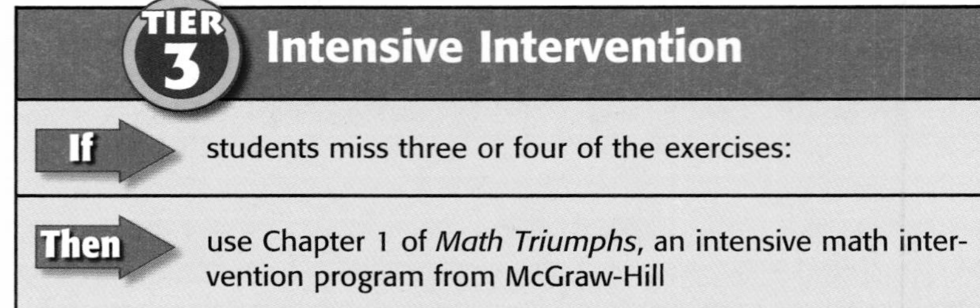

TIER 3 Intensive Intervention

If	students miss three or four of the exercises:
Then	use Chapter 1 of *Math Triumphs*, an intensive math intervention program from McGraw-Hill

Dinah Zike's Foldables

Guide students to create an Accordion Book Foldable for creating a number line to order numbers 11–20.

1. Fold four pieces of paper into hamburgers. Fold one side one half inch shorter than the other side.

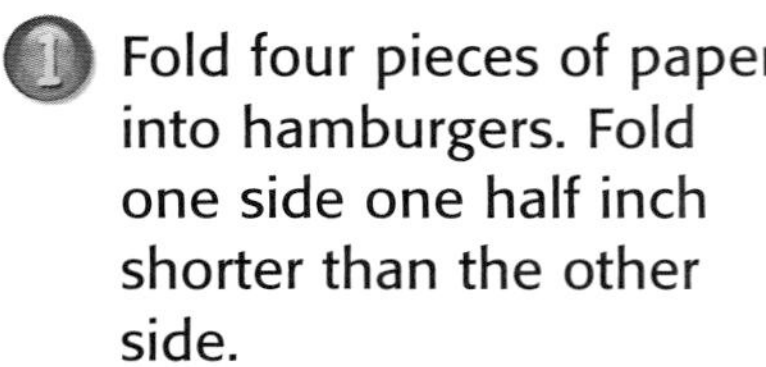

2. Fold this tab forward over the shorter side, and then fold it back away from the shorter piece of paper.

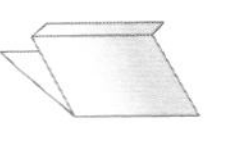

3. Glue together to form an accordion by gluing a straight edge of one section into the valley of another section.

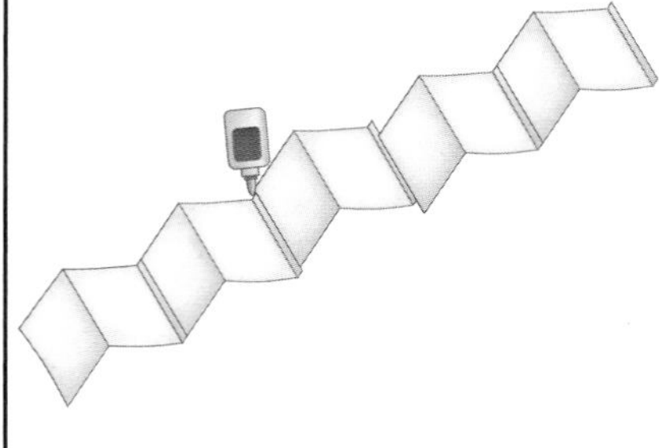

4. Write one number on the top left side of each of the three sections and have students find and place pictures on the appropriate sections to illustrate each of the numbers.

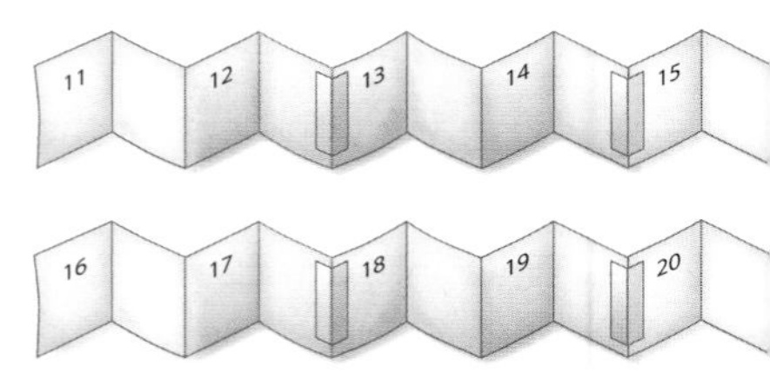

When to Use It *Lessons 6-1, 6-2, 6-3, 6-4, 6-5, and 6-6 (Additional instructions for using the Foldable with these lessons are found on pp. 159 and 171.)*

CHAPTER 6
Use Numbers to 20
Key Vocabulary
twenty
Explore
Draw a circle on the puppets with hats and a box on the puppets without hats.
Are there more puppets with hats or puppets without hats? puppets with hats
Chapter 6
one hundred forty-nine 149

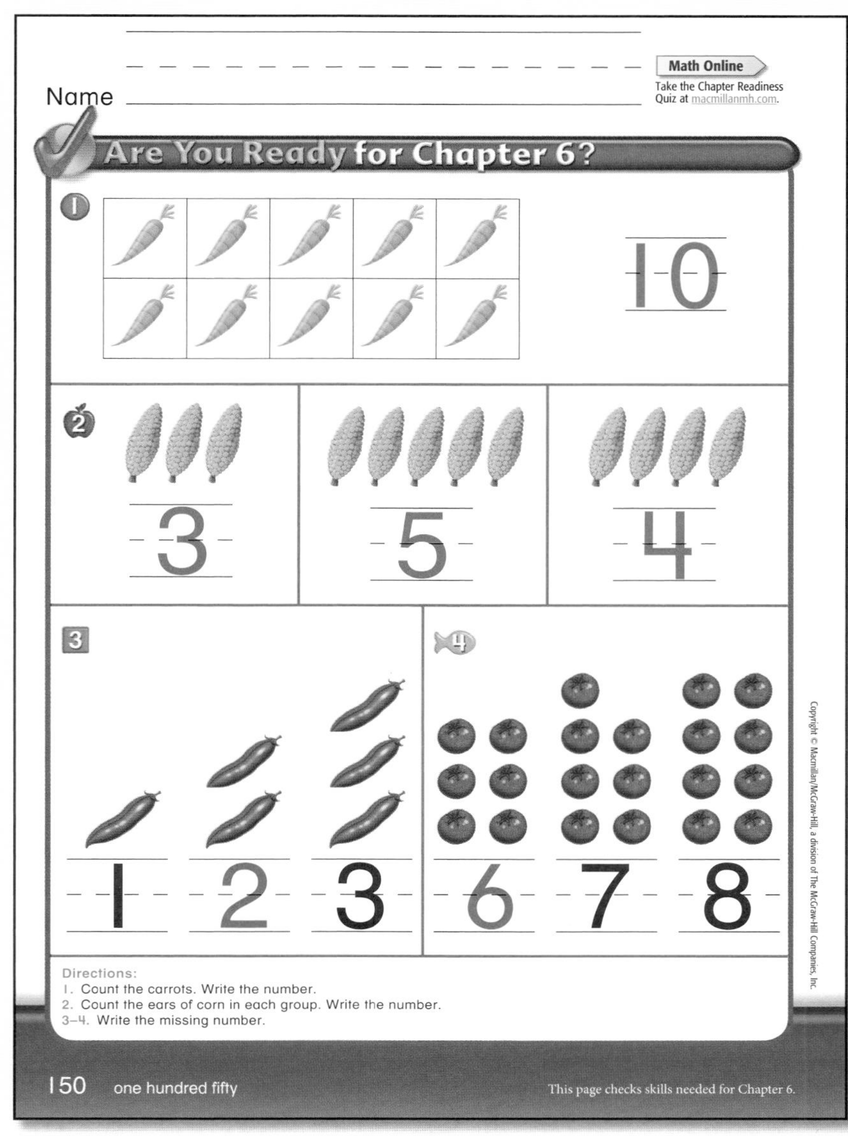

Name
Math Online
Take the Chapter Readiness Quiz at macmillanmh.com.
Are You Ready for Chapter 6?
10
3
5
4
1 2 3
6 7 8
Directions:
1. Count the carrots. Write the number.
2. Count the ears of corn in each group. Write the number.
3–4. Write the missing number.
150 one hundred fifty
This page checks skills needed for Chapter 6.

RTI (Response to Intervention)

TIER 2 Strategic Intervention below/approaching grade level	TIER 1 On-Level	Above/Beyond Level
If students miss two in: **Exercises 1–4**	**If** students miss one in: **Exercises 1–4**	**If** students miss none in: **Exercises 1–4**
Then Choose a resource:	**Then** Choose a resource:	**Then** Choose a resource:
TE Chapter 4 Resource Masters (Reteach Worksheets) Math Online Concepts in Motion	TE Learning Stations (pp. 149G–149H) TE Chapter Project (p. 151) CRM Game: Coin Toss Math Adventures My Math Zone Chapter 5	TE Learning Stations (pp. 149G–149H) TE Chapter Project (p. 151) Real-World Problem Solving: *At the Grocery Store* My Math Zone Chapters 5 and 6 Math Online Game

Starting the Chapter
If students are able, ask them to copy each of the chapter's vocabulary words in their Math Journal. Have them draw a simple illustration to represent each word.

Chapter 6 Project

My Counting Cards

- Have students make counting cards for numbers 11 to 20.
- Students represent quantities by writing one number on each card and then draw that number of objects to illustrate the number on the card. Have students count the total number of objects, starting at one, each time they draw a new object. This will help them draw the correct number of objects.
- Have students count the objects up to 10, then circle that group of 10 objects. Students should count the remaining objects that are not circled. Ask students to describe the number on their card by completing the phrase "a group of 10 and ___ more."
- Students show one card to the class and say the number aloud.

Chapter 6 Literature List

Lesson	Book Title	Author
6-1	**Anno's Counting Book**	Mitsumasa Anno
6-2	**Jack the Builder**	Stuart J. Murphy
6-3	**Jack the Builder**	Stuart J. Murphy
6-4	**Icky Bug Numbers**	Jerry Pallotta
6-5	**Bears at the Beach Counting 10 to 20**	Nikki Yektai
6-6	**Chicka Chicka 1 2 3**	Bill Martin, Jr., Michael Sampson, Lois Ehlert
6-7	**Let's Count It Out, Jesse Bear**	Nancy White Carlstrom
Any	**Gathering: A Northwoods Counting Book**	Betsy Bowen
Any	**How Many Snails? A Counting Book**	Paul Giganti, Jr.

ELL National ESL Standards Alignment for Chapter 6			
Lesson, Page	**ESL Standard**	**Modality**	**Level**
6-1, p. 153B	Goal 2, Standard 1, g	Logical	Intermediate
6-2, p. 155B	Goal 1, Standard 3, g	Kinesthetic	Intermediate
6-3, p. 157B	Goal 2, Standard 2, a	Kinesthetic	Beginning
6-4, p. 161B	Goal 2, Standard 3, c	Intrapersonal	Intermediate
6-5, p. 163B	Goal 1, Standard 3, g	Logical	Intermediate
6-6, p. 165B	Goal 2, Standard 2, f	Logical	Intermediate
6-7, p. 167B	Goal 1, Standard 3, f	Logical	Advanced

The National ESL Standards can be found in the Teacher Reference Handbook.

English

MATH at HOME

Dear Family,

Today my class started Chapter 6, **Use Numbers to 20**. I will be learning to count and order numbers to 20. Here is my vocabulary word, an activity we can do, and a list of books we can read together.

Love, ____________________

Activity

Have your child find 20 or less of an object. For example, have your child find 13 pennies or 17 crayons. Count the objects. Write the number. Compare to show more, less, or the same amounts.

Key Vocabulary

twenty 20

2 tens

Math Online Click on the eGlossary link at macmillanmh.com to find out more about these words. There are 13 languages.

Books to Read

Gathering: A Northwoods Counting Book
by Betsy Bowen
Houghton Mifflin Company, 1999.

Let's Count It Out, Jesse Bear
by Nancy White Carlstrom
Aladdin, 2001.

How Many Snails?
by Paul Giganti
HarperCollins Publishers, 1994.

Español

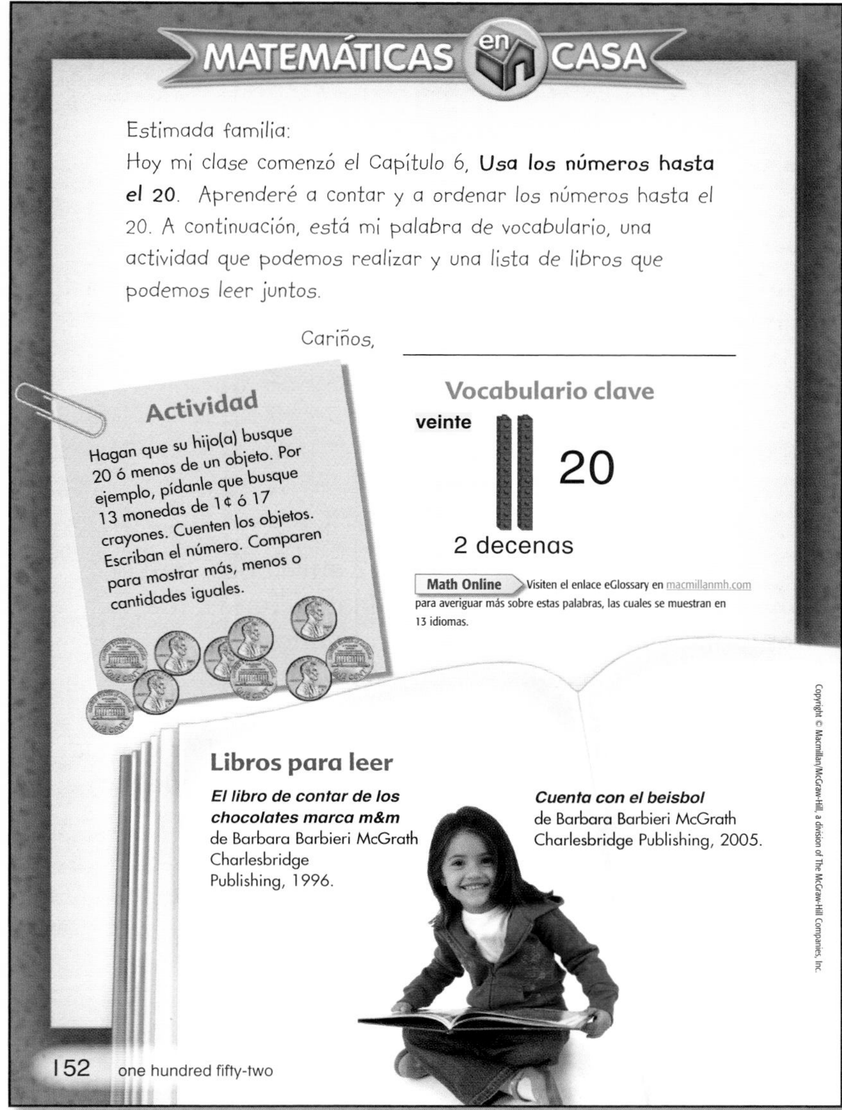

MATEMÁTICAS en CASA

Estimada familia:

Hoy mi clase comenzó el Capítulo 6, **Usa los números hasta el 20**. Aprenderé a contar y a ordenar los números hasta el 20. A continuación, está mi palabra de vocabulario, una actividad que podemos realizar y una lista de libros que podemos leer juntos.

Cariños, ____________________

Actividad

Hagan que su hijo(a) busque 20 ó menos de un objeto. Por ejemplo, pídanle que busque 13 monedas de 1¢ ó 17 crayones. Cuenten los objetos. Escriban el número. Comparen para mostrar más, menos o cantidades iguales.

Vocabulario clave

veinte 20

2 decenas

Math Online Visiten el enlace eGlossary en macmillanmh.com para averiguar más sobre estas palabras, las cuales se muestran en 13 idiomas.

Libros para leer

El libro de contar de los chocolates marca m&m
de Barbara Barbieri McGrath
Charlesbridge Publishing, 1996.

Cuenta con el beisbol
de Barbara Barbieri McGrath
Charlesbridge Publishing, 2005.

- Read the Math at Home letter on p. 151 with the class and have each student sign it.
- Send home copies of the Math at Home letter with each student.
- Use the Spanish letter on p. 152 for students with Spanish-speaking parents or guardians.

Read-Aloud Anthology

For an optional reading activity to introduce this chapter's math concepts, see the Read-Aloud Anthology on p. TR29.

LESSON 6-1

Numbers 11 and 12

Lesson Planner

Objective

Name, recognize, count, and write the numerals 11 and 12 using concrete objects and illustrations.

Vocabulary

eleven, **twelve**

Resources

Materials: chart paper, crayons, 12 envelopes, basket, number cards 11 and 12, WorkMat 5: Ten-Frame
Manipulatives: connecting cubes, counters
Literature Connection: *Anno's Counting Book* by Mitsumasa Anno
Alternate Lesson: Adapt *Junk Boxes* on page 175 of *Math Their Way* for practice with recognition of and writing numerals 11 and 12.
Teacher Technology
TeacherWorks

Focus on Math Background

As the numbers they are asked to count become greater, students need to develop their counting and grouping skills. Allow plenty of time for students to work on these skills. Give them many opportunities to count a variety of objects in different-sized sets and have them record the numbers.

Daily Routine

Use these suggestions before beginning the lesson on p. 153.

5-Minute Check

(Reviews Lesson 5-5)
Give each student a cup with attribute buttons. Have them make a graph of figures using the buttons, and then make a graph of colors.

Problem of the Day

Show students a group with nine objects. Show them a group with six objects. Ask: Which group has more? group with nine objects

LINE UP Have five pairs of students line up. **How many students are lined up?** 10 **How many more need to line up to make 11?** one Have one more student join the line. **How many more need to line up to now make 12?** one

Building Math Vocabulary

Materials: number/name cards 11 and 12

- Give number/name cards 11 and 12 to each student. Draw a ten frame on the chalkboard with 10 counters plus one counter, counting each counter aloud. Have students show the card that matches the total number of counters.
- **How do you know the number on the card matches the number of counters?** 11 is one more than 10.
- Have students write 11 in the air.
- Draw 10 stars, counting aloud. Circle the group. Draw two more stars. Have students show the card that matches the stars.
- **How do you know the number on the card matches the number of stars?** 12 is one more than 11.
- Have students count on from 10: "**eleven**, **twelve**." Have students write 12 in the air.

Differentiated Instruction

Small Group Options

Option 1 Below/Approaching Level BL

LOGICAL

Materials: WorkMat 5: Ten-Frame, green and red connecting cubes

- Have students describe quantities symbolically by putting 10 green connecting cubes ("apples") in a ten-frame ("basket").
- Have students add one red "apple." Count the apples.
- Have students continue to add one apple and count the total until they reach 12.

Option 2 English Language Learners ELL

LOGICAL

Core Vocabulary: group, tell, find
Common Use Verb: count out

Talk Math This strategy teaches recognizing quantities 11 and 12.

- Have students describe quantities verbally by counting out 11 crayons and 12 pencils. Instruct groups of students to find 11 items in the classroom that are similar.
- Have groups tell the items they selected and then count them aloud. Repeat with 12 items.

Independent Work Options

Option 1 Early Finishers OL AL

VISUAL

Materials: egg cartons, rocks (12 per crate)

- Have students describe quantities verbally, counting from 1 to 12, by putting a rock in each space in the egg carton.
- Discuss that a dozen means 12.
- Have students empty the carton and put 11 rocks in it.
- **How many spaces are empty with 11 rocks in the carton?** 1 space
- Add one more rock.
- **How many rocks are in the carton now?** 12 rocks

Option 2 Student Technology

Math Online macmillanmh.com

Math Adventures

Option 3 Learning Station: Science (p. 149G)

Direct students to the Science Learning Station for opportunities to explore and extend the lesson concept.

Leveled Lesson Resources

Reteach (p. 6) BL

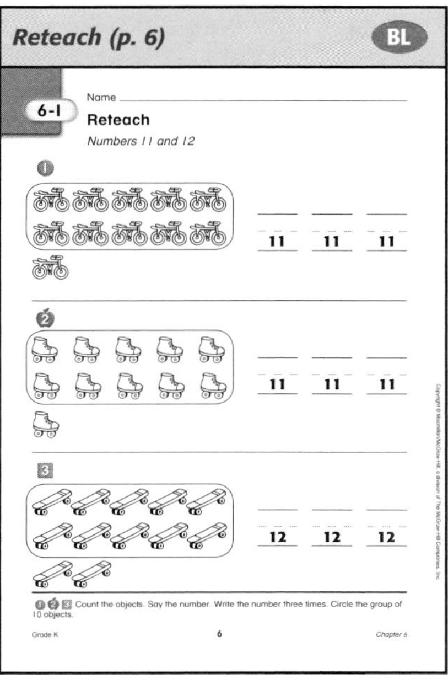

6-1 Name
Reteach
Numbers 11 and 12

1. 11 11 11
2. 11 11 11
3. 12 12 12

Count the objects. Say the number. Write the number three times. Circle the group of 10 objects.

Skills Practice (p. 7) OL

6-1 Name
Skills Practice
Numbers 11 and 12

11 flowers are drawn. 12 rocks are drawn.

Draw 11 flowers. Draw 12 rocks.

Enrich (p. 9) AL

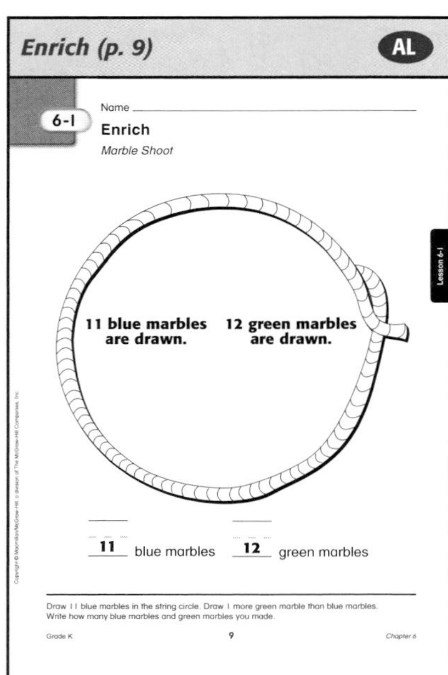

6-1 Name
Enrich
Marble Shoot

11 blue marbles are drawn. 12 green marbles are drawn.

11 blue marbles 12 green marbles

Draw 11 blue marbles in the string circle. Draw 1 more green marble than blue marbles. Write how many blue marbles and green marbles you made.

Homework Practice (p. 8) OL

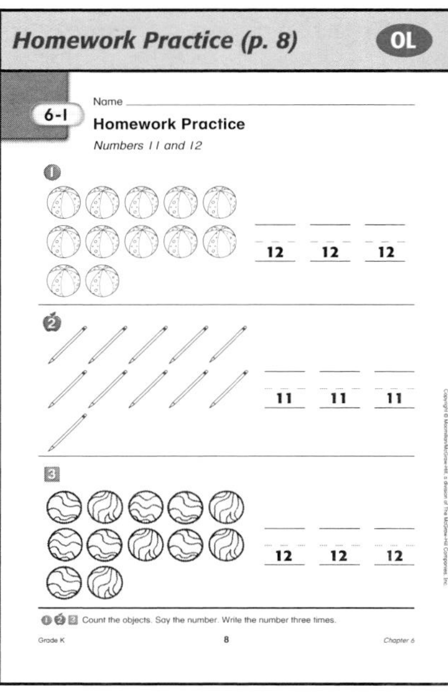

6-1 Name
Homework Practice
Numbers 11 and 12

1. 12 12 12
2. 11 11 11
3. 12 12 12

Count the objects. Say the number. Write the number three times.

1 Introduce

Circle Time

Activity Choice 1 • Literature

Anno's Counting Book
by Mitsumasa Anno

- Read and discuss the book, counting objects of that particular number.
- On the pages that illustrate numbers **eleven** and **twelve**, ask students to count items on the page.
- Using two pieces of chart paper with headings "11" and "12," have the students describe quantities symbolically by drawing pictures to illustrate either number 11 or 12. Encourage students to write the corresponding number beside it.

Activity Choice 2 • Hands-On 

Materials: 12 envelopes, basket, number cards 11 and 12

- Put 10 envelopes in a basket, having students count from one to 10 as each envelope is counted.
- **What number comes after 10? How do you know?** 11; 11 is one more than 10.
- Put an envelope in the basket.
- Ask what 11 looks like. Show the 11 card. Have students write 11 in the air, then jump as they count to 11.
- Repeat with 12. Have students write 12 in the air and then nod as they count to 12.

2 Teach

- Direct students to the top of p. 153. Describe quantities verbally by counting the bunnies together. Practice writing 11 in the air.
- Count the horses together. Say that 12 is one more than 11. Have students practice writing 12 in the air.

BL Alternate Teaching Strategy

If students have trouble understanding how to count to 11 or 12 . . .

Then use one of these reteach options.

1  **Daily Reteach Worksheet** (p. 6)

2 **Counting 11 and 12** Use connecting cubes to review counting.

- Describe quantities verbally by connecting 10 cubes to make a train, having students count from one to 10. Make several ten-cube trains—enough for students to work in groups of three with each group having its own train. Divide students into groups of three, and give each group a train and two additional connecting cubes.
- Ask how many cubes will be on the train if one more cube is added. Have one student in each group add one more cube. Count the cubes from one to 11.
- Ask how many cubes will be on the train if one more cube is added. Have a second student in each group add one cube. Count the cubes from one to 12.
- Have the third student in each group take the cubes apart, with all students in the group counting from one to 12.

COMMON ERROR!

Students may struggle with counting on from 10. Start by counting from one, and then gradually build until they count from 10.

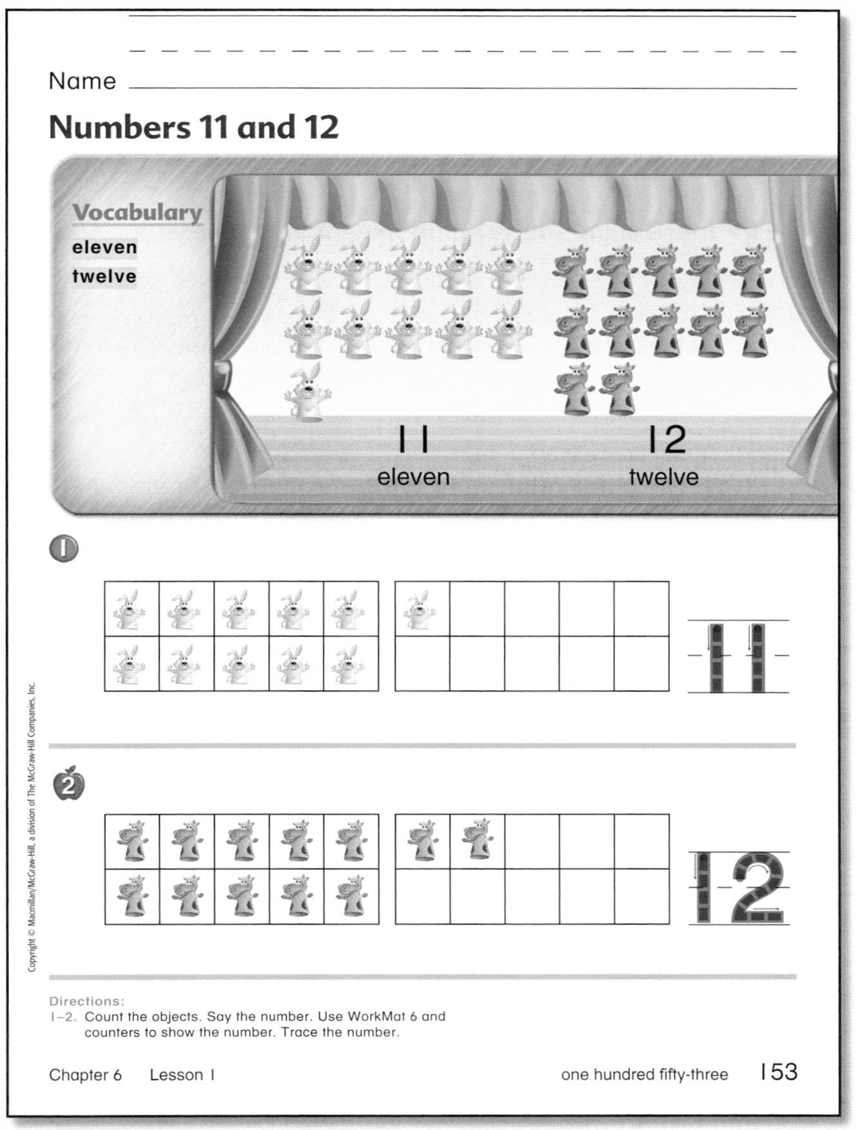

Name
Numbers 11 and 12
Vocabulary
eleven
twelve
11
eleven
12
twelve
Directions:
1–2. Count the objects. Say the number. Use WorkMat 6 and counters to show the number. Trace the number.
Chapter 6 Lesson 1
one hundred fifty-three 153

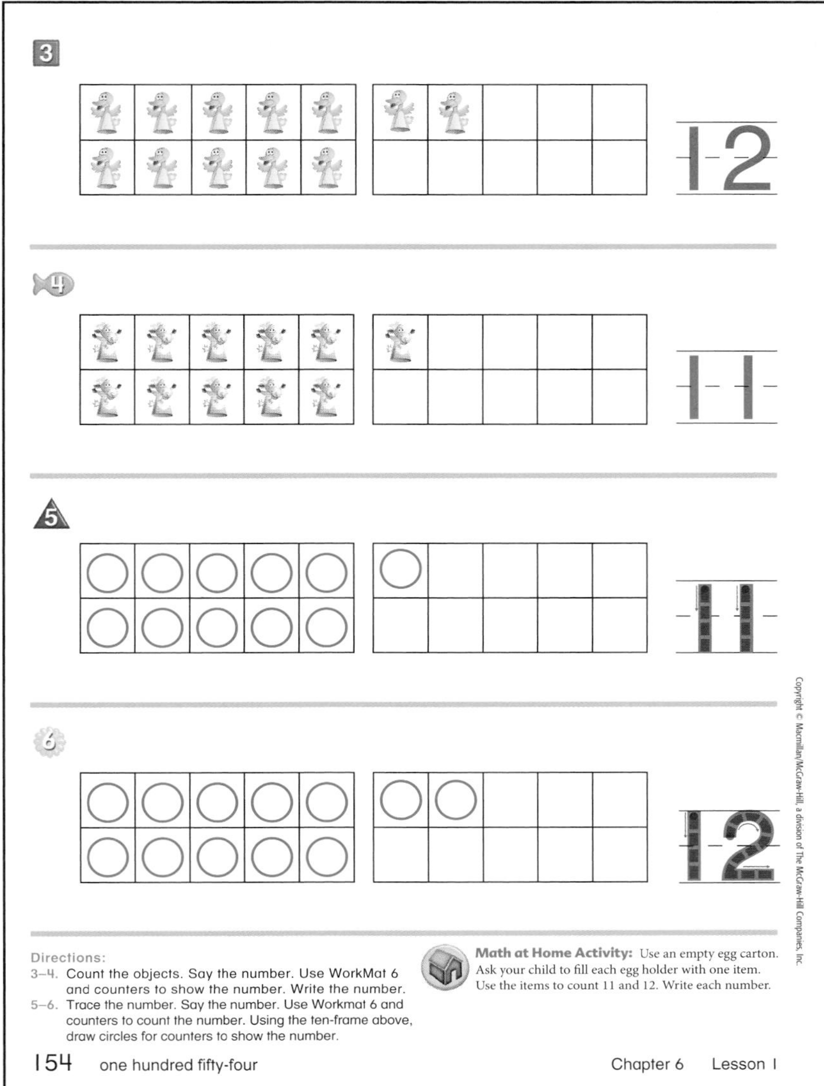

Directions:
3–4. Count the objects. Say the number. Use WorkMat 6 and counters to show the number. Write the number.
5–6. Trace the number. Say the number. Use Workmat 6 and counters to count the number. Using the ten-frame above, draw circles for counters to show the number.
Math at Home Activity: Use an empty egg carton. Ask your child to fill each egg holder with one item. Use the items to count 11 and 12. Write each number.
154 one hundred fifty-four
Chapter 6 Lesson 1

3 Practice

Guided Practice

- Direct students to Exercise 1 on p. 153. Say that these are the same bunnies as on the puppet stage. Have students count the bunnies. Distribute 11 counters and WorkMat 6 and count them aloud with students. Say that there are 11 bunnies and 11 counters. Have students use Workmat 6 and counters to model the number. Tell students to trace the number.
- Work Exercise 2 in the same way, counting 12 horses and using WorkMat 6 and 12 counters. Have students practice writing by tracing the number 12.

Independent Practice

Have students turn to p. 154 and work independently on Exercises 3–4. Explain the directions for Exercises 5 and 6. Have students complete Exercises 5 and 6 independently.

4 Assess

Formative Assessment

Put 10 counters on a ten-frame mat.

- **How many counters are on the mat?** 10 counters
- **How would you show 11 and how would you show 12 on the mat?** Add one more counter to 10 to make 11. Add one more counter to 11 to make 12.

Quick Check **Are students still struggling to count and write numbers 11 and 12?**

If Yes → Small Group Options (p. 153B)

If No → Independent Work Options (p. 153B)

CRM Skills Practice Worksheet (p. 7)

CRM Enrich Worksheet (p. 9)

LESSON 6-2

Numbers 13, 14, and 15

Lesson Planner

Objective

Name, recognize, count, and write the numerals 13, 14, and 15 using concrete objects and illustrations.

Vocabulary

thirteen, **fourteen**, **fifteen**

Resources

Materials: chart paper, crayons, paper cups, WorkMat 5: Ten-Frame
Manipulatives: geometric solids, connecting cubes, two-color counters
Literature Connection: *Jack the Builder* by Stuart J. Murphy
Alternate Lesson: Adapt *Numeral Sequence Cards* on page 47 of *Math Their Way* for practice recognizing and writing the numbers 13, 14, and 15.
Teacher Technology
TeacherWorks

Focus on Math Background

When organizing sets into groups of tens and ones, students learn to visualize the relationship between 10 and the "teen" numbers. They begin to connect the meaning of the word *fifteen* and the symbol *15* as one ten and five ones. Provide many opportunities to work with sets of ten and more.

Daily Routine

Use these suggestions before beginning the lesson on p. 155.

5-Minute Check

(Reviews Lesson 6-1)

1. Describe quantities symbolically by drawing 11 circles.
2. Write the number 11 three times.
3. Draw 12 triangles.
4. Write the number 12 three times.
5. Which is more, 11 or 12? 12

Problem of the Day

What is one more than 11? 12 Draw a picture to explain your answer.

LINE UP Have 12 students line up, each holding an object from the classroom. **How many more do we need to make 13? 14? 15?** one; two; three Have students holding objects join the line, counting on from 12: "thirteen, fourteen, fifteen."

Building Math Vocabulary

Materials: glue stick, small blue squares, 9″ × 12″ construction paper

- Distribute to each student a glue stick, small plastic bag of blue construction paper squares, and a sheet of yellow construction paper with 13, 14, or 15 written on it.
- Have students trace the written number with a glue stick and then paste on the number of squares equal to the number drawn on the paper.
- Tell students that if they have the number that is 10 and three more, they should stand and hold up their papers. Ask the class if only students holding **thirteen** are standing.
- Repeat for **fourteen** and **fifteen**.

Differentiated Instruction

Small Group Options

Option 1 Gifted and Talented (AL)

LOGICAL

- Split class into five groups.
- Give each group a large paper circle, cut into equal pieces of a different number: 11, 12, 13, 14, 15.
- Tell students each circle is a pizza. Have students take turns taking a piece of pizza until it is gone. Have them represent the quantities verbally by counting their own pieces, then counting the group total.
- Ask students to compare their number of pieces with other groups, and tell which pizza has the most pieces.

Option 2 English Language Learners (ELL)

KINESTHETIC

Materials: yarn, 3 colors of beads
Core Vocabulary: of a, of another, on a string
Common Use Verb: put

Do Math This strategy allows students to visualize 13-15.

- Have students represent quantities verbally by counting out 13 beads of one color, 14 beads of another color, and 15 beads of a third color.
- Have them put each set of beads on a piece of yarn.
- Have students lay the string of 15 beads on the bottom, 14 beads in the middle, and 13 beads on top.

Independent Work Options

Option 1 Early Finishers (OL) (AL)

SPATIAL

Materials: crayons, paper, small classroom objects

- Have a student search the room for 13, 14, or 15 of a small object (crayons, cubes, paper clips, etc.).
- A partner counts the number of the objects found.
- The students draw the same number of objects as the number found and write that number on the paper.
- Repeat, with partners switching roles.

Option 2 Student Technology

Math Online macmillanmh.com

Math Adventures

Option 3 Learning Station: Art (p. 149H)

Direct students to the Art Learning Station for opportunities to explore and extend the lesson concept.

Leveled Lesson Resources

Reteach (p. 10) BL

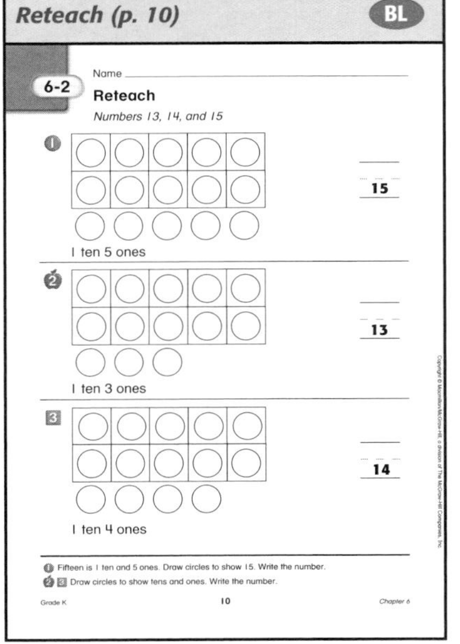

Name
6-2 Reteach
Numbers 13, 14, and 15

1 — 15
I ten 5 ones

2 — 13
I ten 3 ones

3 — 14
I ten 4 ones

1 Fifteen is I ten and 5 ones. Draw circles to show 15. Write the number.
2 3 Draw circles to show tens and ones. Write the number.

Grade K 10 Chapter 6

Skills Practice (p. 11) OL

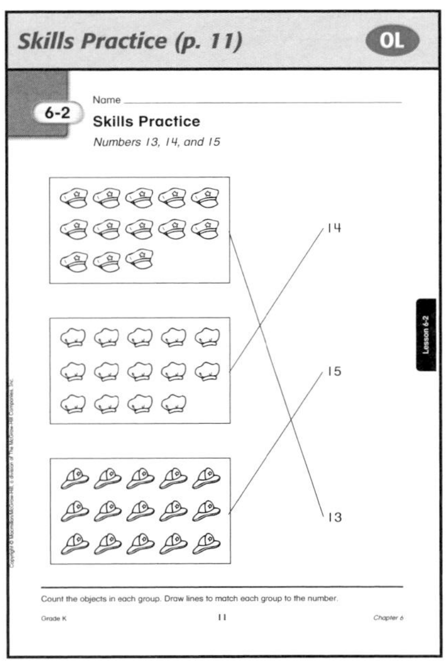

Name
6-2 Skills Practice
Numbers 13, 14, and 15

14
15
13

Count the objects in each group. Draw lines to match each group to the number.

Grade K 11 Chapter 6

Enrich (p. 13) AL

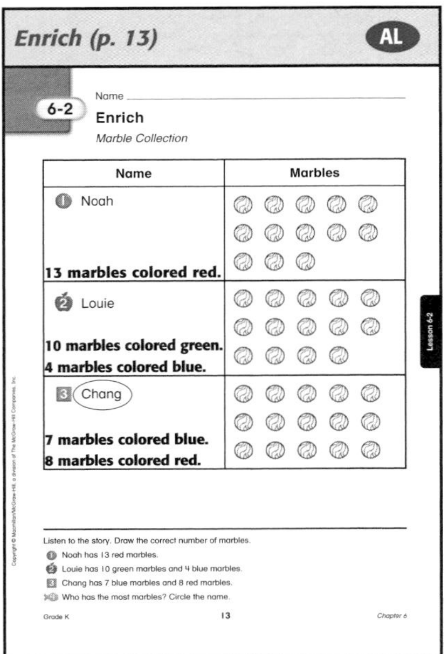

Name
6-2 Enrich
Marble Collection

Name	Marbles
1 Noah 13 marbles colored red.	
2 Louie 10 marbles colored green. 4 marbles colored blue.	
3 Chang 7 marbles colored blue. 8 marbles colored red.	

Listen to the story. Draw the correct number of marbles.
1 Noah has 13 red marbles.
2 Louie has 10 green marbles and 4 blue marbles.
3 Chang has 7 blue marbles and 8 red marbles.
Who has the most marbles? Circle the name.

Grade K 13 Chapter 6

Homework Practice (p. 12) OL

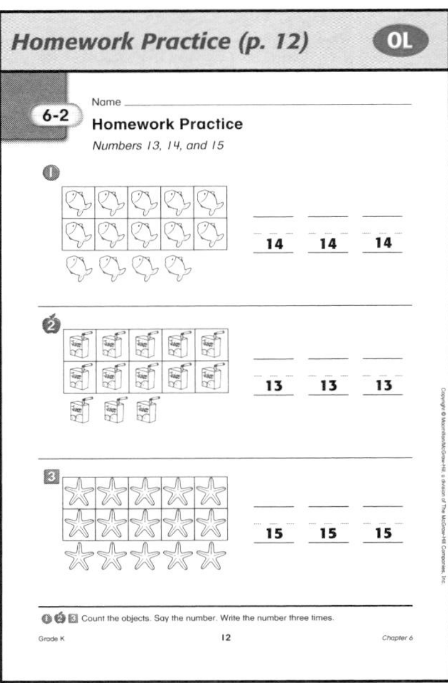

Name
6-2 Homework Practice
Numbers 13, 14, and 15

1 — 14 14 14

2 — 13 13 13

3 — 15 15 15

1 2 3 Count the objects. Say the number. Write the number three times.

Grade K 12 Chapter 6

1 Introduce

Activity Choice 1 • Literature

Jack the Builder
by Stuart J. Murphy

- Read and discuss the book, counting the geometric figures.
- Allow students to work in pairs to build a rocket, with **thirteen, fourteen,** or **fifteen** geometric solids.
- Have students represent quantities verbally by counting out the number of figures used to build the rocket.
- Have students create a class chart or graph recording the number of figures each student pair used.

Activity Choice 2 • Hands-On 

Materials: counters, cups

- Drop 12 counters into a cup one by one, having students count aloud.
- **How many counters will be in the cup if one more is added?** 13 counters
- Add another counter.
- Take the counters out of the cup one by one, having students count aloud, clapping their hands as they count to 13.
- Repeat with 14 counters, having students tap their feet as they count to 14.
- Repeat with 15 counters, having students touch their toes as they count to 15.

2 Teach

- Direct students to the top of p. 155. Identify the items in the cupboard.
- Represent quantities verbally by counting the cups together. Have students practice writing 13 in the air.
- Count the plates together. Say that 14 is one more than 13. Have students practice writing 14 in the air.
- Count the bowls together. Say that 15 is one more than 14. Have students practice writing 15 in the air.

BL Alternate Teaching Strategy

 students have trouble understanding how to count to 13, 14, or 15 . . .

 use one of these reteach options.

1 CRM **Daily Reteach Worksheet** (p. 10)

2 **Use Manipulatives** Give a student 12 cups. Have the student put cups in the ten-frame with two below.

- **What number is one more than 12?** 13
- Have the student put a cup beside cup 12 and count to 13.
- Ask what 13 looks like. Show a number card with 13. Have students write 13 in the air.
- Repeat with 14 and 15 cups.

COMMON ERROR!

Students may have trouble using ten-frames for numbers greater than 10. Have them line up counters under the frame, one per divided area, or use a second frame.

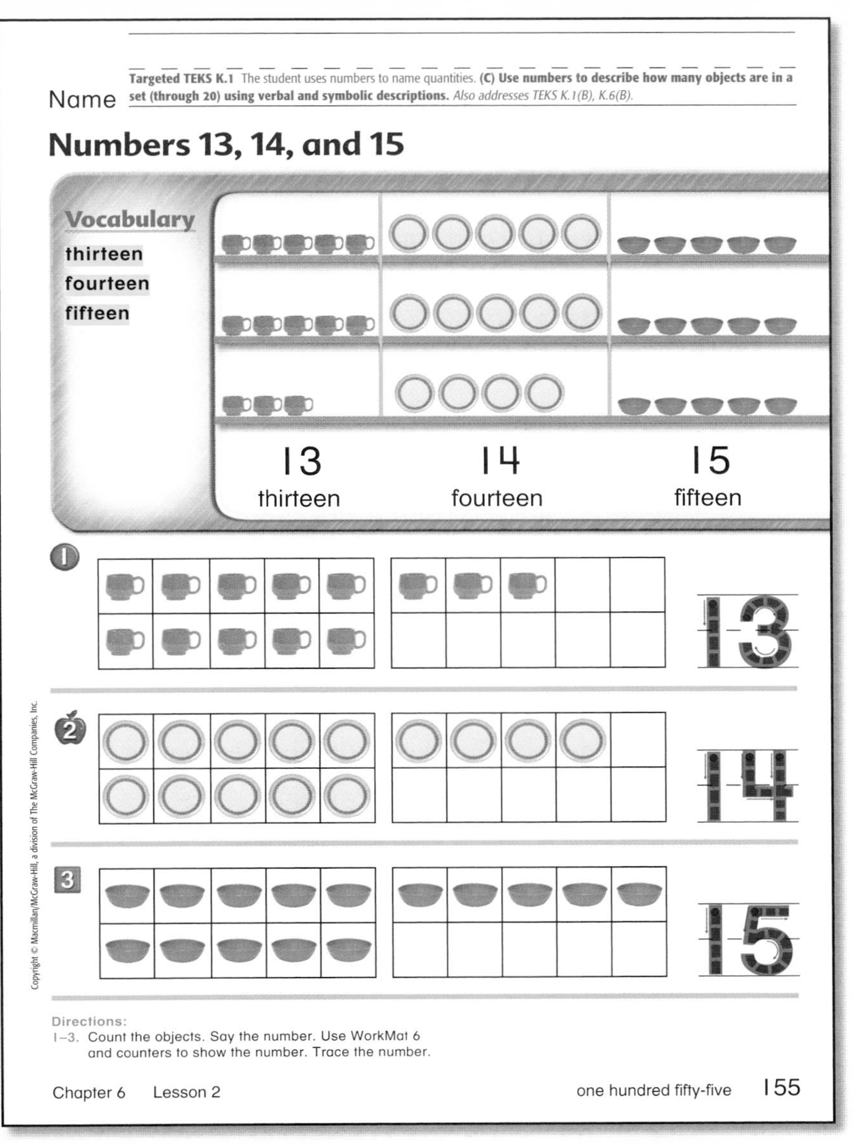

Name

Targeted TEKS K.1 The student uses numbers to name quantities. (C) Use numbers to describe how many objects are in a set (through 20) using verbal and symbolic descriptions. *Also addresses TEKS K.1(B), K.6(B).*

Numbers 13, 14, and 15

Vocabulary
thirteen
fourteen
fifteen

13 thirteen
14 fourteen
15 fifteen

1. 13
2. 14
3. 15

Directions:
1–3. Count the objects. Say the number. Use WorkMat 6 and counters to show the number. Trace the number.

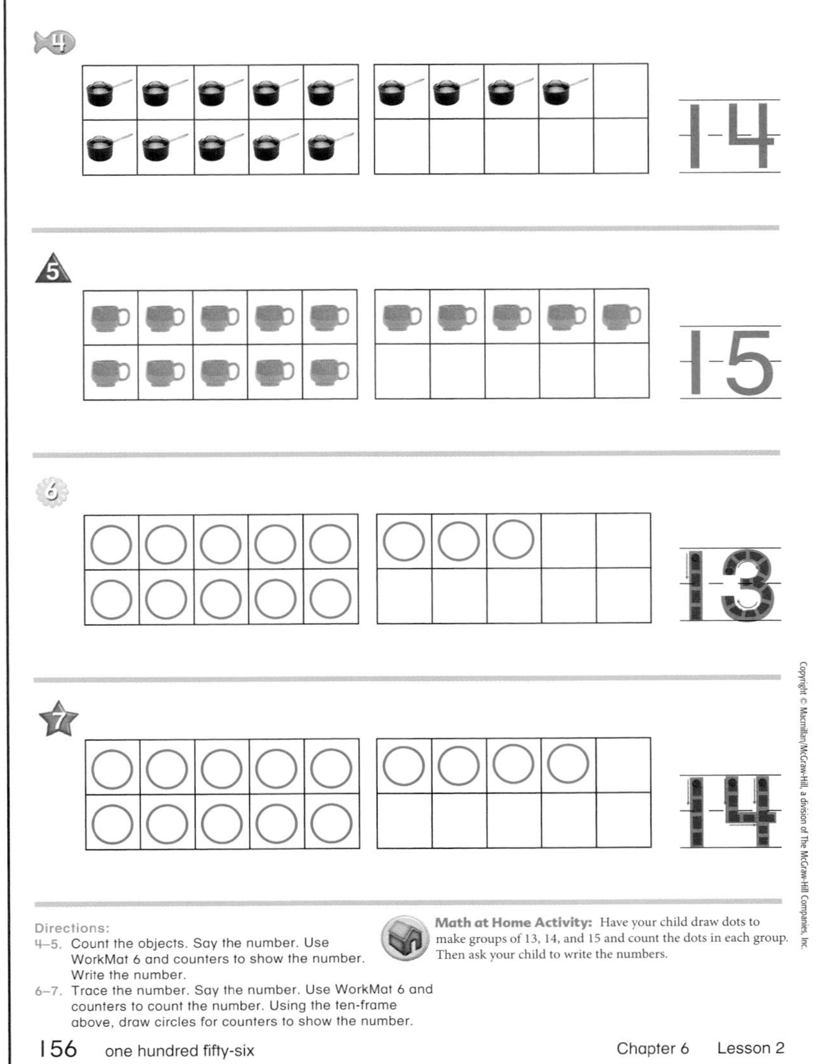

4. 14
5. 15
6. 13
7. 14

Directions:
4–5. Count the objects. Say the number. Use WorkMat 6 and counters to show the number. Write the number.
6–7. Trace the number. Say the number. Use WorkMat 6 and counters to count the number. Using the ten-frame above, draw circles for counters to show the number.

Math at Home Activity: Have your child draw dots to make groups of 13, 14, and 15 and count the dots in each group. Then ask your child to write the numbers.

3 Practice

Guided Practice

- Direct students to Exercise 1 on p. 155.
- **Is the number of cups the same as in the cupboard above?** yes
- Have students count the cups. Distribute 13 counters and WorkMat 6. Have students count how many as they place counters on the WorkMat. Have students practice writing by tracing the number 13.
- Work through Exercises 2 and 3 in the same way, counting plates and bowls.

Independent Practice

Have students turn to p. 156 and work independently on Exercises 4 and 5. Explain directions for Exercises 6 and 7. Have students complete Exercises 6 and 7 independently.

Assess

Formative Assessment

Make a train of 12 connecting cubes.

- **How many cubes are in the train?** 12 cubes
- **How can you show 13?** Add one cube.
- Add a cube, and show the train of 13 cubes.
- Repeat with 14 and 15.

Quick Check **Are students still struggling to count and write numbers 13, 14, and 15?**

If Yes → Small Group Options (p. 155B)

If No → Independent Work Options (p. 155B)

CRM Skills Practice Worksheet (p. 11)

CRM Enrich Worksheet (p. 13)

LESSON 6-3

Numbers 16 and 17

Lesson Planner

Objective

Name, recognize, count, and write the numerals 16 and 17.

Vocabulary

sixteen, **seventeen**

Resources

Materials: WorkMat 5: Ten-Frame, drum, number cards 15, 16, 17, chart, string
Manipulatives: geometric solids, counters, attribute buttons
Literature Connection: *Jack the Builder* by Stuart J. Murphy
Alternate Lesson: Adapt *People Counting Game* on pages 96 and 97 of *Math Their Way* for practice in counting and naming numbers 11 through 20.
Teacher Technology
TeacherWorks

Focus on Math Background

When students hear the word *sixteen* and learn to represent the quantity in a ten frame, they associate the word, the symbol, and the quantity. Arranging quantities into tens and ones will help students when they begin developing mental math skills and an understanding of mathematical algorithms.

Daily Routine

Use these suggestions before beginning the lesson on p. 157.

5-Minute Check

(Reviews Lesson 6-2)

1. Draw 13 flowers. Represent the quantity by writing 13.
2. Draw 14 trees. Represent the quantity by writing 14.
3. Draw 15 suns. Represent the quantity by writing 15.
4. How many smiley faces do you see below?
   14 faces

Problem of the Day

What comes next in the pattern: 11, 12, 11, 12, 11, 12? 11

LINE UP Call students to find a classroom object, bring it to the front of the room, and place it in a line on the floor. Continue until there are 16 objects, counting aloud as each object is added. **How many objects are in the line?** 16 objects Have a student add one more object to the line. Have students say the total.

Building Math Vocabulary

Materials: number word cards for 15, 16, 17; dot cards; cards, index cards, sticker dots

- Show the word card for fifteen. Say "fifteen."
- Have a volunteer find the 15 dot card and another volunteer find the 15 number card.
- Repeat for **sixteen** and **seventeen**.
- Students may create dot cards using index cards and sticker dots.

Differentiated Instruction

Small Group Options

Option 1 Gifted and Talented (AL)

KINESTHETIC

Materials: magazines, scissors, glue, poster board

- Have students cut out eight pictures of unhealthful foods and eight pictures of healthful foods from magazines.
- Write headings on the poster board: *Healthy Foods* and *Unhealthy Foods.* Have students glue pictures under the correct heading, then represent the quantity verbally by counting all pictures.
- Have students draw a food item under one of the headings. **What is the total now?** 17

Option 2 English Language Learners (ELL)

KINESTHETIC

Materials: blocks
Core Vocabulary: tall, taller, side by side
Common Use Verb: stack

Do Math This strategy helps students visualize numbers 16 and 17.

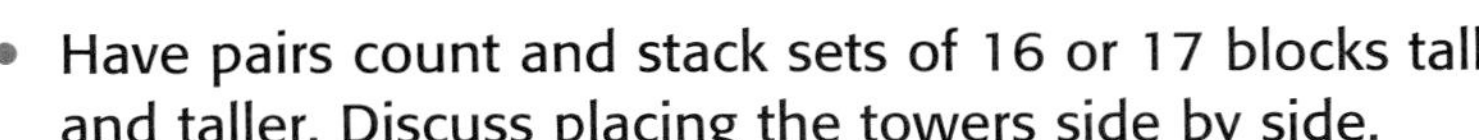

- Have pairs count and stack sets of 16 or 17 blocks tall and taller. Discuss placing the towers side by side.
- Ask which set is taller.
- Repeating until students begin to show understanding.

Independent Work Options

Option 1 Early Finishers (OL) (AL)

KINESTHETIC

Materials: attribute buttons, string

- Have students string 15 attribute buttons together.
- Using a different string, string together 16 buttons.
- How could you change your first string so that it has 16 buttons? How could you change your second string so that it has 17 buttons?
- Change strings to show 16 and 17 and then count buttons on each string.

Option 2 Student Technology

Math Online macmillanmh.com

Math Adventures

Option 3 Learning Station: Language Arts (p. 149H)

Direct students to the Language Arts Learning Station for opportunities to explore and extend the lesson concept.

Leveled Lesson Resources

Reteach (p. 14) (BL)

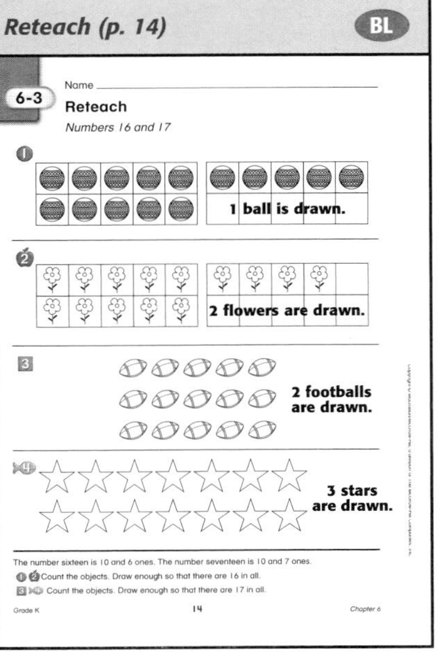

6-3 Name
Reteach
Numbers 16 and 17

1. 1 ball is drawn.
2. 2 flowers are drawn.
3. 2 footballs are drawn.
4. 3 stars are drawn.

The number sixteen is 10 and 6 ones. The number seventeen is 10 and 7 ones.
1 2 Count the objects. Draw enough so that there are 16 in all.
3 4 Count the objects. Draw enough so that there are 17 in all.

Grade K 14 Chapter 6

Skills Practice (p. 15) (OL)

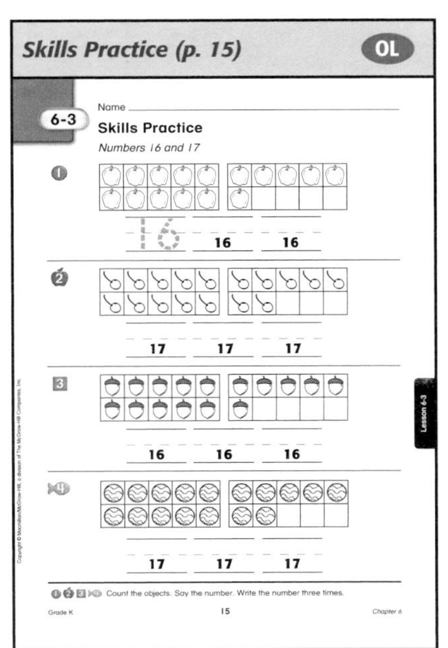

6-3 Name
Skills Practice
Numbers 16 and 17

1. 16 16 16
2. 17 17 17
3. 16 16 16
4. 17 17 17

1 2 3 4 Count the objects. Say the number. Write the number three times.

Grade K 15 Chapter 6

Enrich (p. 17) (AL)

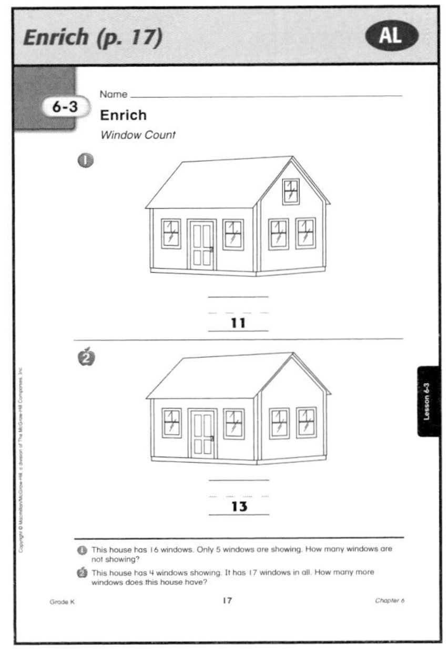

6-3 Name
Enrich
Window Count

1. 11
2. 13

1 This house has 16 windows. Only 5 windows are showing. How many windows are not showing?
2 This house has 4 windows showing. It has 17 windows in all. How many more windows does this house have?

Grade K 17 Chapter 6

Homework Practice (p. 16) (OL)

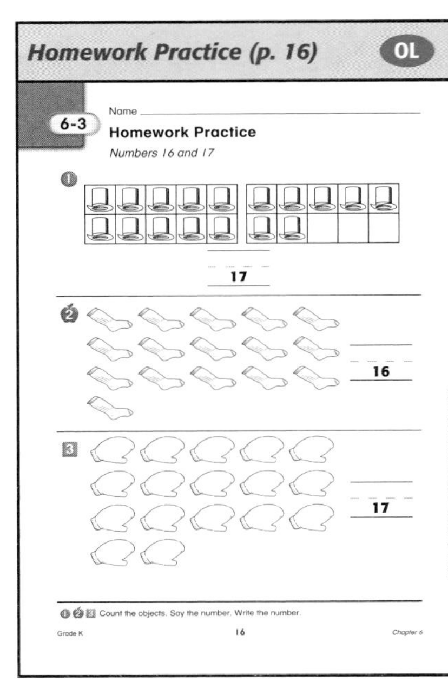

6-3 Name
Homework Practice
Numbers 16 and 17

1. 17
2. 16
3. 17

1 2 3 Count the objects. Say the number. Write the number.

Grade K 16 Chapter 6

1 Introduce

Circle Time

Activity Choice 1 • Literature

Jack the Builder
by Stuart J. Murphy
Materials: geometric solids

- Read the book aloud, counting the geometric figures.
- Have students work in small groups to create a structure using either **sixteen** or **seventeen** geometric solids.
- Have students represent the quantity verbally by counting out the number of figures used to build each structure.
- Have students create a class chart to record the number of figures each group used.

Activity Choice 2 • Hands-On

Materials: drum; number word cards for 15, 16, 17; two ten-frames

- Have three students each find five objects in the classroom and put their objects one at a time into two ten-frames counting aloud to 15 as each object is placed in a ten-frame.
- Beat the drum 15 times, having students count each beat. Other students should pretend to beat the drum by slapping their thighs at the same time.
- **What number comes next? How do you know?** 16; 16 is one more than 15.
- Have a student beat the drum 16 times. Ask what 16 looks like. Show card 16. Have students write 16 in the air.
- Have a student find one more object and place it in the ten-frame that is not full.
- **What number is one more than 16?** 17
- Have a student beat the drum 17 times as the class counts.
- Ask a student to find one more object and place it in the ten-frame that is not full. Have students count the 17 objects in the ten-frame.

2 Teach

- Direct students to the top of p. 157. Discuss sports and the sports that students know of or are involved in.
- Identify a basketball. Count together the basketballs. Have students practice writing 16 in the air.
- Represent the quantity verbally by counting out the soccer balls. Say that 17 is one more than 16. Have students practice writing 17 in the air.

BL Alternate Teaching Strategy

If students have trouble understanding how to count to 15, 16, and 17 . . .

Then use one of these reteach options.

1 CRM **Daily Reteach Worksheet** (p. 14)

2 **Use Manipulatives** Use attribute buttons to review counting.

- String 15 attribute buttons into a necklace one by one, having students count aloud from one to 15.
- **How many buttons will be on the string if one more is added?** 16 buttons
- Add another button to the string.
- Take the buttons off of the string one-by-one, having students count one to 16 aloud.
- Repeat with 17 buttons.

COMMON ERROR!

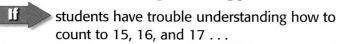

Students may not count each instrument sound as one. Have them slowly and carefully count one number for each drum beat.

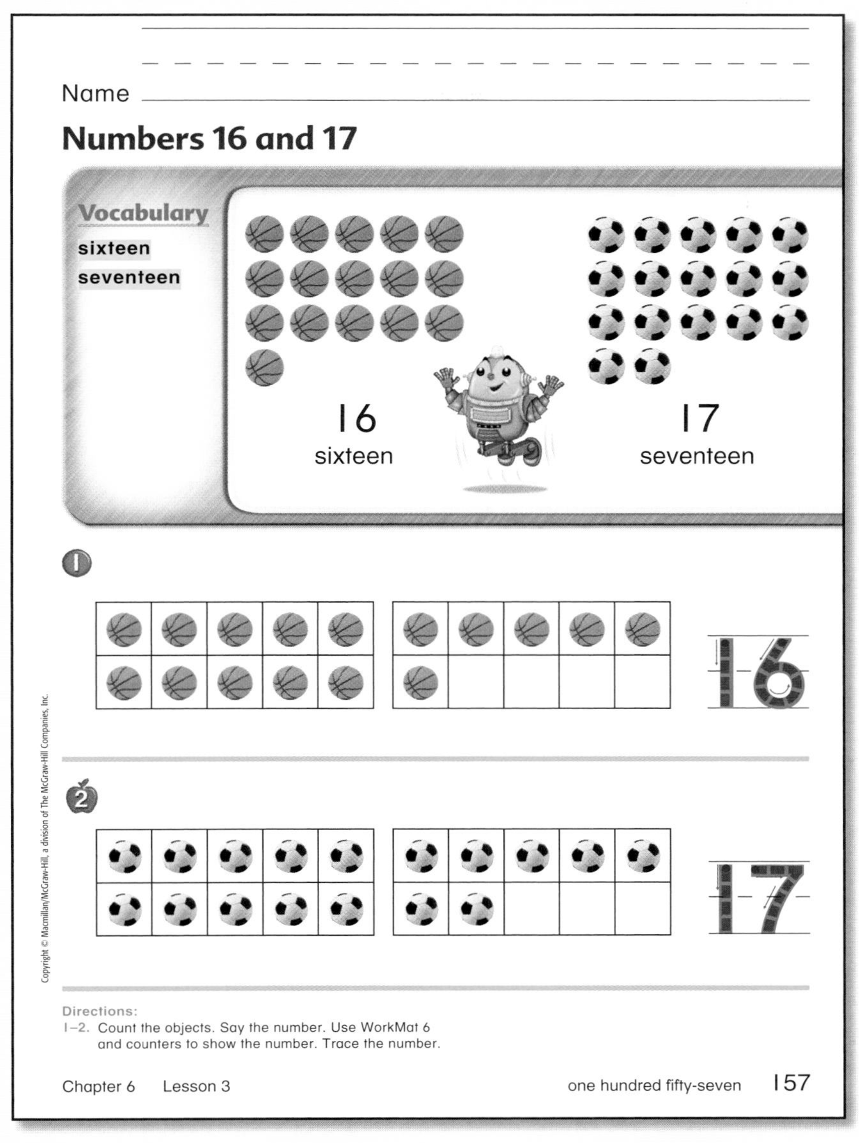

Name

Numbers 16 and 17

Vocabulary
sixteen
seventeen

16
sixteen

17
seventeen

1

16

2

17

Directions:
1–2. Count the objects. Say the number. Use WorkMat 6 and counters to show the number. Trace the number.

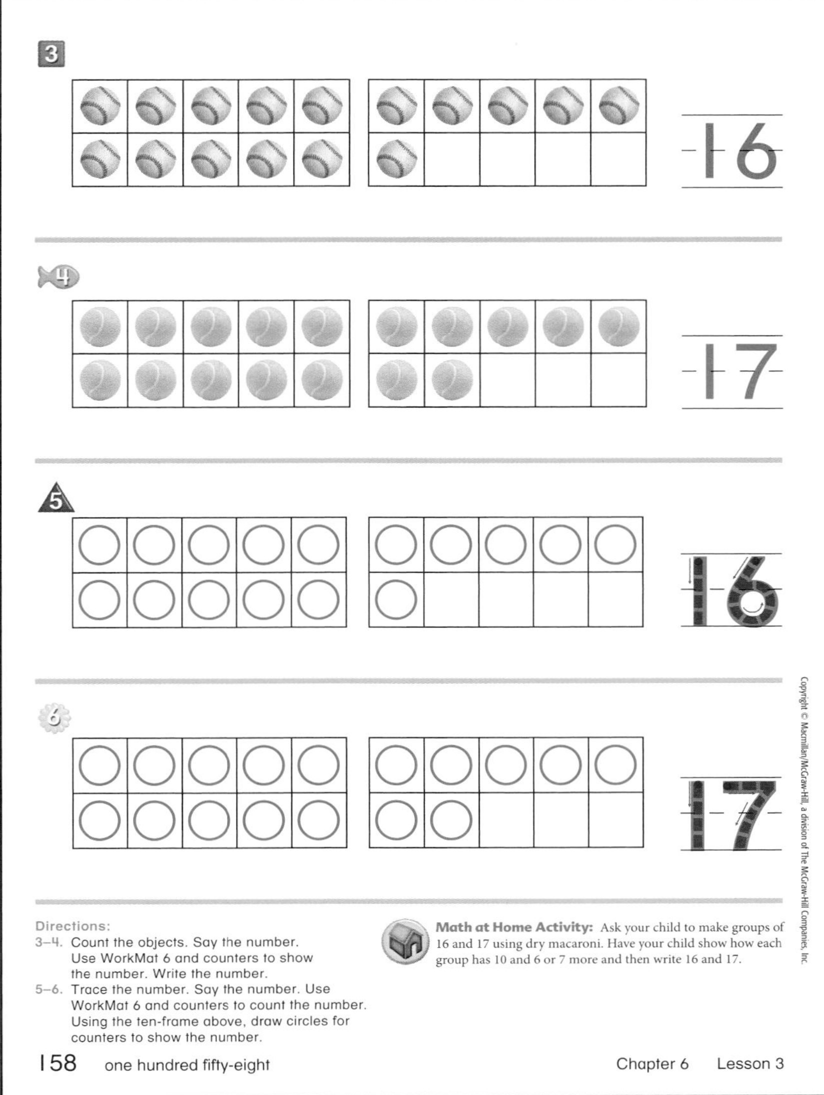

3

16

4

17

5

16

6

17

Directions:
3–4. Count the objects. Say the number. Use WorkMat 6 and counters to show the number. Write the number.
5–6. Trace the number. Say the number. Use WorkMat 6 and counters to count the number. Using the ten-frame above, draw circles for counters to show the number.

Math at Home Activity: Ask your child to make groups of 16 and 17 using dry macaroni. Have your child show how each group has 10 and 6 or 7 more and then write 16 and 17.

3 Practice

Guided Practice

- Direct students to Exercise 1 on p. 157.
- **Do you think there is the same number of balls in the ten-frames as above?** Sample answer: yes
- Have them count the basketballs. Distribute 16 counters and WorkMat 6. Count how many. Have students use WorkMat 6 and counters to show the number.
- Have students practice writing by tracing the number 16 on their papers.
- Work through Exercise 2 in the same way, counting soccer balls.

Independent Practice

Have students turn to p. 158 and work independently on Exercises 3 and 4. Explain directions for Exercises 5 and 6. Allow students to complete Exercises 5 and 6 independently.

4 Assess

Formative Assessment

Put 10 counters on a ten-frame mat. Place another ten-frame mat below it. Fill the second ten-frame mat with six counters.

- **How many counters are there?** 16 counters Add one more counter.
- **How many counters are there now? How do you know?** 17; 17 is the one more than 16.

Quick Check **Are students still struggling to count and write numbers 16 and 17?**

If Yes → Small Group Options (p. 157B)

If No → Independent Work Options (p. 157B)
CRM Skills Practice Worksheet (p. 15)
CRM Enrich Worksheet (p. 17)

Mid-Chapter Check

Lessons 6-1 to 6-3

Formative Assessment

Use the Mid-Chapter Check to assess students' progress in the first half of the chapter.

ExamView Assessment Suite Customize and create multiple versions of your Mid-Chapter Check and their answer keys.

FOLDABLES Dinah Zike's Foldables

Use these lesson suggestions for incorporating the Foldables during the chapter.

Lesson 6-1 Make and glue together two sections of the Foldable Number Line. Write the numbers 11 and 12 on the top left side of each of the two sections and have students find and place pictures on the appropriate sections to illustrate each of the numbers.

Lesson 6-2 Glue three more sections to the Foldable Number Line. Write the numbers 13, 14, and 15 on the top left side of each section and have students find and place pictures on the appropriate sections to illustrate each number.

Lesson 6-3 Make and glue two more Foldable sections to the number line. Write the numbers 16 and 17 on the top left side of each section and have students find and place pictures on the appropriate sections to illustrate each of the numbers.

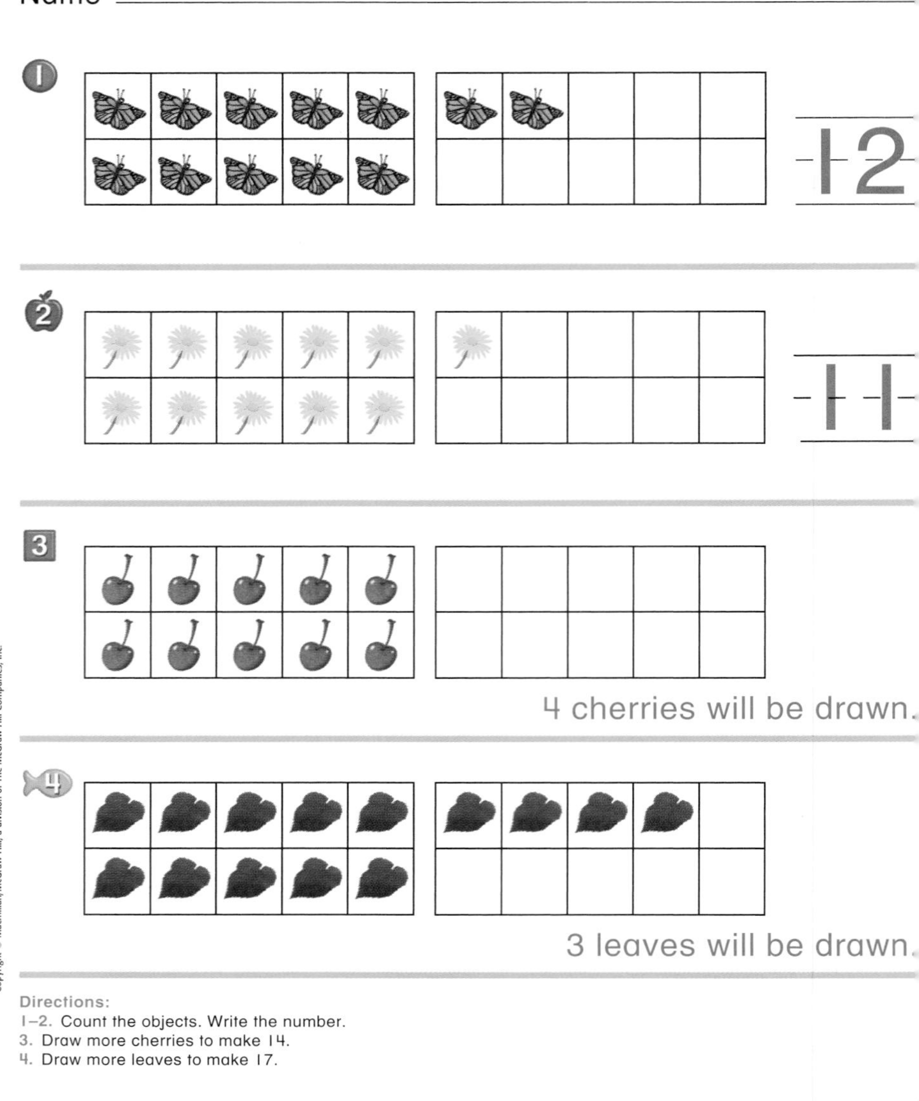

Mid-Chapter Check
Lessons 1-3
Name
12
11
4 cherries will be drawn.
3 leaves will be drawn.
Directions:
1–2. Count the objects. Write the number.
3. Draw more cherries to make 14.
4. Draw more leaves to make 17.
Chapter 6
one hundred fifty-nine 159

Data Driven Decision Making

Based on the results of the Mid-Chapter Check, use the following resources to review concepts that continue to give students problems.

Exercises	State/Local Standards	What's the Math?	Error Analysis	Resources for Review
1–2 Lesson 6-1		Understand the relationship between numbers and quantities. Name, recognize, count and write numbers up to 12.	Does not count correctly. Does not write the correct number.	CRM Chapter 6 Resource Masters (Reteach Worksheets) Math Online Concepts in Motion Math Adventures
3 Lesson 6-2		Understand the relationship between numbers and quantities. Name, recognize, count and write the number of objects up to 15.	Does not draw in spaces provided. Does not draw correct number of objects.	
4 Lesson 6-3		Understand the relationship between numbers and quantities. Name, recognize, count and write the number of objects up to 17.	Does not draw in spaces provided. Does not draw correct number of objects.	

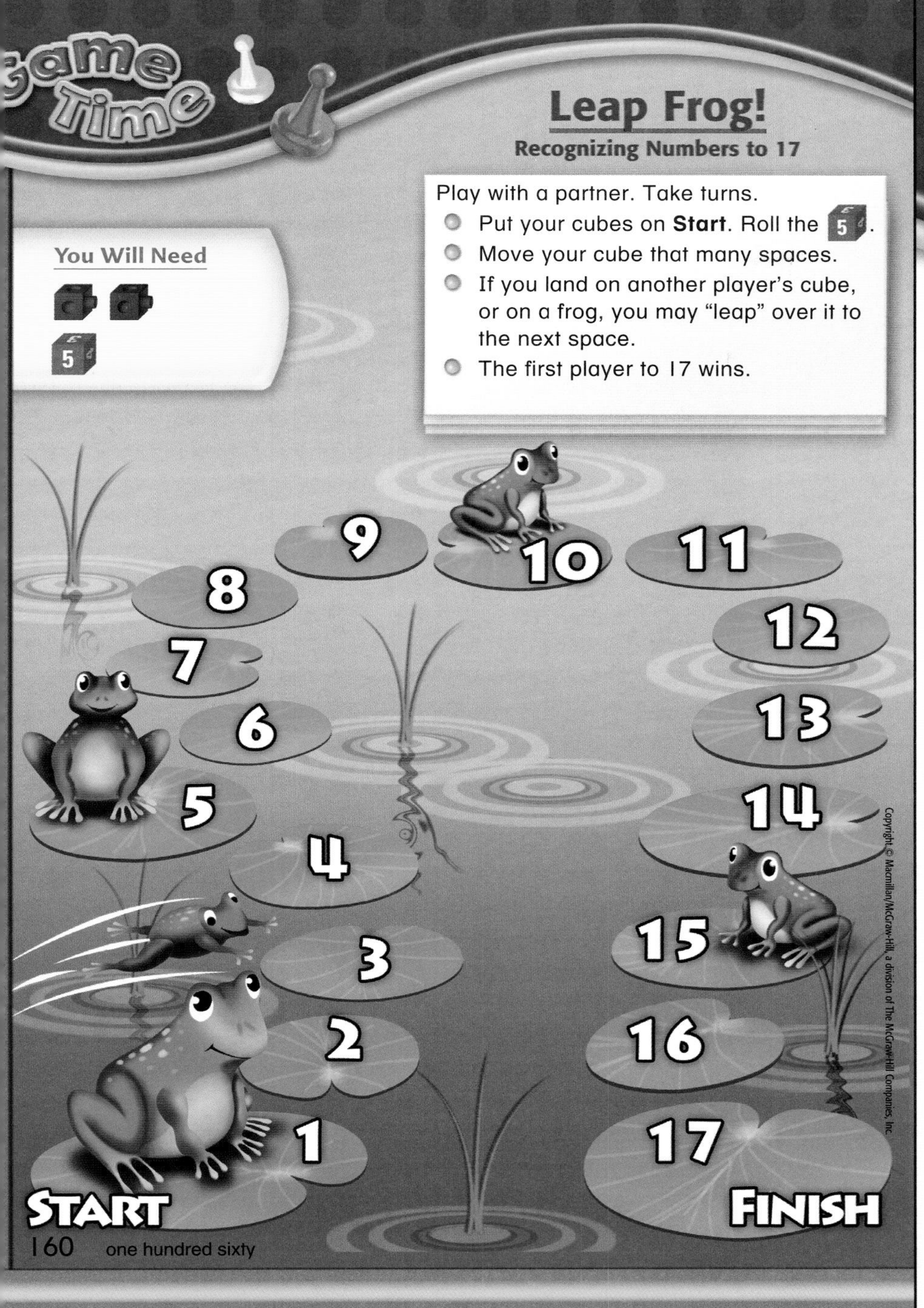

Game Time

Leap Frog!

Recognizing Numbers to 17

You Will Need

Play with a partner. Take turns.

- Put your cubes on **Start**. Roll the 5.
- Move your cube that many spaces.
- If you land on another player's cube, or on a frog, you may "leap" over it to the next space.
- The first player to 17 wins.

Leap Frog!

Math Concept: Recognizing Numbers to 17

Manipulatives: red number cube, one red cube, one purple cube

Introduce the game on page 160 to your students to play as a class, in small groups, or at a learning workstation to review concepts introduced in this chapter.

Instructions

- Assign each student a color.
- Have students play in pairs and take turns moving their cubes along the path.
- Have a player roll the number cube.
- The player moves his or her cube (frog) that many spaces.
- If students come to another player's frog on one of the game squares, they leap over it to the next square.
- The first player to 17 wins.

Extend the Game

Have students draw cards with greater numbers instead of rolling a number cube.

Differentiated Practice

Use these leveled suggestions to differentiate the game for all learners.

Level	Assignment
BL Below/Approaching Level	Have students share a square instead of leaping.
OL On Level	Have students play the game with the rules as written.
AL Above/Beyond Level	Have students predict what square they think they will land on before moving at each turn.

6-4 Problem-Solving Strategy
Look for a Pattern

Lesson Planner

Objective

Name, recognize, represent, and count the numerals 11–17 using illustrations.

Resources

Materials: string, paper clips, paper, pencils
Manipulatives: connecting cubes, attribute buttons
Literature Connection: *Icky Bug Numbers* by Jerry Pallotta
Teacher Technology
TeacherWorks

Real-World Problem Solving Library
Math and Science: ***At the Grocery Store***
Use these leveled readers to reinforce and extend problem-solving skills and strategies.

Leveled for:

- OL On Level
- ELL Sheltered English
- SP Spanish

For additional support, see the Real-World Problem Solving Teacher Guide.

On-level title is available in classroom Big book.

Daily Routine

Use these suggestions before beginning the lesson on p. 161.

5-Minute Check

(Reviews Lesson 6-3)
Have students count the objects and write the number.

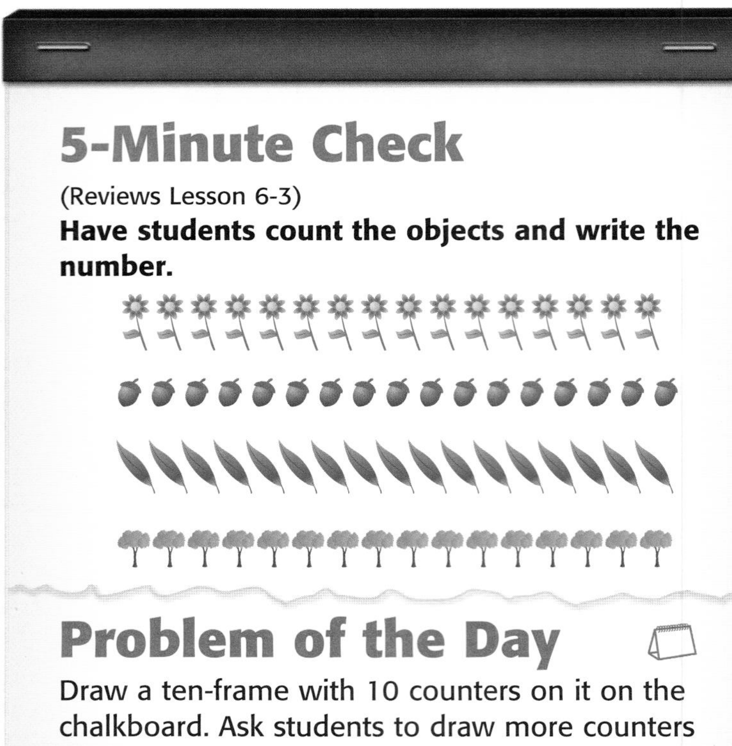

Problem of the Day

Draw a ten-frame with 10 counters on it on the chalkboard. Ask students to draw more counters to show 12. 2 Draw more counters to show 15. 5 Draw more counters to show 17. 7

LINE UP Have students line up in the following pattern: 2, 4, 6, 8. Count each group as they line up. Ask students to identify the pattern they find in the numbers.

Differentiated Instruction

Small Group Options

Option 1 Gifted and Talented AL

KINESTHETIC, LOGICAL

Materials: paper, crayons

- Have students work in pairs.
- Each partner takes a turn creating a number pattern, leaving out one number. The other partner needs to turn away while their partner is writing so they cannot see the pattern.
- The partner turns around and tries to solve the missing number.
- Once the partner has figured out the pattern, this student will take a turn creating a pattern using numbers for their pattern.

Option 2 English Language Learners ELL

INTRAPERSONAL

Core Vocabulary: table, set a table, group of things
Common Use Verb: set

Hear Math This strategy shows words can have two meanings.

- Say: "**Set and table** have more than one meaning. This is a **table**." Say "This is also a **table.**" Show a math table.
- Repeat for **set** (group of objects, putting something down, and setting a table).

Independent Work Options

Option 1 Early Finishers OL AL

INTERPERSONAL

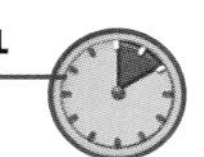

Materials: stickers, paper, pencil

- Give each student 30 stickers, a sheet of paper, and a pencil.
- Have students write the numbers 15, 10, and 5 at the top of the paper.
- Tell them to put that number of stickers in a column under each number.
- Ask them to find the pattern in the numbers.

Option 2 Student Technology

Option 3 Learning Station: Science (p. 149G)

Direct students to the Science Learning Station for opportunities to explore and extend the lesson concept.

Leveled Lesson Resources

Reteach (p. 18-19) BL

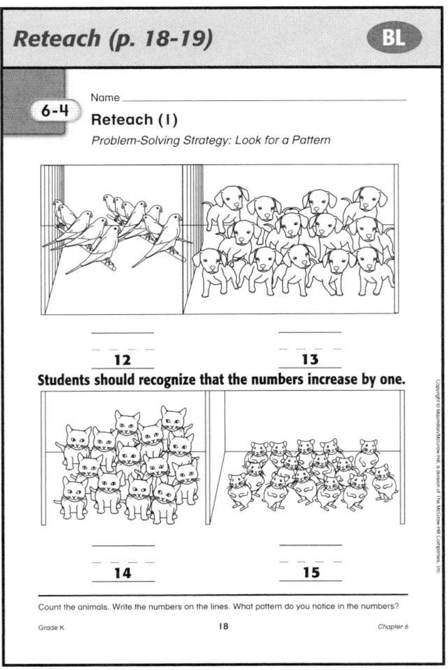
6-4 Name
Reteach (1)
Problem-Solving Strategy: Look for a Pattern

12 13
Students should recognize that the numbers increase by one.
14 15

Count the animals. Write the numbers on the lines. What pattern do you notice in the numbers?
Grade K 18 Chapter 6

Skills Practice (p. 20) OL

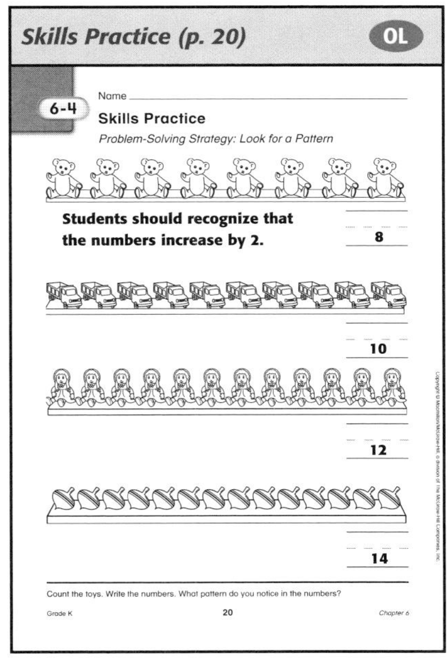
6-4 Name
Skills Practice
Problem-Solving Strategy: Look for a Pattern

Students should recognize that the numbers increase by 2.
8
10
12
14

Count the toys. Write the numbers. What pattern do you notice in the numbers?
Grade K 20 Chapter 6

Enrich (p. 22) AL

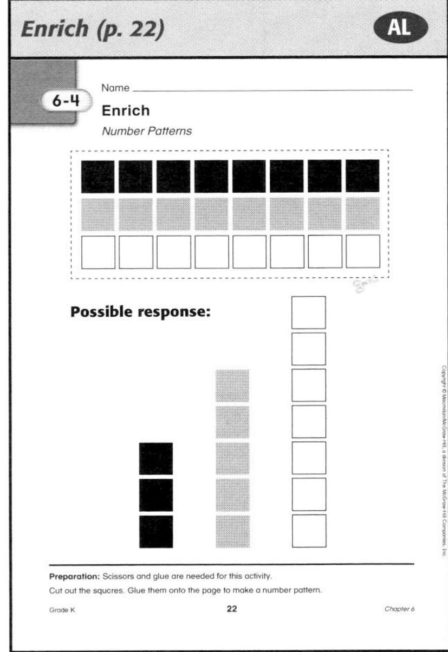
6-4 Name
Enrich
Number Patterns

Possible response:

Preparation: Scissors and glue are needed for this activity.
Cut out the squares. Glue them onto the page to make a number pattern.
Grade K 22 Chapter 6

Homework Practice (p. 21) OL

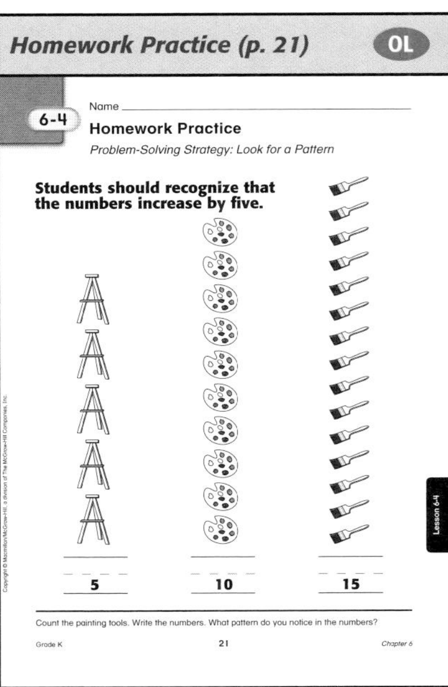
6-4 Name
Homework Practice
Problem-Solving Strategy: Look for a Pattern

Students should recognize that the numbers increase by five.

5 10 15

Count the painting tools. Write the numbers. What pattern do you notice in the numbers?
Grade K 21 Chapter 6

1 Introduce

Activity Choice 1 • Literature

Icky Bug Numbers
by Jerry Pallotta

- Read the first two to three sentences of each page.
- Pass out connecting cubes. Read a page with a one-digit number. Have students take out that many connecting cubes and count them to match the number.
- Turn to a page with a two-digit number and have the students take out that many cubes. As they count, demonstrate that as you get to ten it makes a stick. The rest are ones. For example: 15 is one ten stick and 5 ones.
- Repeat this with other numbers in the book as time allows, up to 17 connecting cubes.

Activity Choice 2 • Hands-On 

Manipulatives: attribute buttons, string

- Divide students into groups of four.
- Give each student in the group a different number of buttons to string. Be sure the number of buttons follows a pattern such as 2, 4, 6, 8.
- Ask groups to find a pattern in the number of buttons that the group members have.
- Discuss the patterns that students found.
- Repeat the activity with different numbers of buttons.

2 Teach

Direct students to the top of p. 161.

Understand Review what students know and what they need to find for each problem.

Plan Have students discuss their strategy for solving the problems.

Solve Guide students to look for a pattern to solve the problem. Review patterns with students and explain that patterns can be made in many ways, including numbers. Have students find patterns in the room.

Check Have students look back at the problem to be sure that the answers fit what they already know about the problem.

BL Alternate Teaching Strategy

If students have trouble looking for a pattern . . .

Then use one of these reteach options.

1 CRM **Daily Reteach Worksheet** (p. 18–19)

2 **Use Paper Clips** Give students chains of paper clips that are in a pattern, such as 6, 8, 10.

- Have students count the paper clips in each chain and write the numbers.
- Discuss with students what is happening to the chains by finding a pattern in the numbers. **What pattern do you see?** Each chain has 2 more paper clips than the chain before it. That means each number is two more.

COMMON ERROR!

Students may struggle to identify a pattern in the numbers. Have them describe what is happening to the objects and explain that this is also what is happening to the numbers.

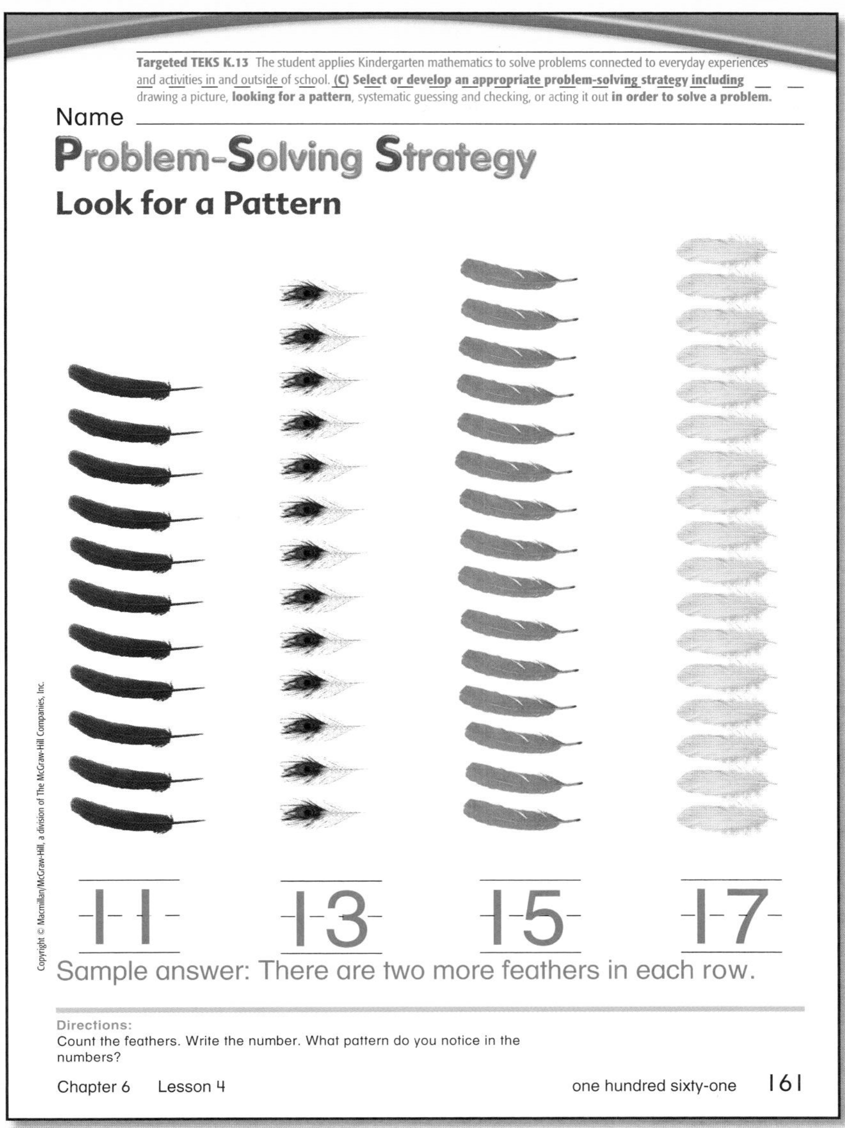

Targeted TEKS K.13 The student applies Kindergarten mathematics to solve problems connected to everyday experiences and activities in and outside of school. **(C) Select or develop an appropriate problem-solving strategy including** drawing a picture, **looking for a pattern**, systematic guessing and checking, or acting it out **in order to solve a problem.**

Name ______

Problem-Solving Strategy

Look for a Pattern

11 13 15 17

Sample answer: There are two more feathers in each row.

Directions:
Count the feathers. Write the number. What pattern do you notice in the numbers?

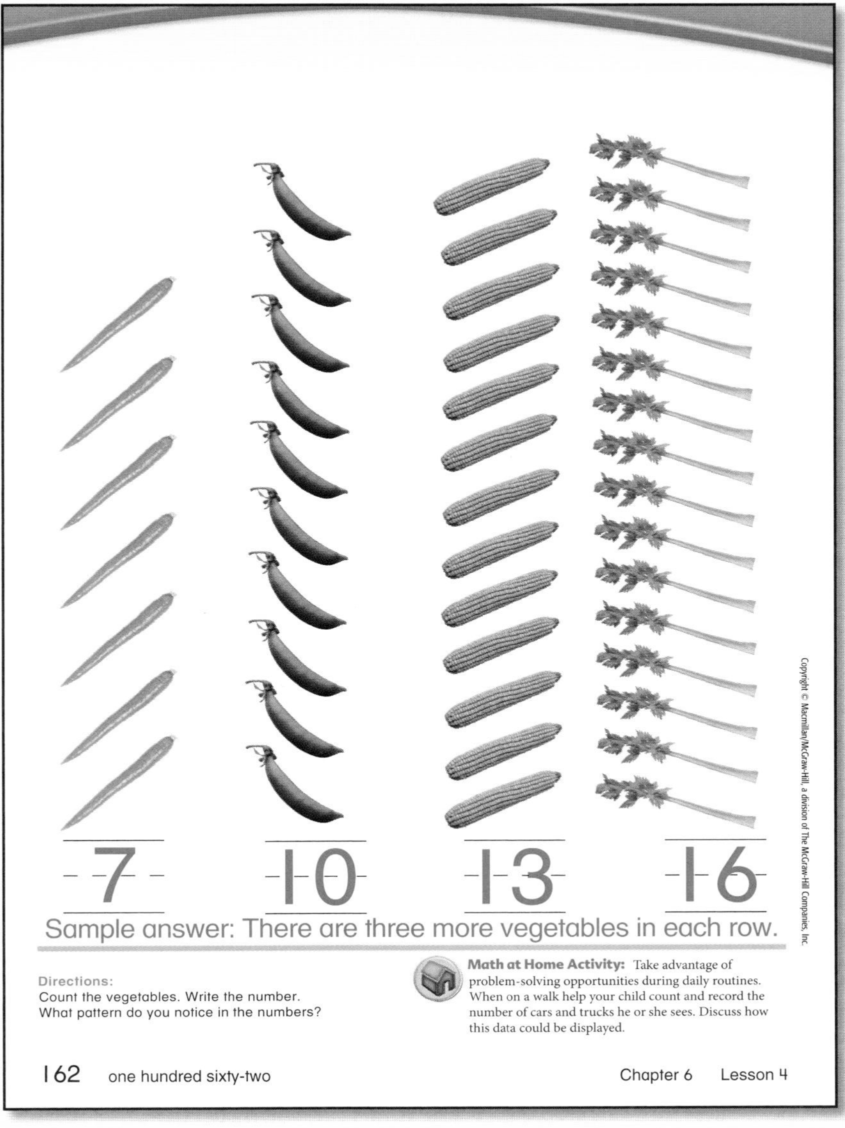

7 10 13 16

Sample answer: There are three more vegetables in each row.

Directions:
Count the vegetables. Write the number. What pattern do you notice in the numbers?

Math at Home Activity: Take advantage of problem-solving opportunities during daily routines. When on a walk help your child count and record the number of cars and trucks he or she sees. Discuss how this data could be displayed.

3 Practice

Guided Practice

- Direct students to p. 161.
- Have students count the feathers in the first column and write the number.
- Repeat for the other columns.
- Have students identify the pattern in the numbers.
- **What pattern do you see?** Each number is 2 more.

Independent Practice

Have students turn to p. 162 and work independently on the exercises.

4 Assess

Formative Assessment

- Draw four rows of apples with 16, 15, 14, and 13 apples respectively.
- Tell students to write how many apples are in each row.
- Have students look at the numbers they wrote. **What pattern do you see?** Each number is one less.

Quick Check **Are students still struggling to identify patterns?**

If Yes → Small Group Options (p. 161B)

If No → Independent Work Options (p. 161B)

CRM Skills Practice Worksheet (p. 20)

CRM Enrich Worksheet (p. 22)

LESSON 6-5

Numbers 18, 19, and 20

Lesson Planner

Objective

Name, recognize, count, and write the numerals 18, 19, and 20 using concrete objects and illustrations.

Vocabulary

eighteen, **nineteen**, **twenty**

Resources

Materials: WorkMat 5: Ten-Frame, crayons, picture of an 18-wheel truck, paper, number cards 18, 19, 20
Manipulatives: counters, connecting cubes
Literature Connection: *Bears at the Beach Counting 10 to 20* by Nikki Yektai
Alternate Lesson: Adapt *Geoboards* Numerals on page 48 of *Math Their Way* for practice in recognizing and writing the numbers 18, 19, and 20.
Teacher Technology
TeacherWorks • Concepts in Motion • Math Songs Track 3

Focus on Math Background

When keeping track of the number of days they have been in school, students will be able to practice bundling ones into groups of ten. This experience will reinforce that 20 can be represented by two groups of ten.

Daily Routine

Use these suggestions before beginning the lesson on p. 163.

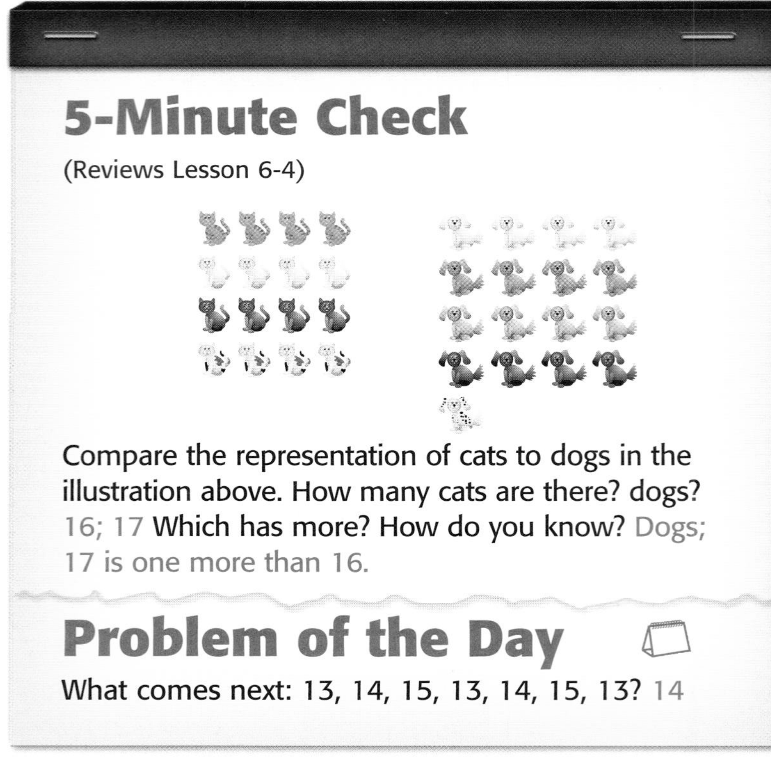

5-Minute Check

(Reviews Lesson 6-4)

Compare the representation of cats to dogs in the illustration above. How many cats are there? dogs? 16; 17 Which has more? How do you know? Dogs; 17 is one more than 16.

Problem of the Day

What comes next: 13, 14, 15, 13, 14, 15, 13? 14

LINE UP Have students line up one at a time. Have students count how many shoes are in line. At 20, start over with one.

Building Math Vocabulary

Materials: number/name cards for 18, 19, 20

- Have students form groups of three. Give a number/name card of **eighteen**, **nineteen**, or **twenty** to each group. Draw two ten-frames and stars to show 18 on the chalkboard.
- **What card matches the picture on the chalkboard?** 18
- Have students with the 18 card come to the front of the room, showing the card.
- Repeat, drawing 19 and then 20 on the chalkboard and having students with corresponding cards come to the front.

Differentiated Instruction

Small Group Options

Option 1 Below/Approaching Level BL

LOGICAL

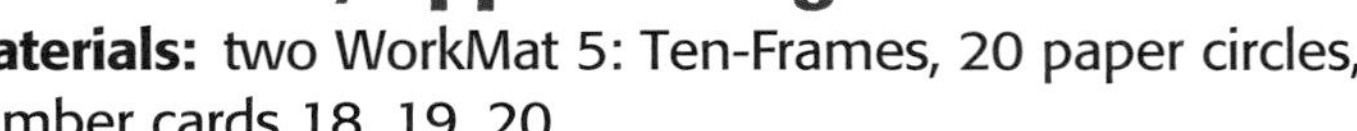

Materials: two WorkMat 5: Ten-Frames, 20 paper circles, number cards 18, 19, 20

- Select a volunteer to put 18 circles ("wheels") in the ten-frames as students count.
- **What number comes after 18? How do you know?** 19; 19 is one more than 18.
- Show card 19. Have students practice writing 19 in the air.
- Have a student add a wheel to the ten-frame and represent the quantity verbally by saying "19." Repeat for 20.

Option 2 English Language Learners ELL

LOGICAL

Materials: classroom objects, sticky notes, bags
Core Vocabulary: in, how many
Common Use Verb: find out

Do Math This strategy helps students recognize numbers 18–20.

- Write 18, 19, and 20 on sticky notes. Give each student a bag with 18, 19, or 20 objects in the bag.
- Have students count the objects and sort them, putting the sticky note on the bag.

Independent Work Options

Option 1 Early Finishers OL AL

SOCIAL

Materials: number cards 17, 18, and 19, paper, crayons

- Put the cards in a pile in the middle of the table. Have students work in pairs.
- The first student should draw one card and hold it up for their partner to see.
- The partner should identify the number, and say the number that is one more.
- Have the first student draw Xs on a piece of paper equal to the number on the card, while the partner draws Xs equal to the number that is one more.
- Have partners count the Xs aloud on each piece of paper to check which number is more.

Option 2 Student Technology

Math Online macmillanmh.com

Math Song Track 3

Math Adventures

Option 3 Learning Station: Art (p. 149H)

Direct students to the Art Learning Station for opportunities to explore and extend the lesson concept.

Leveled Lesson Resources

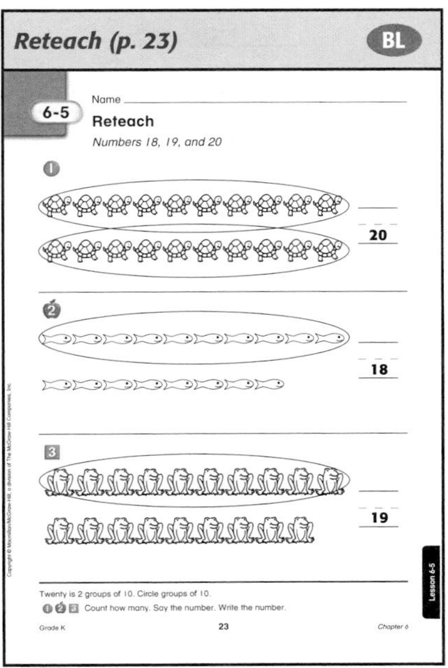
Reteach (p. 23) BL

6-5 Reteach
Numbers 18, 19, and 20

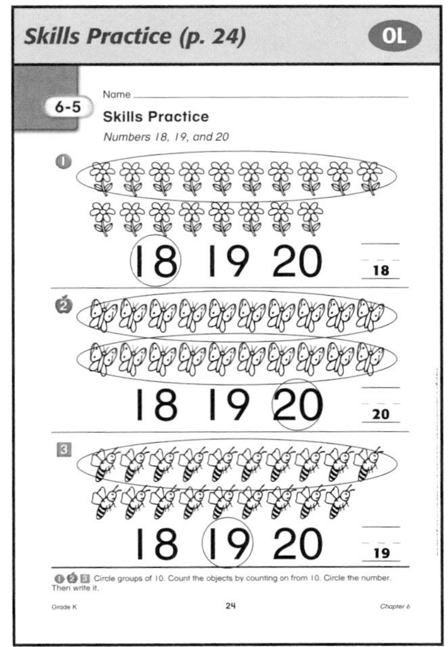
Skills Practice (p. 24) OL

6-5 Skills Practice
Numbers 18, 19, and 20

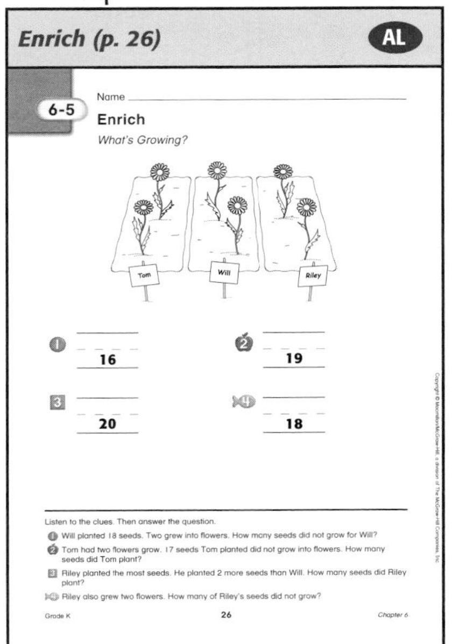
Enrich (p. 26) AL

6-5 Enrich
What's Growing?

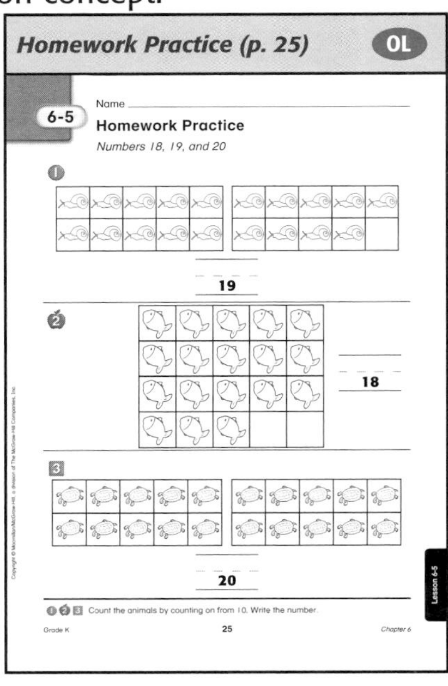
Homework Practice (p. 25) OL

6-5 Homework Practice
Numbers 18, 19, and 20

1 Introduce

Circle Time

Activity Choice 1 • Literature

Bears at the Beach Counting 10 to 20
by Nikki Yektai
Materials: counters, paper, crayons

- Read the book aloud, counting the numbers of objects in each picture.
- Have students make groups of **eighteen, nineteen,** and **twenty** counters.
- Have students represent the quantities by writing the numbers on a sheet of paper that correspond to the groups they made.

Activity Choice 2 • Hands-On 

Materials: picture of an 18-wheel truck, number card 18, 19, 20

- Show a picture of an 18-wheel truck and ask how it got its name. Count 18 wheels.
- Ask what 18 looks like. Show card 18. Have students practice writing 18 in the air.
- Tell students to move their hands in a circular motion, like a wheel. Model making a circle with hands as if rolling, having students join, counting one to 18.
- Repeat with 19 and 20.

2 Teach

- Direct students to the top of p. 163. Explain that some truckers drive 18-wheel trucks to bring food to stores.
- Represent the quantity verbally by counting the apples together. Have students write 18 in the air.
- Count the oranges together. Say that 19 is one more than 18. Have students practice writing 19 in the air.
- Count the peaches together. Say that 20 is one more than 19. Have students practice writing 20 in the air.

BL Alternate Teaching Strategy

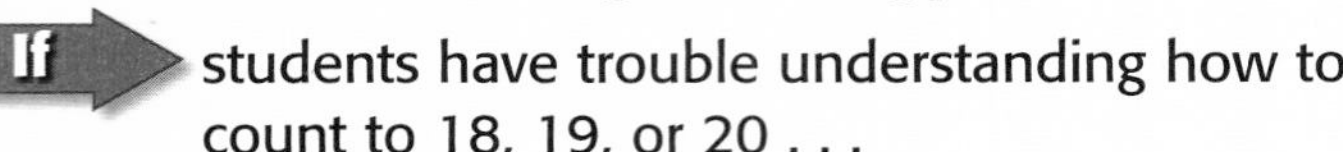

If students have trouble understanding how to count to 18, 19, or 20 . . .

Then use one of these reteach options.

1 CRM **Daily Reteach Worksheet** (p. 23)

2 **Use Connecting Cubes** Use connecting cubes to review counting.

- Connect 18 cubes to make an 18-wheeler, having students count cubes.
- **How many wheels will be on the truck if one more is added? Two more?** 19 wheels; 20 wheels
- Add a cube to the truck and recount. Add another cube and recount.
- Take the cubes apart, counting one to 20.

COMMON ERROR!

Students may have difficulty transitioning from the teens to 20. Practice counting from teen numbers to 20 to reinforce the change in number-word patterns.

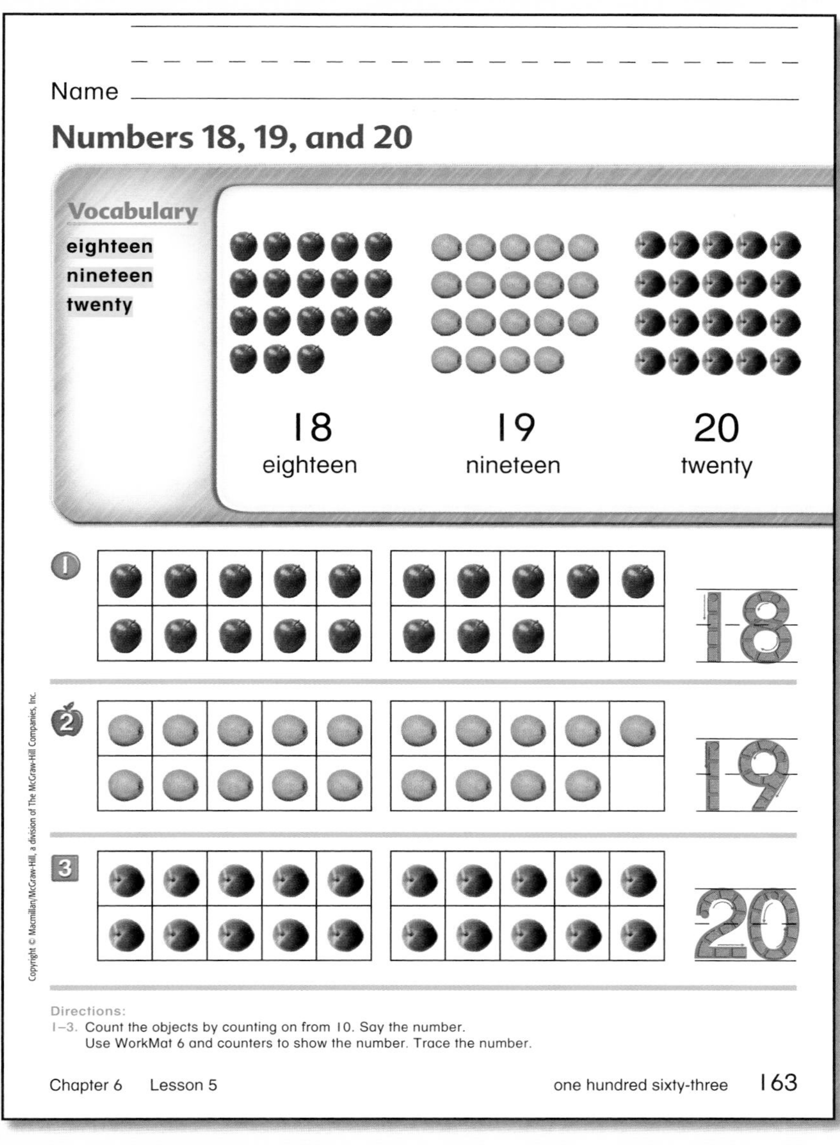

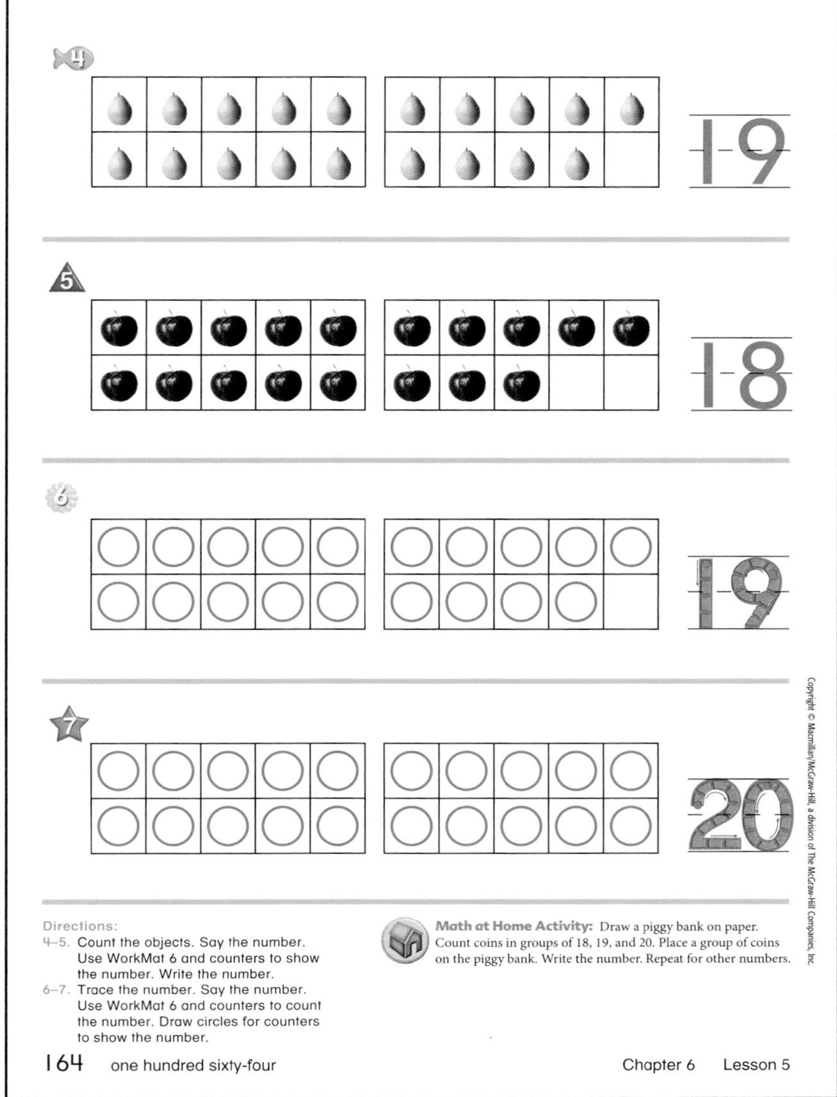

3 Practice

Guided Practice

- Direct students to Exercise 1 on p. 163.
- **Is the number of apples the same as in the apple bin above?** yes Have students count the apples aloud to check their answers.
- Distribute 18 counters and WorkMat 6 to each student. Have students count aloud the counters as they place each one in a ten-frame on WorkMat 6.
- Have students practice writing by tracing the number 18 on their papers.
- Work through Exercises 2 and 3 in the same way.

Independent Practice

Have students turn to p. 164 and work independently on the Exercises 4 and 5. Explain directions for 6 and 7. Have students complete Exercises 6 and 7 independently.

4 Assess

Formative Assessment

Put 10 counters on a ten-frame mat. Place another ten-frame mat below it. Fill the second ten-frame mat with eight counters.

- **How many counters are there?** 18 counters Add one more counter.
- **How many counters are there now? How do you know?** 19; 19 is one more than 18. Repeat to show 20.

Quick Check **Are students still struggling to count and write numbers 18, 19, and 20?**

If Yes → Small Group Options (p. 163B)

If No → Independent Work Options (p. 163B)

CRM Skills Practice Worksheet (p. 24)

CRM Enrich Worksheet (p. 26)

LESSON 6-6

Compare Numbers to 20

Lesson Planner

Objective

Count to compare to 20 and determine which has more, less, or are the groups the same.

Review Vocabulary

more, **less**

Resources

Materials: paper, crayons, paper bags, classroom objects such as crayons, paper clips, beads, clothespins, number cards 0-20

Manipulatives: connecting cubes, pattern blocks

Literature Connection: *Chicka Chicka 1 2 3* by Bill Martin, Jr., Michael Sampson, Lois Ehlert

Alternate Lesson: Adapt *Recording at the Number Stations* on page 177 of *Math Their Way* for practice using one-to-one correspondence and comparing groups to determine more or less.

Use *IMPACT Mathematics*: Unit C to provide practice with comparing sets.

Teacher Technology

TeacherWorks • Concepts in Motion • Math Songs Track 3

Focus on Math Background

Students gradually develop number sense, an ongoing process. As students are exposed to greater numbers, they learn to recognize and name the numerals as well as understand the relative magnitude of the numbers.

Daily Routine

Use these suggestions before beginning the lesson on p. 165.

5-Minute Check

(Reviews Lesson 6-5)

1. Draw 18 squares. Write the number 18.
2. Draw 19 Xs. Write the number 19.
3. Draw 20 Os. Write the number 20.
4. Is 20 more than 19? How do you know? Yes; 20 is one more than 19. 20 comes after 19.

Problem of the Day 

If two full ten-frames show the number 20, what number would one full ten-frame and nine show? 19

Have boys line up and then girls. **Are there more boys or girls? How do you know?** Sample answer: Count boys and girls. Compare the two numbers.

Review Math Vocabulary

Materials: connecting cubes, paper bags, markers

- Put 11 to 20 cubes in each paper bag. Give each student a bag and a marker. Have students work in pairs. Have one partner count the cubes in a bag. Have the other partner recount. Have each pair write the number of cubes on the bag and return the cubes to the bag.
- Have students switch roles and repeat.
- Have pairs exchange bags and compare the number of cubes in each bag. Pairs should identify whose bag has **more** and whose bag has **less**.

Differentiated Instruction

Small Group Options

Option 1 Below/Approaching Level (BL)

LOGICAL

Materials: 2 paper bags, small objects such as crayons, paper clips, beads, clothespins

- Fill one bag with nine crayons and one bag with 14 paper clips. Label each bag with the number of objects.
- Have a student count the crayons.
- Repeat with the paper clips in the other bag.
- Ask comparison questions such as "Which is more, nine crayons or 14 paper clips?"
- Repeat the activity with different numbers and objects.

Option 2 English Language Learners (ELL)

LOGICAL

Materials: sticky notes numbered 1 to 20
Core Vocabulary: what number, before, after
Common Use Verb: comes

Do Math This strategy models comparing numbers to 20.

- Give each student a numbered sticky note.
- Call students up to place themselves from 1 to 20, using the vocabulary.
- Place "10" in the middle and say: "Ten is in the middle. What number comes before, or after 10?"

Independent Work Options

Option 1 Early Finishers (OL) (AL)

LOGICAL

Materials: index cards, markers

- Make two sets of cards with dots from 10 to 20. Give each student five cards. Put remaining cards facedown in a pile. Have students take turns asking the others if they are holding a card that matches theirs.
- If the person asked has the card, they give it to the student. If not, the student draws from the pile.
- Have students lay down their matching pair of cards face up. The winner is the person who has the most matches. Repeat with students asking for cards that are more or less than theirs.

Option 2 Student Technology

Math Online macmillanmh.com

Math Adventures

Option 3 Learning Station: Reading (p. 149G)

Direct students to the Reading Learning Station for opportunities to explore and extend the lesson concept.

Leveled Lesson Resources

Additional support for English Language Learners can be found in the ELL Guide (p. 61). (ELL)

Reteach (p. 27) (BL)

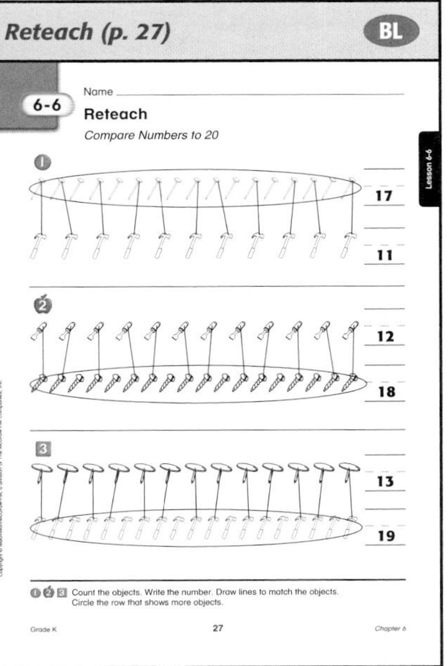
6-6 Name
Reteach
Compare Numbers to 20
Lesson 6-6
1 17 11
2 12 18
3 13 19
1 2 3 Count the objects. Write the number. Draw lines to match the objects. Circle the row that shows more objects.
Grade K 27 Chapter 6

Skills Practice (p. 28) (OL)

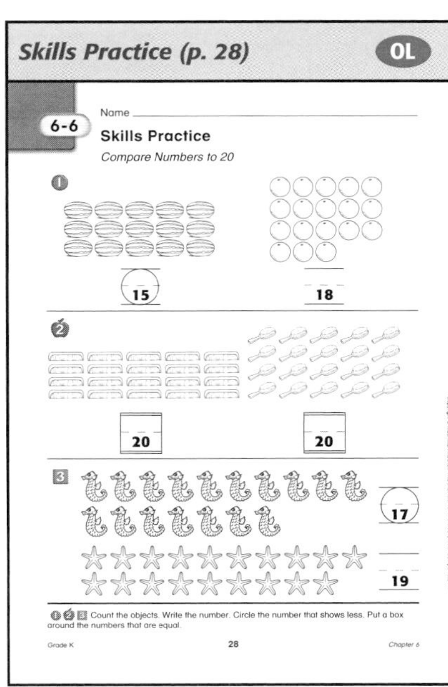
6-6 Name
Skills Practice
Compare Numbers to 20
1 15 18
2 20 20
3 17 19
1 2 3 Count the objects. Write the number. Circle the number that shows less. Put a box around the numbers that are equal.
Grade K 28 Chapter 6

Enrich (p. 30) (AL)

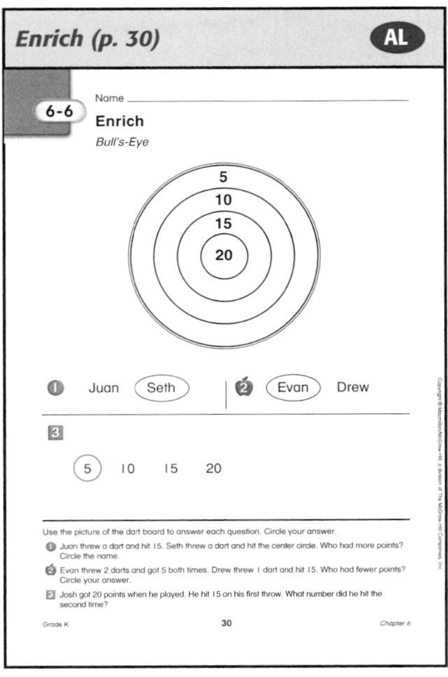
6-6 Name
Enrich
Bull's-Eye
5 10 15 20
1 Juan Seth
2 Evan Drew
3 5 10 15 20
Use the picture of the dart board to answer each question. Circle your answer.
1 Juan threw a dart and hit 15. Seth threw a dart and hit the center circle. Who had more points? Circle the name.
2 Evan threw 2 darts and got 5 both times. Drew threw 1 dart and hit 15. Who had fewer points? Circle your answer.
3 Josh got 20 points when he played. He hit 15 on his first throw. What number did he hit the second time?
Grade K 30 Chapter 6

Homework Practice (p. 29) (OL)

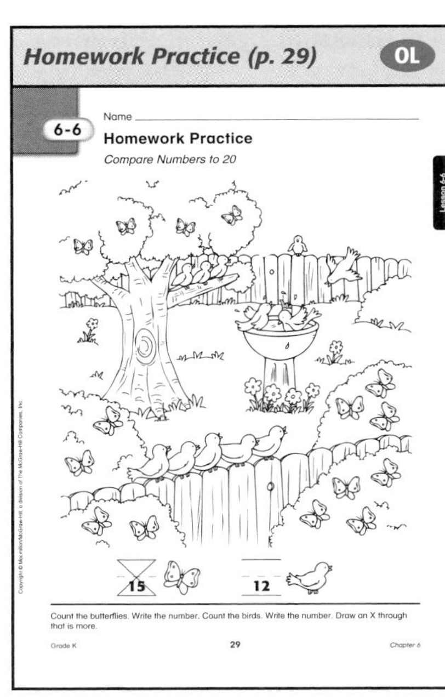
6-6 Name
Homework Practice
Compare Numbers to 20
Lesson 6-6
15 12
Count the butterflies. Write the number. Count the birds. Write the number. Draw an X through that is more.
Grade K 29 Chapter 6

1 Introduce

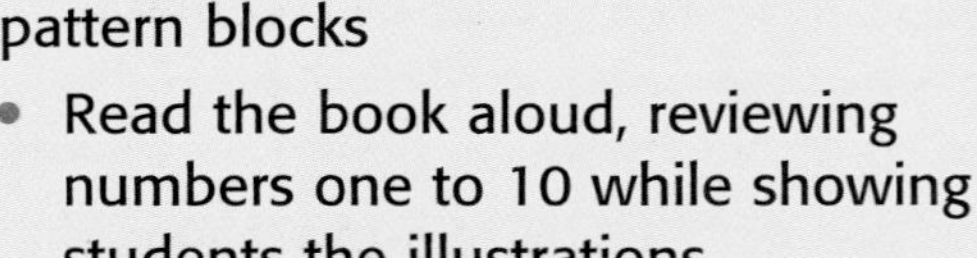

Circle Time

Activity Choice 1 • Literature

Chicka Chicka 1 2 3 by Bill Martin, Jr., Michael Sampson, Lois Ehlert
Manipulative Materials: paper, crayons, bags, classroom items, pattern blocks

- Read the book aloud, reviewing numbers one to 10 while showing students the illustrations.
- Continue counting from 11 to 20. Write each number on the chalkboard.
- Have sample collections of 11 to 20 classroom items prepared in bags (for example, 11 pattern blocks, 16 crayons).
- Describe quantities verbally by counting each collection with the class and put it by the correct number on the chalkboard.
- Assign each student a number from 11 to 20 to draw and color. Then create a class *Chicka Chicka 1 2 3* book. Put the book in the Math Center so that students can review it.

Activity Choice 2 • Hands-On

Materials: connecting cubes

- Have students sit in a circle. Give each student five connecting cubes. Tell them they will have a train-building race, and that the winner of the round will build the train with the most cubes.
- Give one cube to the student on your left and one cube to the student on your right so that two trains are being built. Each of those students adds a cube to the train and passes it to the next student. All students should add a cube to only one train.
- **How can we compare the number of cubes on the trains to decide which is more?** Compare lengths and count to compare numbers. Use a summary statement, such as "12 is **more** than 11" or "13 is **less** than 14."

2 Teach

- Direct students to the top of p. 165. Describe the amount verbally by counting together the crackers in the first and second plates. Write the numbers.
- Discuss which plate has more, which has less, and which has the same amount.
- Have students place an X through the number that describes the set with more objects, or a box around the numbers that are the same.
- Count the crackers on each yellow plate and write the numbers.
- Ask students what they notice about the crackers on the yellow plates. Emphasize that they are the *same number* thus they are equal.

BL Alternate Teaching Strategy

If students have trouble understanding how to compare numbers . . .

Then use one of these reteach options.

1 CRM **Daily Reteach Worksheet** (p. 27)

2 **Compare Numbers** Use connecting cubes to review counting.

- Make two trains of 16 cubes and 19 cubes, having students count aloud.
- Lay the trains next to each other.
- **Which is more, 16 or 19?** 19
- **Which is less, 16 or 19?** 16
- Take one cube off the 19 train. Add two cubes to the 16 train.
- **How do the trains compare?** Same number; both have 18 cubes.

COMMON ERROR!

Students may be confused when asked questions using more and less. Use the words in statements and questions, discussing the differences.

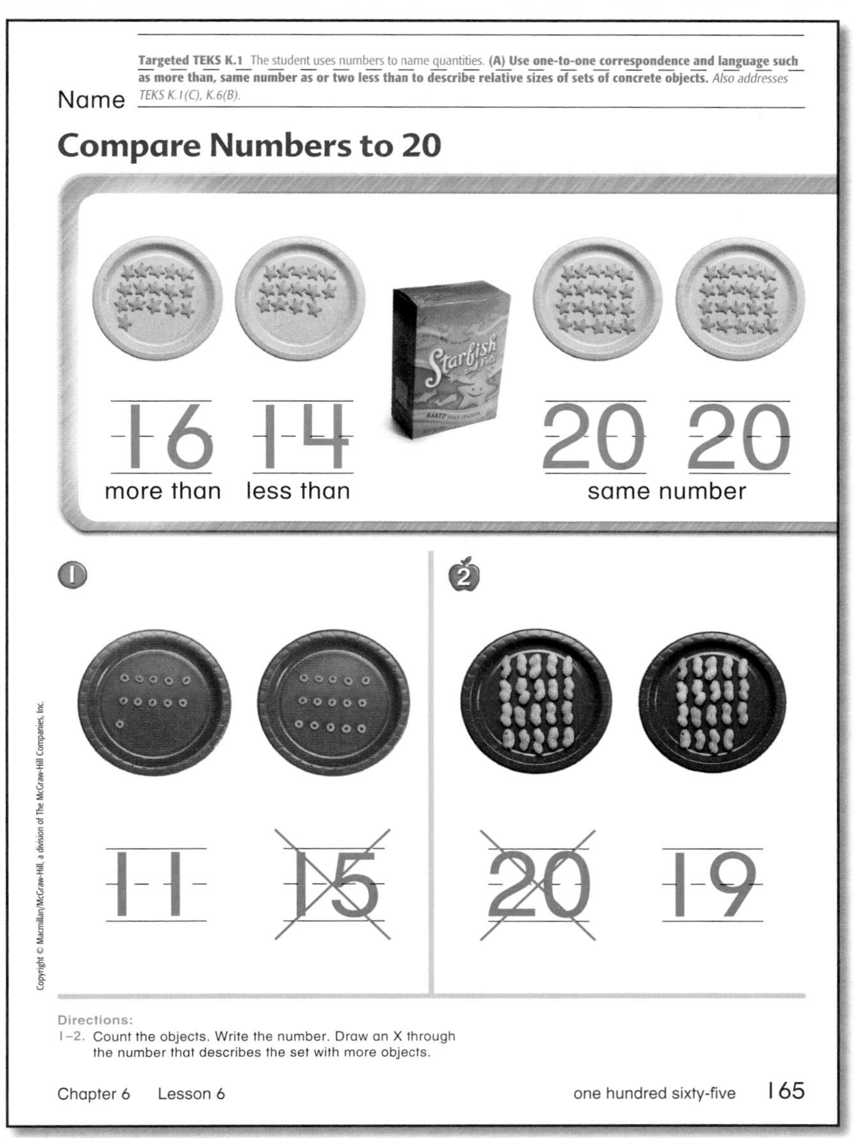

Targeted TEKS K.1 The student uses numbers to name quantities. (A) Use one-to-one correspondence and language such as more than, same number as or two less than to describe relative sizes of sets of concrete objects. Also addresses TEKS K.1(C), K.6(B).
Name
Compare Numbers to 20
16
14
20
20
more than
less than
same number
1
2
11
15
20
19
Directions:
1–2. Count the objects. Write the number. Draw an X through the number that describes the set with more objects.
Chapter 6 Lesson 6
one hundred sixty-five 165

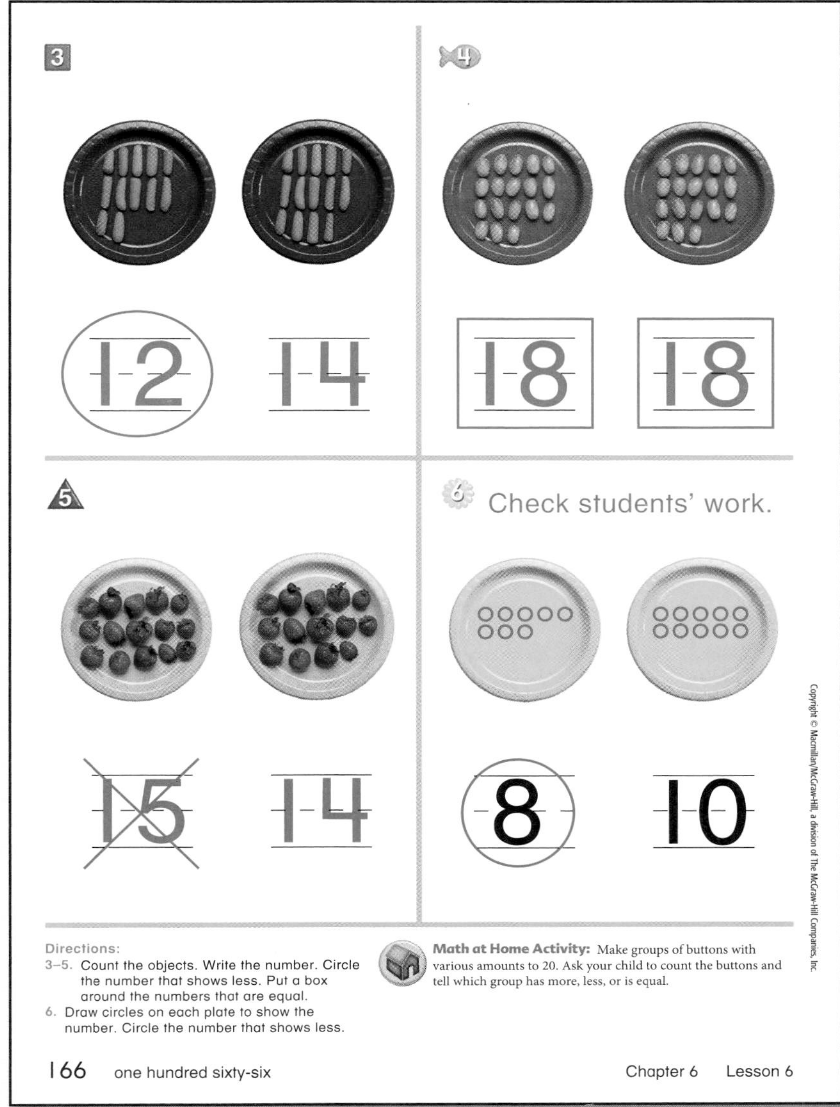

3
4
12
14
18
18
5
6
Check students' work.
15
14
8
10
Directions:
3–5. Count the objects. Write the number. Circle the number that shows less. Put a box around the numbers that are equal.
6. Draw circles on each plate to show the number. Circle the number that shows less.
Math at Home Activity: Make groups of buttons with various amounts to 20. Ask your child to count the buttons and tell which group has more, less, or is equal.
166 one hundred sixty-six
Chapter 6 Lesson 6

3 Practice

Guided Practice

- Direct students to Exercise 1 on p. 165. Have student count the pieces of cereal and put the total amount below the plate. Help them determine which plate has more cereal and put an X on the number.
- Work Exercise 2 in the same way, counting and comparing peanuts on plates.

Independent Practice

Have students turn to p. 166. Explain the directions and have students work independently on the exercises.

4 Assess

Formative Assessment

Hold up two number cards, one with a single-digit number and one with a double-digit number up to 20.

- Have students compare the numbers.
- **Which number is more?** Sample answer: 14
- Repeat with different cards, asking students which number is more than, less than, or the same (equal) number.

Quick Check **Are students still struggling to compare numbers to 20?**

If Yes → Small Group Options (p. 165B)

If No → Independent Work Options (p. 165B)

CRM Skills Practice Worksheet (p. 28)

CRM Enrich Worksheet (p. 30)

LESSON 6-7

Order Numbers to 20

Lesson Planner

Objective

Order numbers from 1 to 20 in sequence using a number line.

Review Vocabulary

order

Resources

Materials: number cards 0–20

Literature Connection: *Let's Count It Out, Jesse Bear* by Nancy White Carlstrom

Alternate Lesson: Adapt *Dot to Dots* on page 49 of *Math Their Way* for practice in ordering numbers 0 through 20. Use *IMPACT Mathematics*: Unit C to provide practice with ordering numbers.

Teacher Technology

TeacherWorks • Math Songs Track 3

Focus on Math Background

As students begin counting greater numbers, they may struggle with the order of the "teen" numbers. By using ten frames, students will learn to carefully compare the number of ones and will then be better able to order the numbers from one to 20.

Daily Routine

Use these suggestions before beginning the lesson on p. 167.

5-Minute Check

(Reviews Lesson 6-6)

1. Which is more, 17 or 14? 17
2. Which is less, 19 or 12? 12
3. Which is more, 18 or 18? Neither; they are equal.
4. Which is more, 13 or 16? 16
5. Which is less, 11 or 15? 11

Problem of the Day

What comes next: 10, 9, 8, 7, ___? 6

LINE UP Give each student a number card from one to 20. Call up students with cards one to five in random order, and ask them to line up so that their numbers are ordered correctly. Repeat with numbers five to 10, 11 to 15, and 16 to 20.

Review Math Vocabulary

Materials: index cards numbered 1–20, two-colored counters, ten-frames

- Have students work in pairs. Have each student draw a number card, then use ten-frames and counters to show the number.
- Have pairs form groups of four. Have each group put their four cards in **order** from least to greatest.
- Verify number order. Repeat the activity with different cards.

Differentiated Instruction

Small Group Options

Option 1 Gifted and Talented (AL)

LOGICAL

Materials: 10 laminated number lines ending with 20 but missing a variety of numbers, overhead markers

- Students will need washable overhead markers to fill in the missing numbers on the laminated number lines. Encourage students to check their work by counting out the numbers.
- Students need to complete each of the 10 number lines with the markers, and then wipe their answers off of the number line so that it is ready for the next student.

Option 2 English Language Learners (ELL)

LOGICAL

Materials: strings, sets of sticky notes numbered 1-20
Core Vocabulary: out of order, in order, revising
Common Use Verb: place

Talk Math This strategy teaches ordering numbers through cooperative groups and auditory recognition.

- Tape strings to the wall for groups. Put sticky notes next to the strings in any order.
- Have the class count chorally from one to twenty as a group orders their notes on the string.
- Repeat for all groups.
- Have groups check the order by reading the notes, revising as necessary.

Independent Work Options

Option 1 Early Finishers (OL) (AL)

LOGICAL

Materials: number cards 0–20

- Have students work in pairs. Have each pair shuffle a set of number cards zero to 20. Have them put the number cards in order in a row from left to right.
- Have one partner look away while the other partner removes a card. Have the first partner say which number is missing.
- Repeat twice, and then have pairs switch roles.

Option 2 Student Technology

Math Online macmillanmh.com

Math Adventures

Option 3 Learning Station: Music (p. 149G)

Direct students to the Music Learning Station for opportunities to explore and extend the lesson concept.

Leveled Lesson Resources

Additional support for English Language Learners can be found in the ELL Guide (p. 47). (ELL)

Reteach (p. 31) (BL)

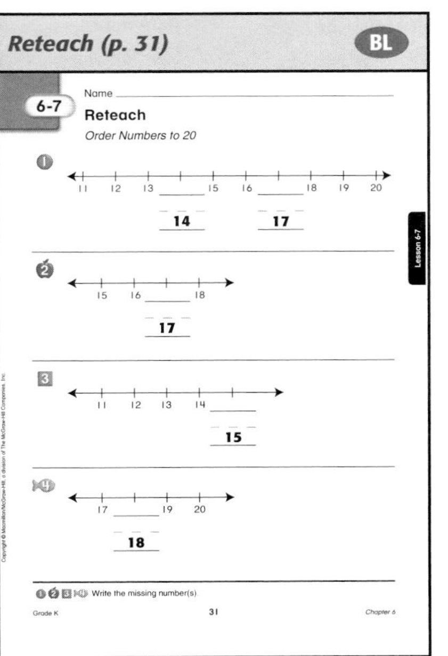
Name
6-7 Reteach
Order Numbers to 20

1. 11 12 13 ___ 15 16 ___ 18 19 20 — 14, 17
2. 15 16 ___ 18 — 17
3. 11 12 13 14 ___ — 15
4. 17 ___ 19 20 — 18

Write the missing number(s).
Grade K 31 Chapter 6

Skills Practice (p. 32) (OL)

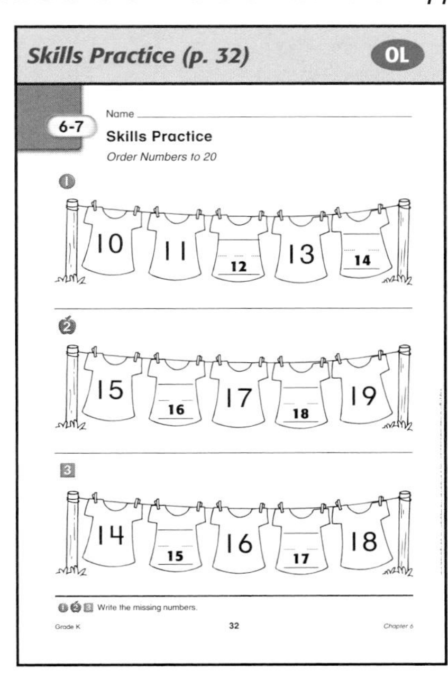
Name
6-7 Skills Practice
Order Numbers to 20

1. 10 11 ___ 13 ___ — 12, 14
2. 15 ___ 17 ___ 19 — 16, 18
3. 14 ___ 16 ___ 18 — 15, 17

Write the missing numbers.
Grade K 32 Chapter 6

Enrich (p. 34) (AL)

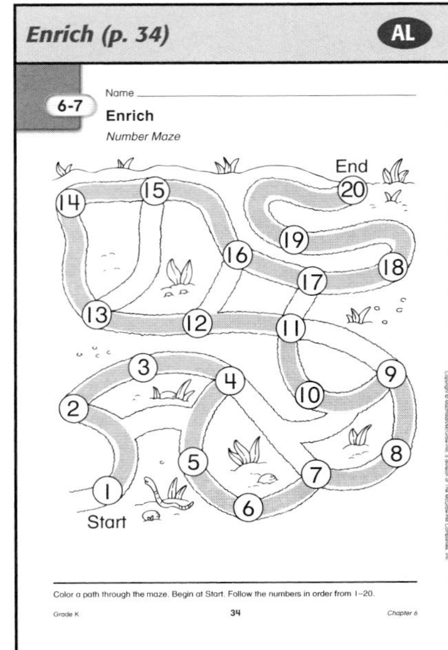
Name
6-7 Enrich
Number Maze

Color a path through the maze. Begin at Start. Follow the numbers in order from 1–20.
Grade K 34 Chapter 6

Homework Practice (p. 33) (OL)

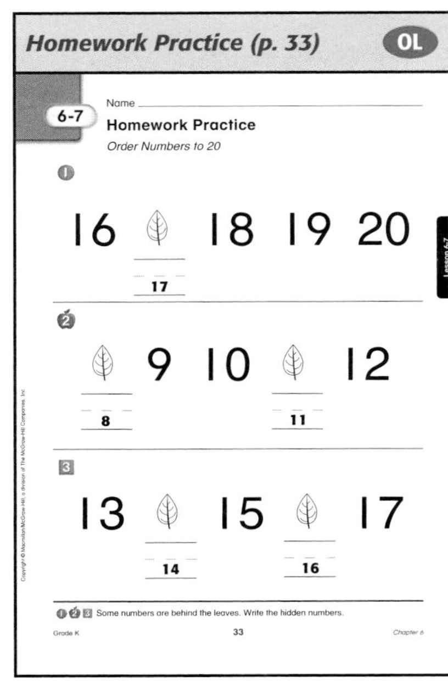
Name
6-7 Homework Practice
Order Numbers to 20

1. 16 ___ 18 19 20 — 17
2. ___ 9 10 ___ 12 — 8, 11
3. 13 ___ 15 ___ 17 — 14, 16

Some numbers are behind the leaves. Write the hidden numbers.
Grade K 33 Chapter 6

1 Introduce

Circle Time

Activity Choice 1 • Literature

Let's Count It Out, Jesse Bear
by Nancy White Carlstrom
Materials: number cards 1–20

- Read the book aloud. Randomly distribute number cards one to 20, one per student.
- Ask the student with the number card for one to stand. Ask the student with "one and one more" to line up. Have students continue lining up in order from numbers one to 20.

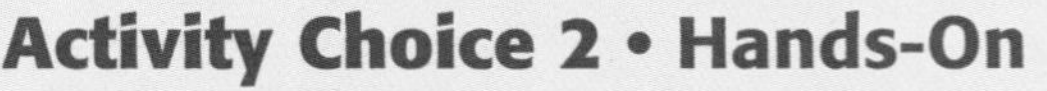

Activity Choice 2 • Hands-On

Materials: number cards 0–20

- Distribute number cards zero to 20 in order, one per student. Have students line up in order and count out their numbers.
- Tell them that they formed a number line, or a line with numbers on it in order. Explain that number lines help us count and know the order of numbers.
- **Do all number lines end with 20?** No, the number at the end can be less than 20 or more than 20.

2 Teach

- Direct students to the top of p. 167. Discuss the weather shown on the page. Ask students to count from zero to 20, pointing to each number.
- Practice using the number line by asking students questions such as "What number comes just after three?" or "What number is just before 12?"

BL Alternate Teaching Strategy

If students have trouble understanding how to order numbers . . .

Then use one of these reteach options.

1. CRM **Daily Reteach Worksheet** (p. 31)
2. **Use Number Cards** Distribute number cards one to five to five different students—one card for each student. Have students line up in order.
   - Mix up the students in line so that their numbers are out of order. Have the class call out the correct order by counting aloud.
   - Repeat with new groups of students, using number cards six to 10, 11 to 15, and 16 to 20.

! COMMON ERROR!

Students may have difficulty putting numbers on a number line. Explain that they look at it like they are reading or writing. Then, numbers are greater the further they move along the number line.

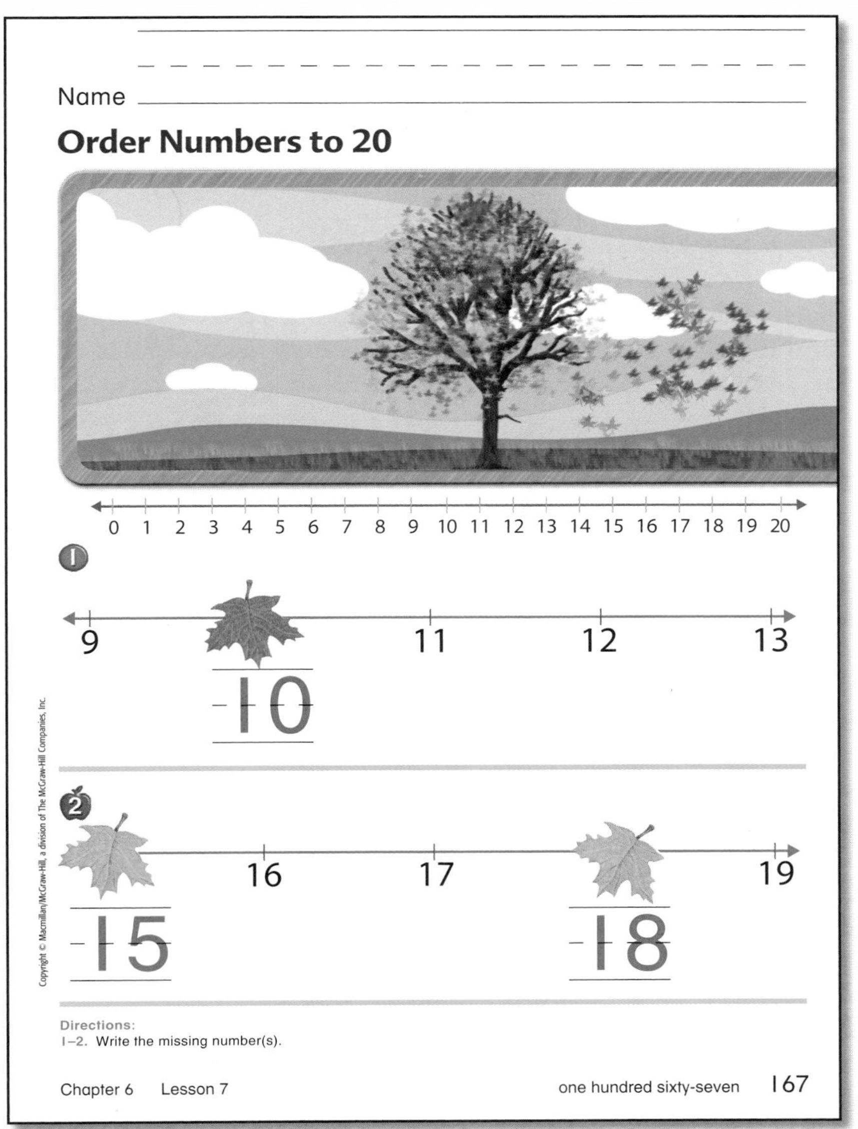

3 Practice

Guided Practice

- Direct students to Exercise 1 on p. 167. Tell them that this is also a number line, but only part of it is showing. Say that a leaf is hiding a number. Have students say the hidden number aloud. Write the number below the leaf.
- Repeat for Exercise 2.

Independent Practice

Have students turn to p. 168. Explain the directions. Have students work independently on the exercises.

4 Assess

Formative Assessment

- Draw a number line from zero to 20 on the chalkboard. Point to any number, asking what comes before and after.
- Have students close their eyes and erase a number(s) from the number line.
- Have students identify the missing number(s).

Quick Check **Are students still struggling to order numbers to 20?**

If Yes → Small Group Options (p. 167B)

If No → Independent Work Options (p. 167B)
CRM Skills Practice Worksheet (p. 32)
CRM Enrich Worksheet (p. 34)

Problem Solving
in Social Studies
Real-World MATH
Some people have collections.
A collection is many of the same kind of thing.
This book belongs to
A

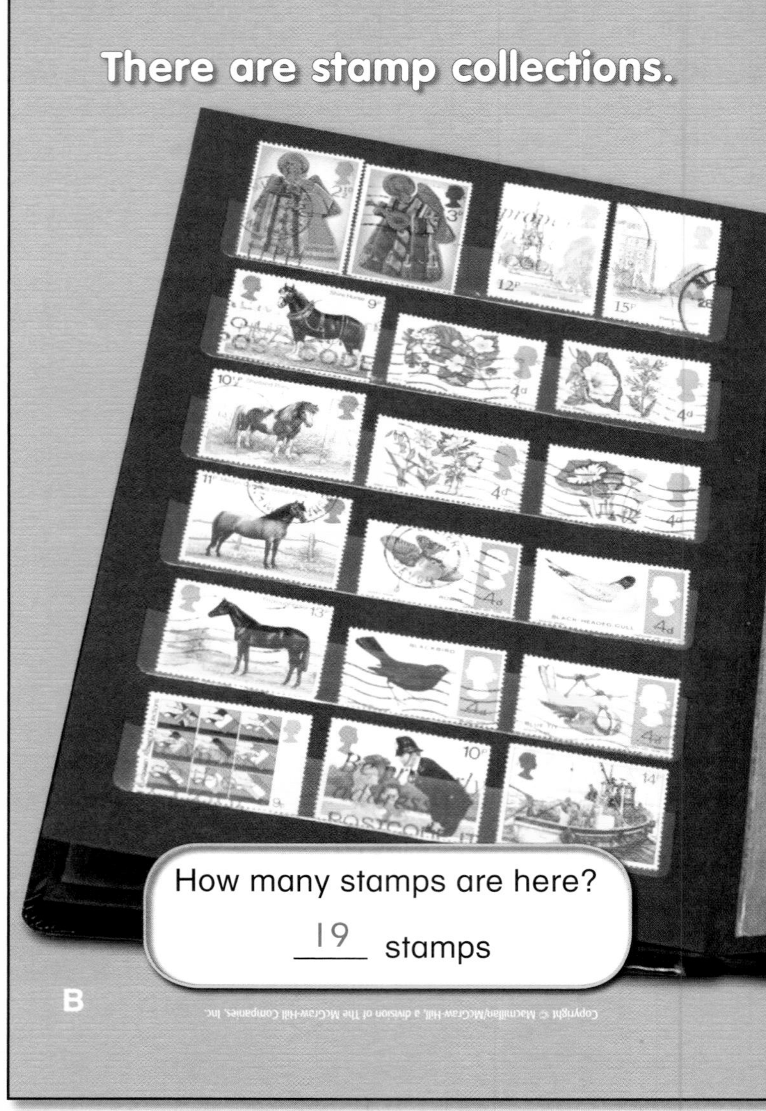

There are stamp collections.
How many stamps are here?
19 stamps
B

Lesson Planner

Objective

To count objects in a collection.

National Standard 

Students learn about distinctive characteristics of American society.

Activate Prior Knowledge

Before you turn students' attention to the pages, discuss collections.

- **What is a collection?** a group of the same kind of things
- **What types of things do people collect?** Sample answers: stamps, coins, shells, rocks

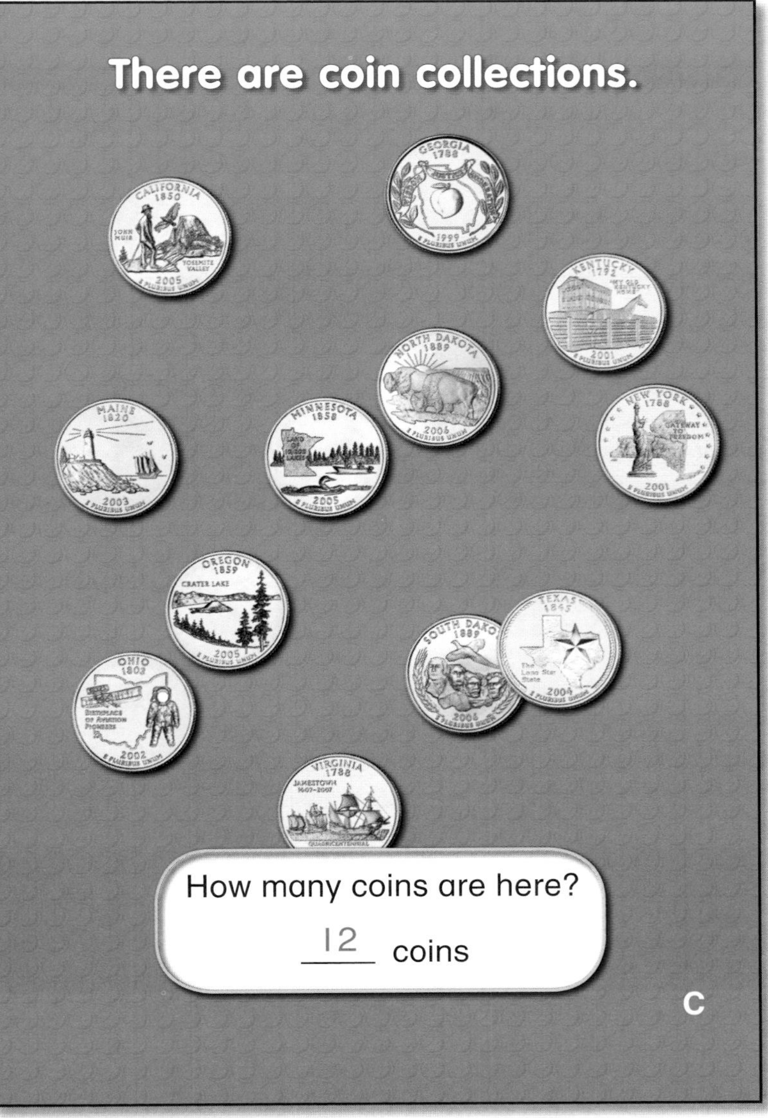

There are coin collections.
How many coins are here?
12 coins
C

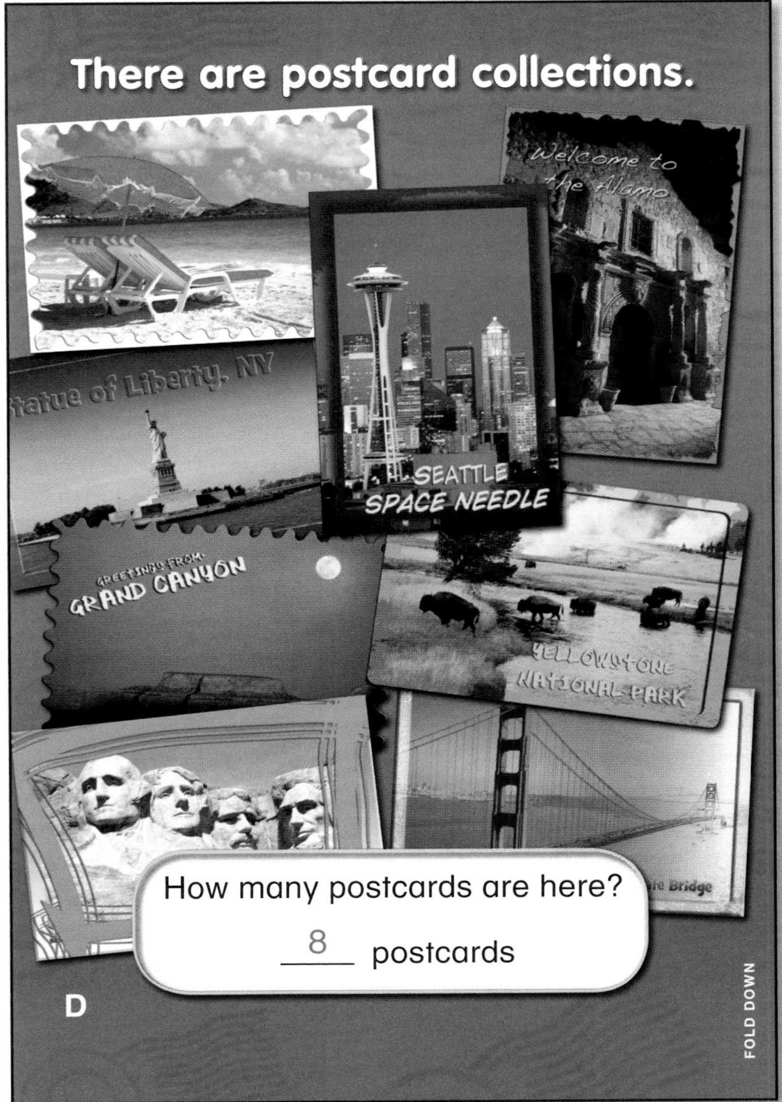

Create the Book

Guide students to create their book.

- Have them fold the page in half.
- Ask them to write their name on page A.
- Explain that page A is the front cover and page D is the back cover. If necessary, have them practice flipping through the book in order.
- Guide them in reading the information and word problems on each of the pages.

Use the Student Page

Have students work individually or in pairs to solve the word problems on pages B–D.

Page B Have students mark each stamp as it is counted.

Page C Have students group large numbers to help them keep track of which objects they have counted.

Page D If necessary, review the problem-solving strategies suggested in Lesson 6-4, p. 161.

WRITING IN MATH Have students draw their own collection by drawing pictures of something they collect or would like to collect.

Dinah Zike's Foldables

Use these lesson suggestions for incorporating the Foldables during the chapter.

Lesson 6-5 Make and add three more sections to the Foldable Number Line. Write the numbers 18, 19, and 20 on the top left side of each section and have students find and place pictures on the appropriate sections to illustrate each of the numbers.

Lesson 6-6 Use the display cases made in Chapter 1 to compare numbers one to 20. Place one to 20 objects in each of the two display cases. Determine which groups have *more*, *less*, or *the same (equal)* number of objects.

Lesson 6-7 Use the number line to review the order of numbers from zero to 20.

NOTE: Stand the sections on end to form an accordion to help students visualize how to glue them together. Always place the extra tab at the back of the book so you can add more pages later.

Chapter 6 Project

My Counting Cards

Lead a discussion on the results of the completed chapter project with the class.

Vocabulary Review

Review chapter vocabulary using the **eGlossary** at macmillanmh.com.

Data-Driven Decision Making

Based on the results of the Chapter/Review Test, use the following to review concepts that continue to present students with problems.

Exercises	State/Local Standards	What's the Math?	Error Analysis	Resources for Review
1–3 Lesson 6-3		Understand the relationship between numbers and quantities. Name and write numbers up to 17.	Does not count correctly. Writes wrong number.	CRM Chapter 6 Resource Masters (Reteach Worksheets) Math Online Concepts in Motion Math Adventures
4 Lesson 6-5		Understand the relationship between numbers and quantities. Name, recognize, count and write numbers up to 20.	Does not count correctly. Writes wrong number. Does not circle group with more.	
5 Lesson 6-7		Order numbers up to 20 using a number line.	Writes wrong numbers. Writes numbers in wrong places.	

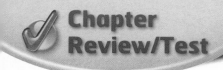

Chapter Review/Test

Name

1. 12
2. 15
3. 17
4. 14 12
5. 16 17 18 19 20

Directions:
1–3. Count the objects. Write the number.
4. Count the objects in each group. Write the number. Circle the group that has more.
5. Write the hidden numbers.

Chapter 6 one hundred seventy-one 171

Copyright © Macmillan/McGraw-Hill, a division of The McGraw-Hill Companies, Inc.

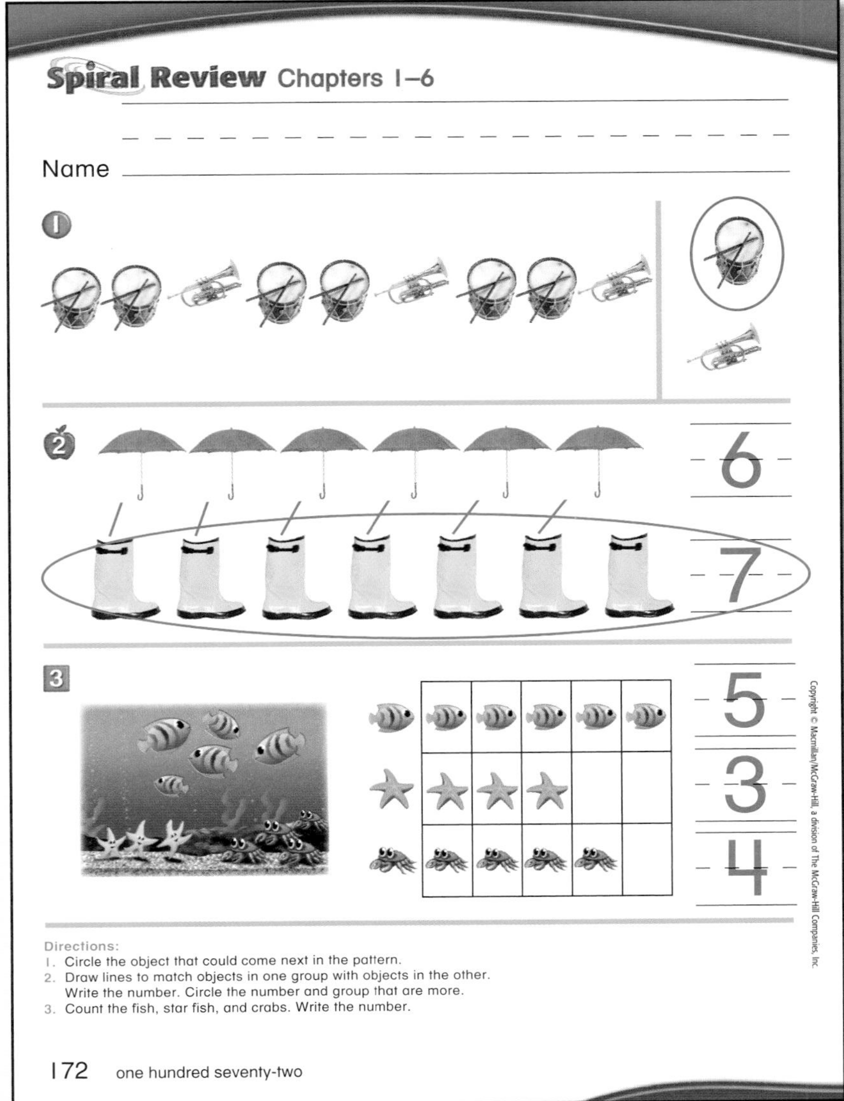
Spiral Review Chapters 1–6

Name

1.
2. 6 7
3. 5 3 4

Directions:
1. Circle the object that could come next in the pattern.
2. Draw lines to match objects in one group with objects in the other. Write the number. Circle the number and group that are more.
3. Count the fish, star fish, and crabs. Write the number.

172 one hundred seventy-two

Copyright © Macmillan/McGraw-Hill, a division of The McGraw-Hill Companies, Inc.

Summative Assessment

Use these alternate leveled chapter tests to differentiate assessment for the specific needs of your students.

Leveled Chapter 6 Tests			
Form	**Type**	**Level**	**CRM Pages**
1	Multiple Choice	BL	42–43
2A	Multiple Choice	OL	44–45
2C	Multiple Choice	OL	46–47
2D	Free Response	AL	48–49

BL = below/approaching grade level
OL = on grade level
AL = above/beyond grade level

Spiral Review

Reviews Chapters 1 to 6

Objective: Review and assess mastery of skills and concepts from previous chapters.

Resources for Review

Based on student results, refer to these lessons for remediation.

- **Exercise 1: Lesson 3-5** (p. 81)
- **Exercise 2: Lesson 4-7** (p. 115)
- **Exercise 3: Lesson 5-1** (p. 131)

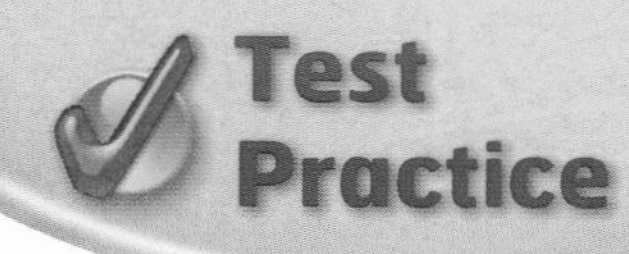

Chapter 1-6

Formative Assessment

- You can use Student Edition pp. 173-174 to benchmark student progress.
- Additional practice pages can be found in Chapter 6 Resource Masters.

Chapter 6 Resource Masters
Cumulative Test Practice

- Multiple Choice format (pp. 42–47)
- Free Response format (pp. 48–49)

Create additional practice worksheets or tests.

Math Online For additional practice with the NCTM Focal Points and Focal Connections, visit macmillanmh.com.

Test-Taking Tips

For the Teacher

- You may repeat orally administered directions if necessary.
- Read oral test questions at a moderate, steady pace.

For the Student

- Make sure students check that they have filled in an oval for each test question.
- Pay close attention when you hear the teacher's voice.

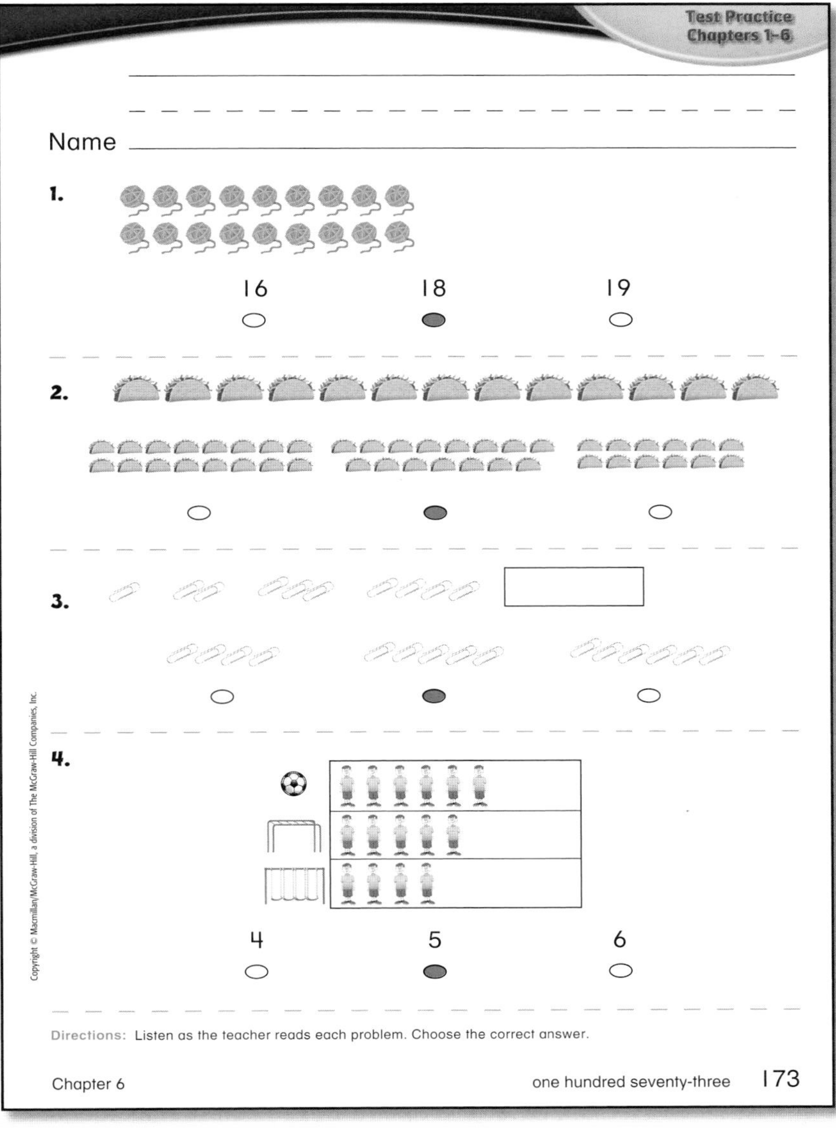

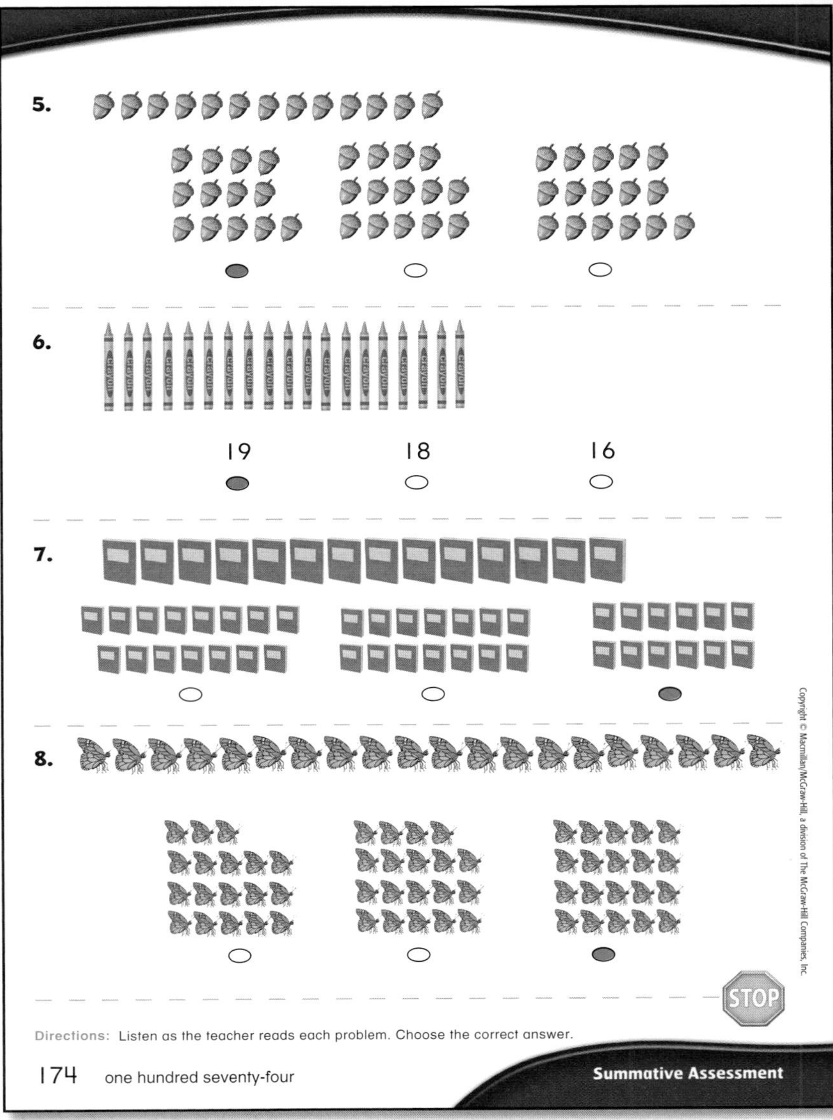

Test Directions for Teachers

Read the following directions to students before they begin. Then read each question followed by a pause to allow students time to work and choose an answer. The first test item can be worked as a class example.

- **Write your name at the top of the page.**
- **I am going to read each question to you. Listen carefully to the entire question before you choose an answer.**

1. Look at the balls of yarn. Count all the balls of yarn. Mark the number that tells how many balls of yarn in all.
2. Look at the group of tacos. Mark the group of tacos that shows 2 more.
3. Look at the pattern of paper clips. Mark the number of paper clips that could come next.
4. Look at the graph. It shows fun things to do at recess. Below the graph, mark the number of boys who like to play on the monkey bars.

- **Turn the page over.**

5. Look at the group of acorns. Mark the group of acorns that shows the same number.
6. Look at the crayons. Count all the crayons. Mark the number that tells how many crayons in all.
7. Look at the books. Find the group that has less books. Mark the group that has less books.
8. Look at the butterflies. Find the group that has exactly the same number of butterflies. Mark the group that has exactly the same number of butterflies.

Chapter Overview

Chapter-at-a-Glance

In Chapter 7, the emphasis is on measuring length, weight, capacity, area, and temperature comparing objects based on these attributes, and ordering objects by length.

Lesson		Math Objective	State/Local Standards
7-1	**Compare Length** (pp. 179–180)	Compare length to a reference object.	
7-2	**Order Length** (pp. 181–182)	Order objects by length from shortest to longest.	
7-3	**Compare Weight** (pp. 183–184)	Compare weight to a reference object.	
7-4	**Problem-Solving Strategy: Guess and Check** (pp. 185–186)	Compare length to a reference object.	
7-5	**Compare Capacity** (pp. 189–190)	Compare capacity to a reference object.	
7-6	**Compare Area** (pp. 191–192)	Compare the area of two objects.	
7-7	**Compare Temperature** (pp. 193–194)	Compare objects or situations by using terms hot and cold.	

Compare Measurements

BIG Idea Understanding and performing measurements with nonstandard units gives students the opportunity to compare relative sizes.

- Opportunities to measure in a hands-on way with different units, such as connecting cubes, give students an intuitive sense of measurement.
- Opportunities to measure items help students understand that objects have different properties.

Algebra Students begin using manipulatives to compare the sizes of objects. This lays the groundwork for students to understand balanced equalities. Lessons 7-1, 7-2, 7-3, 7-5

Measurement All of the lessons in this chapter focus on measurement. Students have opportunities to work with "small" measurements, setting the stage for them to work with larger measurements and other units. Lessons 7-1, 7-2, 7-3, 7-4, 7-5, 7-6, 7-7

GK-FP1 *Measurement:* **Ordering objects by measurable attributes**

Children use measurable attributes, such as length or weight, to solve problems by comparing and ordering objects. They compare the lengths of two objects both directly (by comparing them with each other) and indirectly (by comparing both with a third object), and they order several objects according to length.

Skills Trace

Vertical Alignment

PreKindergarten

In PreK, students learned to:

- Begin to make size comparisons between objects (e.g., taller than, smaller than).
- Begin to order two or three objects by size (seriation) (e.g., largest to smallest) (age 4).

Kindergarten

During this chapter, students learn to:

- Compare length, height, weight, area, temperature, and capacity to reference objects.
- Order objects by length from shortest to longest.
- Discuss how height and length are alike and different.

After this chapter, students will learn to:

- Use measures of time, such as days of the week and today, tomorrow, and yesterday.

First Grade

In first grade, students will learn to:

- Measure and compare with nonstandard units.
- Make a table to solve problems.
- Measure volume with nonstandard units.

BackMapping and Vertical Alignment **McGraw-Hill's *Math Connects*** program was conceived and developed with the final results in mind: student success in Algebra 1 and beyond. The authors, using the **NCTM Focal Points and Focal Connections** as their guide, developed this brand new series by backmapping from Algebra 1 concepts, and vertically aligning the topics so that they build upon prior skills and concepts and serve as a foundation for future topics.

Math Vocabulary

The following math vocabulary words for Chapter 7 are listed in the glossary of the ***Student Edition***. You can find interactive definitions in 13 languages in the ***eGlossary*** at macmillanmh.com.

area (p. 191)

covers more   covers less

capacity the amount a container can hold (p. 189)

holds less/holds more (p. 189)

holds less holds more

length (p. 179)

lighter/heavier (p. 183)

lighter

heavier

longer/longest, shorter/shortest (pp. 179, 181)

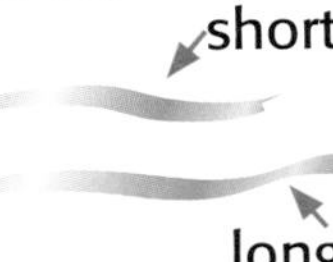

temperature, hot, cold (p. 193)

hot   cold

weight a measurement that tells how heavy or light an object is (p. 183)

Visual Vocabulary Cards Use Visual Vocabulary Cards 16, 17, 18, 21, 22, 35 to introduce and reinforce the vocabulary in this chapter. (The Define/Example/Ask routine is printed on the back of each card.)

holds more

Chapter Planner

Suggested Pacing		
Instruction	Review and Assessment	TOTAL
7 days	2 days	**9 days**

Diagnostic Assessment
Are You Ready? (p. 176)

	Lesson 7-1 (Pacing: 1 day)	Lesson 7-2 (Pacing: 1 day)	Lesson 7-3 (Pacing: 1 day)
Lesson/ Objective	**Compare Length** (pp. 179–180) **Objective:** Compare length to a reference object.	**Order Length** (pp. 181–182) **Objective:** Order objects by length from shortest to longest.	**Compare Weight** (pp. 183–184) **Objectives:** Compare weight to a reference object.
State/Local Standards			
Math Vocabulary	**length, longer, shorter, same as**	**longest, shortest**	**weight, heavier, lighter, equal to**
Lesson Resources	**Materials** number cards 1–20, bag, pencils, classroom objects **Manipulatives** connecting cubes **Other Resources** CRM Leveled Worksheets (pp. 6–9) Daily Reteach Problem of the Day	**Materials** classroom objects **Manipulatives** connecting cubes, counters **Other Resources** CRM Leveled Worksheets (pp. 10–13) Daily Reteach Problem of the Day	**Materials** pencil, book, dictionary, story book, containers, crayons, glue, scale, classroom objects, blocks **Other Resources** CRM Leveled Worksheets (pp. 14–17) Daily Reteach Problem of the Day
Technology Math Online	Math Adventures	Math Song Track 6 Math Adventures Concepts in Motion	Concepts in Motions
Reaching All Learners	English Learners, p. 179B ELL Gifted and Talented, p. 179B AL Early Finishers, p. 179B OL AL	English Learners, p. 181B ELL Below Level, p. 181B BL Early Finishers, p. 181B OL AL	English Learners, p. 183B ELL Gifted and Talented, p. 183B AL Early Finishers, p. 1835B OL AL
Alternate Lesson	*Math Their Way*, p. 118 *IMPACT Mathematics*: Unit I	*Math Their Way*, p. 159 *IMPACT Mathematics*: Unit I	*Math Their Way*, p. 122 *IMPACT Mathematics*: Unit J

KEY

BL Below/Approaching Level — OL On Level — AL Above/Beyond Level — ELL English Learners
SE Student Edition — TE Teacher Edition — CRM Chapter 7 Resource Masters — CD-Rom
Transparency — Flip Chart — Real-World Problem Solving Library

	Lesson 7-4 (Pacing: 1 day)	Lesson 7-5 (Pacing: 1 day)	Lesson 7-6 (Pacing: 1 day)
Lesson/ Objective	Problem-Solving Strategy **Guess and Check** (pp. 185–186) **Objective:** Compare length to a reference object.	**Compare Capacity** (pp. 189–190) **Objective:** Compare capacity to a reference object.	**Compare Area** (pp. 191–192) **Objective:** Compare the area of two objects.
State/Local Standards			
Math Vocabulary		**capacity, holds more, holds less, holds the same**	**area, covers more, covers less, covers the same**
Lesson Resources	**Materials** pencils, classroom objects, paper, posterboard **Manipulatives** connecting cubes **Other Resources** CRM Leveled Worksheets (pp. 18–22) Daily Reteach Problem of the Day *Bigger or Smaller?*	**Materials** small classroom objects, mittens, dry cereal, containers, cups, bottles, dried beans, bags, juice can, juice pitcher, crayons, chart paper, dry rice **Manipulatives** connecting cubes **Other Resources** CRM Leveled Worksheets (pp. 23–26) Daily Reteach Problem of the Day	**Materials** classroom objects, juice can, coffee can, drawing paper, pencils, scissors, sticky note, note book paper, books **Manipulatives** pattern blocks **Other Resources** CRM Leveled Worksheets (pp. 27–30) Daily Reteach Problem of the Day
Technology Math Online		Concepts in Motion	
Reaching All Learners	English Learners, p. 185B ELL Below Level, p. 185B BL Gifted and Talented, p. 185B AL	English Learners, p. 189B ELL Gifted and Talented, p. 189B AL Early Finishers, p. 189B OL AL	English Learners, p. 191B ELL Below Level, p. 191B BL Early Finishers, p. 191B OL AL
Alternate Lesson		*Math Their Way*, p. 132 *IMPACT Mathematics*: Unit J	

Formative Assessment
Mid-Chapter Check (p. 187)

Game Time: Building a Snake (p. 188)

Chapter Planner

Lesson 7-7

Pacing: 1 day

Lesson/ Objective	**Compare Temperature** (pp. 193–194) **Objective:** Compare objects and situations by using terms hot and cold.
State/Local Standards	
Math Vocabulary	**hot, cold, temperature**
Lesson Resources	**Materials** chart paper, pencils, file folder, scissors, crayons, glue **Other Resources** CRM Leveled Worksheets (pp. 31–34) Daily Reteach; Problem of the Day
Technology Math Online	
Reaching All Learners	English Learners, p. 193B ELL Below Level, p. 193B BL Early Finishers, p. 193B OL AL
Alternate Lesson	*IMPACT Mathematics*: Unit J

Problem Solving in Science (p. 195)

Summative Assessment
- Chapter Review/Test (p. 197)
- Test Practice (p. 199)

Assessment Options

Diagnostic Assessment

- SE *Option 1:* Are You Ready? (p. 176)
- *Option 2:* Online Quiz (macmillanmh.com)
- CRM *Option 3:* Diagnostic Test (p. 36)

Formative Assessment

- TE Alternate Teaching Strategy (every lesson)
- TE Writing in Math (every lesson)
- TE Line Up (every lesson)
- SE Mid-Chapter Check (p. 187)
- CRM Mid-Chapter Test (p. 37)

Summative Assessment

- SE Chapter Review/Test (p. 197)
- SE Test Practice (p. 199)
- CRM Leveled Chapter Tests (pp. 42–49)
- CRM Cumulative Test Practice (p. 50–51)
- CRM Listening Assessment (p. 40–41)
- CRM Oral Assessment (p. 38–39)
- Exam*View*® Assessment Suite
- Advance Tracker

McGraw Hill Professional Development

Targeted professional development has been articulated throughout **McGraw-Hill's *Math Connects*** program. The **McGraw-Hill Professional Development Video Library** provides short videos that support the **NCTM Focal Points and Focal Connections**. For more information, visit macmillanmh.com.

Model Lessons

Instructional Strategies

Assessment Tips

Students will learn about nonstandard measurement by using different objects to measure length, weight, and capacity.

- During this chapter, students can be in partners or small groups to do the measuring activities.
- Create a chart listing the objects you want the students to measure.
- As groups of students complete the various measurement activities, check them off on the chart.
- Ask students clarifying questions during these measurement activities to get them to elaborate and extend their thinking.

Teacher Notes

Learning Stations

Cross-Curricular Links

Reading

group | INDIVIDUAL/ LOGICAL

Read All About It

- Listen to the story.
- Tell about the objects.
- Point to the objects.

Teacher Note: Before reading, prepare questions for the class about length, weight, capacity, area, and temperature of objects on the pages. Ask the questions while reading the book aloud. Have students point to the objects on the pages, checking their work.

Materials:

- a picture book, such as *Is It Larger, Is It Smaller?* by Tana Hoban

Social Studies

individual | SPATIAL

Make a Train

- Make a train of 8 cubes.
- Lay a pencil next to the train.
- Put the train on paper. Trace the train.

Teacher Note: Give each student a sheet of white paper, a pencil, and 8 connecting cubes. Have students make a train of 8 connecting cubes. Have them lay their pencil next to their train to measure how long their pencil is. Tell them to add or take away cubes from their train to show how long their pencil is. Have them lay the train on paper and trace it to show the length of their pencil on paper.

Materials:

- white paper, $8\frac{1}{2} \times 11$
- pencils
- connecting cubes

Science

individual | LOGICAL

Ways to Measure

- Make a train of connecting cubes.
- Line toothpicks up end to end next to the cube train.
- Tell how many toothpicks you used.
- Tell how you used the toothpicks to measure.

Teacher Note: Show students the proper way to line up toothpicks end to end. Be sure to use toothpicks with rounded ends. Lead a discussion about other objects that can be used to measure length, such as paper clips or cotton swabs. Make sure the connecting cube train is long enough that students must use several toothpicks. Have students turn train vertically and remeasure. Tell them length turned up is called height.

Materials:

- connecting cubes
- round-ended toothpicks

Health

group | SPATIAL

Covering Area

- Cover each shape with paper.
- Count the paper. Which shape covers more area?

Teacher Note: Create two different sized squares on the floor with masking tape. Have students cover squares with paper. Have students count how many pieces of paper it took to cover the squares to determine which square covers more or less area.

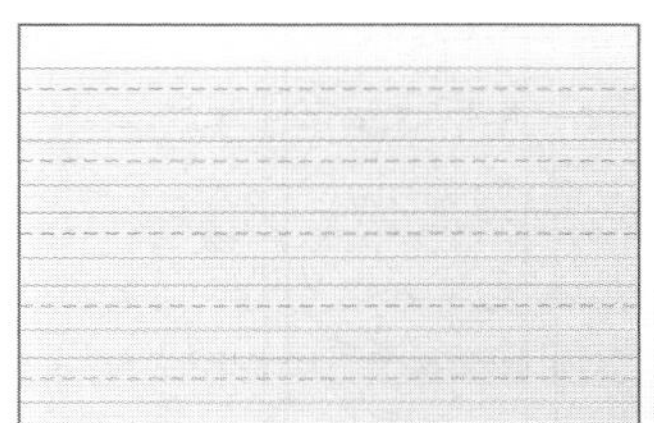

Materials:

- masking tape
- paper

Music

group | AUDITORY, KINESTHETIC

Weather Song

- "What's the weather like today?" "My Fair Lady."
- Identify the weather for today.
- Talk about hot and cold weather.

Teacher Note: Teach children a weather song such as: What's the weather like today? (to the tune of My Fair Lady)
What's the weather like today like today, like today?

What's the weather like today?

Today is _________? (Children insert the current type of weather)

Discuss the current weather as well as weather that is hotter and colder.

Materials:

- none

Calendar Time

"Train" the Days

- Write the name of the current month on a calendar poster.
- Write the numbers for the days of the month.
- Start a train with one cube on the first day of the month.
- Make a new cube train each day. Be sure the number of cubes equals the number/date on the calendar.
- Compare each day's cube train to the train(s) from the day(s) before. Order the trains by length.

Teacher Note: Help students write the month's name and numbers of the days on a calendar poster. Help them check regularly that the number of cubes on their trains equals the calendar number. When the number of the calendar date is greater than 10, have students group their cubes in trains of 10 cubes as a review of the previous chapter.

Introduce the Chapter

Real World: Measurement

Share with students that they are going to learn about measurement. Explain that when people measure something, they figure out how long, tall, or heavy something is. People can compare things and put them in order when they measure.

- Have students sit in a circle on the floor.
- Display an object such as a straw. Tell students that this object can be used to measure other objects by comparing lengths.
- **What can you measure with this object?** Answers will vary. Sample answer: the length of a crayon
- Prompt discussion about measurement with other objects, such as cotton swabs, paper clips, crayons, and so on.
- Allow time for students to experiment, using various classroom objects to measure length.

Use the Student Page

Have students turn to p. 175. Guide students to discuss the images on the page and answer the Explore questions.

Key Vocabulary

Intoduce the key vocabulary in the chapter using the routine below.

Define: Something **holds more** when you can get a greater amount to fit inside.
Example: A pitcher holds more than a glass.
Ask: What holds more than a shoe box?

Diagnostic Assessment

Check for students' prerequisite skills before beginning the chapter.

- **Option 1:** ***Are You Ready for Chapter 7?***
  SE Student Edition, p. 176
- **Option 2:** ***Online Assessment Quiz***
  Math Online macmillanmh.com
- **Option 3:** ***Diagnostic Test***
  CRM Chapter 7 Resource Masters, p. 36

RTI (Response to Intervention)

Apply the Results Based on the results of the diagnostic assessment on p. 176, use the chart on the next page to address individual needs before and during the chapter.

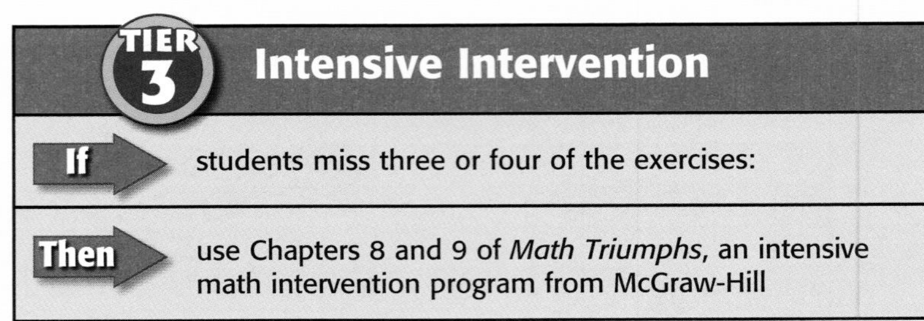

TIER 3 **Intensive Intervention**

If	students miss three or four of the exercises:
Then	use Chapters 8 and 9 of *Math Triumphs*, an intensive math intervention program from McGraw-Hill

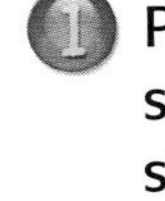

Dinah Zike's Foldables

Guide students to create a Four-Door Foldable graphic organizer to illustrate measurement.

1. Provide each student with a sheet of 11″ by 17″ paper or use a sheet of poster board to make a shutter fold.

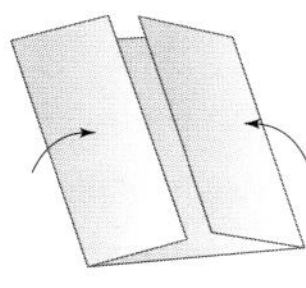

2. Fold the shutter in half like a hamburger. Crease well.

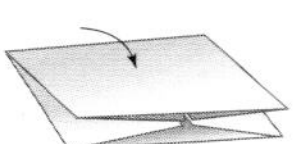

3. Open the paper and cut along the two inside valley folds. These cuts form four doors.

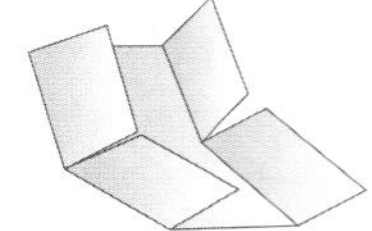

4. This foldable can be used by each student or the class to record what they learn about measurement.

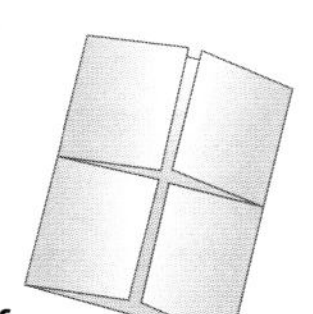

5. Write *Length*, *Height*, *Weight*, and *Capacity* on separate tabs, or doors of the Foldable.

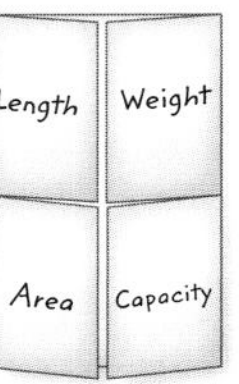

When to Use It *Lessons 7-2, 7-3, 7-5, and 7-6 (Additional instructions for using the Foldable with these lessons are found on pp. 187 and 197.)*

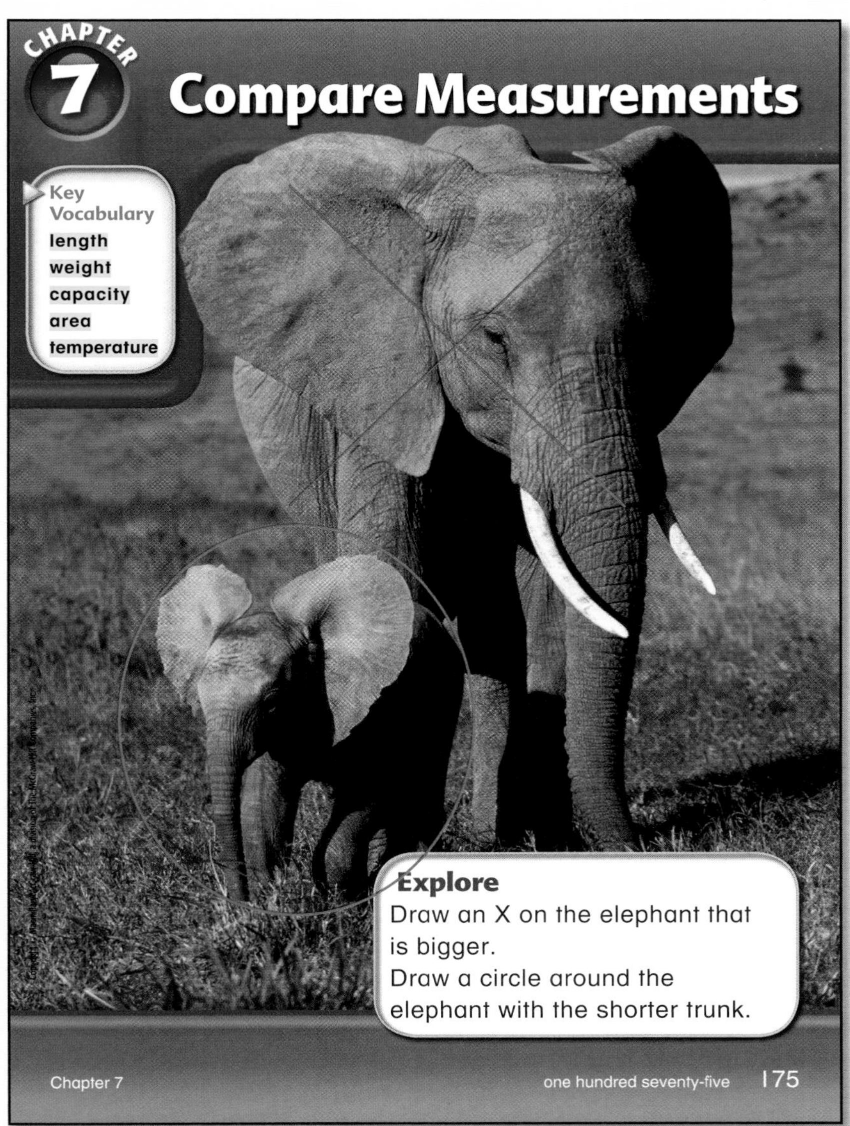

Chapter 7 Compare Measurements

Key Vocabulary
length
weight
capacity
area
temperature

Explore
Draw an X on the elephant that is bigger.
Draw a circle around the elephant with the shorter trunk.

Chapter 7 one hundred seventy-five 175

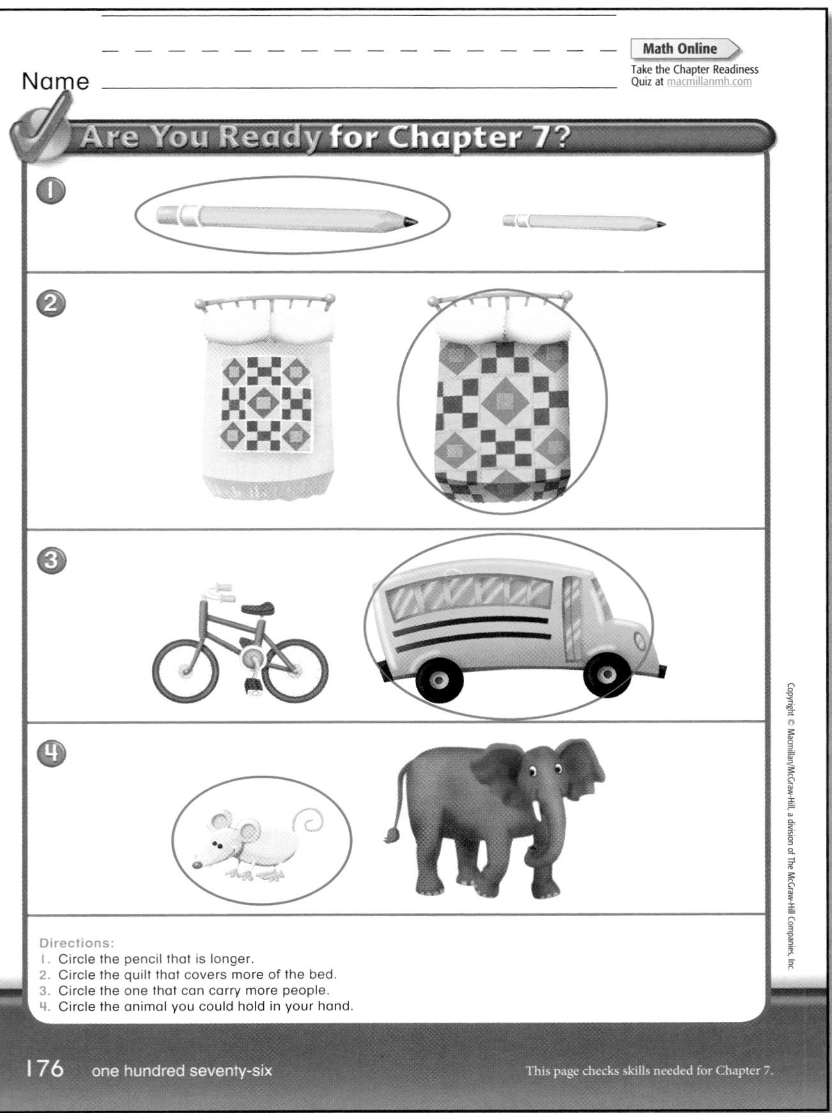

Name ______________________

Math Online
Take the Chapter Readiness Quiz at macmillanmh.com

Are You Ready for Chapter 7?

1
2
3
4

Directions:
1. Circle the pencil that is longer.
2. Circle the quilt that covers more of the bed.
3. Circle the one that can carry more people.
4. Circle the animal you could hold in your hand.

176 one hundred seventy-six This page checks skills needed for Chapter 7.

RTI (Response to Intervention)

TIER 2 Strategic Intervention below/approaching grade level	TIER 1 On-Level	Above/Beyond Level
If students miss two in: **Exercises 1–4** **Then** choose a resource:	**If** students miss one in: **Exercises 1–4** **Then** choose a resource:	**If** students miss none in: **Exercises 1–4** **Then** choose a resource:
CRM Chapter 1 Resource Masters (Reteach Worksheets) Math Online Concepts in Motion	TE Learning Stations (pp. 175G–175H) TE Chapter Project (p. 177) CRM Game: Estimation Chain Math Adventures My Math Zone Chapter 6	TE Learning Stations (pp. 175G–175H) TE Chapter Project (p. 177) Real-World Problem Solving: *Bigger or Smaller?* My Math Zone Chapters 6 and 7 Math Online Game

WRITING IN ➤ MATH

Starting the Chapter
Ask students to write one of the chapter's vocabulary words in their Math Journal. Have them draw a simple illustration to represent the word. Have students use the glossary if they need ideas for their drawing. Require only one word to copy or trace and draw the picture.

Chapter 7 Project

Measurement Vocabulary Cards

- Throughout the chapter, ask students to write the vocabulary words they learn from the chapter on separate index cards: *longest, shortest, longer, shorter, heavier, lighter, holds more, holds less, covers more, covers less, hotter, colder.*
- Below each word, have students draw or glue pictures cut out of magazines to illustrate the meaning of each vocabulary word.
- Give students a plastic zip bag to keep their cards in.
- Students can use their cards to play memory, matching, or flashcard games with a partner or in small groups.

Chapter 7 Literature List

Lesson	Book Title	Author
7-1	**The Long and Short of It**	Cheryl Nathan and Lisa McCourt
7-2	**Fish Eyes: A Book You Can Count On**	Lois Ehlert
7-3	**Just a Little Bit**	Ann Tompert
7-4	**Much Bigger Than Martin**	Steven Kellogg
7-5	**The Mitten**	Jan Brett
7-6	**Not Enough Room!**	Joanne Rocklin
7-7	**Math for All Seasons**	Greg Tang
Any	**Super Sand Castle Saturday**	Stuart J. Murphy
Any	**The Best Bug Parade**	Stuart J. Murphy
Any	**Length**	Henry Arthur Pluckrose

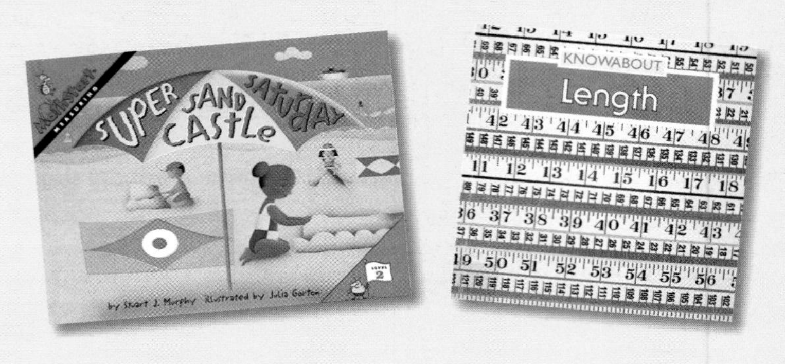

ELL National ESL Standards Alignment for Chapter 7			
Lesson, Page	**ESL Standard**	**Modality**	**Level**
7-1, p. 179B	Goal 2, Standard 2, a	Logical	Intermediate
7-2, p. 181B	Goal 2, Standard 2, f	Logical	Intermediate
7-3, p. 183B	Goal 1, Standard 3, f	Visual	Beginning
7-4, p. 185B	Goal 2, Standard 2, j	Logical/Spatial	Intermediate
7-5, p. 189B	Goal 2, Standard 2, g	Kinesthetic	Intermediate
7-6, p. 191B	Goal 2, Standard 1, h	Visual/Spatial, Kinesthetic	Advanced
7-7, p. 193B	Goal 3, Standard 2, a	Linguistic	Beginning

The National ESL Standards can be found in the Teacher Reference Handbook.

English

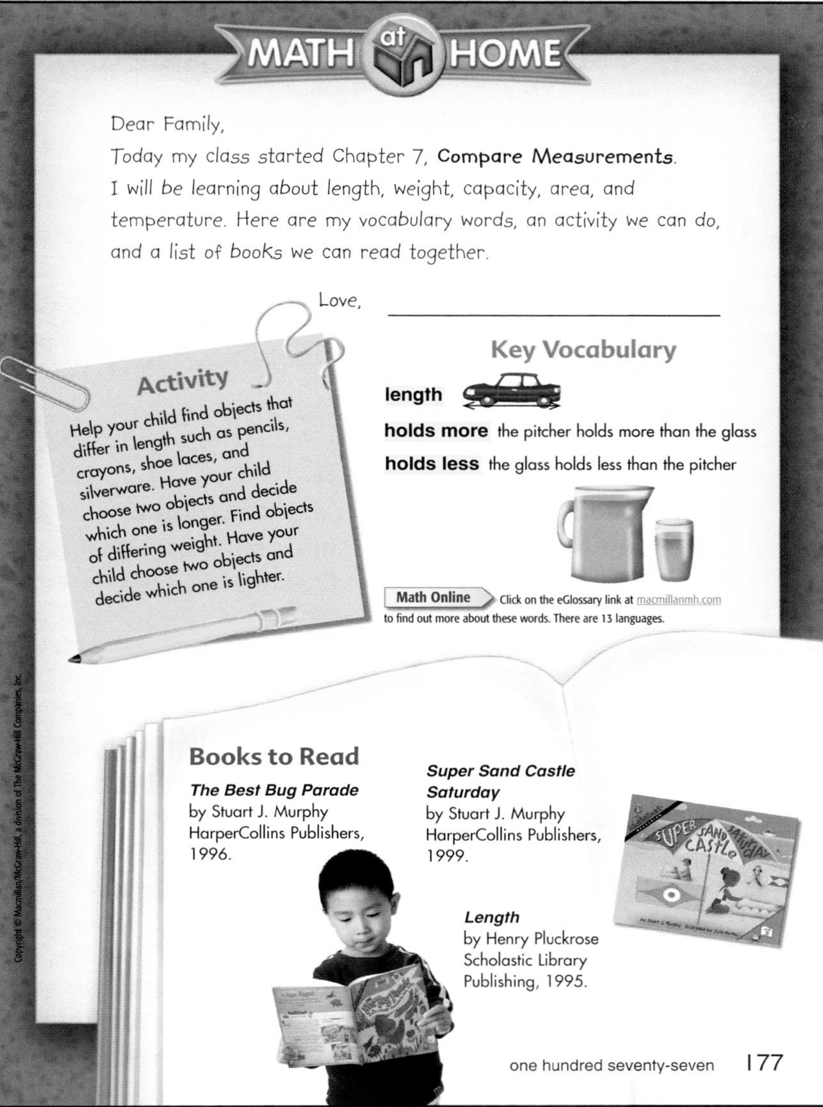

MATH at HOME

Dear Family,

Today my class started Chapter 7, **Compare Measurements**. I will be learning about length, weight, capacity, area, and temperature. Here are my vocabulary words, an activity we can do, and a list of books we can read together.

Love, ____________________

Activity

Help your child find objects that differ in length such as pencils, crayons, shoe laces, and silverware. Have your child choose two objects and decide which one is longer. Find objects of differing weight. Have your child choose two objects and decide which one is lighter.

Key Vocabulary

length

holds more the pitcher holds more than the glass

holds less the glass holds less than the pitcher

Math Online Click on the eGlossary link at macmillanmh.com to find out more about these words. There are 13 languages.

Books to Read

The Best Bug Parade by Stuart J. Murphy HarperCollins Publishers, 1996.

Super Sand Castle Saturday by Stuart J. Murphy HarperCollins Publishers, 1999.

Length by Henry Pluckrose Scholastic Library Publishing, 1995.

one hundred seventy-seven 177

Español

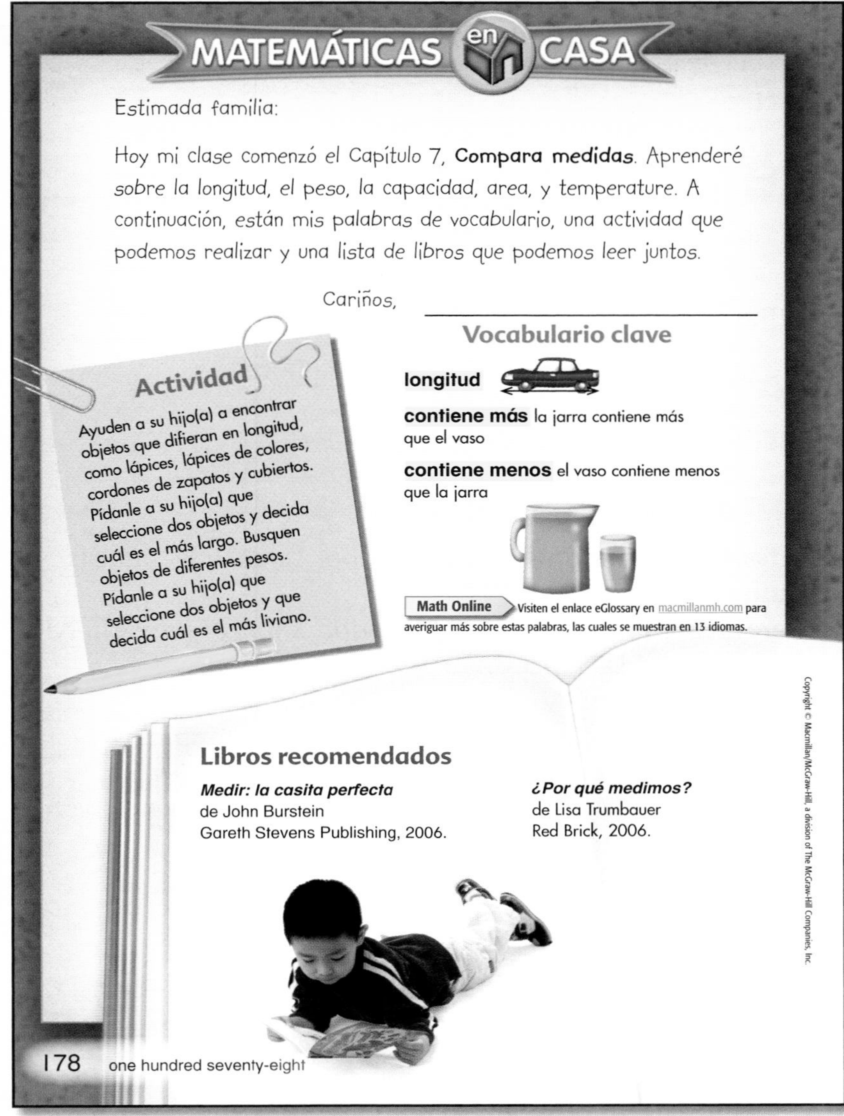

MATEMÁTICAS en CASA

Estimada familia:

Hoy mi clase comenzó el Capítulo 7, **Compara medidas**. Aprenderé sobre la longitud, el peso, la capacidad, area, y temperature. A continuación, están mis palabras de vocabulario, una actividad que podemos realizar y una lista de libros que podemos leer juntos.

Cariños, ____________________

Actividad

Ayuden a su hijo(a) a encontrar objetos que difieran en longitud, como lápices, lápices de colores, cordones de zapatos y cubiertos. Pídanle a su hijo(a) que seleccione dos objetos y decida cuál es el más largo. Busquen objetos de diferentes pesos. Pídanle a su hijo(a) que seleccione dos objetos y que decida cuál es el más liviano.

Vocabulario clave

longitud

contiene más la jarra contiene más que el vaso

contiene menos el vaso contiene menos que la jarra

Math Online Visiten el enlace eGlossary en macmillanmh.com para averiguar más sobre estas palabras, las cuales se muestran en 13 idiomas.

Libros recomendados

Medir: la casita perfecta de John Burstein Gareth Stevens Publishing, 2006.

¿Por qué medimos? de Lisa Trumbauer Red Brick, 2006.

178 one hundred seventy-eight

- Read the Math at Home letter on p. 177 with the class and have each student sign it.
- Send home copies of the Math at Home letter with each student.
- Use the Spanish letter on p. 178 for students with Spanish-speaking parents or guardians.

Read-Aloud Anthology

For an optional reading activity to introduce this chapter's math concepts, see the Read-Aloud Anthology on p. TR30.

LESSON 7-1

Compare Length

Lesson Planner

Objective

Compare length to a reference object.

Vocabulary

length, **longer**, **shorter**, **same as**

Resources

Materials: classroom objects, number cards, bag, pencils
Manipulatives: connecting cubes
Literature Connection: *The Long and Short of It* by Cheryl Nathan and Lisa McCourt
Alternate Lesson: Adapt *Comparing Names* on page 118 of *Math Their Way* to provide practice in comparing length to a reference object.
Use *IMPACT Mathematics*: Unit I to provide practice with comparing length.
Teacher Technology
TeacherWorks

Focus on Math Background

In this lesson, students explore the measurable attribute of length. Length is the most concrete and easily understood property of measurement because students can look at an object and see how long or short it is. Kindergartners need hands-on experience directly comparing the length of two items before they can determine an appropriate size unit—e.g., a tongue depressor versus an inch cube—by which to quantify an object's length.

Daily Routine

Use these suggestions before beginning the lesson on p. 179.

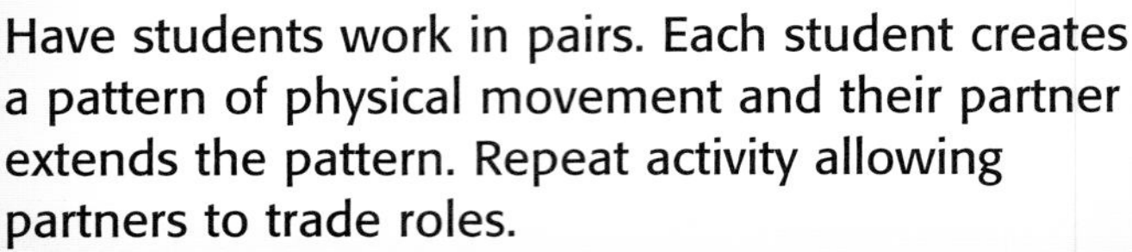

5-Minute Check

(Reviews Lesson 6-7)
Have students put numbers one to 20 on a number line. Then ask questions such as "What is a number between four and seven?" five, six

Problem of the Day

Have students work in pairs. Each student creates a pattern of physical movement and their partner extends the pattern. Repeat activity allowing partners to trade roles.

LINE UP Using a train of three connecting cubes as reference, have students walk around the room to find an object longer than the train. Have them line up with arms outstretched so they can see the line lengthening.

Building Math Vocabulary

Materials: classroom objects of different lengths

- Have students sit in two lines across from each other, with one line much **shorter** than the other.
- Explain that **length** tells us how long or short something is. Define the words ***longer*** and *shorter* by using the two lines of students.
- Have students form a line that is the **same as** a line of eight students.
- Tell students that length is described as height when it stands straight up. Have students stand classroom objects on end to show how length relates to height.

Visual Vocabulary Cards

Use Visual Vocabulary Card 22 to reinforce the vocabulary introduce in this lesson. (The Define/Example/Ask routine is printed on the back of each card.)

Differentiated Instruction

Small Group Options

Option 1 Gifted and Talented AL

KINESTHETIC, LOGICAL

Materials: yarn, scissors, tape, paper, pencils

- Have students choose three classroom objects.
- Have them measure and compare the length of each object with yarn, cutting the yarn the length of the object.
- Have them tape the yarn on paper.
- Have students label the yarn by drawing the three objects.

Option 2 English Language Learners ELL

LOGICAL

Materials: classroom objects
Core Vocabulary: side by side, short, long
Common Use Verb: lay down

See Math This strategy teaches the protocol for comparing length.

- Have students find two similar objects and put them side by side on the floor.
- Model identifying and comparing short and long objects.
- Verbalize choices. Encourage students to compare objects. Restate student language in complete sentences as needed.

Independent Work Options

Option 1 Early Finishers OL AL

VISUAL

Materials: connecting cubes, classroom objects

- Have each student make a train with 12 connecting cubes.
- Have students find classroom objects shorter than their trains. Then have them find objects longer than their trains.
- Have students justify their thinking by measuring the objects with cubes and telling a classmate how many cubes long each object is.

Option 2 Student Technology

Math Online macmillanmh.com

Math Adventures

Option 3 Learning Station: Health (p. 175H)

Direct students to the Health Learning Station for opportunities to explore and extend the lesson concept.

Leveled Lesson Resources

Reteach (p. 6) BL

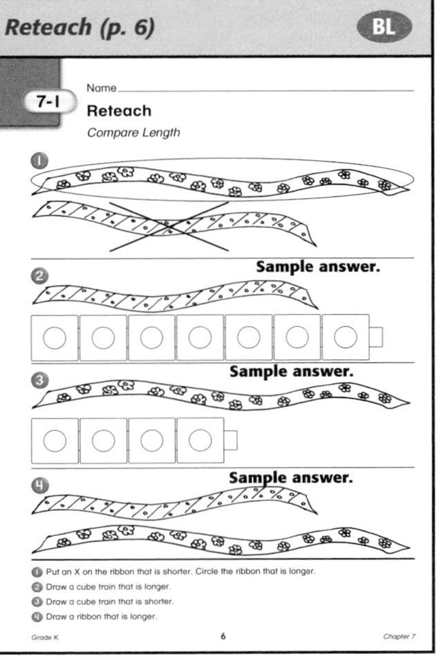

7-1 Name
Reteach
Compare Length

Sample answer.

Sample answer.

Sample answer.

1. Put an X on the ribbon that is shorter. Circle the ribbon that is longer.
2. Draw a cube train that is longer.
3. Draw a cube train that is shorter.
4. Draw a ribbon that is longer.

Grade K 6 Chapter 7

Skills Practice (p. 7) OL

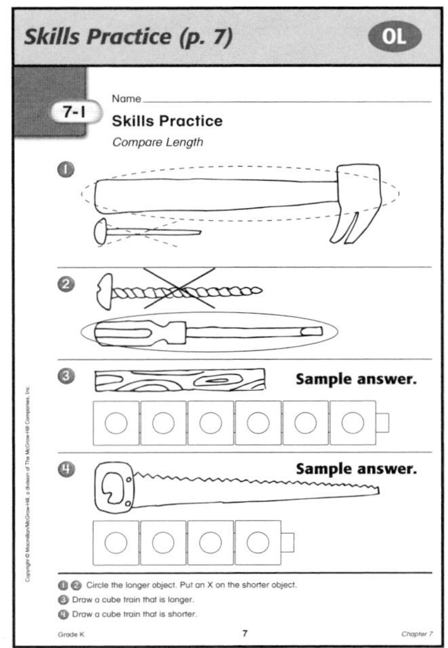

7-1 Name
Skills Practice
Compare Length

Sample answer.

Sample answer.

1. 2. Circle the longer object. Put an X on the shorter object.
3. Draw a cube train that is longer.
4. Draw a cube train that is shorter.

Grade K 7 Chapter 7

Enrich (p. 9) AL

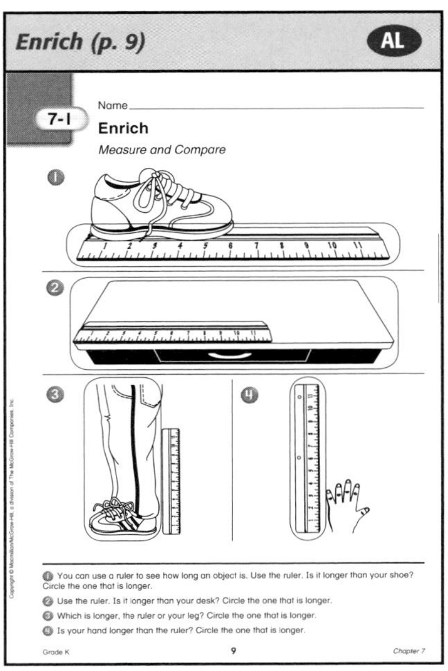

7-1 Name
Enrich
Measure and Compare

1. You can use a ruler to see how long an object is. Use the ruler. Is it longer than your shoe? Circle the one that is longer.
2. Use the ruler. Is it longer than your desk? Circle the one that is longer.
3. Which is longer, the ruler or your leg? Circle the one that is longer.
4. Is your hand longer than the ruler? Circle the one that is longer.

Grade K 9 Chapter 7

Homework Practice (p. 8) OL

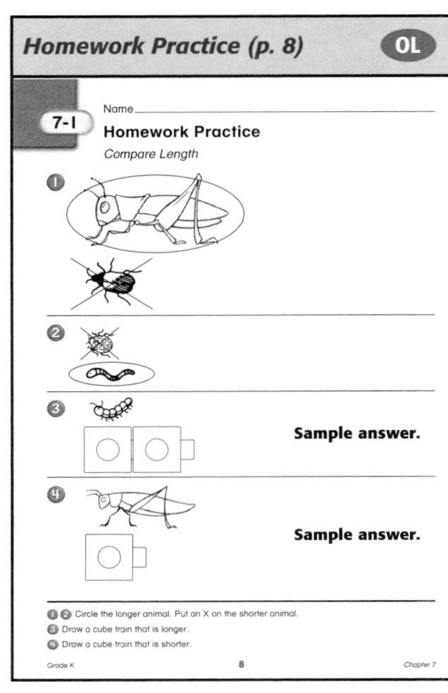

7-1 Name
Homework Practice
Compare Length

Sample answer.

Sample answer.

1. 2. Circle the longer animal. Put an X on the shorter animal.
3. Draw a cube train that is longer.
4. Draw a cube train that is shorter.

Grade K 8 Chapter 7

1 Introduce

Circle Time

Activity Choice 1 • Literature

The Long and Short of It by Cheryl Nathan and Linda McCourt

Materials: classroom objects such as pencils, markers, books, paper, crayons

- Read the book aloud. Discuss the book using lesson vocabulary.
- Discuss **longer** and **shorter** using concrete objects. Use examples such as pencils, desks, or books.
- Have students draw pictures to demonstrate the concept of **length**, drawing longer and shorter objects.

Activity Choice 2 • Hands-On 

Materials: number cards 1–20, bag, connecting cubes

- Put number cards in a bag. Ask each student to take one card.
- Have students make trains with the same number of connecting cubes as the number on their card.
- Have students work in pairs.
- Have each pair say which train is shorter and which train is longer.

2 Teach

- Direct students to the top of p. 179.
- Instruct them to compare the picture of the two fish.
- **Which fish is shorter?** The top fish is shorter.
- **Which fish is longer?** The bottom fish is longer.

BL Alternate Teaching Strategy

 students have trouble identifying the difference between longer and shorter . . .

 use one of these reteach options.

1 CRM **Daily Reteach Worksheet** (p. 6)

2 **Make a Train** Have students make trains and compare them.

- Have students form groups of three.
- Have one student in the group make a train of connecting cubes.
- Have another student make a train that is longer, and have the third student make a train that is shorter.
- Repeat the activity, trading partners so that each student makes all three trains.

COMMON ERROR!

Students may forget to line up the ends of objects when comparing lengths. Show them how to place the objects so that the ends are parallel.

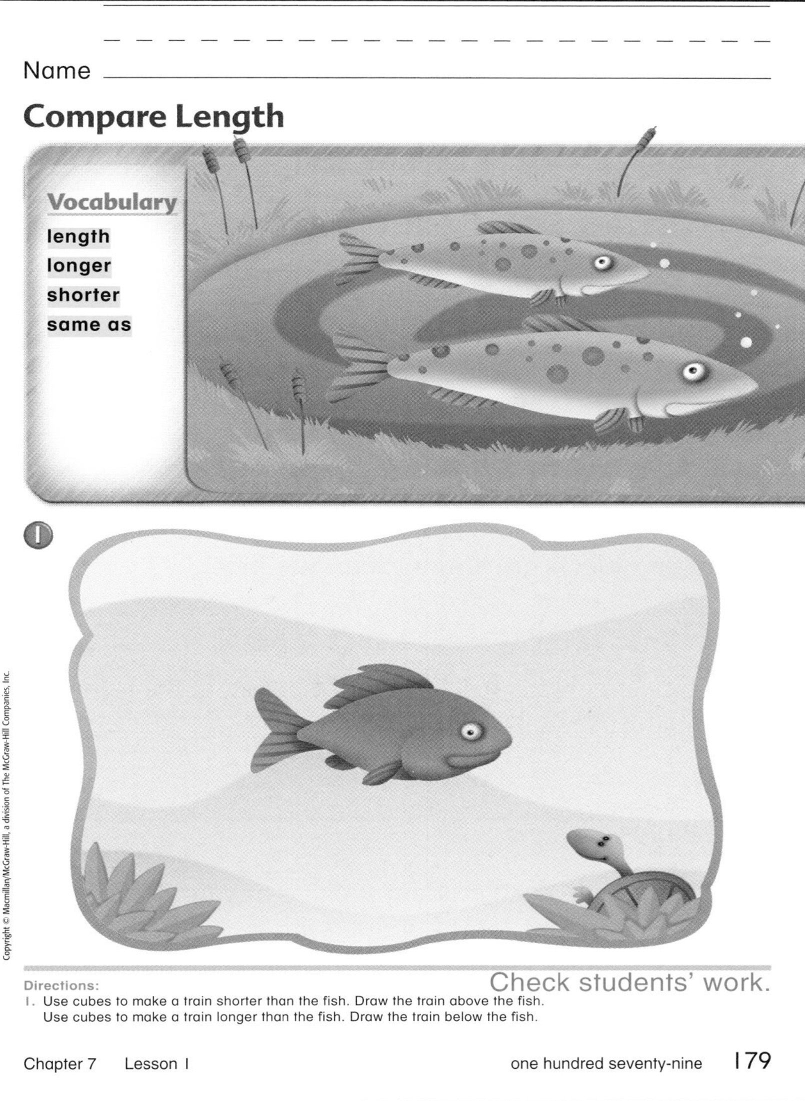

Name
Compare Length
Vocabulary
length
longer
shorter
same as
Check students' work.
Directions:
1. Use cubes to make a train shorter than the fish. Draw the train above the fish.
Use cubes to make a train longer than the fish. Draw the train below the fish.
Chapter 7 Lesson 1 one hundred seventy-nine 179

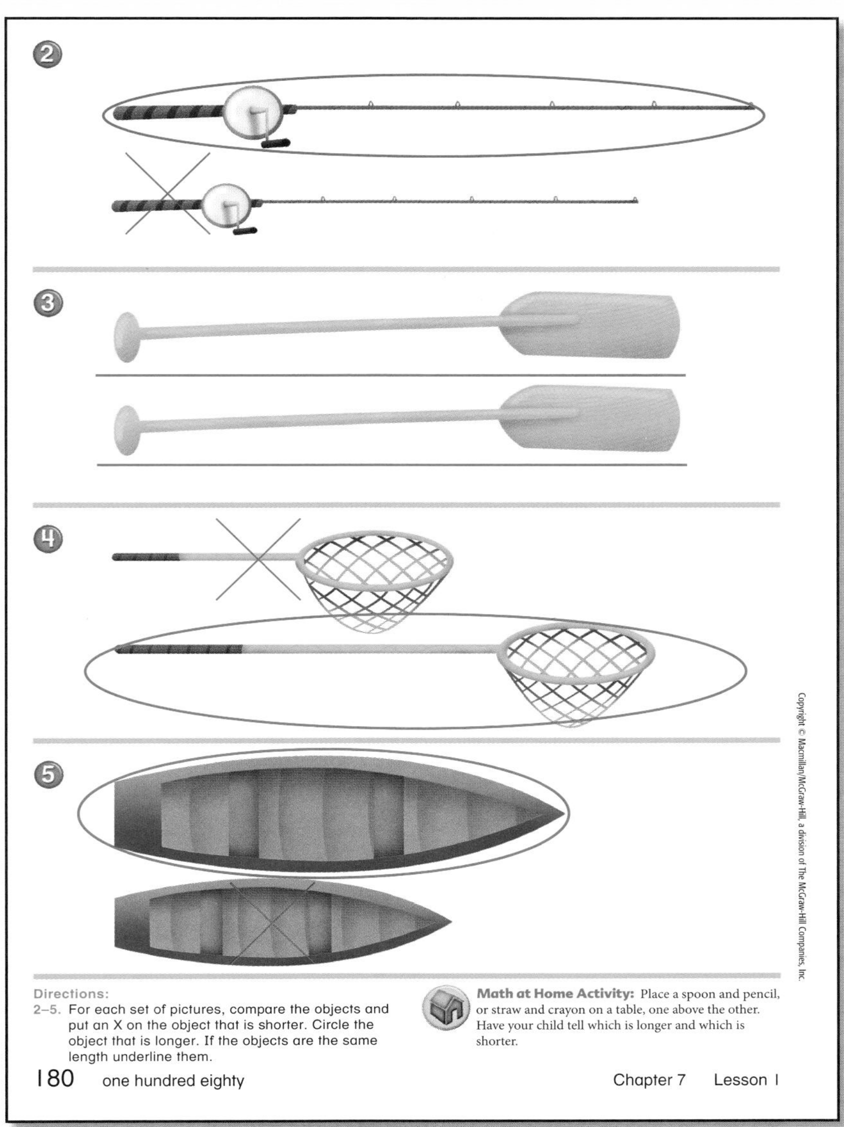

Directions:
2–5. For each set of pictures, compare the objects and put an X on the object that is shorter. Circle the object that is longer. If the objects are the same length underline them.
Math at Home Activity: Place a spoon and pencil, or straw and crayon on a table, one above the other. Have your child tell which is longer and which is shorter.
180 one hundred eighty Chapter 7 Lesson 1

3 Practice

Guided Practice

Direct students to Exercise 1 on p. 179.

- Help students choose the number of cubes to make a train shorter than the fish. Draw the train above the fish.
- Help students choose the number of cubes to make a train longer than the fish. Be sure the train will fit on the page. Draw the train below the fish.
- Have students identify shorter and longer with reference to the fish.

Independent Practice

Have students turn to p. 180. Explain the directions. Have students work independently on the exercises.

4 Assess

Formative Assessment

Show two objects of different lengths.

- **Which is longer? Shorter?** Answers will vary.
- Hold up one of the objects. Have students find another object in the room that is longer or shorter than that object.

Quick Check **Are students still struggling with concepts of shorter and longer?**

If Yes → Small Group Options (p. 179B)

If No → Independent Work Options (p. 179B)

CRM Skills Practice Worksheet (p. 7)

CRM Enrich Worksheet (p. 9)

LESSON 7-2

Order Length

Lesson Planner

Objective

Order objects by length from shortest to longest.

Vocabulary

longest, **shortest**

Resources

Materials: classroom objects
Manipulatives: connecting cubes, counters
Literature Connection: *Fish Eyes: A Book You Can Count On* by Lois Ehlert
Alternate Lesson: Adapt *Sorting on the Overhead Projector* on page 159 of *Math Their Way* for practice sorting and classifying objects.
Use *IMPACT Mathematics*: Unit I to provide practice with ordering length.
Teacher Technology
TeacherWorks • Concepts in Motion

Focus on Math Background

This lesson continues to develop students' awareness of length. It focuses on ordering three or more objects in a series arranged from longest to shortest or vice versa. This skill is called seriation. It lays the foundation for more advanced mathematics and science work in understanding and using the hierarchy of units—i.e. there are 12 inches in one foot—to measure length.

Daily Routine

Use these suggestions before beginning the lesson on p. 181.

5-Minute Check

(Reviews Lesson 7-1)
Show a block. Ask students what objects in the classroom are longer than the block. Then ask what objects are shorter than the block.

Problem of the Day

Compare objects that are shorter, longer, or the same length as (equal to) the yarn.

LINE UP Give each student a piece of yarn. Have each student form a group with two other students so that their pieces are long, longer, and longest. Have each group get in line.

Building Math Vocabulary

- Have students sit on the floor in three unequal lines.
- Remind students that they have already described lines using the words *long* and *short*. Have them compare the three lines using the words *long*, *longer*, and ***longest***.
- Continue the discussion by renaming the lines *short*, *shorter*, and ***shortest***. Use classroom objects to show order such as different pencil lengths, crayon lengths, and/or students' shoe lengths.

Visual Vocabulary Cards

Use Visual Vocabulary Card 35 to reinforce the vocabulary introduced in this lesson. (The Define/Example/Ask routine is printed on the back of each card.)

Differentiated Instruction

Small Group Options

Option 1 Below/Approaching Level BL

KINESTHETIC, VISUAL

Materials: connecting cubes

- Make two different lengths of connecting cubes. Have students work in small groups to compare and determine which cube train is short or long.
- Add a third cube train of a different length. Have groups order the cube trains from shortest to longest and make new cube trains to repeat the activity.

Option 2 English Language Learners ELL

LOGICAL

Materials: straws, teacher straw (mid-sized)
Core Vocabulary: mine, shorter, longer
Common Use Verb: look

Do Math This strategy teaches the vocabulary for comparing length.

- Display your straw. Say: "This **straw** is **mine**."
- Compare your straw to a longer and shorter straw. Write and say: "Look, mine is longer" or "mine is shorter."
- Prompt students to repeat with their straws with other students.
- Restate students responses.

Independent Work Options

Option 1 Early Finishers OL AL

LOGICAL, VISUAL

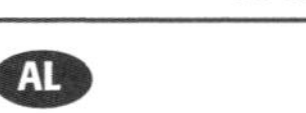

Materials: paper, pencil

- Give each student a pencil and paper.
- Have students make a graph with two columns: *Longer Than a Pencil* and *Shorter Than a Pencil*.
- Show students a pencil. Ask them to find two longer objects and two shorter objects in the room. Have them draw the objects in the correct column on the graph.
- Have students find an object with a length that is in between the short and long pencils.

Option 2 Student Technology

Math Online macmillanmh.com

Math Adventures

Option 3 Learning Station: Music (p. 175H)

Direct students to the Music Learning Station for opportunities to explore and extend the lesson concept.

Leveled Lesson Resources

Additional support for English Language Learners can be found in the ELL Guide (p. 113). ELL

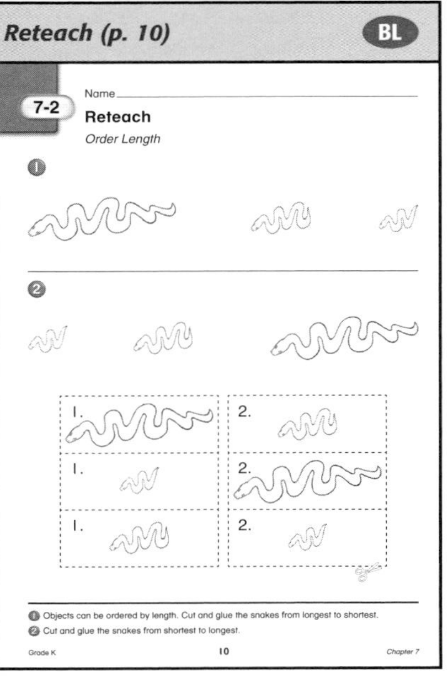

Reteach (p. 10) BL

7-2 Name
Reteach
Order Length

1. Objects can be ordered by length. Cut and glue the snakes from longest to shortest.
2. Cut and glue the snakes from shortest to longest.

Grade K 10 *Chapter 7*

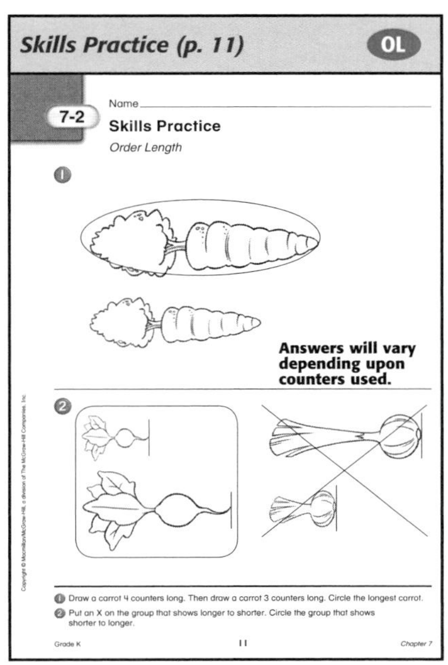

Skills Practice (p. 11) OL

7-2 Name
Skills Practice
Order Length

Answers will vary depending upon counters used.

1. Draw a carrot 4 counters long. Then draw a carrot 3 counters long. Circle the longest carrot.
2. Put an X on the group that shows longer to shorter. Circle the group that shows shorter to longer.

Grade K 11 *Chapter 7*

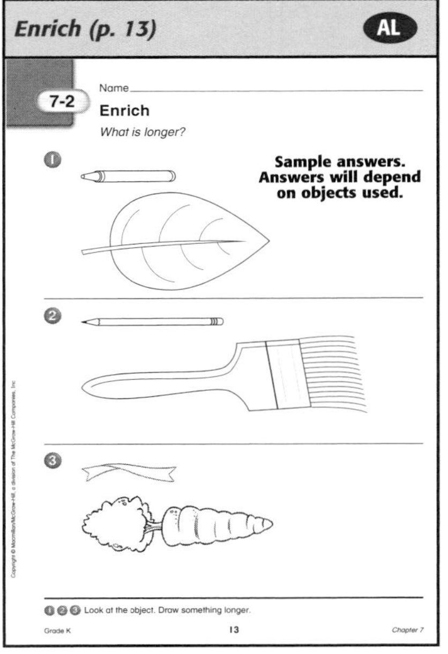

Enrich (p. 13) AL

7-2 Name
Enrich
What is longer?

Sample answers. Answers will depend on objects used.

1, 2, 3 Look at the object. Draw something longer.

Grade K 13 *Chapter 7*

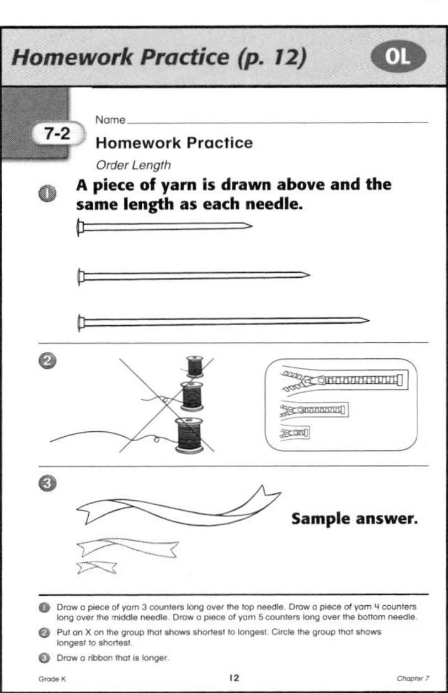

Homework Practice (p. 12) OL

7-2 Name
Homework Practice
Order Length

A piece of yarn is drawn above and the same length as each needle.

Sample answer.

1. Draw a piece of yarn 3 counters long over the top needle. Draw a piece of yarn 4 counters long over the middle needle. Draw a piece of yarn 5 counters long over the bottom needle.
2. Put an X on the group that shows shortest to longest. Circle the group that shows longest to shortest.
3. Draw a ribbon that is longer.

Grade K 12 *Chapter 7*

1 Introduce

Activity Choice 1 • Literature

Fish Eyes: A Book You Can Count On by Lois Ehlert

Materials: connecting cubes

- Read the book aloud, using connecting cubes to compare fish sizes.
- Ask students to look at the two jumping fish. Ask which fish is longer. Use connecting cubes to find the length of each fish. Ask students was their answer correct.
- Repeat for the three, four, and five fish pages using the connecting cube procedure used with the two jumping fish.
- Work with students to find the **shortest** and **longest** fish, then putting the fish in order by longest size.
- Place the book in the Math Center. Encourage students to use connecting cubes during their independent work time to identify fish in the book that are the same size, longest, and shortest.

Activity Choice 2 • Hands-On 

- Show two different objects lying side by side. Ask students what is longer and what is shorter.
- Show a third object in the line. Ask students what is longest and what is shortest.
- Invite volunteers in groups of three to arrange other objects in order: short, shorter, shortest or long, longer, longest. Have the class say the order with the volunteers.
- Repeat this activity with objects standing on end to compare height.

2 Teach

- Direct students to the top of p. 181.
- Instruct students to look at the picture of the three caterpillars.
- Have students point to the bottom caterpillar. Say that this caterpillar is short.
- Have students point to the middle caterpillar. Say that this caterpillar is shorter.
- **Which is the shortest caterpillar?** the top caterpillar
- Now start with the shortest caterpillar and tell students it is long. Prompt students to identify the longer and longest caterpillars.

BL Alternate Teaching Strategy

If students have trouble ordering objects by length . . .

Then use one of these reteach options.

1  **Daily Reteach Worksheet** (p. 10)

2 **Find What Is Longer** Have students arrange objects in order by length. Review the terms *long, longer, short,* and *shorter*.

- Gather classroom objects such as pencils, clothespins, and erasers.
- Ask students to choose two items and put them in order, with the long item first and the longer item second.
- Repeat the activity, having students choose different objects to compare. This time, have students order objects from short to shorter.

COMMON ERROR!

Students may have difficulty comparing three objects. Help students align all three objects at one end and to observe the difference in length at the other end.

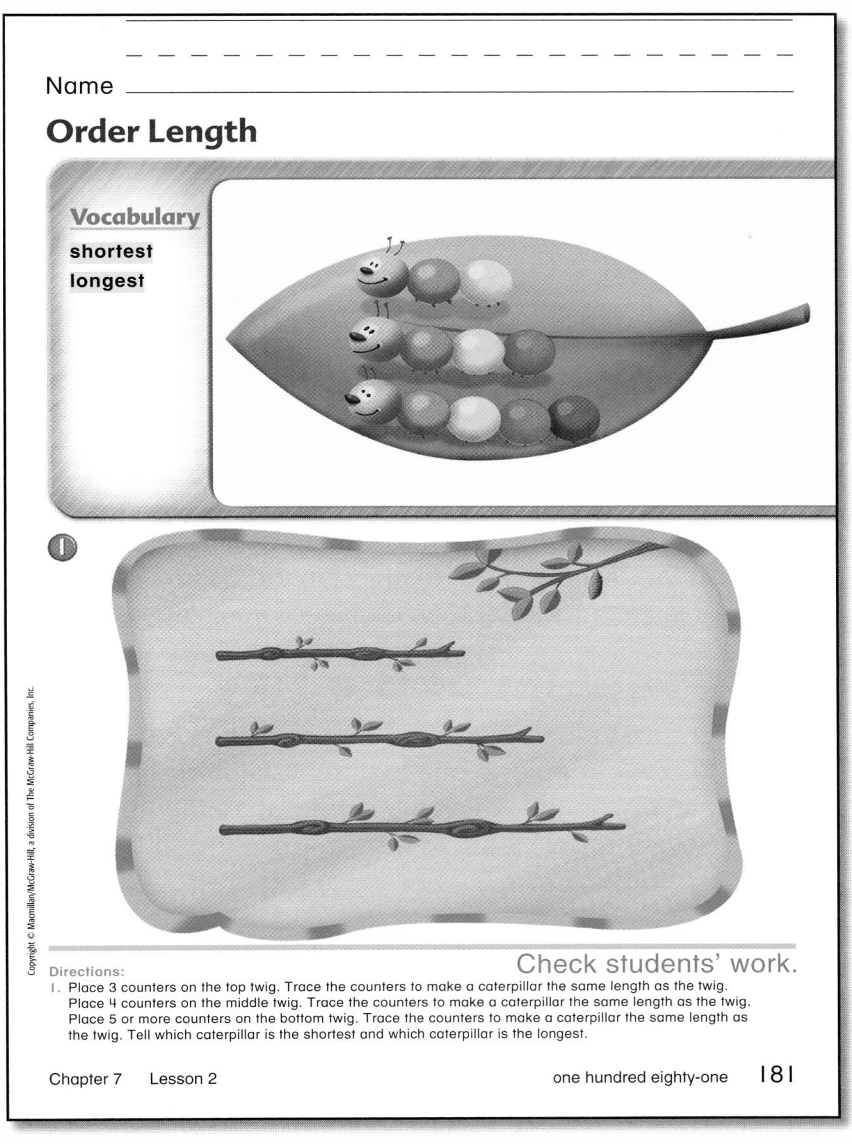

Name

Order Length

Vocabulary
shortest
longest

1

Check students' work.

Directions:
1. Place 3 counters on the top twig. Trace the counters to make a caterpillar the same length as the twig. Place 4 counters on the middle twig. Trace the counters to make a caterpillar the same length as the twig. Place 5 or more counters on the bottom twig. Trace the counters to make a caterpillar the same length as the twig. Tell which caterpillar is the shortest and which caterpillar is the longest.

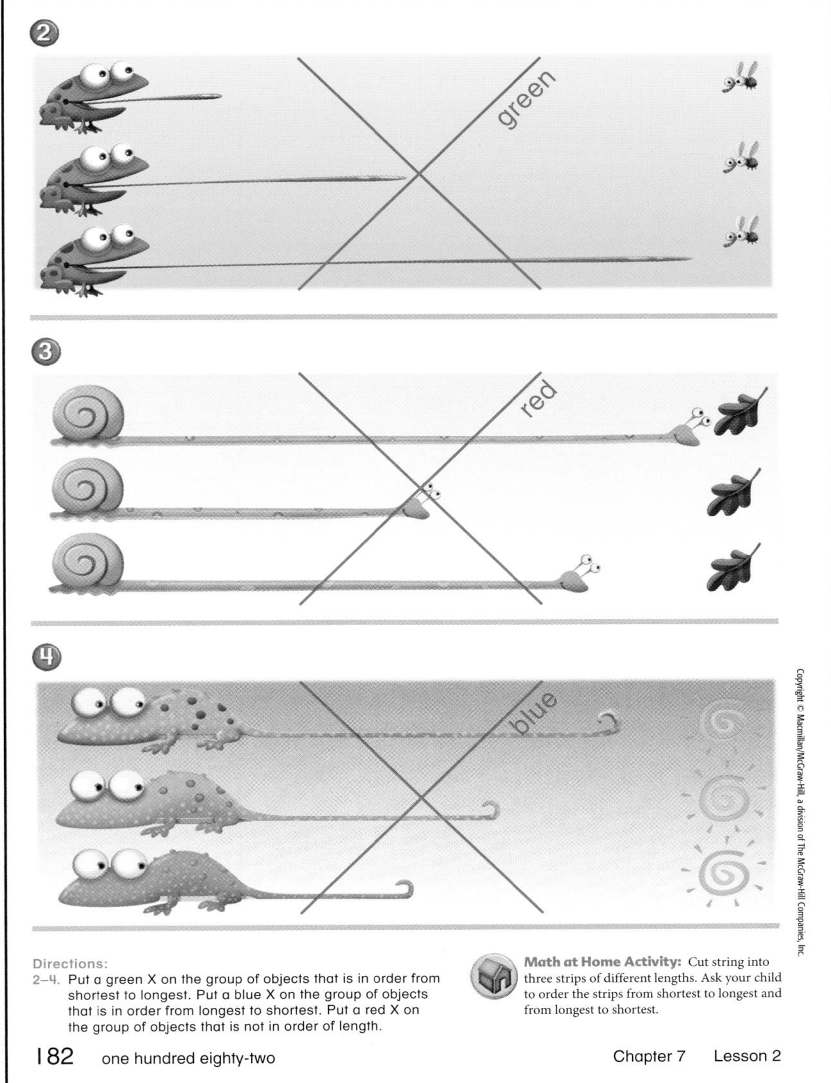

2 green

3 red

4 blue

Directions:
2–4. Put a green X on the group of objects that is in order from shortest to longest. Put a blue X on the group of objects that is in order from longest to shortest. Put a red X on the group of objects that is not in order of length.

Math at Home Activity: Cut string into three strips of different lengths. Ask your child to order the strips from shortest to longest and from longest to shortest.

3 Practice

Guided Practice

- Direct students to Exercise 1 on p. 181.
- Give 12 counters to each student. Ask them to line up in a row the counters that will fit on the top twig.
- **How many counters fit?** three counters
- Have them trace around their counters to draw their caterpillars. Repeat with the middle and bottom twigs.
- **How many counters fit on the middle twig? The bottom twig?** four counters; five or more counters
- Guide students to order the caterpillars using: long, longer, longest then short, shorter, shortest.

Independent Practice

Have students turn to p. 182. Explain the directions. Have students work independently on the exercises.

4 Assess

Formative Assessment

Make three trains of different numbers of connecting cubes.

- Show the shortest train.
- **Which train is longer? Longest?** Answers will vary.
- Have students re-order the trains by shorter and shortest.
- Repeat the activity using trains of different lengths.

Quick Check **Are students still struggling to order objects by lengths?**

If Yes → Small Group Options (p. 181B)

If No → Independent Work Options (p. 181B)

CRM Skills Practice Worksheet (p. 11)

CRM Enrich Worksheet (p. 13)

LESSON 7-3 Compare Weight

Lesson Planner

Objective

Compare weight to a reference object.

Vocabulary

weight, **heavier**, **lighter**, **equal to**

Resources

Materials: pencil, book, dictionary, storybooks, containers, crayons, glue, scale, classroom objects, blocks
Literature Connection: *Just a Little Bit* by Ann Tompert
Alternate Lesson: Use *Teeter Totter* on page 122 of *Math Their Way* to provide practice in comparing weight to a reference object.
Use *IMPACT Mathematics*: Unit J to provide practice with comparing weight.
Teacher Technology
TeacherWorks • Concepts in Motion

Focus on Math Background

In this lesson, students explore weight as a measurable attribute. Length is a more concrete attribute in that students can see the distance between two points. Weight is more abstract and less easy to visualize because students must feel how heavy or light two objects are when directly compared to each other. Direct comparison of two objects helps students distinguish between unlike properties such as heavy and light.

Daily Routine

Use these suggestions before beginning the lesson on p. 183.

5-Minute Check

(Reviews Lesson 7-2)
Have students compare multiple lengths of connecting cubes and order them by length. Tell them to find a concrete object in the classroom that is longer or shorter than each section of cubes.

Problem of the Day

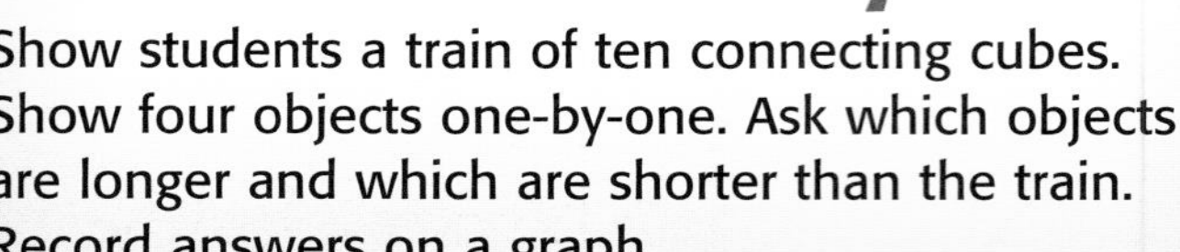

Show students a train of ten connecting cubes. Show four objects one-by-one. Ask which objects are longer and which are shorter than the train. Record answers on a graph.

Ask students to line up as they name something very light or name something very heavy.

Building Math Vocabulary

Materials: classroom scale, classroom objects

- Ask students if they can lift a car or an elephant. Ask if they can lift a pencil or a banana. Have them explain their answer.
- Explain that the words *heavy* and *light* describe **weight** and that weight tells how heavy an object is.
- Use the classroom scale to show what **heavier** and **lighter** look like, and to show that the heavier object makes the scale go down.
- Show students that when one object is **equal to** another object the scale will balance.

Visual Vocabulary Cards

Use Visual Vocabulary Card 16 to reinforce the vocabulary introduced in this lesson. (The Define/Example/Ask routine is printed on the back of each card.)

Differentiated Instruction

Small Group Options

Option 1 LOGICAL

Gifted and Talented AL

Materials: balance scale, classroom objects, cubes

- Hold up two different objects. Ask students to compare objects and decide which weighs more. Record their guesses, then weigh them.
- Ask students to estimate/guess how many cubes are needed to balance the scale before cubes are added. Ask if estimate is reasonable. Have students add cubes.

Option 2 VISUAL

English Language Learners ELL

Materials: classroom objects, balance scales
Core Vocabulary: lighter, heavier, (goes) up/down
Common Use Verb: goes

Do Math This strategy allows students to compare weight.

- Pantomime weighing two objects by hand.
- Show and say using a scale: "This is lighter. It goes up."
- Repeat for heavier, saying: "This is heavier. It goes down."
- Restate language as necessary.

Independent Work Options

Option 1 LOGICAL, VISUAL

Early Finishers OL AL

Materials: drawing paper, crayons, apples, balance scales

- Have students draw a picture of an apple and a picture of a crayon.
- Ask students if an apple or a crayon is heavier. Ask which is lighter.
- Have students weigh the two objects with the scale to check their guesses.

Option 2

Student Technology

Math Online macmillanmh.com

Option 3

Learning Station: Science (p. 175G)

Direct students to the Science Learning Station for opportunities to explore and extend the lesson concept.

Leveled Lesson Resources

Additional support for English Language Learners can be found in the ELL Guide (p. 115). ELL

Reteach (p. 14) BL

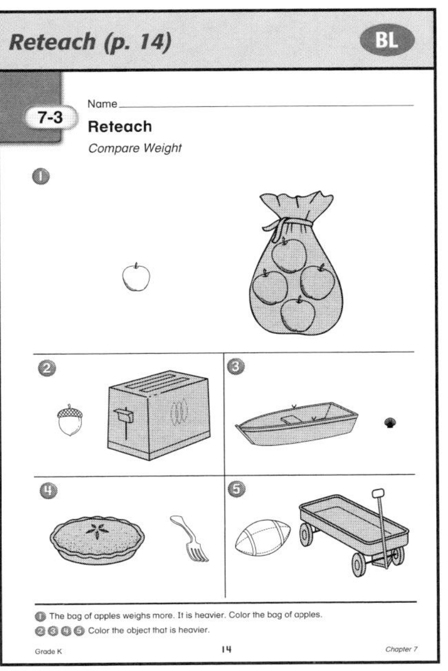

Name

7-3 Reteach

Compare Weight

1 The bag of apples weighs more. It is heavier. Color the bag of apples.

2 3 4 5 Color the object that is heavier.

Grade K 14 Chapter 7

Skills Practice (p. 15) OL

Name

7-3 Skills Practice

Compare Weight

1 2 Trace or draw a line from each object to its correct place on the scale.

3 4 Circle the heavier object. Put an X on the lighter object.

Grade K 15 Chapter 7

Enrich (p. 17) AL

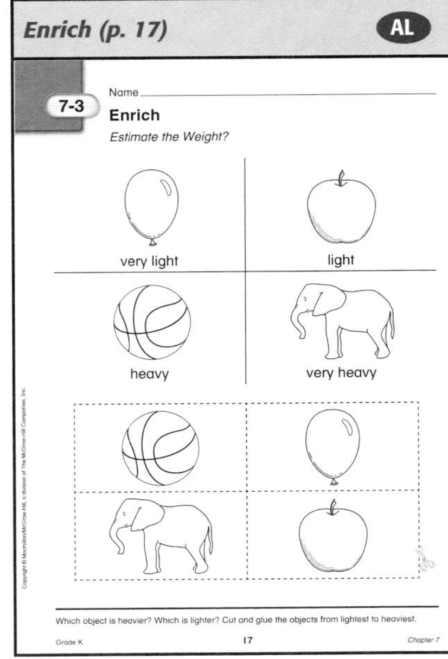

Name

7-3 Enrich

Estimate the Weight?

Which object is heavier? Which is lighter? Cut and glue the objects from lightest to heaviest.

Grade K 17 Chapter 7

Homework Practice (p. 16) OL

Name

7-3 Homework Practice

Compare Weight

1 2 Circle the heavier object. Put an X on the lighter object.

3 4 Draw a line from each object to its correct place on the scale.

Grade K 16 Chapter 7

1 Introduce

Circle Time

Activity Choice 1 • Literature

Just a Little Bit by Ann Tompert

- Discuss how a seesaw works and why it is necessary for the seesaw to balance.
- Ask students to describe how much an elephant weighs: a lot, more than the teacher, etc.
- Discuss why the seesaw did not work for elephant and mouse and why it did not work for elephant, mouse, zebra, lion, and bear.
- **Why did it finally work?** total weight was about the same as elephant's weight
- Display a seesaw chart showing elephant on one side and all the other animals on the other side.

Activity Choice 2 • Hands-On

Materials: pencil, book, dictionary

- Ask students to compare a pencil and a book. **Which is heavier and which is lighter?** book is heavier; pencil is lighter
- Have students pick up the objects to confirm their guesses. Ask them if their guess was reasonable.
- Show a large dictionary with the pencil and book. **Which is heaviest and which is lightest?** dictionary is heaviest; pencil is lightest
- Have students pick up the objects to confirm their guesses. Ask if their guess was reasonable.
- Ask students what items in the room weigh more than the dictionary or weigh less than the pencil. Invite volunteers to share their answers.
- Have students pick up the objects to confirm their guesses.

2 Teach

- Direct students to the top of p. 183.
- Put out a pile of children's storybooks and a bottle of glue that match the picture. Discuss that the student is thinking what is heavier, a book or a bottle of glue.
- Explain that we will see what is heavier, a book or a bottle of glue. Have each student get a book and glue bottle.
- Have students hold the book in their right hand as you model. **Is the book heavier than, lighter than, or the same (equal to)?** heavier than
- Have students hold the glue bottle in their left hand as you model. **Is the glue heavier than, lighter than, or the same (equal to)?** lighter than
- Point out that heavier items push our hand down and light items are easier to hold up.

BL Alternate Teaching Strategy

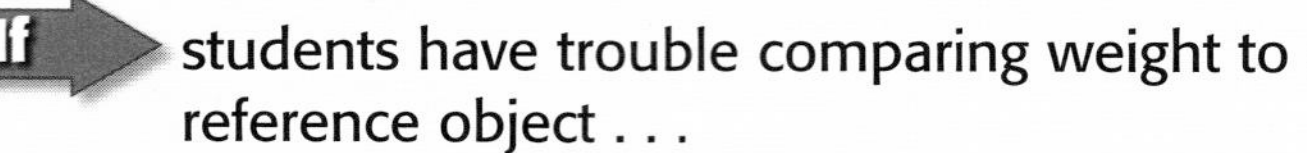

If students have trouble comparing weight to a reference object . . .

Then use one of these reteach options.

1 CRM **Daily Reteach Worksheet** (p. 14)

2 **Comparing Weights** Give students 11 identical blocks and two identical containers.

- Ask students to put one block in a container and 10 blocks in a second container.
- Have students hold a container in each hand and say what container is heavier and what container is lighter.
- Have them weigh the two containers on the scale to check their guesses.

COMMON ERROR!

Students may confuse size with weight and be unable to judge how heavy an object is by seeing it on paper. Tell students to imagine holding the object to get an idea of its weight.

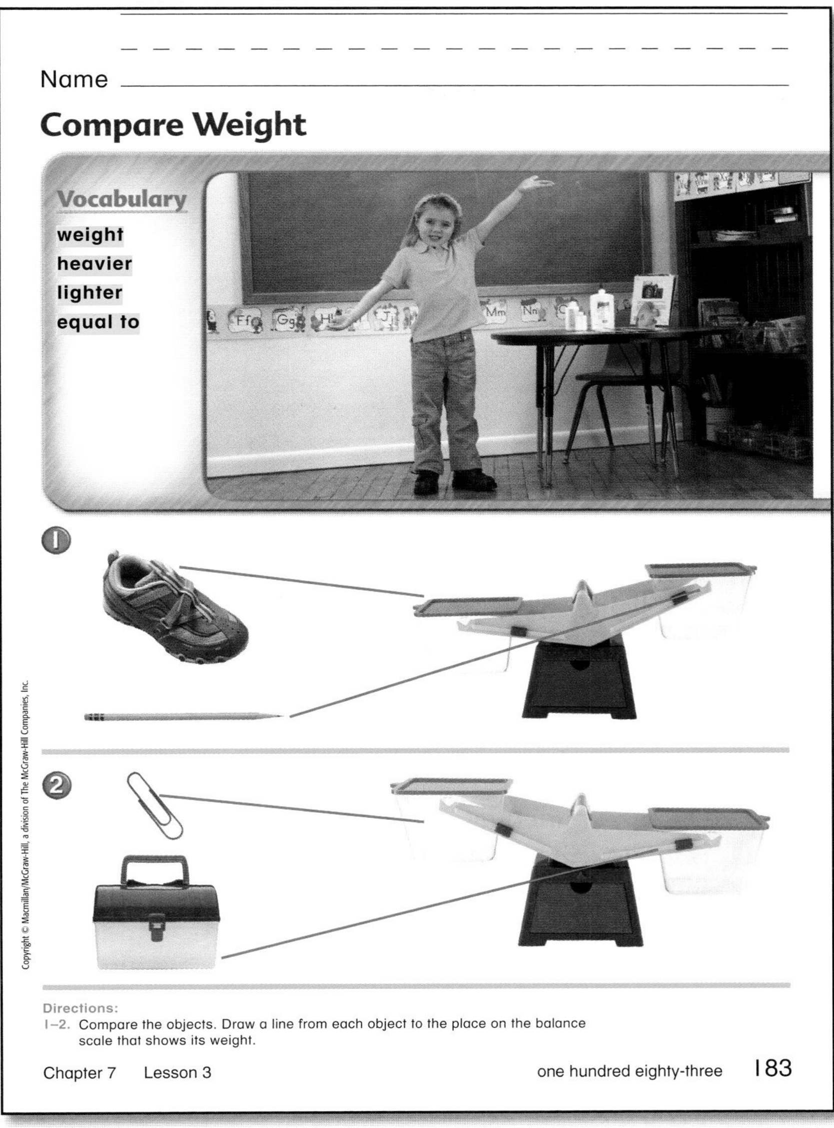

Name

Compare Weight

Vocabulary
weight
heavier
lighter
equal to

1

2

Directions:
1–2. Compare the objects. Draw a line from each object to the place on the balance scale that shows its weight.

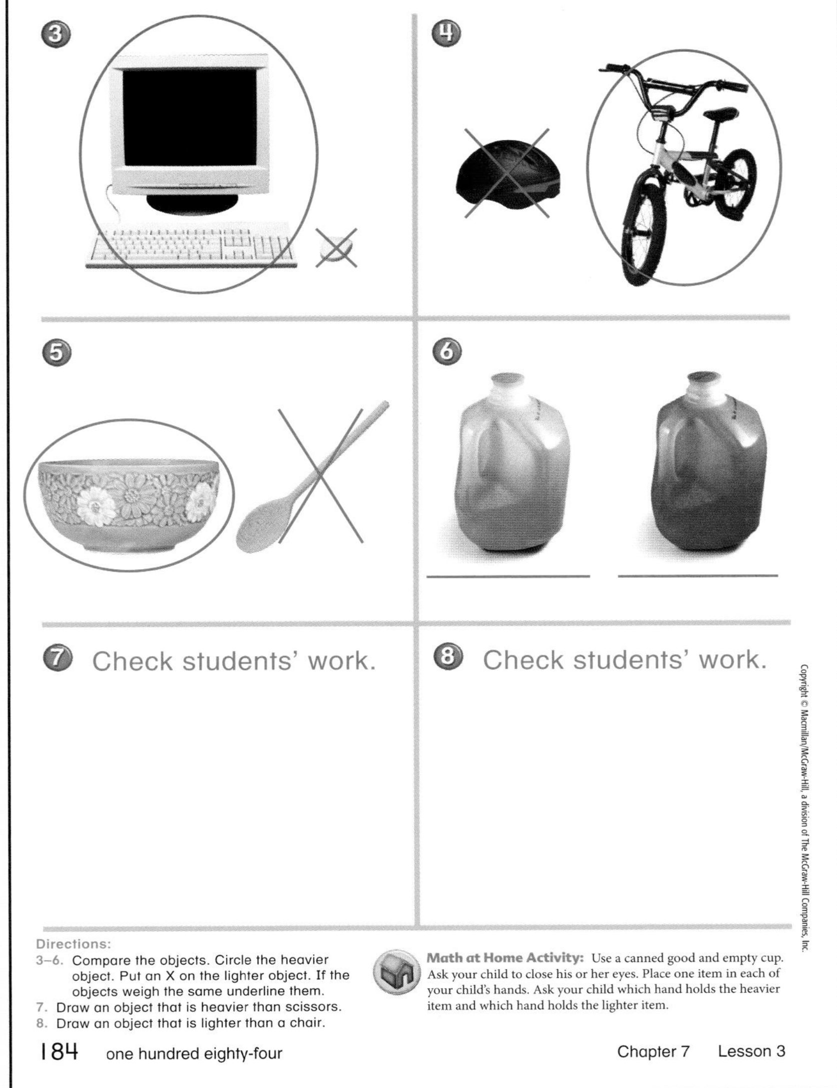

3

4

5

6

7 Check students' work.

8 Check students' work.

Directions:
3–6. Compare the objects. Circle the heavier object. Put an X on the lighter object. If the objects weigh the same underline them.
7. Draw an object that is heavier than scissors.
8. Draw an object that is lighter than a chair.

Math at Home Activity: Use a canned good and empty cup. Ask your child to close his or her eyes. Place one item in each of your child's hands. Ask your child which hand holds the heavier item and which hand holds the lighter item.

3 Practice

Guided Practice

- Direct students to p. 183.
- **What objects do you see in Exercise 1?** shoe, pencil, scale
- Have students put one of their shoes in one hand and a pencil in the other hand. Demonstrate that heavier objects push our hands down while lighter objects are easy to hold up.
- **Which is heavier, the shoe or pencil?** shoe
- Guide students to draw a line from each object to the correct place on the scale that shows its weight.
- Repeat the activity for Exercise 2.

Independent Practice

Have students turn to p. 184. Explain the directions. Have students work independently on the exercises.

4 Assess

Formative Assessment

- **What do we use to measure weight?** a scale
- Show a heavy book and a crayon.
- **Which object is heavier? Which is lighter?** book; crayon
- Give students a classroom object such as a crayon. Have them find a heavier and a lighter classroom object.

Quick Check **Are students still struggling to compare weights of objects?**

If Yes → Small Group Options (p. 183B)

If No → Independent Work Options (p. 183B)

CRM Skills Practice Worksheet (p. 15)

CRM Enrich Worksheet (p. 17)

7-4 Problem-Solving Strategy
Guess and Check

Lesson Planner

Objective

Compare length to a reference object.

Resources

Materials: pencils, classroom objects, paper, posterboard
Manipulatives: connecting cubes
Literature Connection: *Much Bigger Than Martin* by Steven Kellogg
Teacher Technology
TeacherWorks

Real-World Problem Solving Library
Math and Science: *Bigger or Smaller?*
Use these leveled readers to reinforce and extend problem-solving skills and strategies.

Leveled for:

- OL On Level
- ELL Sheltered English
- SP Spanish

For additional support, see the Real-World Problem Solving Teacher Guide.

On-level title is available in classroom Big Book.

Daily Routine

Use these suggestions before beginning the lesson on p. 185.

5-Minute Check

(Reviews Lesson 7-3)

1. Ask students riddles: What weighs more than me, lives in Africa, and has a trunk with it wherever it goes? an elephant What (object) is lighter than me but heavier than (another object)? a desk
2. Have students make height riddles.

Problem of the Day

Draw two unequal horizontal lines. Ask which line is longer. Guess how many connecting cubes long the lines are. Measure with cubes to check your answer. Check students work

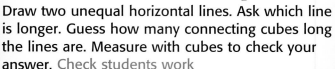

LINE UP Have pairs of students draw straws of two different lengths. Have them determine which is long (or tall) and which is short. Ask the students with the short straws to form a line. Students with the long/tall straws can form a second line.

Differentiated Instruction

Small Group Options

Option 1 LOGICAL

Gifted and Talented AL

Materials: number cards 1–5, squares of paper of the same size, glue, graph paper

- Have pairs mix up number cards 1 to 5.
- Have each partner take a number and glue that many squares in a row, using a sheet of paper for each partner.
- Have the first partner guess what line is longer. Have the pair check by cutting out their rows and comparing their side by side. Have pairs repeat taking turns.

Option 2 LOGICAL/SPATIAL

English Language Learners ELL

Materials: classroom objects, connecting cubes
Core Vocabulary: guess, correct, close
Common Use Verb: measure

Write Math This strategy allows students to guess and check varying measurements.

- Have students guess how many blocks will equal the length of an object. Write their guesses.
- Measure the objects with cubes.
- Count the number of correct or close guesses.
- Repeat with another object.

Independent Work Options

Option 1 KINESTHETIC

Early Finishers OL AL

Materials: paper, pencils, blocks

- Have students form pairs. Have each partner print his or her name, using a separate sheet of paper.
- Have each partner count the number of letters in his or her name, then stack that many blocks.
- Include an opportunity for students to guess which stack will be taller based on the number of letters in children's names before blocks are stacked. Ask students if this guess is reasonable.
- Have one partner say what stack of blocks is taller. Have the pair check by comparing the stacks.

Option 2

Student Technology

Math Online macmillanmh.com

Option 3

Learning Station: Reading (p. 175G)

Direct students to the Reading Learning Station for opportunities to explore and extend the lesson concept.

Leveled Lesson Resources

Reteach (pp. 18–19) BL

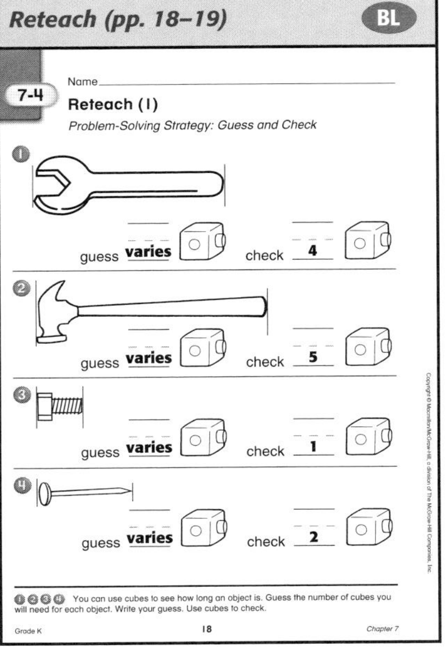

7-4 Name
Reteach (1)
Problem-Solving Strategy: Guess and Check

1. guess varies check 4
2. guess varies check 5
3. guess varies check 1
4. guess varies check 2

1 2 3 4 You can use cubes to see how long an object is. Guess the number of cubes you will need for each object. Write your guess. Use cubes to check.

Grade K 18 Chapter 7

Skills Practice (p. 20) OL

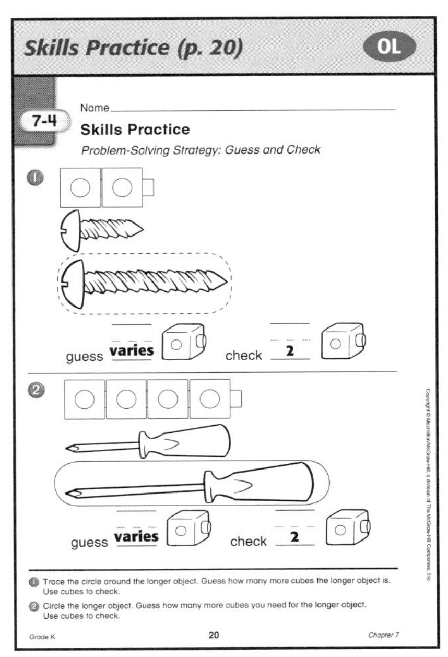

7-4 Name
Skills Practice
Problem-Solving Strategy: Guess and Check

1. guess varies check 2
2. guess varies check 2

1 Trace the circle around the longer object. Guess how many more cubes the longer object is. Use cubes to check.
2 Circle the longer object. Guess how many more cubes you need for the longer object. Use cubes to check.

Grade K 20 Chapter 7

Enrich (p. 22) AL

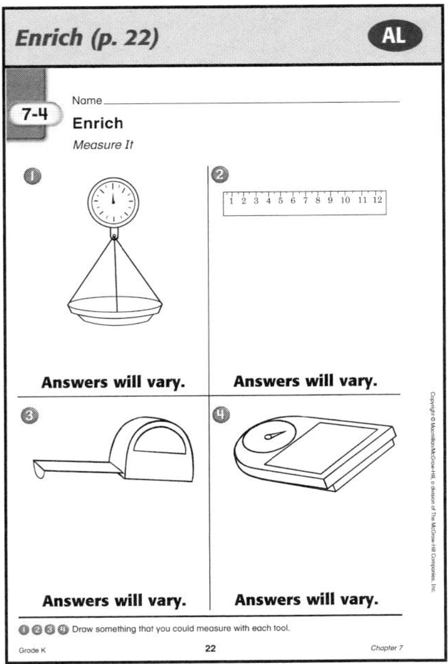

7-4 Name
Enrich
Measure It

1. Answers will vary.
2. Answers will vary.
3. Answers will vary.
4. Answers will vary.

1 2 3 4 Draw something that you could measure with each tool.

Grade K 22 Chapter 7

Homework Practice (p. 21) OL

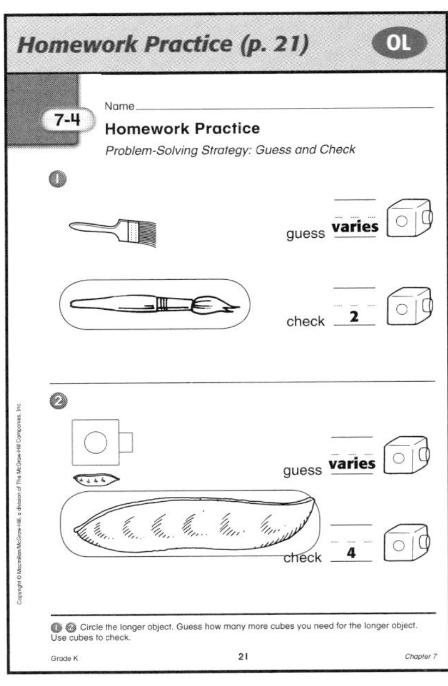

7-4 Name
Homework Practice
Problem-Solving Strategy: Guess and Check

1. guess varies check 2
2. guess varies check 4

1 2 Circle the longer object. Guess how many more cubes you need for the longer object. Use cubes to check.

Grade K 21 Chapter 7

1 Introduce

Circle Time

Activity Choice 1 • Literature

Much Bigger Than Martin
by Steven Kellogg

- Introduce the book stressing this story is about size. Tell students that when they hear the words, *big, bigger,* or *biggest*, they quickly will stand up (grow) and then sit down. Read the story aloud.
- Explain that words other than *big* are used to compare size (*longer, taller*, etc.) and each word means something slightly different.
- Have students sit and locate an object in the room "bigger" than their thumb and an object bigger than themselves.
- Have students physically compare their objects to check if their guesses were correct.
- Have students report their results. Make responses into a class book with student drawings.
- Repeat the activity with smaller or shorter items.

Activity Choice 2 • Hands-On 

- **How do we measure the length of objects?** Sample answer: We line up the end of the object with the object we are using to measure.
- **How can connecting cubes help us know how long objects are?** Sample answer: Cubes are all the same length so put them side by side to check the length of a longer object.
- Have students measure the length of three classroom objects. Be sure they line up the ends of the cube strip with the object.
- Provide students with two more objects. Have students use what they know about the cubes and the lengths of the other objects to guess the lengths of the new objects.
- Have students use cubes to check their guesses.

2 Teach

The *guess and check* strategy helps students find out if their estimate is reasonable and leads them to further thoughtful guessing rather than random answers.

Understand Review what students know and what they need to find for each problem.

Plan Have students discuss their strategy for solving the problems.

Solve Guide students to guess and check to solve the problems. Instruct students to look at the objects and use what they know about the problem to make a systematic guess about the length of each object. Have students measure each object with cubes to check their guesses.

Check Have students look back at the problem to be sure that the answers fit what they already know about the problem.

BL Alternate Teaching Strategy

If students have trouble using the *guess and check* strategy . . .

Then use one of these reteach options.

1 CRM **Daily Reteach Worksheet** (p. 18–19)

2 **Measure Length** Have students practice measuring with manipulatives.

- Give students 10 connecting cubes.
- Have them make a train with the cubes.
- Have them guess the length of classroom objects, then measure the objects using their ten-cube train.
- Repeat the activity with a five-cube train.

COMMON ERROR!

Students may not line up the ends of cube trains with the ends of objects. Model how to line up the end of a cube with the end of an object.

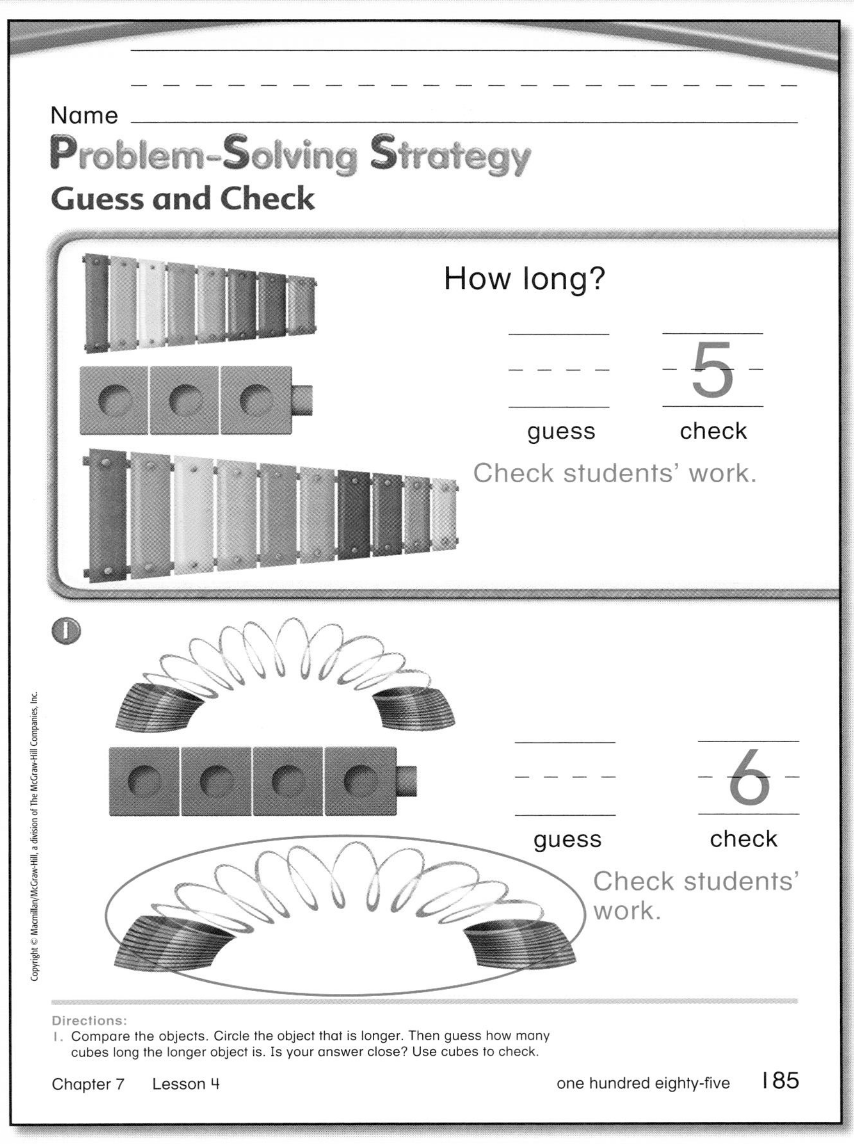
Name

Problem-Solving Strategy
Guess and Check

How long?

guess | check 5

Check students' work.

1

guess | check 6

Check students' work.

Directions:
1. Compare the objects. Circle the object that is longer. Then guess how many cubes long the longer object is. Is your answer close? Use cubes to check.

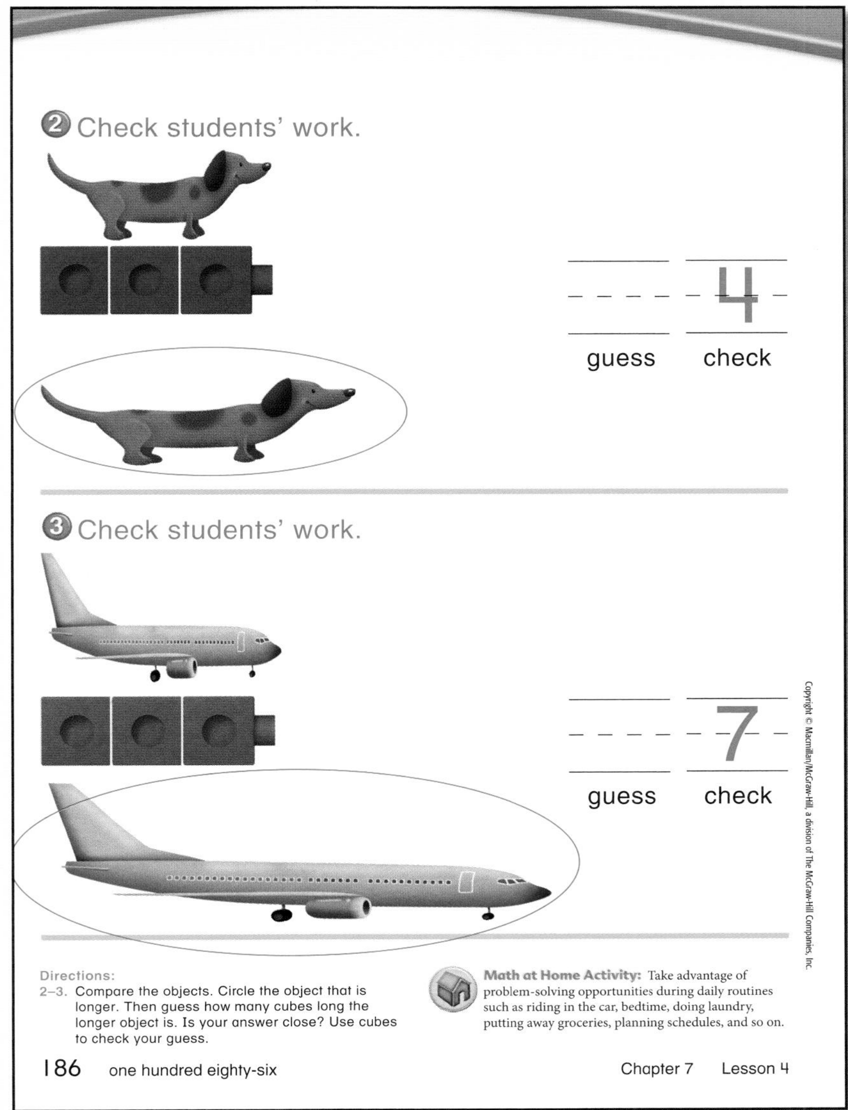
2 Check students' work.

guess | check 4

3 Check students' work.

guess | check 7

Directions:
2–3. Compare the objects. Circle the object that is longer. Then guess how many cubes long the longer object is. Is your answer close? Use cubes to check your guess.

Math at Home Activity: Take advantage of problem-solving opportunities during daily routines such as riding in the car, bedtime, doing laundry, putting away groceries, planning schedules, and so on.

3 Practice

Guided Practice

- Direct students to Exercise 1 on p. 185.
- Have students circle the longer spring.
- Instruct students to guess how many cubes long the longer spring is and to write the number.
- Have students use cubes to check and then write the number.

Independent Practice

Have students turn to p. 186. Explain the directions. Have students work independently on the exercises.

- **What other materials could be used to check the length of the objects? Would the answers be the same?** Sample answers: paper clips, erasers; no
- Ask students to share another approach/strategy that could be used and how it might be used.

4 Assess

Formative Assessment

- Draw a line on a poster board. Use cubes to show how many cubes long the line is.
- Draw a line of a different length beneath the first line.
- Ask students how many cubes long they think the line is.
- Have students use cubes to check their answers at the poster board. Ask students if their guess was close.

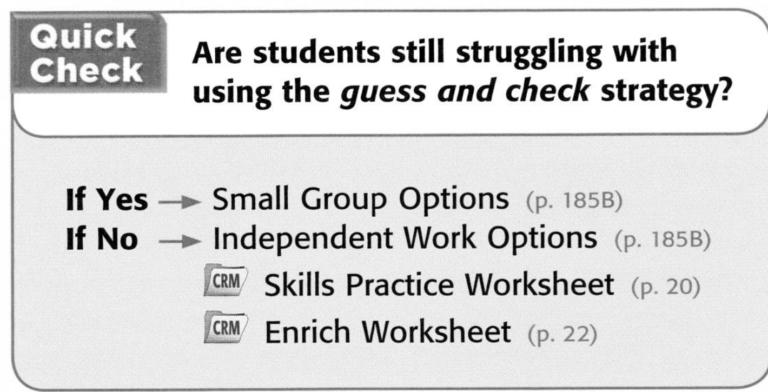
Quick Check **Are students still struggling with using the *guess and check* strategy?**

If Yes → Small Group Options (p. 185B)

If No → Independent Work Options (p. 185B)

CRM Skills Practice Worksheet (p. 20)

CRM Enrich Worksheet (p. 22)

Mid-Chapter Check

Lessons 7-1 to 7-4

Formative Assessment

Use the Mid-Chapter Check to assess students' progress in the first half of the chapter.

Customize and create multiple versions of your Mid-Chapter Check and the test answer keys.

FOLDABLES® Dinah Zike's Foldables

Use these lesson suggestions for incorporating the Foldables during the chapter.

Lesson 7-2 Under the *Length* tab of the Foldable, glue different lengths of materials such as yarn, ribbon, or paper strips. Use the terms *longer* and *shorter* and *longest* and *shortest* when describing the different materials.

Lesson 7-3 Under the *Weight* tab of the Foldable, glue pictures of objects that vary greatly in weight. A picture of an elephant and a mouse might be glued under the tab with *heavier* and *lighter* used to describe, compare, and contrast.

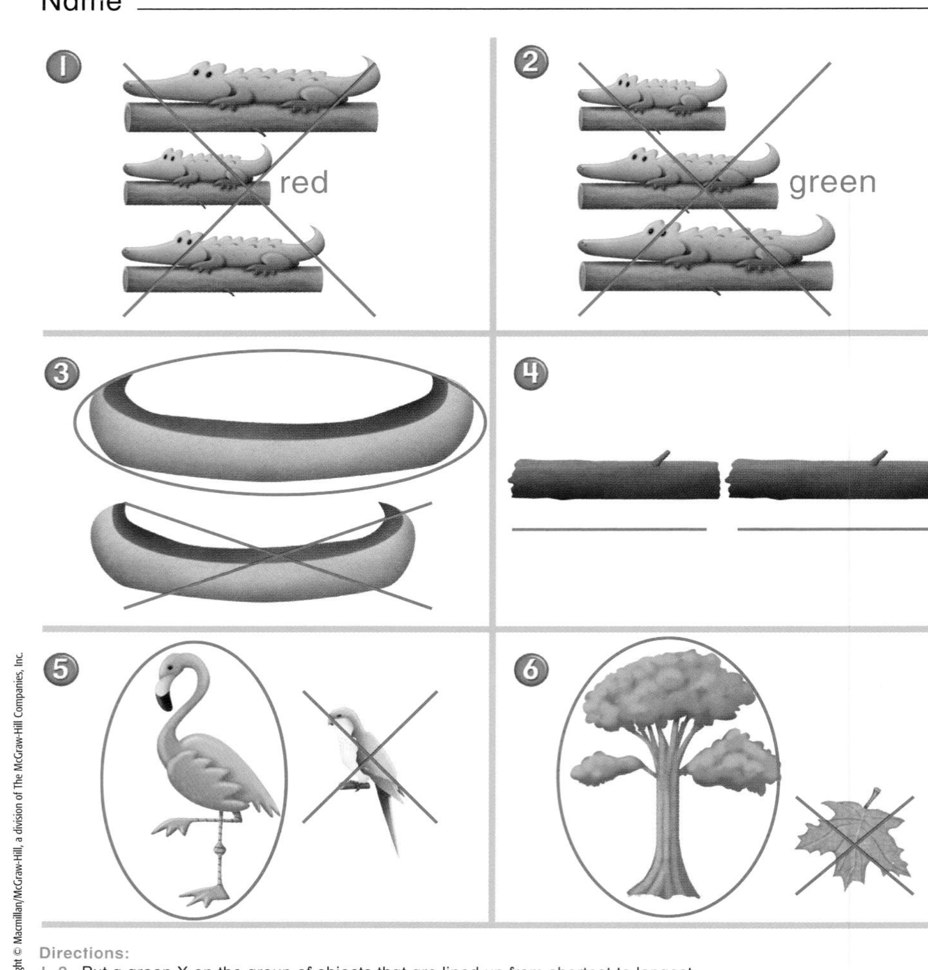

Mid-Chapter Check
Lessons 1-4

Name

Directions:
1–2. Put a green X on the group of objects that are lined up from shortest to longest. Put a red X on the group of objects that are not lined up from shortest to longest.
3. Circle the canoe that is longer. Put an X on the canoe that is shorter.
4–6. Circle the object that is heavier. Put an X on the object that is lighter. If the objects weigh the same underline them.

Chapter 7 one hundred eighty-seven 187

Data-Driven Decision Making

Based on the results of the Mid-Chapter Check, use the following resources to review concepts that continue to give students problems.

Exercises	State/Local Standards	What's the Math?	Error Analysis	Resources for Review
1–2 **Lesson 7-1**		Compare length of objects by making direct comparisons with reference objects to determine which object is longer or shorter.	Circles shorter canoe. Puts an "X" on taller canoe.	CRM Chapter 7 Resource Masters (Reteach Worksheets) Math Online Concepts in Motion Math Adventures
3 **Lesson 7-2**		Compare and order objects by comparing with reference objects to tell which goes from shortest to longest.	Reverses directions and puts green "X" on wrong group and red "X" on wrong group.	
4–6 **Lesson 7-3**		Compare weights of objects by making direct comparisons with reference objects to determine which objects are lighter or heavier.	Reverses directions and circles the wrong objects and puts "X's" on wrong objects.	

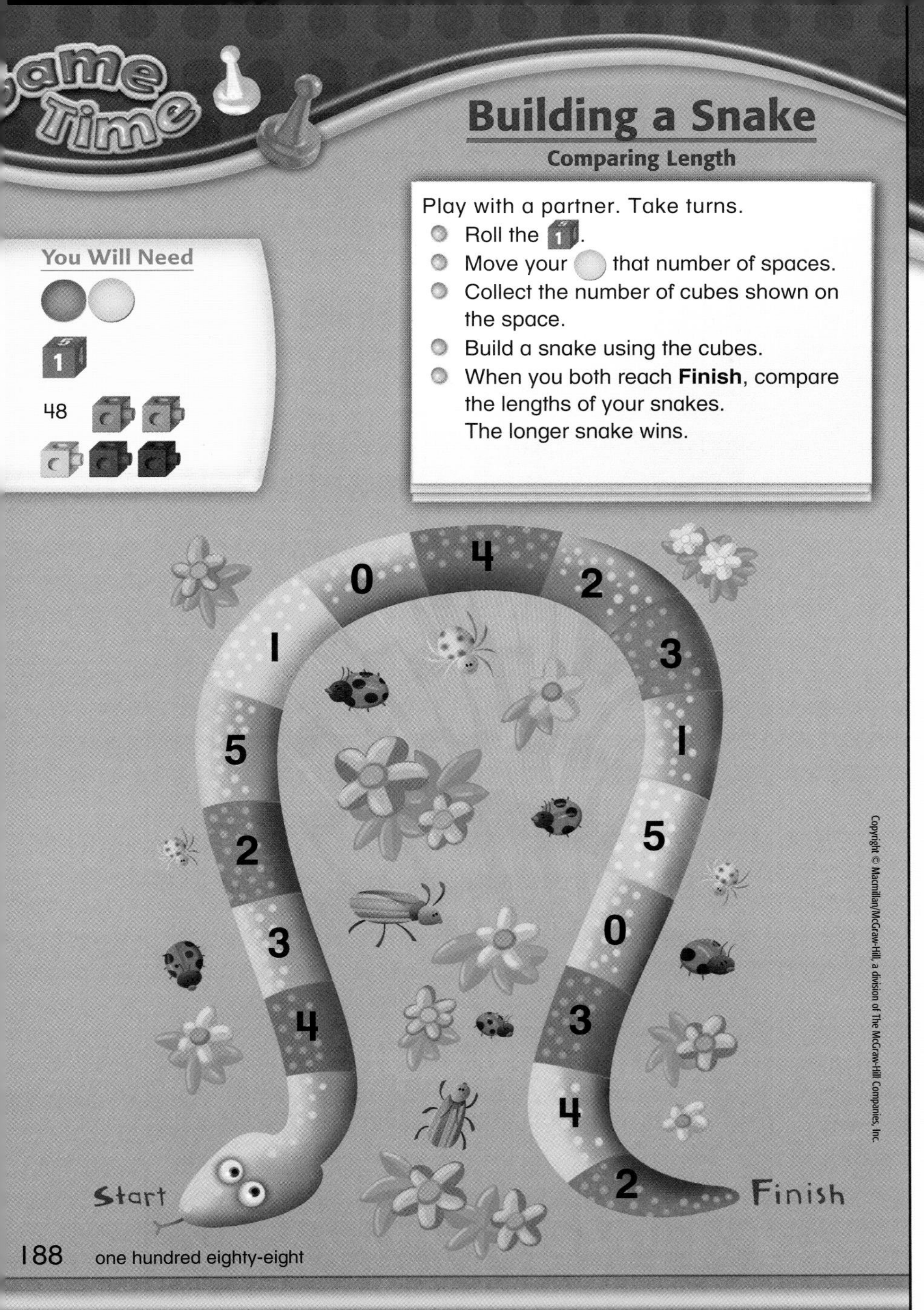
Game Time

Building a Snake

Comparing Length

Play with a partner. Take turns.

- Roll the cube.
- Move your counter that number of spaces.
- Collect the number of cubes shown on the space.
- Build a snake using the cubes.
- When you both reach **Finish**, compare the lengths of your snakes. The longer snake wins.

You Will Need

48

Building a Snake

Math Concept:

Comparing Length

Manipulatives: number cube, two 2-colored counters, 40 connecting cubes

Introduce the game on page 188 to your students to play as a class, in small groups, or at a learning workstation to review concepts introduced in this chapter.

Instructions

- Assign each student a color.
- Students play in pairs, taking turns rolling the number cube and moving that number of squares.
- Players collect the number of cubes that correspond to the number on the square.
- Each player builds a snake with the cubes.
- When both players reach Finish, they compare the lengths of their snakes, with the ends of the snakes next to each other. The player with the longer snake wins.

Extend the Game

Have students create their own game by making a gameboard with different numbers on the squares.

Differentiated Practice

Use these leveling suggestions to differentiate the game for all learners.

Level	Assignment
BL Below/Approaching Level	Change the game board by putting sticky notes over the numbers and using lower numbers. Or, draw dots on the sticky notes for students to count.
OL On Level	Have students play the game with the rules as written.
AL Above/Beyond Level	After students finish playing, have them find the difference in length between the snakes.

LESSON 7-5

Compare Capacity

Lesson Planner

Objective

Compare capacity to a reference object.

Vocabulary

holds more, **holds less**, **holds the same**, **capacity**

Resources

Materials: small classroom objects, mittens, dry cereal, small and large containers, small and large cups, small bottle, dried beans, large bottle, small and large bags, juice can, juice pitcher, crayons, dry rice, chart paper
Manipulatives: connecting cubes
Literature Connection: *The Mitten* by Jan Brett
Alternate Lesson: Adapt *Weighing* and *Comparing* on page 132 of *Math Their Way* for practice with comparing capacity to a reference object.
Use *IMPACT Mathematics*: Unit J to provide practice with comparing capacity.
Teacher Technology
TeacherWorks • Concepts in Motion

Focus on Math Background

This lesson focuses on capacity, which is how much of a solid or a liquid container can hold. Volume and capacity are related. Both are measured by determining how much space to fill. Students must also understand two different attributes simultaneously, such as how *tall* and *thin* a container is.

Daily Routine

Use these suggestions before beginning the lesson on p. 189.

5-Minute Check

(Reviews Lesson 7-3)
Hold a different object in each hand. Have students imagine your hands are a scale. Ask what hand would go lower and why. Repeat using other objects.

Problem of the Day

Show students three different classroom objects. Have them compare and order the objects from shortest to longest. Have students check the lengths by measuring each object with cubes.

LINE UP Give students containers of two different sizes. Have them form two lines: if their container holds more and if their container holds less.

Building Math Vocabulary

Materials: small cup, large cup, box of fish crackers

- Show the two cups and box of fish crackers. Ask which cup you should use to hold more crackers and why.
- Repeat for less crackers.
- Say that **capacity** is the ability of a container to hold something. A container can **hold more**, **hold less**, or **hold the same** as another container.

Visual Vocabulary Cards

Use Visual Vocabulary Card 17 to reinforce the vocabulary introduced in this lesson. (The Define/Example/Ask routine is printed on the back of each card.)

holds less

Differentiated Instruction

Small Group Options

Option 1 KINESTHETIC

Below/Approaching Level BL

Materials: small cups, large cups, scoops, dried beans

- Have students form small groups. Give each group a large cup, a small cup, a scoop, and 3–4 cups of beans.
- Have students use beans to fill large and small cups with scoops, making sure each scoop is full before pouring.
- Have students pour beans from the large container into the small container, and vice versa, to show the difference between containers that hold more and hold less.
- Ask students which cup took more scoops to fill and why.

Option 2 KINESTHETIC

English Language Learners ELL

Materials: small and large plastic bags, connecting cubes

Core Vocabulary: cup your hands, fill, hold

Common Use Verb: pour

Do Math This strategy teaches students one way to compare capacity.

- Model how to cup your hands to hold cubes and how to pour cubes into a bag. Have students repeat.
- Have students count and compare how many handfuls of cubes are needed to fill each bag.

Independent Work Options

Option 1 KINESTHETIC, LOGICAL

Early Finishers OL AL

Materials: tennis balls, small wastepaper basket, large wastepaper basket

- Show students two empty wastepaper baskets of noticeably different sizes.
- Have students guess what basket will hold more tennis balls or less tennis balls.
- Ask students to put their balls in the baskets.
- Have students pour the balls out of each basket into two separate piles. Have them count the number of balls in each pile to check their guesses. Ask if their guess was reasonable.

Option 2

Student Technology

Math Online macmillanmh.com

Option 3

Learning Station: Reading (p. 175G)

Direct students to the Reading Learning Station for opportunities to explore and extend the lesson concept.

Leveled Lesson Resources

Additional support for English Language Learners can be found in the ELL Guide (p. 117). ELL

Reteach (p. 23) BL

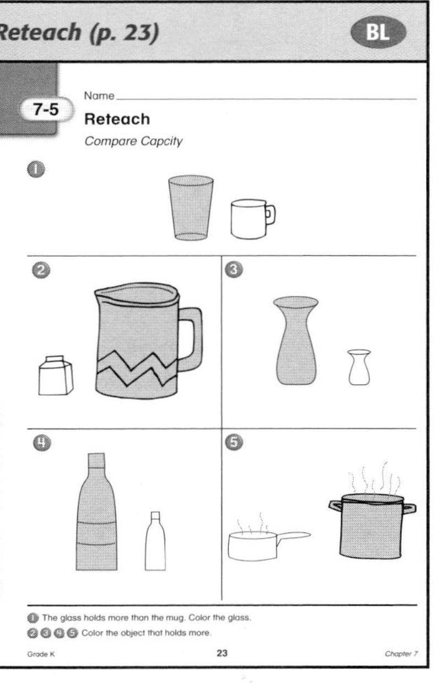
7-5 Name
Reteach
Compare Capacity
1 The glass holds more than the mug. Color the glass.
2 3 4 5 Color the object that holds more.
Grade K 23 Chapter 7

Skills Practice (p. 24) OL

7-5 Name
Skills Practice
Compare Capacity

1 2 3 4 Trace or draw a circle around the object that holds more. Trace or put an X on the object that holds less.
Grade K 24 Chapter 7

Enrich (p. 26) AL

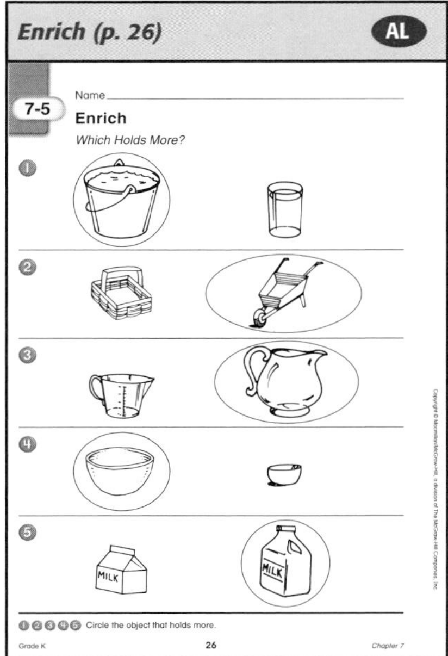
7-5 Name
Enrich
Which Holds More?

1 2 3 4 5 Circle the object that holds more.
Grade K 26 Chapter 7

Homework Practice (p. 25) OL

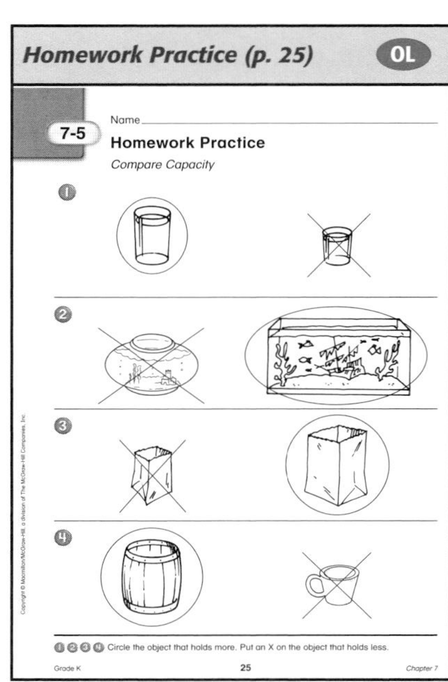
7-5 Name
Homework Practice
Compare Capacity
1 2 3 4 Circle the object that holds more. Put an X on the object that holds less.
Grade K 25 Chapter 7

1 Introduce

Circle Time

Activity Choice 1 • Literature

The Mitten by Jan Brett

Materials: small classroom objects such as crayons or markers, mittens

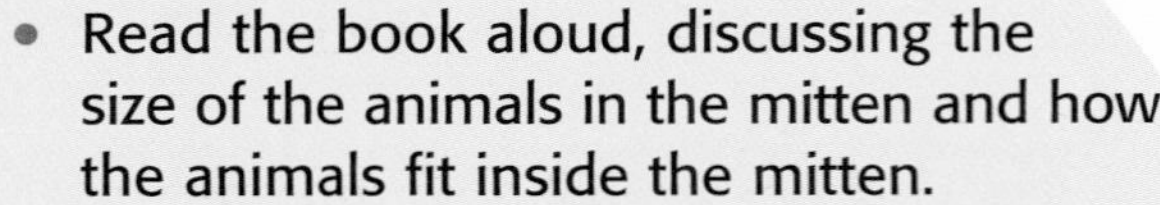

- Read the book aloud, discussing the size of the animals in the mitten and how the animals fit inside the mitten.
- Prepare groups of small classroom objects such as crayons or blocks. Have students put the objects in a child's-sized mitten. Ask them to compare and describe different groupings using ***holds more*** or ***holds less***.
- Have students count the number of objects needed to fill the mitten. Chart this information. Reinforce the lesson vocabulary by asking volunteers to describe the object groupings.

Activity Choice 2 • Hands-On

Materials: half-gallon container filled with dry cereal, half-pint container filled with dry cereal, small cups

- Show students both containers.
- **Which container holds more?** large container
- Have students check by asking volunteers to pour cereal from the small container into cups, having remaining students count the number of cups.
- Ask new volunteers to pour cereal from the large container into cups, having remaining students count the number of cups.
- **Which container holds more?** large container Explain that the large container has the larger **capacity**.
- Repeat with two containers that **hold the same**.
- Tell students that some containers may look different but can **hold the same**.

2 Teach

- Direct students to the top of p. 189.
- Direct them to the picture of the large and small cups. Discuss the picture, pointing out that each cup is filled with connecting cubes. Tell students they will find which cup holds more and which cup holds less.
- Have students form groups. Give each group a small cup, a large cup, and a pile of connecting cubes.
- Have students fill the small cup with cubes.
- Have students pour the small cup of cubes into the large cup. Ask if the large cup is full. Guide students to realize which cup holds more and which cup holds less.

BL Alternate Teaching Strategy

If students have trouble comparing capacity to a reference object . . .

Then use one of these reteach options.

1. CRM **Daily Reteach Worksheet** (p. 23)
2. **Compare Capacities** Show students a very small bottle and a very large bottle. Ask students which bottle holds more and which bottle holds less.
   - To check which holds more, pour dry rice into the large bottle. Ask a student to pour the rice from the large bottle to the small bottle. (Rice will overflow and show that large bottles hold more.)
   - To check which holds less, fill the small bottle with rice. Ask a student to pour the rice from the small bottle into the large bottle. (Rice will not fill the large bottle because small bottles hold less.)
   - Give students opportunities to practice pouring to reinforce capacity of bottles holding more and holding less.

COMMON ERROR!

Students may think that a taller container holds more. Remind them of their activities in this lesson and demonstrate with a short, wide container and a tall, thin container.

3 Practice

Guided Practice

- Direct students to Exercise 1 on p. 189.
- Discuss which bag could hold more connecting cubes.
- Give students a pile of connecting cubes, a small bag, and a large bag. Have them fill the large bag with cubes.
- Have them put the cubes from the large bag into the small bag. **What do you notice about the cubes?** There were leftover cubes.
- Guide students to put a circle on the bag that holds more and to put an X on the bag that holds less.
- Complete Exercise 2 together, discussing the picture.

Independent Practice

Have students turn to p. 190. Explain the directions. Have students work independently on Exercises 3–6.

4 Assess

Formative Assessment

Show students a small juice can and a large juice pitcher.

- **Which container holds more and why?** The pitcher; it is larger.
- **Which container holds less and why?** The juice can; it does not hold as much as the pitcher.

Quick Check **Are students still struggling to compare capacity to a reference object?**

If Yes → Small Group Options (p. 189B)

If No → Independent Work Options (p. 189B)

CRM Skills Practice Worksheet (p. 24)

CRM Enrich Worksheet (p. 26)

LESSON 7-6

Compare Area

Lesson Planner

Objective

Compare the area of two objects.

Vocabulary

area, **covers more**, **covers less**, **covers the same**

Resources

Materials: books, juice can, coffee can, drawing paper, pencils, scissors, sticky note, notebook paper, classroom objects, juice can
Manipulatives: pattern blocks
Literature Connection: *Not Enough Room!* by Joanne Rocklin

Teacher Technology

Teacher Works

Daily Routine

Use these suggestions before beginning the lesson on p. 191.

5-Minute Check

(Reviews Lesson 7-5)

Show a small box and a large box. Ask what box will hold more and what box has the larger capacity. Have students test their answers with cubes.

Problem of the Day

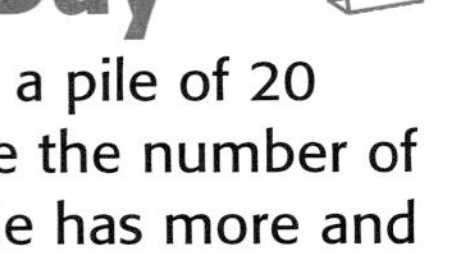

Show a pile of 19 counters and a pile of 20 counters. How can you compare the number of counters in each pile? Which pile has more and which pile has less counters? Count the counter; 20 has more; 19 has less.

LINE UP As students line up, ask questions related to area. **What covers more area, a house or a tent? What covers less area, a shoe box or a pencil box?** house, pencil box

Building Math Vocabulary

Materials: large blanket, baby blanket

- Show a large blanket and a baby blanket.
- **What blanket should I choose to cover my whole body?** large blanket
- Explain that the large blanket covers more **area** than the baby blanket because it is bigger. Tell students that the area is the space inside a shape.
- Tell students that larger objects, such as a large blanket, **cover more** area. Smaller objects such as a baby blanket, **cover less** area. Objects, that are the same size **cover the same** area.

Differentiated Instruction

Small Group Options

Option 1 Below/Approaching Level BL

LOGIICAL, KINESTHETIC

Materials: paper squares of different sizes

- Give each student a square.
- Have them compare the area of the squares by placing one on top of the other.
- Have students determine whose square covers the most area, least area, and if any squares cover the same area.

Option 2 English Language Learners ELL

VISUAL SPATIAL, KINESTHETIC

Core Vocabulary: space inside, fingers, a person
Common Use Verb: fit/doesn't fit
Do Math This strategy helps students understand area.

- Make a circle with your finger and thumb. Say: "Look at the **space inside** my **fingers**. What can **fit inside** the **space**?" Accept answers.
- Repeat for "doesn't fit." Continue comparisons for a circle made from both hands.
- Ask: "How can we make a circle that **a person** can **fit inside**?" Repeat, prompting partners to join hands and have a friend stand inside.

Independent Work Options

Option 1 Early Finishers AL OL

LINGUISTIC/LOGICAL, VISUAL/SPATIAL

Materials: pencils, drawing paper, pattern blocks

- Have students choose a pattern block and trace its shape on paper.
- Tell them to draw a shape that covers more area than the pattern block shape.
- Have them check their drawing by placing the pattern block on top of their drawing, then see which shape covers more area.
- Then have students draw shapes that cover less area and about the same area as their pattern block shape.

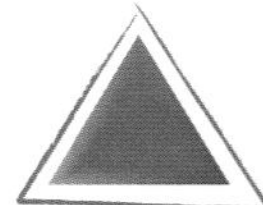

Option 2 Student Technology

Math Online macmillanmh.com

Option 3 Learning Station: Social Studies (p. 175G)

Direct students to the Social Studies Learning Station for opportunities to explore and extend the lesson concept.

Leveled Lesson Resources

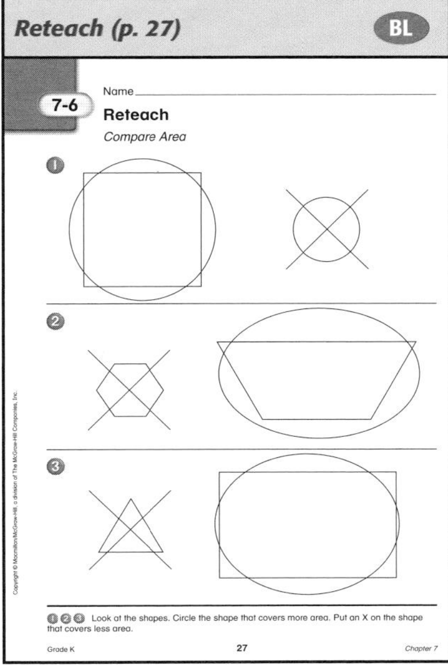

Reteach (p. 27) BL

7-6 Name
Reteach
Compare Area

1 2 3 Look at the shapes. Circle the shape that covers more area. Put an X on the shape that covers less area.

Grade K 27 Chapter 7

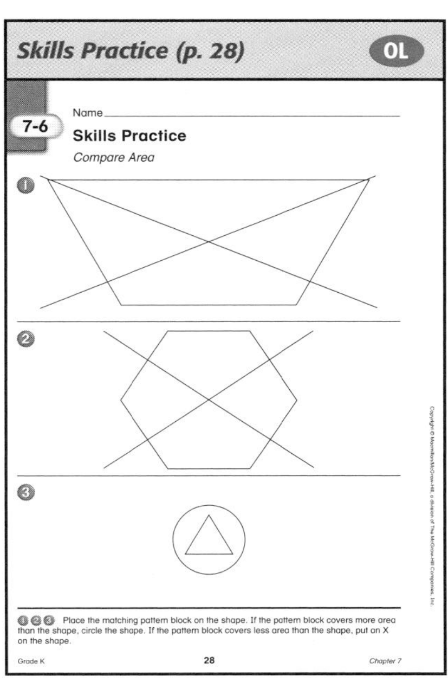

Skills Practice (p. 28) OL

7-6 Name
Skills Practice
Compare Area

1 2 3 Place the matching pattern block on the shape. If the pattern block covers more area than the shape, circle the shape. If the pattern block covers less area than the shape, put an X on the shape.

Grade K 28 Chapter 7

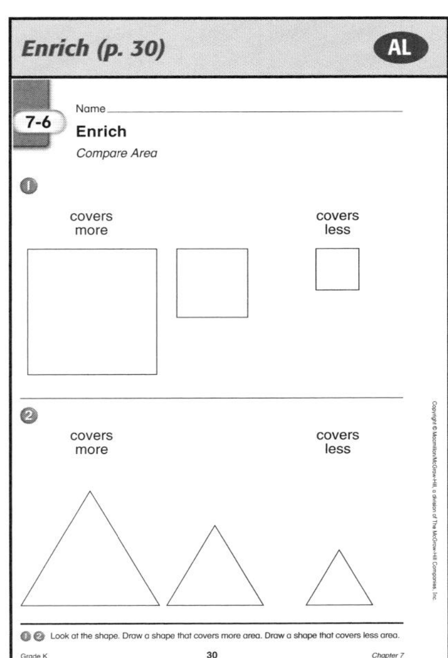

Enrich (p. 30) AL

7-6 Name
Enrich
Compare Area

1 covers more covers less

2 covers more covers less

1 2 Look at the shape. Draw a shape that covers more area. Draw a shape that covers less area.

Grade K 30 Chapter 7

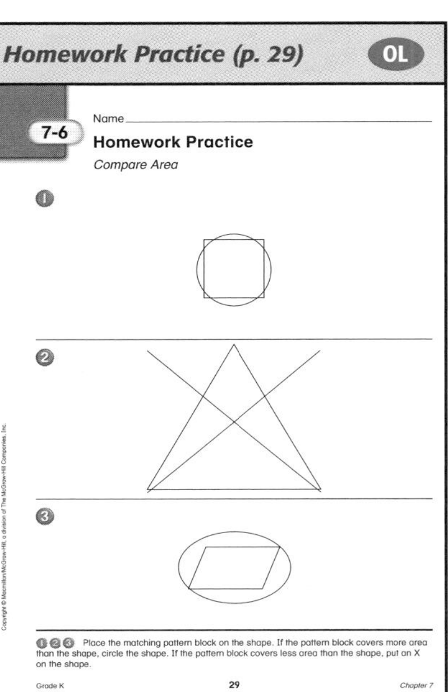

Homework Practice (p. 29) OL

7-6 Name
Homework Practice
Compare Area

1 2 3 Place the matching pattern block on the shape. If the pattern block covers more area than the shape, circle the shape. If the pattern block covers less area than the shape, put an X on the shape.

Grade K 29 Chapter 7

1 Introduce

Circle Time

Activity Choice 1 • Literature

Not Enough Room!
by Joanne Rocklin

- Looking at the diagrams of Kristy's and Pat's rooms, whose room covered more area?
- Provide students with construction paper figures. (Include many different sized squares, rectangles, and circles. Make sure that there are two squares that **cover the same** amount of area.)
- Show students how to compare area by finding two figures that are the same figure and laying one on top of the other to determine which **covers more** area.
- Have students compare the figures to determine which figures cover more area and which figures **cover less** area.
- Ask students to find the two figures that cover the same area.

Activity Choice 2 • Hands-On 

Materials: books of different sizes, juice can, coffee can, drawing paper, pencil, scissors

- Show two books of different sizes. **Which book covers more area? Why?** Larger book, it's bigger.
- Model laying one book on top of the other to prove which book covers more area. Give volunteers two books to determine which book covers more area.
- Show juice and coffee cans. **Which can covers more area? Why?** Coffee can, it's bigger.
- **How can you show this to check your answer?** Put one can on top of the other. Model comparing sizes by tracing the bottom of each can, cutting out the circles, then placing one circle on top of the other.
- Explain that to compare areas, use objects of the same shape and lay one object on top of the other.

2 Teach

Direct students to the top of p. 191.

- Have students identify the notebook paper on the left and the sticky note on the right.
- **How can you show which paper covers more area?** Put the sticky note on top of the notebook paper.
- **Which piece of paper covers more area, the notebook paper or the sticky note? Why?** Notebook paper; the notebook paper is bigger.
- Explain that Matthew Cando is holding signs that show the notebook paper covers more area than the sticky note, and the sticky note covers less area than the notebook paper.

BL Alternate Teaching Strategy

If students have trouble identifying and describing solid figures . . .

Then use one of these reteach options.

1 CRM **Daily Reteach Worksheet** (p. 27)

2 **Comparing Areas** Place a sticky note on a sheet of notebook paper.
- Ask which piece of paper is bigger and why.
- Remind students that the bigger object covers more area.

COMMON ERROR!

Students may not understand Matthew Cando's signs. Explain that the notebook paper is bigger and the sticky note is smaller than the signs. Say the notebook paper covers more area than the sticky note.

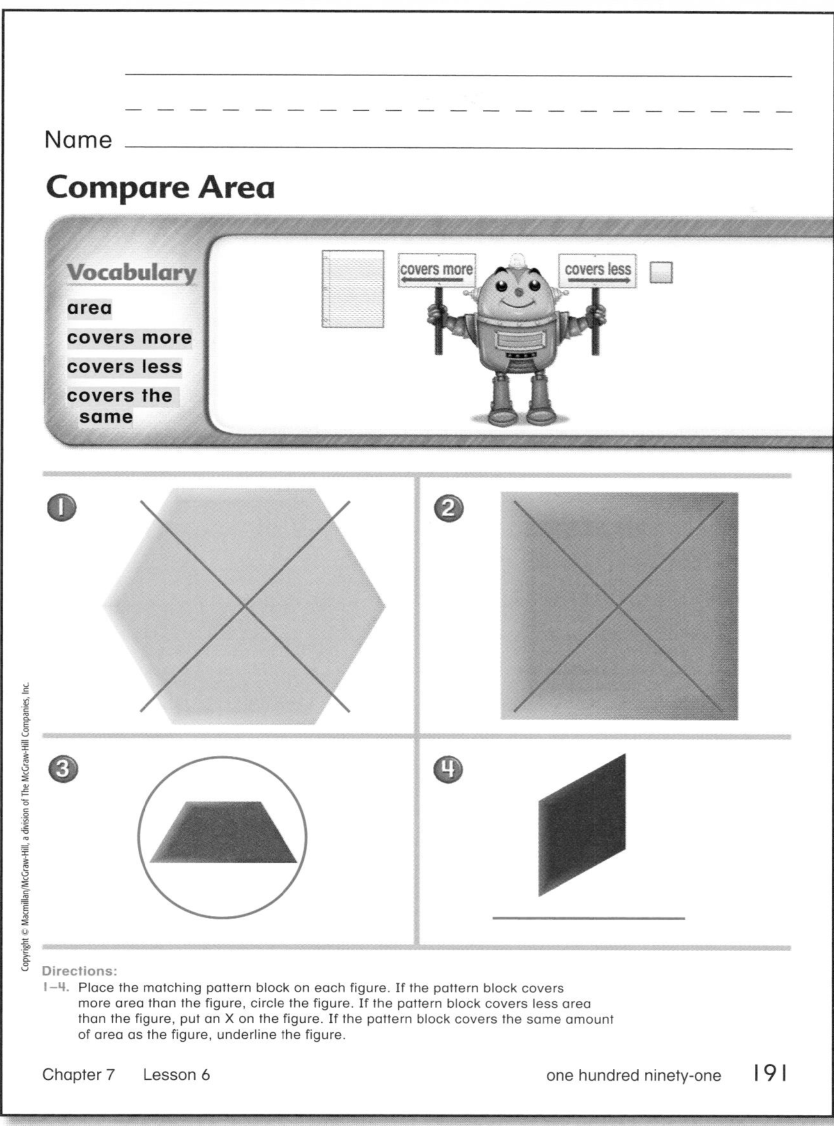

Name
Compare Area
Vocabulary
area
covers more
covers less
covers the same
covers more
covers less
Directions:
1–4. Place the matching pattern block on each figure. If the pattern block covers more area than the figure, circle the figure. If the pattern block covers less area than the figure, put an X on the figure. If the pattern block covers the same amount of area as the figure, underline the figure.
Chapter 7 Lesson 6 one hundred ninety-one 191

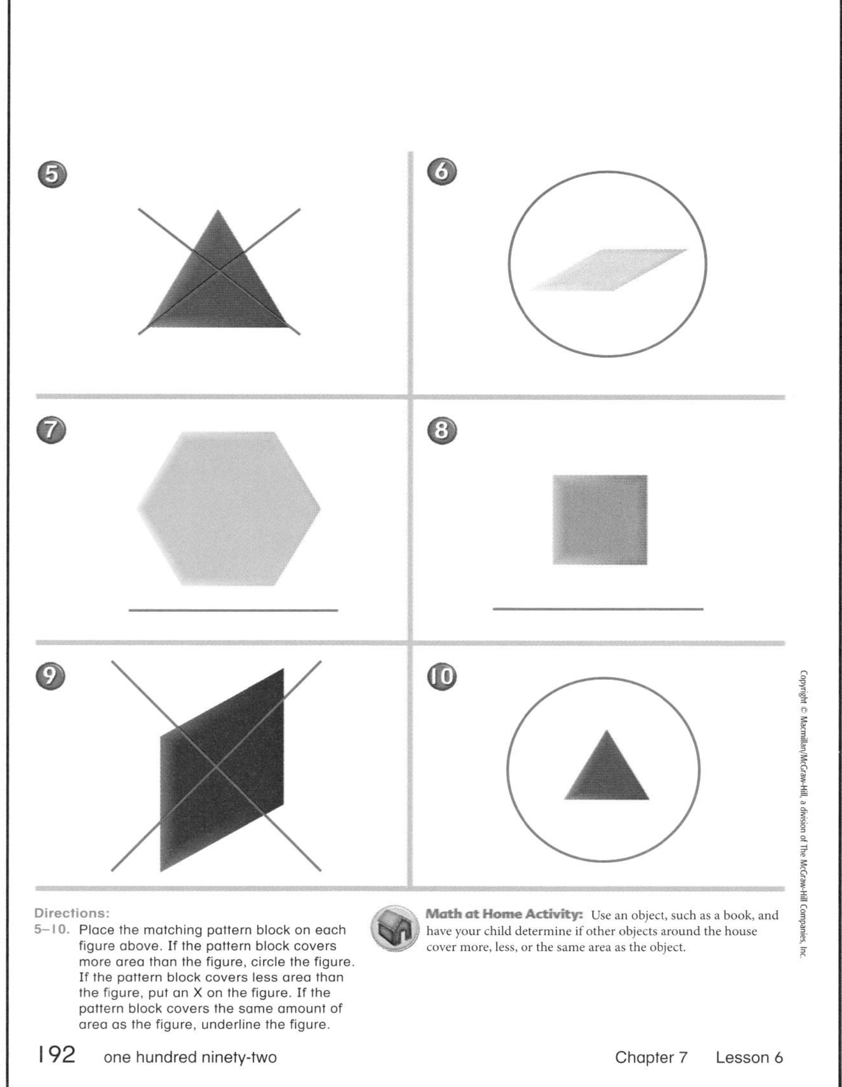

Directions:
5–10. Place the matching pattern block on each figure above. If the pattern block covers more area than the figure, circle the figure. If the pattern block covers less area than the figure, put an X on the figure. If the pattern block covers the same amount of area as the figure, underline the figure.
Math at Home Activity: Use an object, such as a book, and have your child determine if other objects around the house cover more, less, or the same area as the object.
192 one hundred ninety-two Chapter 7 Lesson 6

3 Practice

Guided Practice

- Direct students to p. 191. Give each student pattern blocks.
- Have them lay the yellow hexagon block on top of the hexagon in Exercise 1.
- Have them circle the figure if the pattern block covers more area, put an X on the figure if the pattern block covers less area, or underline the figure if the pattern block covers the same area.
- Repeat the activity for Exercises 2–4.

Independent Practice

Have students turn to p. 192 and work independently on the exercises.

4 Assess

Formative Assessment

- Show two objects of the same figure.
- Ask which object covers more area and which object covers less area.
- Have students prove that their answers are correct.

Quick Check **Are students still struggling to compare the area of two figures?**

If Yes → Small Group Options (p. 191B)

If No → Independent Work Options (p. 191B)

CRM Skills Practice Worksheet (p. 28)

CRM Enrich Worksheet (p. 30)

Compare Temperature

Lesson Planner

Objective
Compare objects or situations by using terms hot and cold.

Vocabulary
hot, cold, temperature

Resources
Materials: chart paper, pencils, file folder, scissors, crayons, glue
Literature Connection: *Math for All Seasons* by Greg Tang
Alternate Lesson:
Use *IMPACT Mathematics*: Unit J to provide practice with comparing temperature.
Teacher Technology
TeacherWorks

Daily Routine

Use these suggestions before beginning the lesson on p. 193.

5-Minute Check
(Reviews Lesson 7-6)

Have students work in pairs. Have them trace each others hand on white paper. After they are finished, encourage them to decide which hand covers more area and which hand covers less area. They can place the two pieces of paper with their hands on top of each other to see if they were correct. Then have them repeat the comparisons with other classmates.

Problem of the Day
Have students draw two triangles that cover the same area.

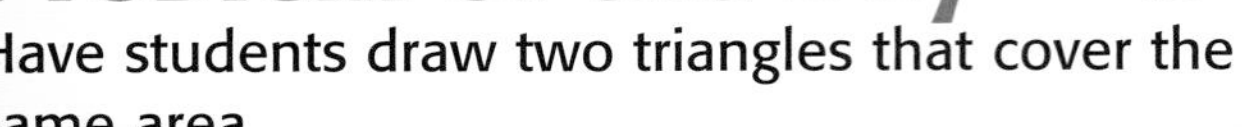

As students line up, ask what they could wear if the outside temperature was hot or cold.

Building Math Vocabulary
Materials: 2 identical containers with lids

- **Hot** and **cold** are words used to describe **temperature.**
- Label a container A and fill with cold water. Label a container *B* and fill with warm water.
- Have students take turns touching the outside of the containers.
- Ask students what they think of when they touch container A. What do they think of when they touch container B?
- Ask which container feels **cold** and which feels **hot**. Talk about ways to change the **temperature** of one of the containers, such as making the container of warm water feel cold.

Differentiated Instruction

Small Group Options

Option 1 Below/Approaching Level BL

KINESTHETIC

Materials: multiple blue and red index cards; paper, pencil

- Have students work in pairs.
- Have the pairs of students choose an index card from a pile of cards. Tell them that blue cards mean "cold," and red cards mean "hot."
- The students then need to draw an object or a picture of an activity that matches the card drawn.

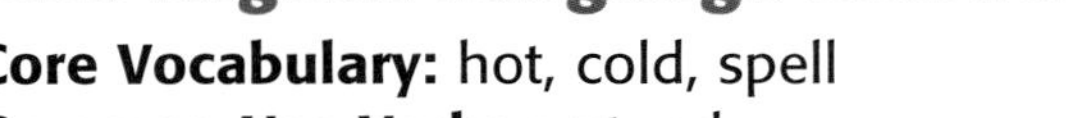

Option 2 English Language Learners ELL

LINGUISTIC

Core Vocabulary: hot, cold, spell
Common Use Verb: pretend

Hear Math This strategy uses a chant to teach vocabulary.

- Say as a chant: "h-o-t, h-o-t, hot, hot, hot." Fan yourself, pretending it is hot.
- Have students act like it is "hot" out.
- Repeat for "cold". Hold your arms as if shivering.
- Call hot/cold randomly as students act it out.

Independent Work Options

Option 1 Early Finishers AL OL

VISUAL/SPATIAL, LOGICAL

Materials: magazines, scissors, glue, construction paper

- Ask students to cut out pictures in magazines of hot objects and cold objects.
- Have them make a collage of hot objects and a collage of cold objects, then glue their collages on paper.
- Display the collages under the words *hot* and *cold*.

Option 2 Student Technology

Math Online macmillanmh.com

Option 3 Option 3 Learning Station: Reading (p. 175G)

Direct students to the Reading Learning Station for opportunities to explore and extend the lesson concept.

Leveled Lesson Resources

Additional support for English Language Learners can be found in the ELL Guide (p. 121). ELL

Reteach (p. 31) BL

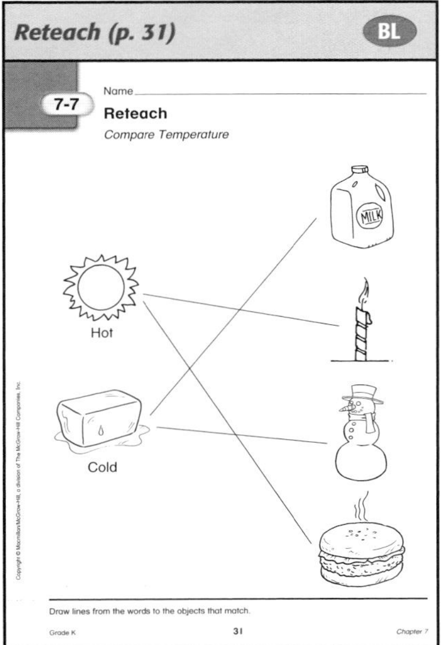

7-7 Name
Reteach
Compare Temperature

Hot
Cold

Draw lines from the words to the objects that match.

Grade K 31 Chapter 7

Skills Practice (p. 32) OL

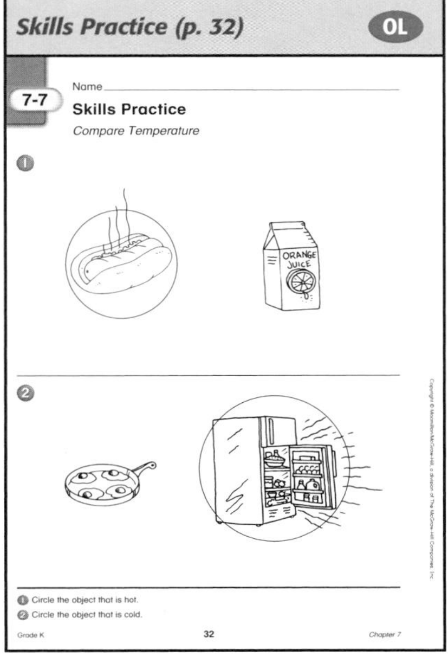

7-7 Name
Skills Practice
Compare Temperature

1. Circle the object that is hot.
2. Circle the object that is cold.

Grade K 32 Chapter 7

Enrich (p. 34) AL

7-7 Name
Enrich
Picture Time

Drawings will vary.

Drawings will vary.

1. Draw something that is hotter than grapes.
2. Draw something that is colder than a pie.

Grade K 34 Chapter 7

Homework Practice (p. 33) OL

7-7 Name
Homework Practice
Compare Temperature

1. Circle the picture that shows a hot day.
2. Circle the object that is cold.

Grade K 33 Chapter 7

1 Introduce

Circle Time

Activity Choice 1 • Literature

Math for All Seasons by Greg Tang

- Ask students to think of things that are hot and things that are cold.
- Create a two-column chart and keep track of each student's contribution. Name the columns "Hot" and "Cold."
- Flip through each page of the book for the class. Stop on each spread, asking students which column the scene could be placed in.
- As you add to each column, have other students verify whether they agree or disagree with the responses.
- Extend the activity by asking students to explain why they agree or disagree with other students.

Activity Choice 2 • Hands-On

Materials: chart paper, marker

- Label a sheet of chart paper ***hot*** and label another sheet ***cold***.
- Have students name hot or cold objects. Write their responses.
- Ask questions to have students compare the **temperatures** of two objects. For example: **What feels colder, bath water or ice water?** ice water **What feels hotter, grapes or soup?** soup **What feels colder, water with ice or juice with ice?** same temperature
- Name a food, point to a student, and say "hotter, colder, about the same temperature." Have the student name a food hotter, colder, or about the same.
- Repeat the activity having students take turns.

2 Teach

Direct students to the top of p. 193.

- Have students point to the picture of the ice cubes. Tell them the word under the ice cubes is *cold.*
- Have students point to the picture of the fire. Tell them the word under the fire is *hot.*
- Ask students what other things are either hot or cold.
- Make a "Hot and Cold Foods" chart using the inside of a file folder. Label the left side "Food Served Hot" and the right side "Food Served Cold".
- Have students work in pairs to color and cut out pictures of many different types of food.
- Encourage students to discuss each food item and determine if the food is usually served hot or cold.
- Have students glue the pictures on the correct side of the folder.

BL Alternate Teaching Strategy

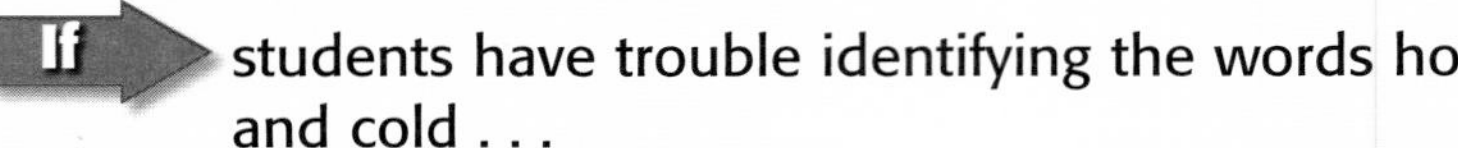

If students have trouble identifying the words hot and cold . . .

Then use one of these reteach options.

1 CRM **Daily Reteach Worksheet** (p. 31)

2 **Use Associations** Have students say *hot*, then isolate and identify the initial sound: /h/.

- Ask students what letter represents the /h/ sound.
- Have students point to the word that begins with *h*.
- Repeat with the /k/ sound and the word *cold*.

COMMON ERROR!

Students may think a cold object must have ice in it or a hot object must be fire. Explain that the pictures are examples of objects that are cold or hot.

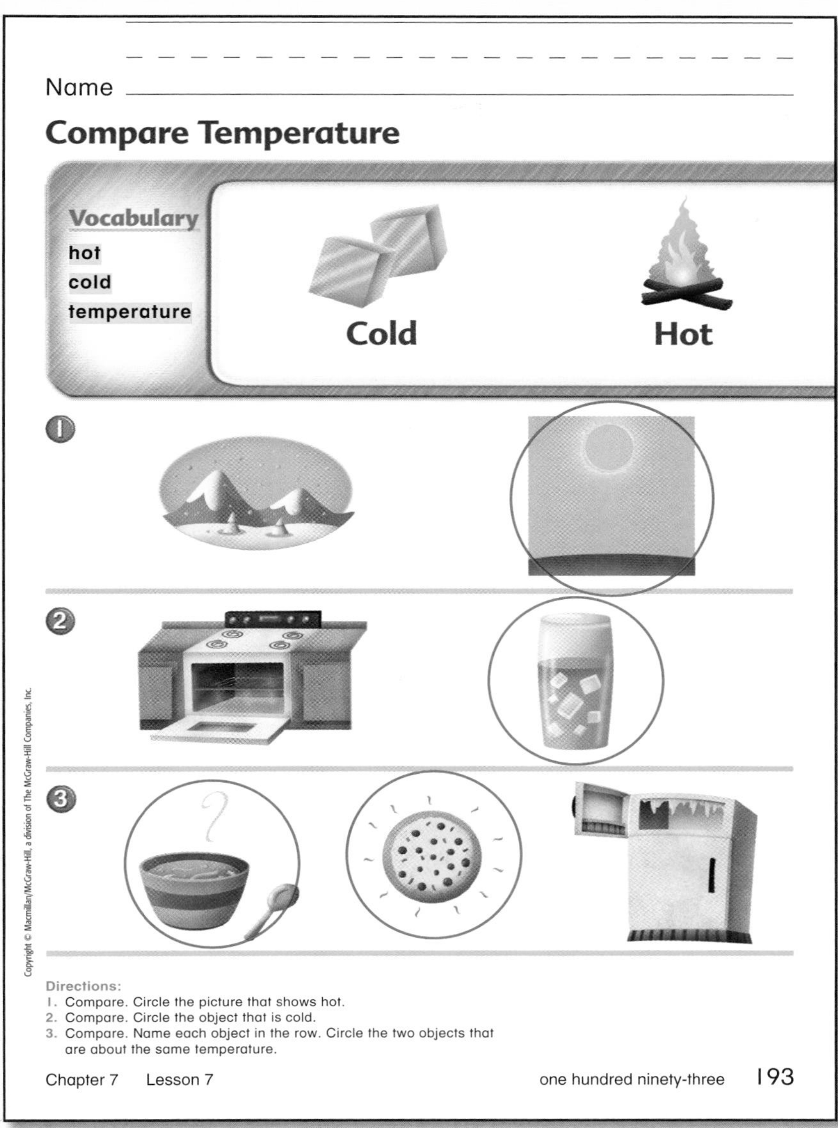

Name

Compare Temperature

Vocabulary
hot
cold
temperature

Cold   Hot

1

2

3

Directions:
1. Compare. Circle the picture that shows hot.
2. Compare. Circle the object that is cold.
3. Compare. Name each object in the row. Circle the two objects that are about the same temperature.

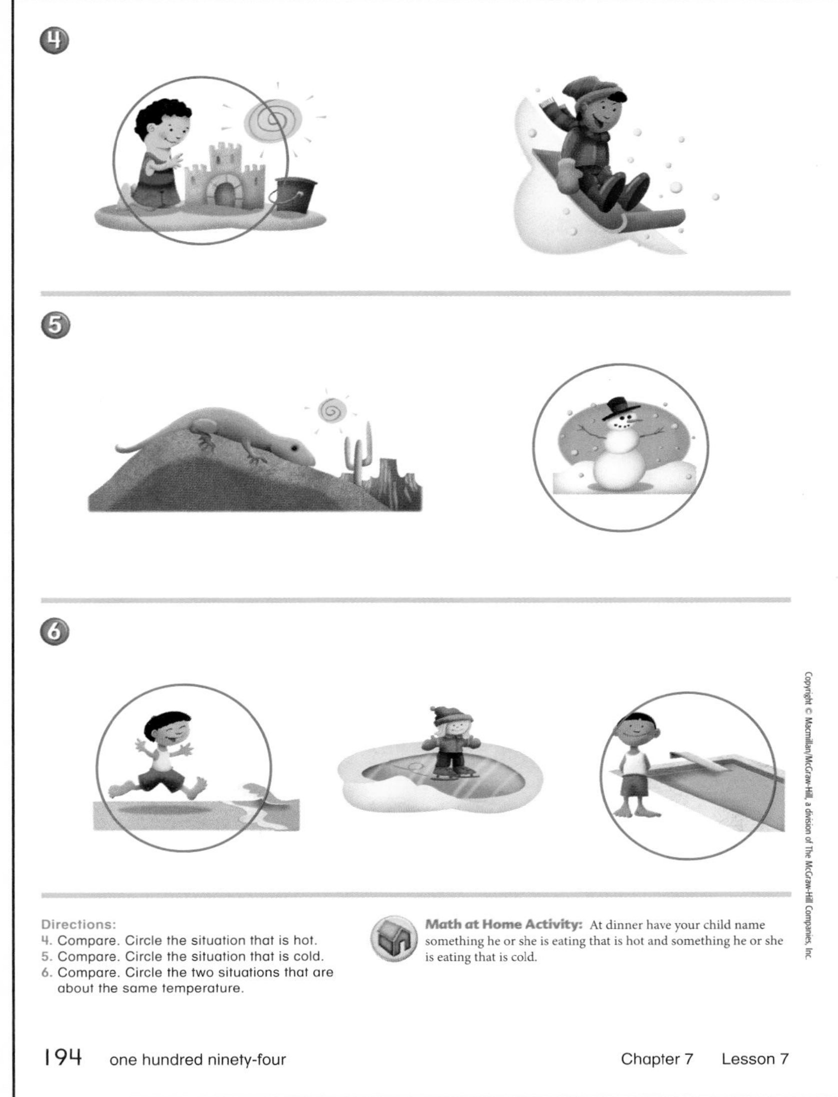

4

5

6

Directions:
4. Compare. Circle the situation that is hot.
5. Compare. Circle the situation that is cold.
6. Compare. Circle the two situations that are about the same temperature.

Math at Home Activity: At dinner have your child name something he or she is eating that is hot and something he or she is eating that is cold.

3 Practice

Guided Practice

- Direct students to p. 193.
- Have students identify each picture in Exercise 1. Have them circle the picture that shows something that is hot.
- Have students identify each picture in Exercise 2. Have them circle the picture that shows an object that is cold.
- Have students identify each picture in Exercise 3. Have them circle the two pictures that show objects that are about the same temperature.

Independent Practice

Have students turn to p. 194 and work independently on the exercises.

4 Assess

Formative Assessment

- Show students several pictures. Have them identify a hot object in one picture and a cold object in another picture.
- Have students pick two pictures that show two objects that are about the same temperature.

Quick Check **Are students still struggling to identify hot and cold objects?**

If Yes → Small Group Options (p. 193B)

If No → Independent Work Options (p. 193B)

CRM Skills Practice Worksheet (p. 32)

CRM Enrich Worksheet (p. 34)

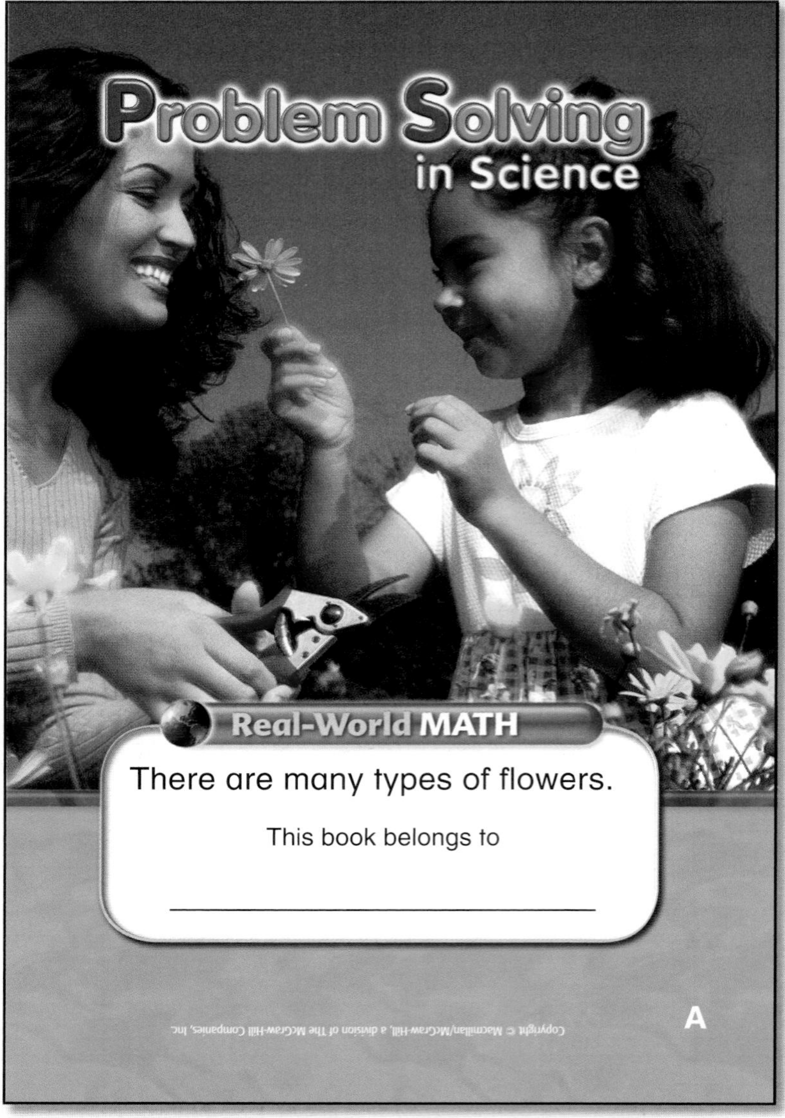

Problem Solving
in Science
Real-World MATH
There are many types of flowers.
This book belongs to
A

Some flowers grow from seeds.
Plant them. Watch them grow!
B

Lesson Planner

Objective
Compare the heights of flowers.

National Standard 

Students will learn about the characteristics of organisms.

Activate Prior Knowledge

Before you turn students' attention to the pages, discuss flowers.

- **How do plants begin? What do plants need to grow?** Sample answers: Most plants begin from seeds. They need soil, water, and light to grow.
- **Which plants and flowers are very tall?** Sample answers: Some trees grow very tall. Sunflowers are flowers that grow tall.

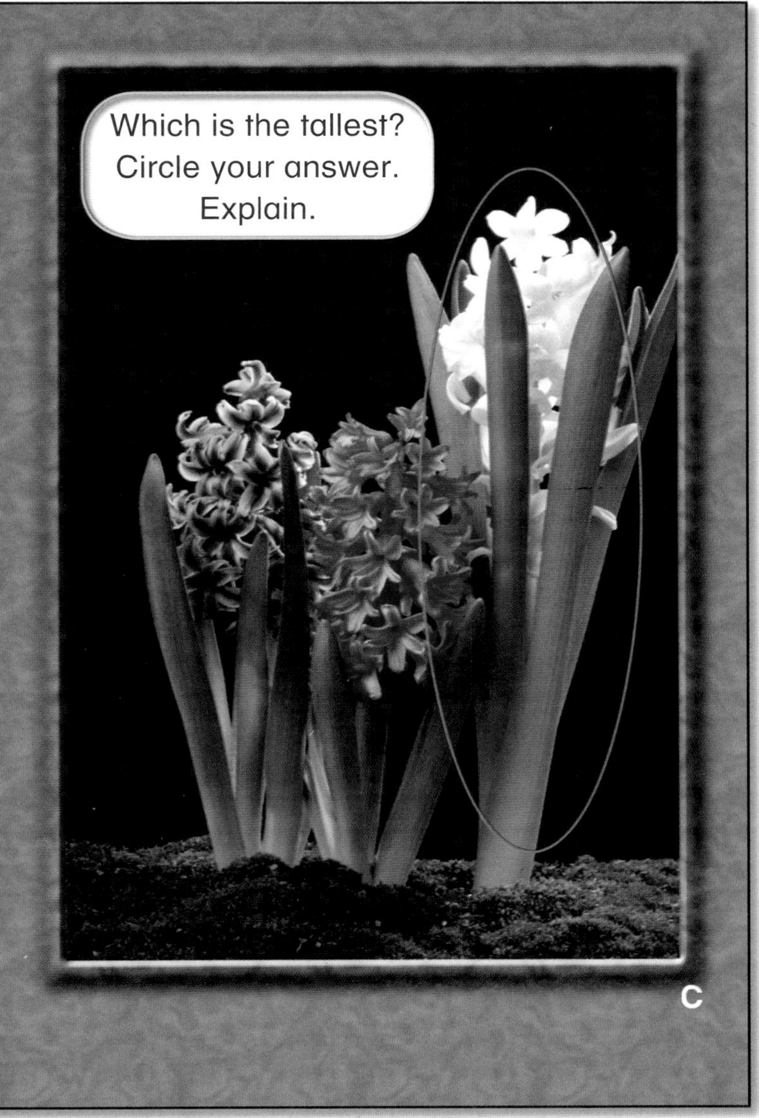

Which is the tallest?
Circle your answer.
Explain.
C

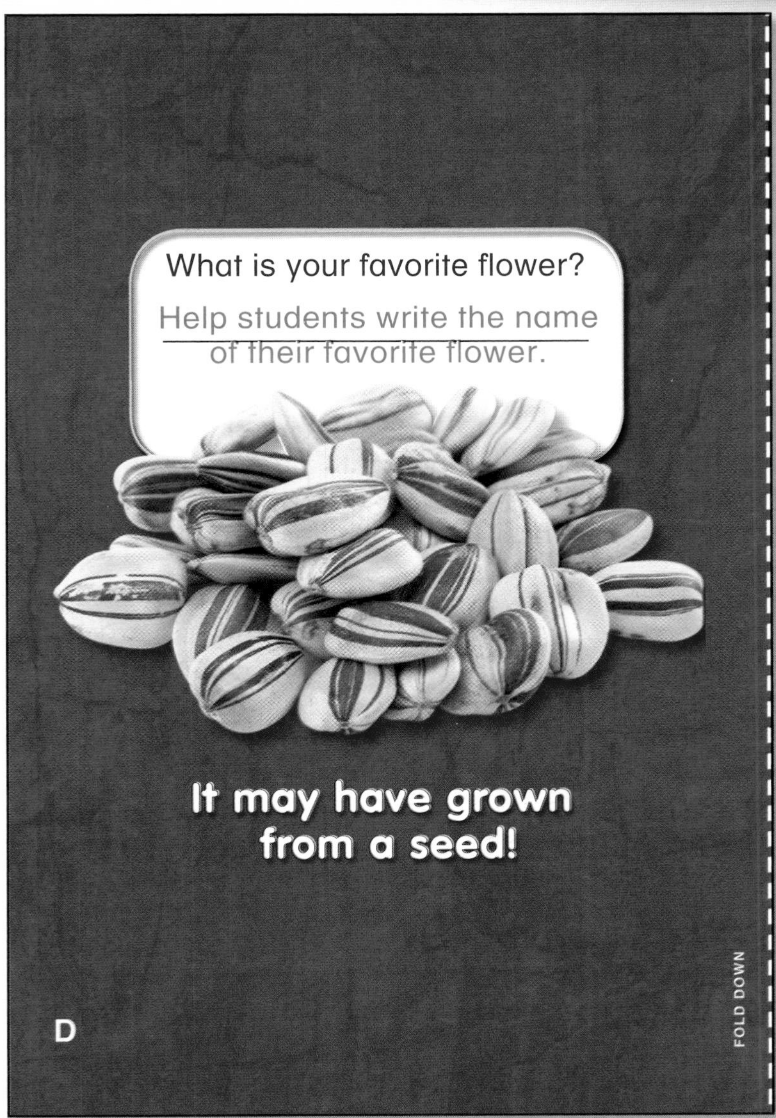

What is your favorite flower?
Help students write the name of their favorite flower.
It may have grown from a seed!
D
FOLD DOWN

Create the Book

Guide students to create their book.

- Have them fold the page in half.
- Ask them to write their name on page A.
- Explain that page A is the front cover and page D is the back cover. If necessary, have them practice flipping through the book in order.
- Guide them in reading the information and word problems on each of the pages.

Use the Student Page

Have students work individually or in pairs to discuss pages B–D.

Page B Engage students in discussion about how flowers grow. Say that the seed in the child's hand will grow into a flower.

Page C Have students use connecting cubes to check their answers.

Page D Prompt discussion about favorite flowers. Have students discuss the size of seeds compared to the flower that could grow from it.

If necessary, review the problem-solving strategies suggested in Lesson 7-4, p. 185.

WRITING IN MATH Have students draw things in nature that are different in height, such as two types of plants (for example, a tree and a flower).

FOLDABLES® Dinah Zike's Foldables

Use these lesson suggestions for incorporating the Foldables during the chapter.

Lesson 7-5 Under the Capacity tab of the Foldable, glue pictures of objects such as cups, glasses, bowls, or pots and pans. Students use the terms holds more or holds less when describing, comparing, and contrasting the capacity of the objects.

Lesson 7-6 Under the Area tab of the Foldable, have students draw pictures of classroom objects such as pencils, paper, desks, glue bottles. Students can place objects under the title covers more area or covers less area.

Chapter 7 Project

Measurement Vocabulary Cards

Lead a discussion on the results of the completed chapter project with the class.

Vocabulary Review

Review chapter vocabulary using one of the following options.

- **Visual Vocabulary Cards** (16, 17, 18, 21, 22, 35, 44)
- **eGlossary** at macmillanmh.com

Data-Driven Decision Making

Based on the results of the Chapter Review/Test, use the following to review concepts that continue to present students with problems.

Exercises	State/Local Standards	What's the Math?	Error Analysis	Resources for Review
1 Lesson 7-1		Compare lengths of objects by making direct comparisons with reference objects to determine which object is shorter or longer.	Does not follow directions. Circles wrong objects.	CRM Chapter 7 Resource Masters (Reteach Worksheets) Math Online Concepts in Motion Math Adventures
2 Lesson 7-5		Compare capacity of objects by making direct comparisons with reference objects to determine which object holds more or holds less.	Does not understand word "heavier." Puts "X" on wrong object.	
3 Lesson 7-6		Compare area of two figures by making direct comparisons with reference objects.	Puts "X" on wrong object.	
4 Lesson 7-7		Compare temperatures of two objects to determine which is hotter or colder.	Circles the wrong object.	

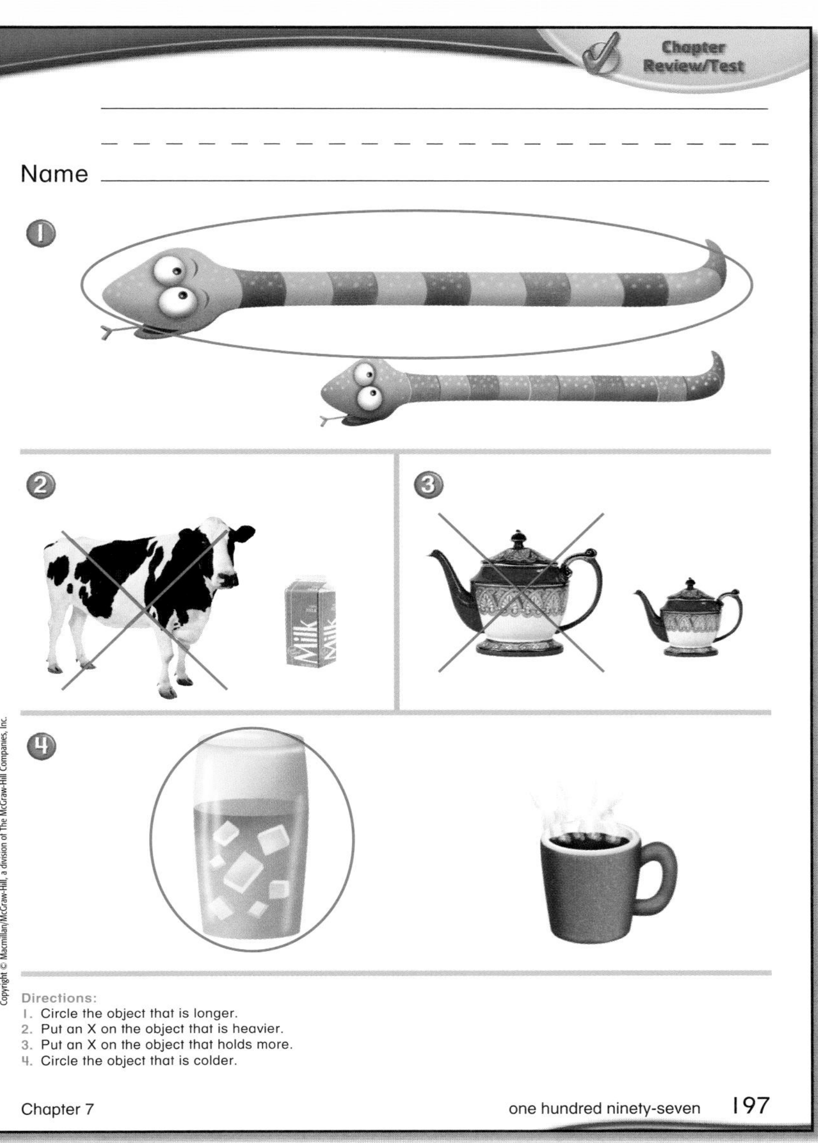

Chapter Review/Test
Name
Directions:
1. Circle the object that is longer.
2. Put an X on the object that is heavier.
3. Put an X on the object that holds more.
4. Circle the object that is colder.
Chapter 7
one hundred ninety-seven 197

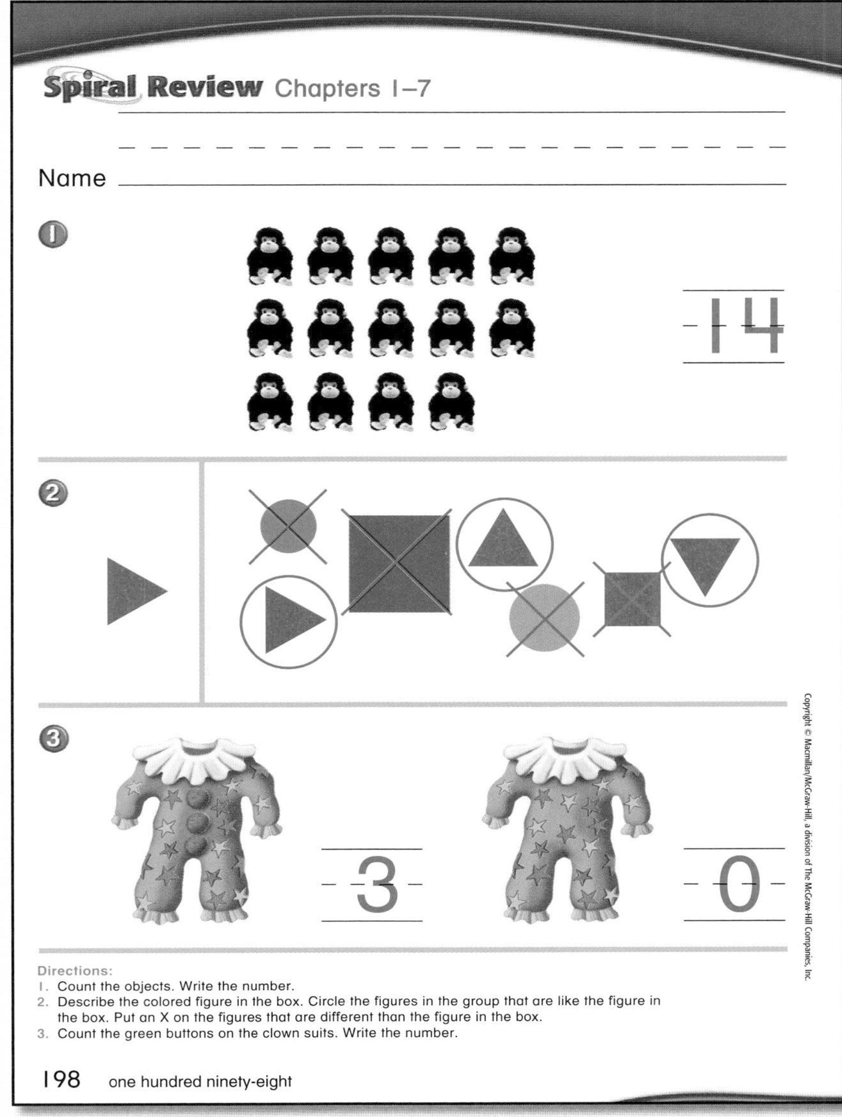

Spiral Review Chapters 1–7
Name
14
3
0
Directions:
1. Count the objects. Write the number.
2. Describe the colored figure in the box. Circle the figures in the group that are like the figure in the box. Put an X on the figures that are different than the figure in the box.
3. Count the green buttons on the clown suits. Write the number.
198 one hundred ninety-eight

Summative Assessment

Use these alternate leveled chapter tests to differentiate assessment for the specific needs of your students.

Leveled Chapter 7 Tests			
Form	**Type**	**Level**	**Pages**
1	Multiple Choice	BL	42–43
2A	Multiple Choice	OL	44–45
2C	Multiple Choice	OL	46–47
2D	Free Response	AL	48–49

BL = below/approaching grade level
OL = on grade level
AL = above/beyond grade level

Spiral Review

Reviews Chapters 1 to 7

Objective: Review and assess mastery of skills and concepts from previous chapters.

Resources for Review

Based on student results, refer to these lessons for remediation.

- **Exercise 1: Lesson 6-2** (p. 155)
- **Exercise 2: Lesson 1-2** (p. 19)
- **Exercise 3: Lesson 2-7** (p. 57)

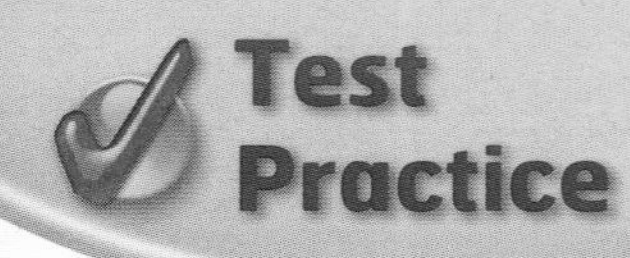

Chapters 1–6

Formative Assessment

- You can see Student Edition pp. 199-200 to benchmark student progress.
- Additional practice pages can be found in the Chapter 7 Resource Masters.

Chapter 7 Resource Masters
Cumulative Test Practice (p. 50)

- Multiple choice format (pp. 42–47)
- Free Response format (pp. 48–49)

Create additional practice worksheets or tests.

Test-Taking Tips

For the Teacher

- Remind students of *length* by holding with a hand at each end a yardstick horizontally and saying that length is how long an object is from end to end.
- Encourage students to look their test over carefully before they turn it in.

For the Student

- Remind students to ask for help if they do not understand the instructions.
- Encourage students to listen carefully when you give instructions.

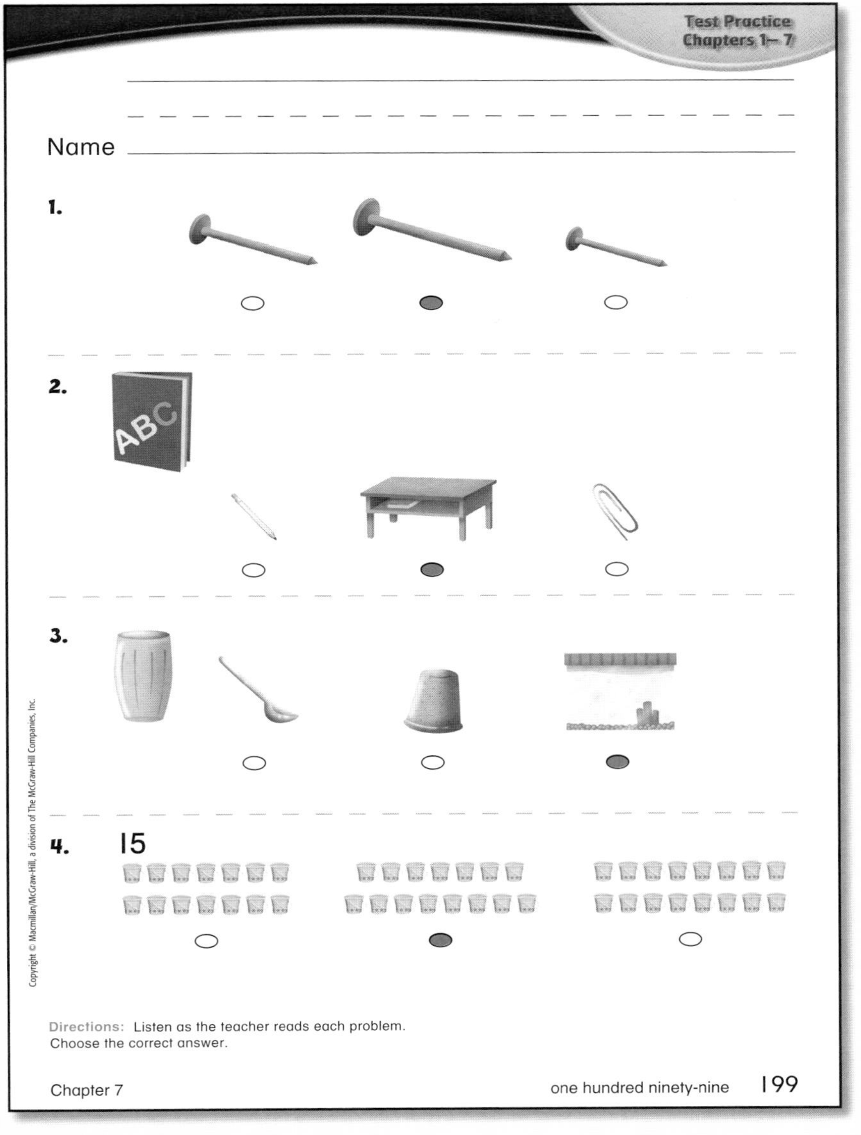

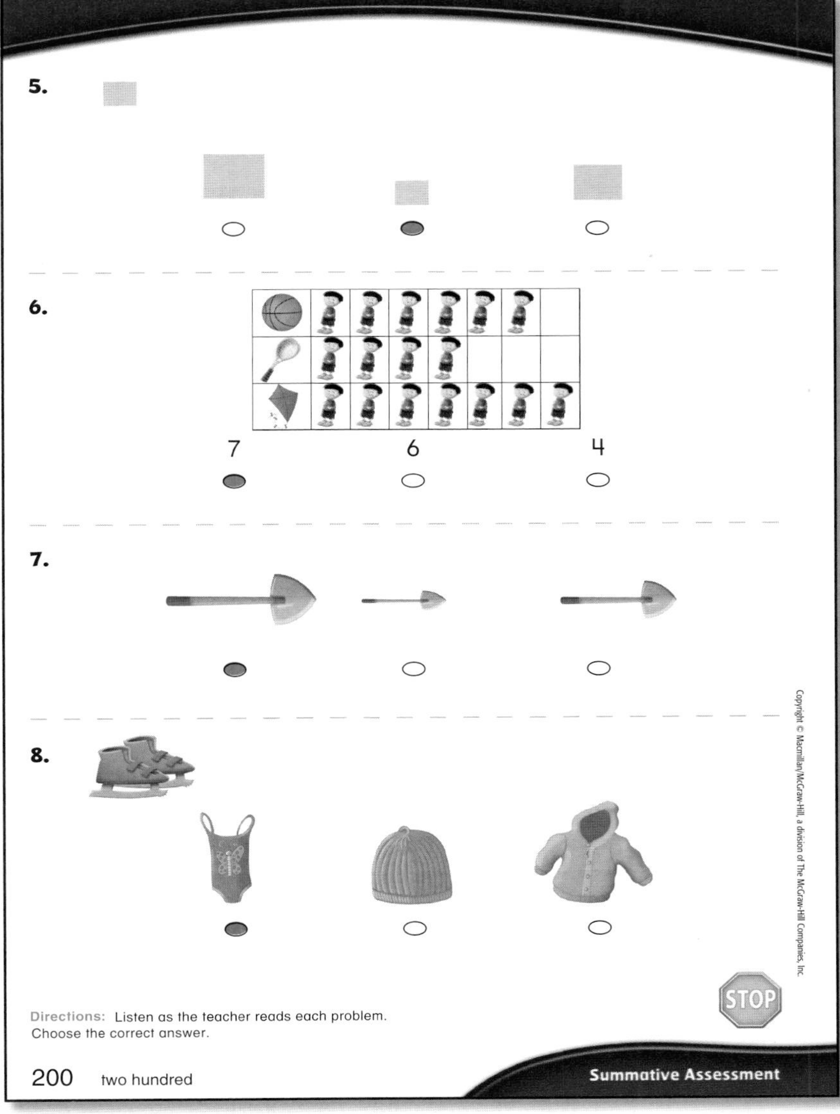

Test Directions for Teachers

Read the following directions to students before they begin. The first test item can be worked as a class example. Then read each question followed by a pause to allow students time to work and choose an answer.

- **Write your name at the top of the page.**
- **I am going to read each question to you. Listen carefully to the entire question before you choose an answer.**

1. Look at the nails. Find the longest nail. Mark the longest nail.
2. Look at the objects. Find the object that is heavier than a book. Mark the object that is heavier than a book.
3. Look at the objects. Find the object that holds more than the drinking glass. Mark the object that holds more than the drinking glass.
4. Look at the number 15. Find the group that has 15 buckets. Mark the group that has exactly 15 buckets.

- **Turn the page over.**

5. Look at the square. Find another square that covers the same area. Mark the other square that covers the same area.
6. Look at the graph. It shows fun things to do at the park. Below the graph, mark the number of children who like to fly kites.
7. Look at the shovels. Find the longest shovel. Mark the longest shovel.
8. Look at the ice skates. Find the object that is used when it is hotter. Mark the object that is used when it is hotter.

Student Handbook

Built-In Workbook

Reference

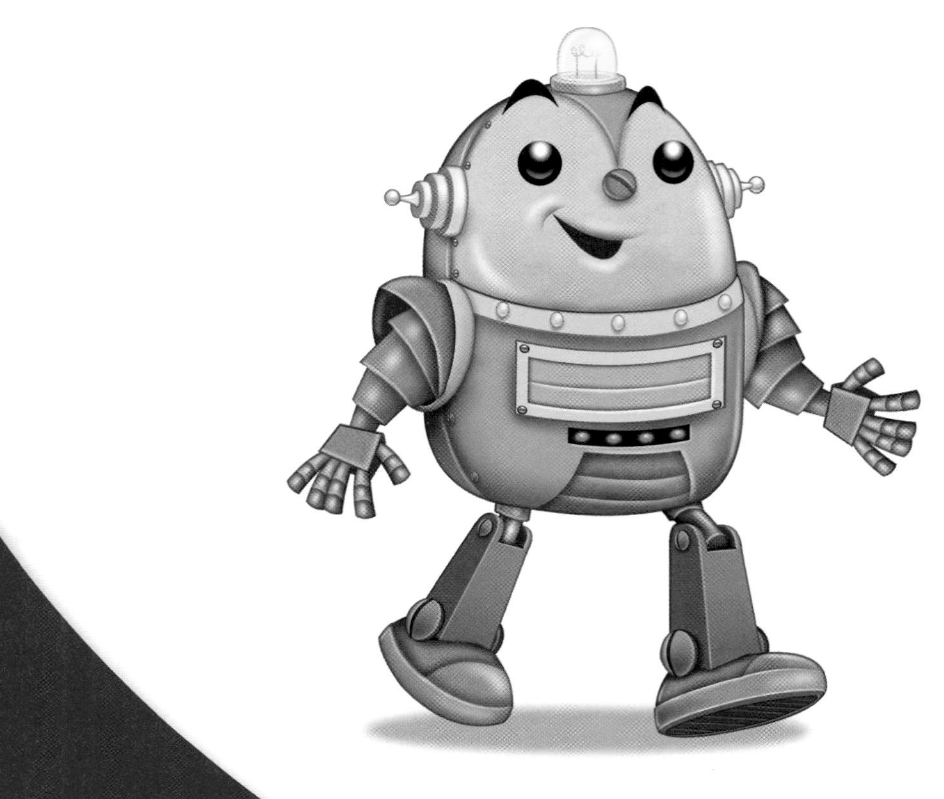

How to Use the Student Handbook

Use the Student Handbook:

- when you need more practice writing numbers
- when you need to know the meaning of a math word
- when you need to find number patterns, to order numbers, or to skip count
- when you need help writing the number names

Glossary/Glosario

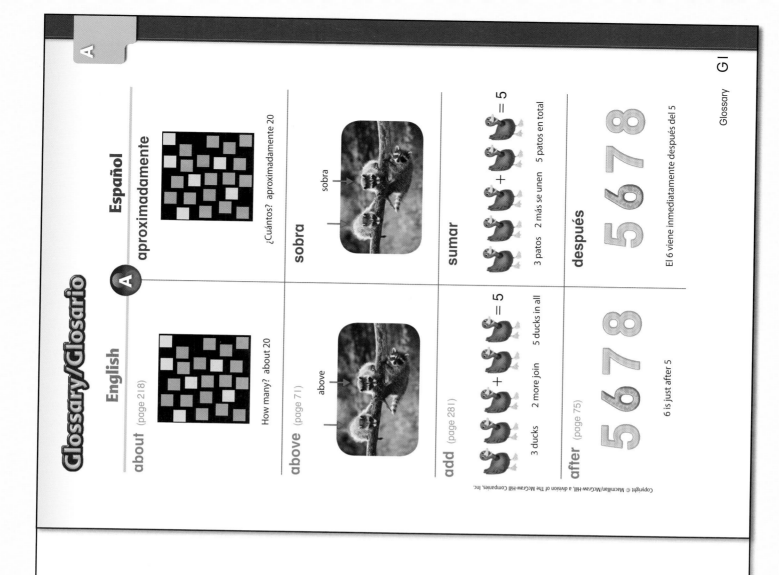

English	A	Español
about (page 218) How many? about 20		**aproximadamente** ¿Cuántos? aproximadamente 20
above (page 71) above		**sobra** sobra
add (page 281) = 5 3 ducks 2 more join 5 ducks in all		**sumar** = 5 3 patos 2 más se unen 5 patos en total
after (page 75) 5678 6 is just after 5		**después** 5678 El 6 viene inmediatamente después del 5

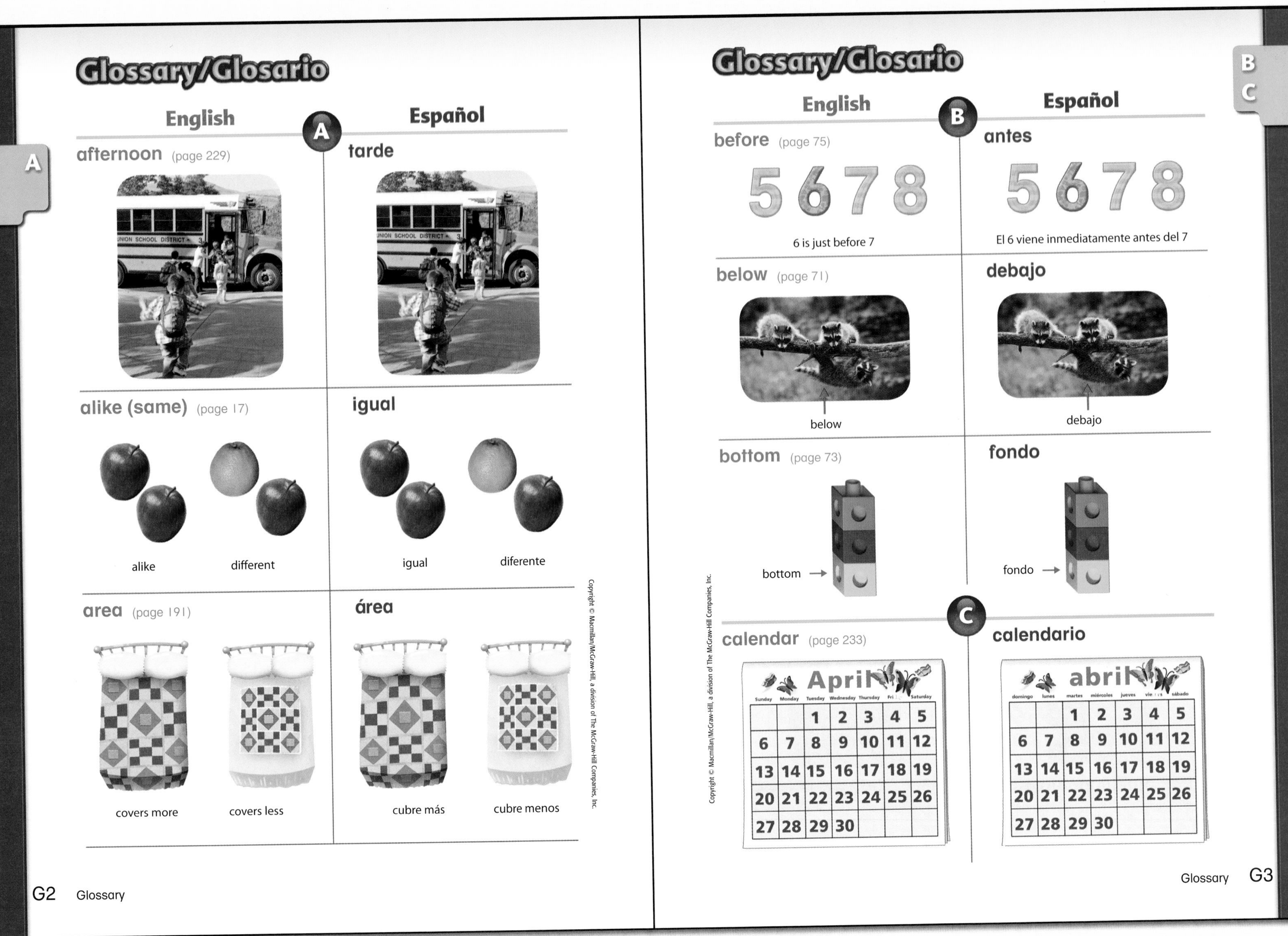

Glossary/Glosario

English	Español
A	
afternoon (page 229)	**tarde**
alike (same) (page 17) — alike, different	**igual** — igual, diferente
area (page 191) — covers more, covers less	**área** — cubre más, cubre menos

Glossary/Glosario

English	Español
B	
before (page 75) — 5 6 7 8 — 6 is just before 7	**antes** — 5 6 7 8 — El 6 viene inmediatamente antes del 7
below (page 71) — below	**debajo** — debajo
bottom (page 73) — bottom →	**fondo** — fondo →
C	
calendar (page 233)	**calendario**

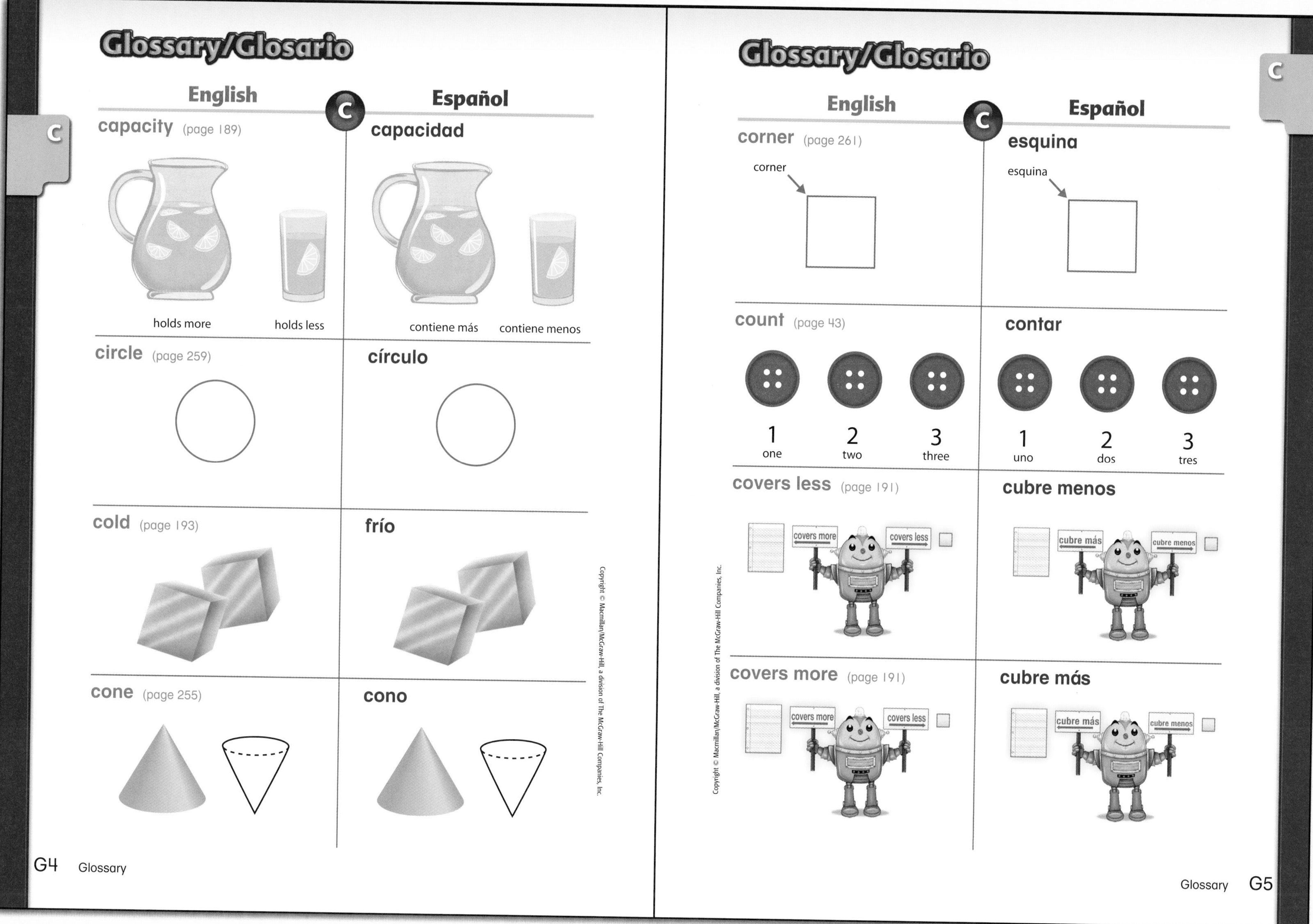

C

Glossary/Glosario

English	Español
capacity (page 189)	**capacidad**
holds more / holds less	contiene más / contiene menos
circle (page 259)	**círculo**
cold (page 193)	**frío**
cone (page 255)	**cono**

C

Glossary/Glosario

English	Español
corner (page 261)	**esquina**
corner	esquina
count (page 43)	**contar**
1 one, 2 two, 3 three	1 uno, 2 dos, 3 tres
covers less (page 191)	**cubre menos**
covers more / covers less	cubre más / cubre menos
covers more (page 191)	**cubre más**
covers more / covers less	cubre más / cubre menos

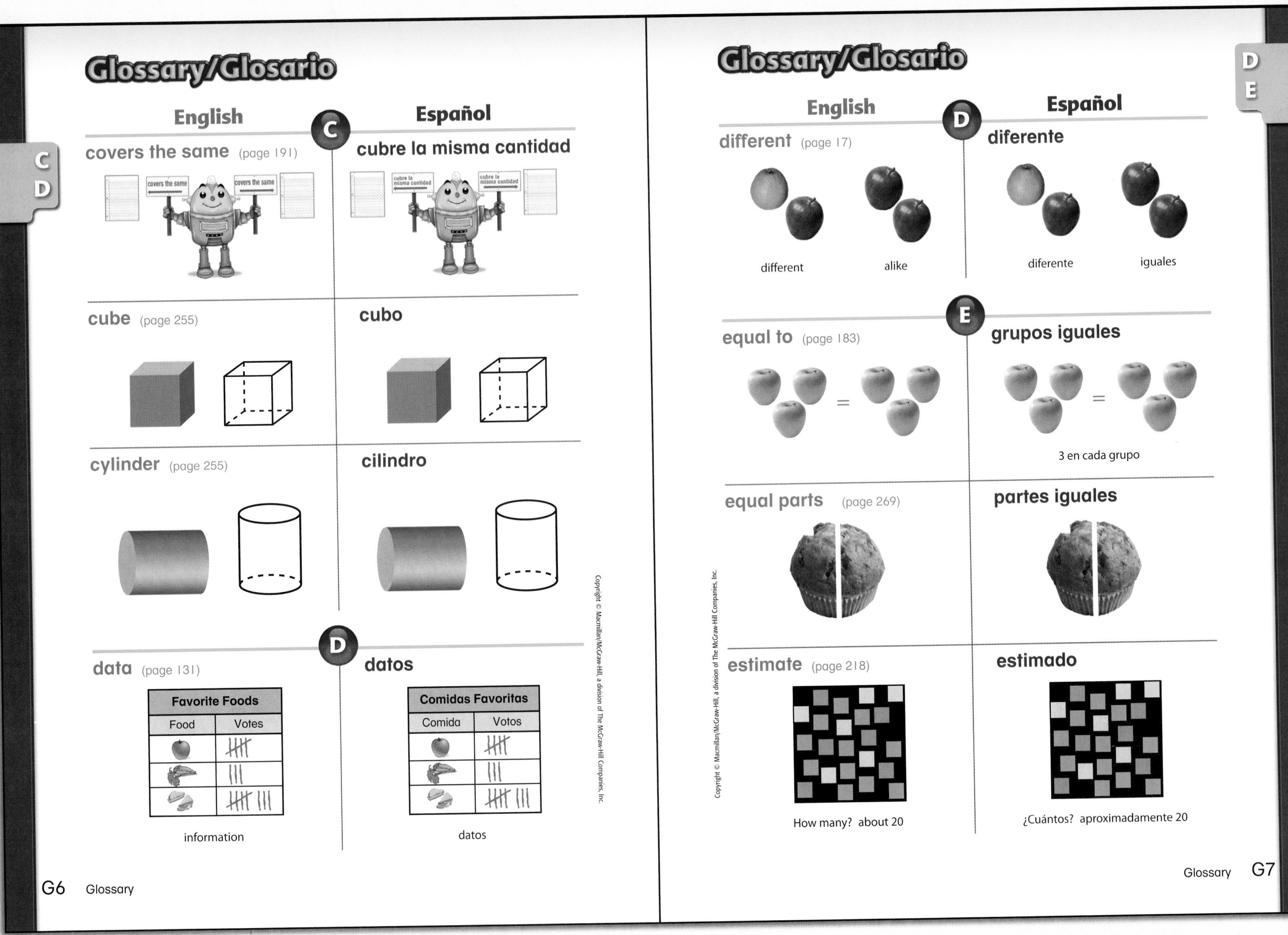

Glossary/Glosario

C D

English		Español
covers the same (page 191)	C	**cubre la misma cantidad**
cube (page 255)		**cubo**
cylinder (page 255)		**cilindro**
data (page 131)	D	**datos**

Favorite Foods	
Food	Votes
(apple)	𝍸
(food)	|||
(sandwich)	𝍸 |||

information

Comidas Favoritas	
Comida	Votos
(apple)	𝍸
(food)	|||
(sandwich)	𝍸 |||

datos

Glossary/Glosario

D E

English		Español
different (page 17)	D	**diferente**
equal to (page 183)	E	**grupos iguales**
equal parts (page 269)		**partes iguales**
estimate (page 218)		**estimado**

different alike

diferente iguales

3 en cada grupo

How many? about 20

¿Cuántos? aproximadamente 20

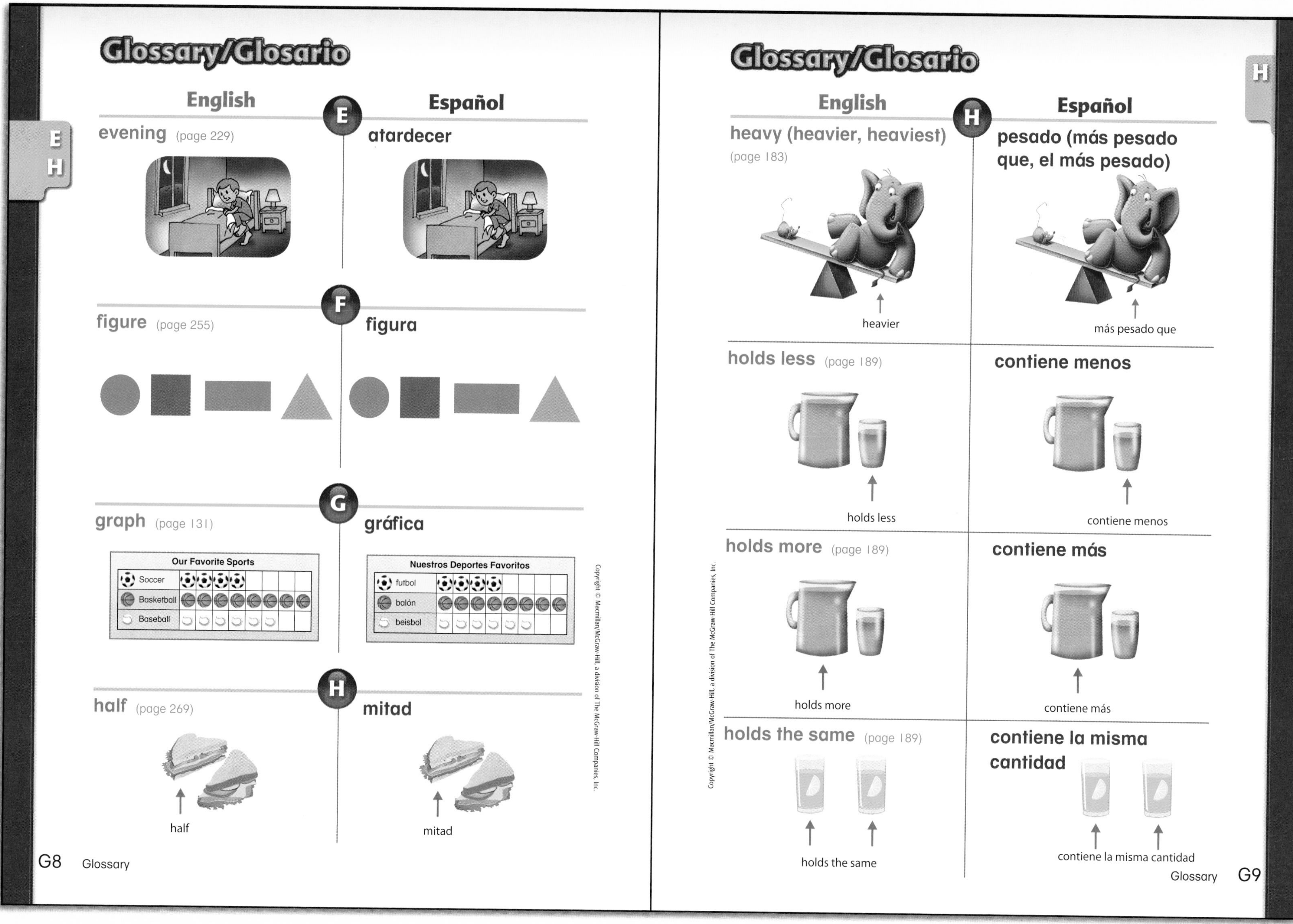

Glossary/Glosario

English		Español
evening (page 229)	E	**atardecer**
figure (page 255)	F	**figura**
graph (page 131)	G	**gráfica**
half (page 269) half	H	**mitad** mitad

Our Favorite Sports

Soccer	⚽	⚽	⚽	⚽				
Basketball	🏀	🏀	🏀	🏀	🏀	🏀	🏀	🏀
Baseball	⚾	⚾	⚾	⚾	⚾	⚾		

Nuestros Deportes Favoritos

futbol	⚽	⚽	⚽	⚽				
balón	🏀	🏀	🏀	🏀	🏀	🏀	🏀	🏀
beisbol	⚾	⚾	⚾	⚾	⚾	⚾		

Glossary/Glosario

English		Español
heavy (heavier, heaviest) (page 183) heavier	H	**pesado (más pesado que, el más pesado)** más pesado que
holds less (page 189) holds less		**contiene menos** contiene menos
holds more (page 189) holds more		**contiene más** contiene más
holds the same (page 189) holds the same		**contiene la misma cantidad** contiene la misma cantidad

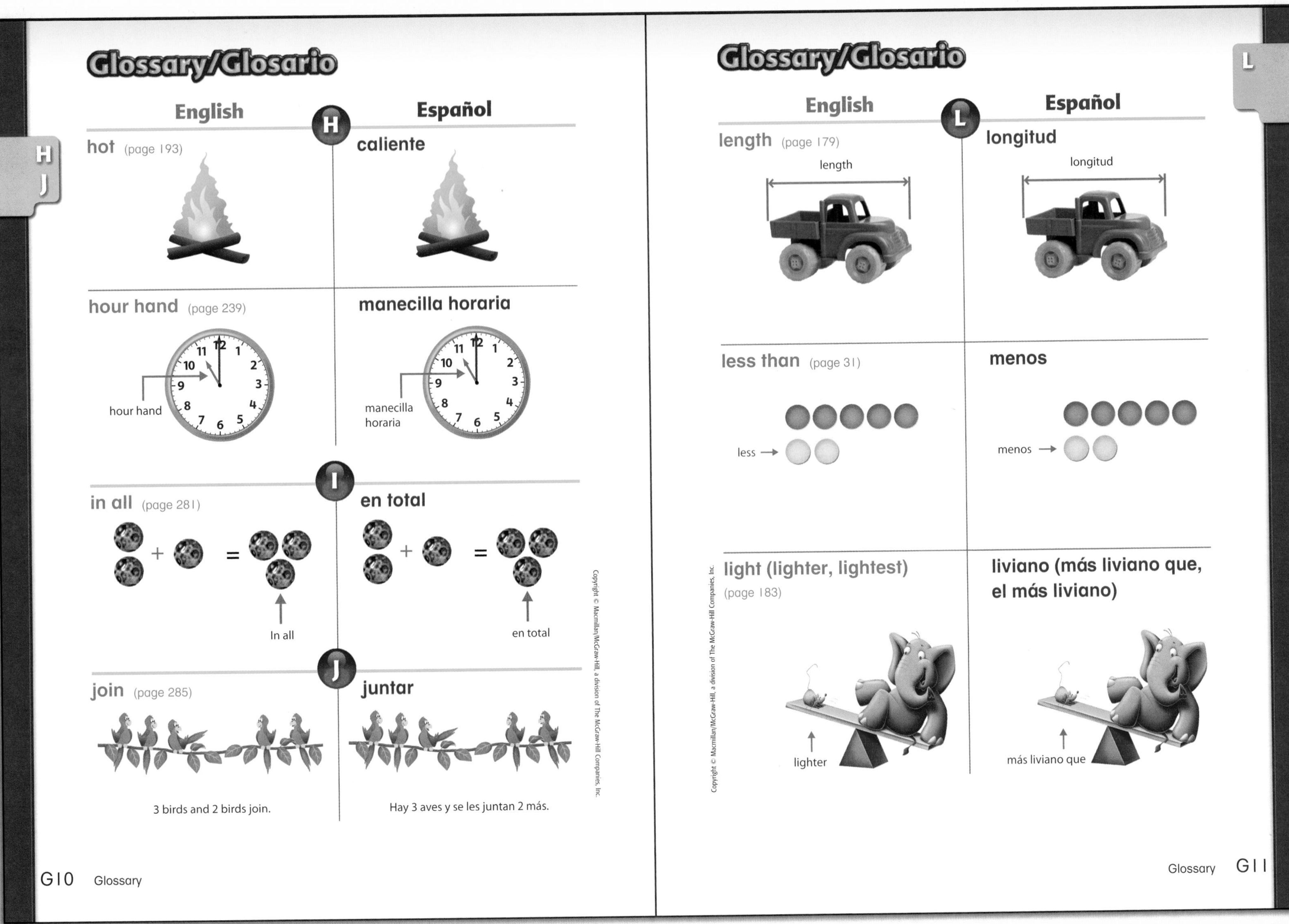

Glossary/Glosario

English		Español
hot (page 193)	H	**caliente**
hour hand (page 239)		**manecilla horaria**
in all (page 281)	I	**en total**
join (page 285)	J	**juntar**

3 birds and 2 birds join.

Hay 3 aves y se les juntan 2 más.

Glossary/Glosario

English		Español
length (page 179)	L	**longitud**
less than (page 31)		**menos**
light (lighter, lightest) (page 183)		**liviano (más liviano que, el más liviano)**

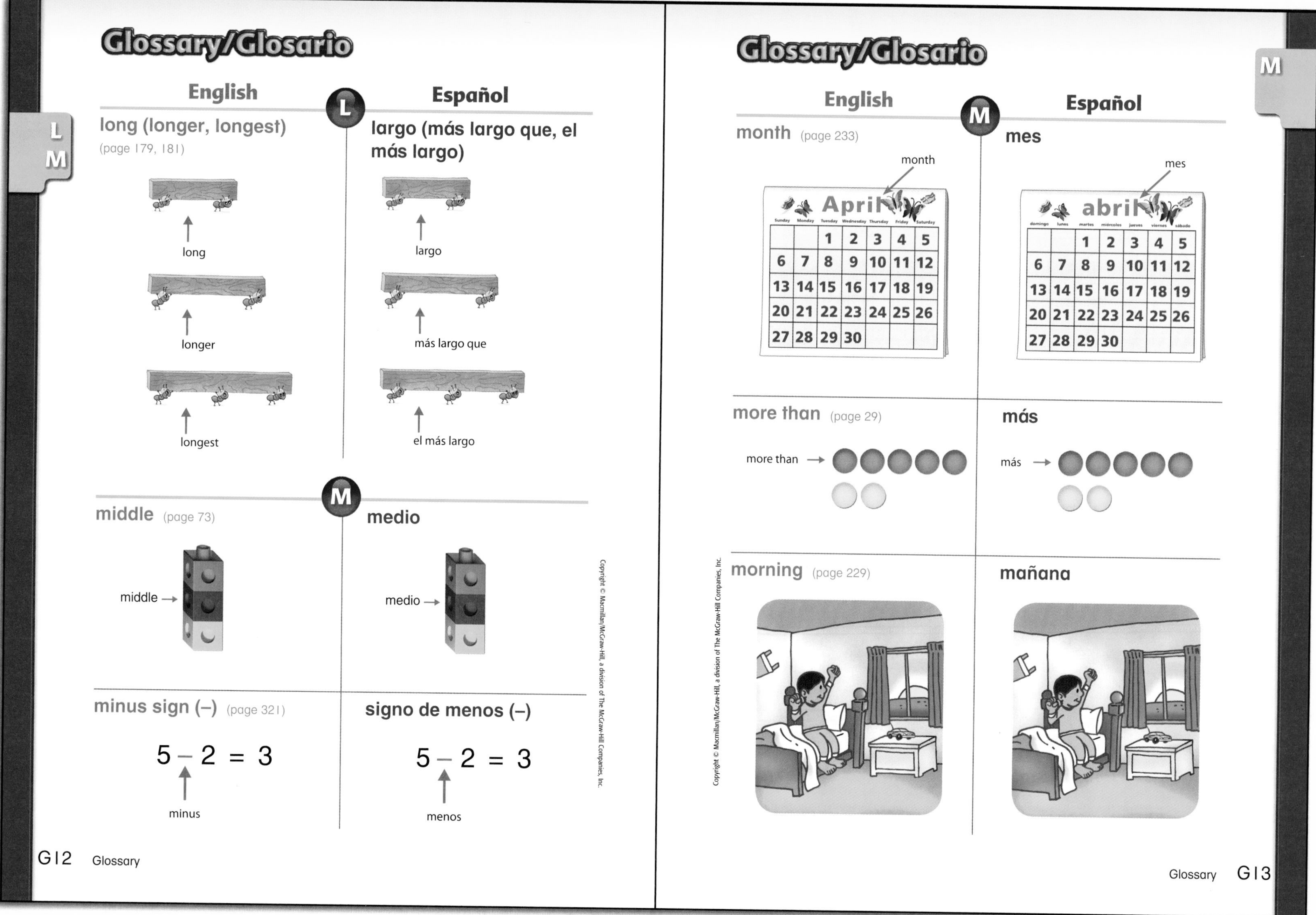

Glossary/Glosario

English		Español
long (longer, longest) (page 179, 181)	L	**largo (más largo que, el más largo)**
long, longer, longest		largo, más largo que, el más largo
middle (page 73)	M	**medio**
middle →		medio →
minus sign (–) (page 321)		**signo de menos (–)**
$5 - 2 = 3$ (minus)		$5 - 2 = 3$ (menos)

Glossary/Glosario

English		Español
month (page 233)	M	**mes**
month (April)		mes (abril)
more than (page 29)		**más**
more than →		más →
morning (page 229)		**mañana**

April / abril calendar:

Sunday	Monday	Tuesday	Wednesday	Thursday	Friday	Saturday
		1	2	3	4	5
6	7	8	9	10	11	12
13	14	15	16	17	18	19
20	21	22	23	24	25	26
27	28	29	30			

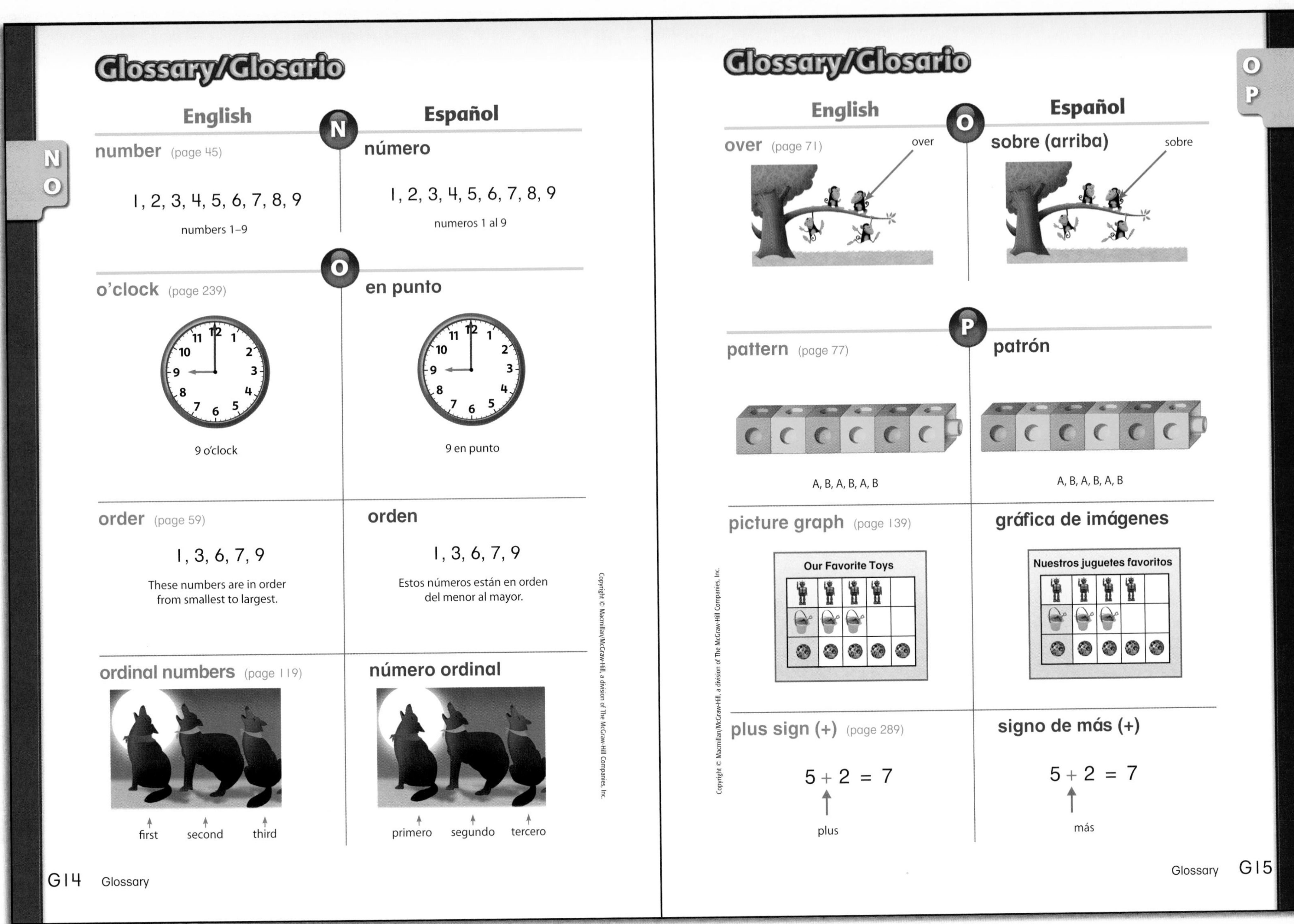

Glossary/Glosario

English		Español
number (page 45) 1, 2, 3, 4, 5, 6, 7, 8, 9 numbers 1–9	N	**número** 1, 2, 3, 4, 5, 6, 7, 8, 9 numeros 1 al 9
o'clock (page 239) 9 o'clock	O	**en punto** 9 en punto
order (page 59) 1, 3, 6, 7, 9 These numbers are in order from smallest to largest.		**orden** 1, 3, 6, 7, 9 Estos números están en orden del menor al mayor.
ordinal numbers (page 119) first second third		**número ordinal** primero segundo tercero

Glossary/Glosario

English		Español
over (page 71) over	O	**sobre (arriba)** sobre
pattern (page 77) A, B, A, B, A, B	P	**patrón** A, B, A, B, A, B
picture graph (page 139)		**gráfica de imágenes**
plus sign (+) (page 289) 5 + 2 = 7 plus		**signo de más (+)** 5 + 2 = 7 más

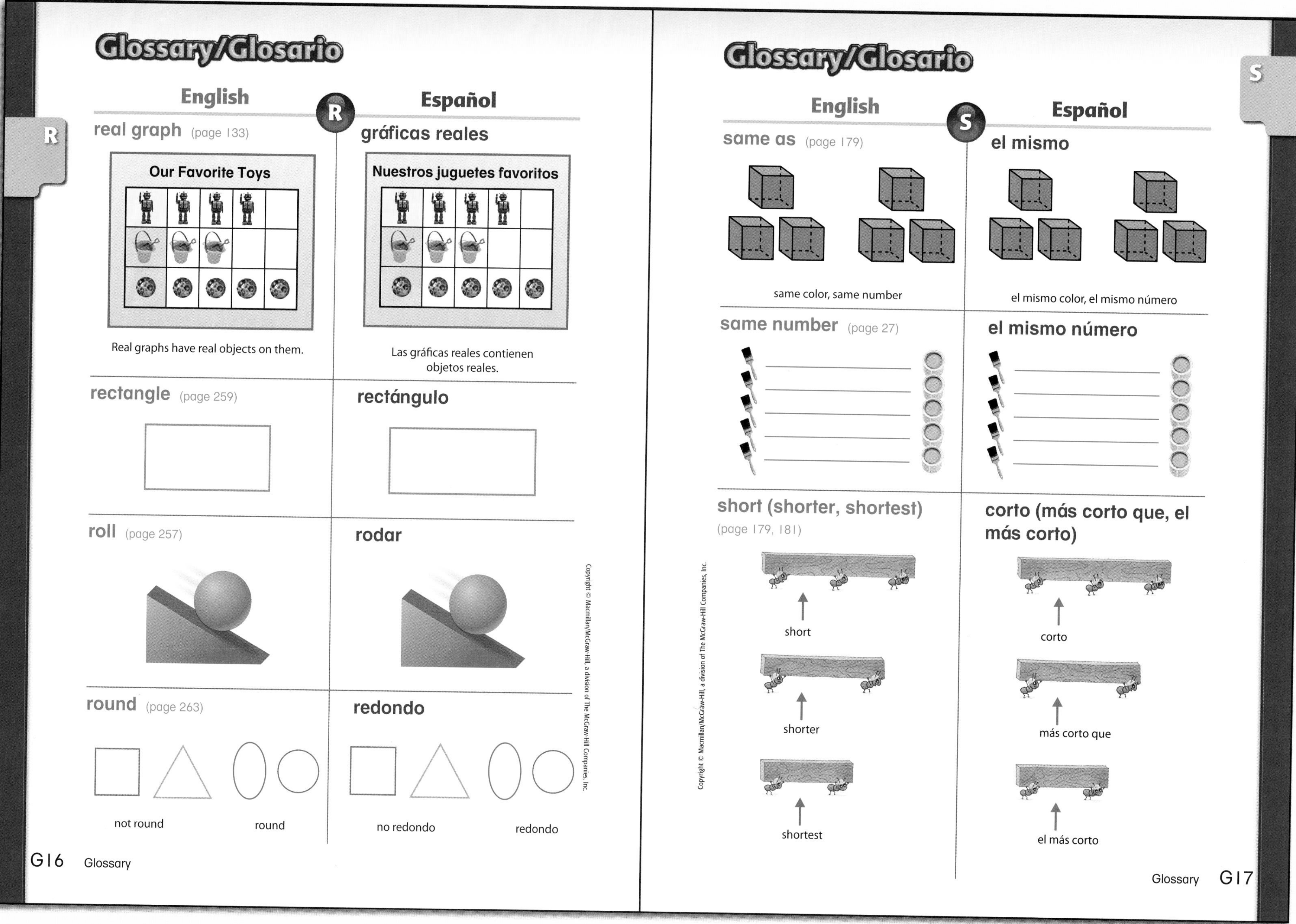

Glossary/Glosario

English	Español
real graph (page 133)	**gráficas reales**
Our Favorite Toys	Nuestros juguetes favoritos
Real graphs have real objects on them.	Las gráficas reales contienen objetos reales.
rectangle (page 259)	**rectángulo**
roll (page 257)	**rodar**
round (page 263)	**redondo**
not round / round	no redondo / redondo

Glossary/Glosario

English	Español
same as (page 179)	**el mismo**
same color, same number	el mismo color, el mismo número
same number (page 27)	**el mismo número**
short (shorter, shortest) (page 179, 181)	**corto (más corto que, el más corto)**
short	corto
shorter	más corto que
shortest	el más corto

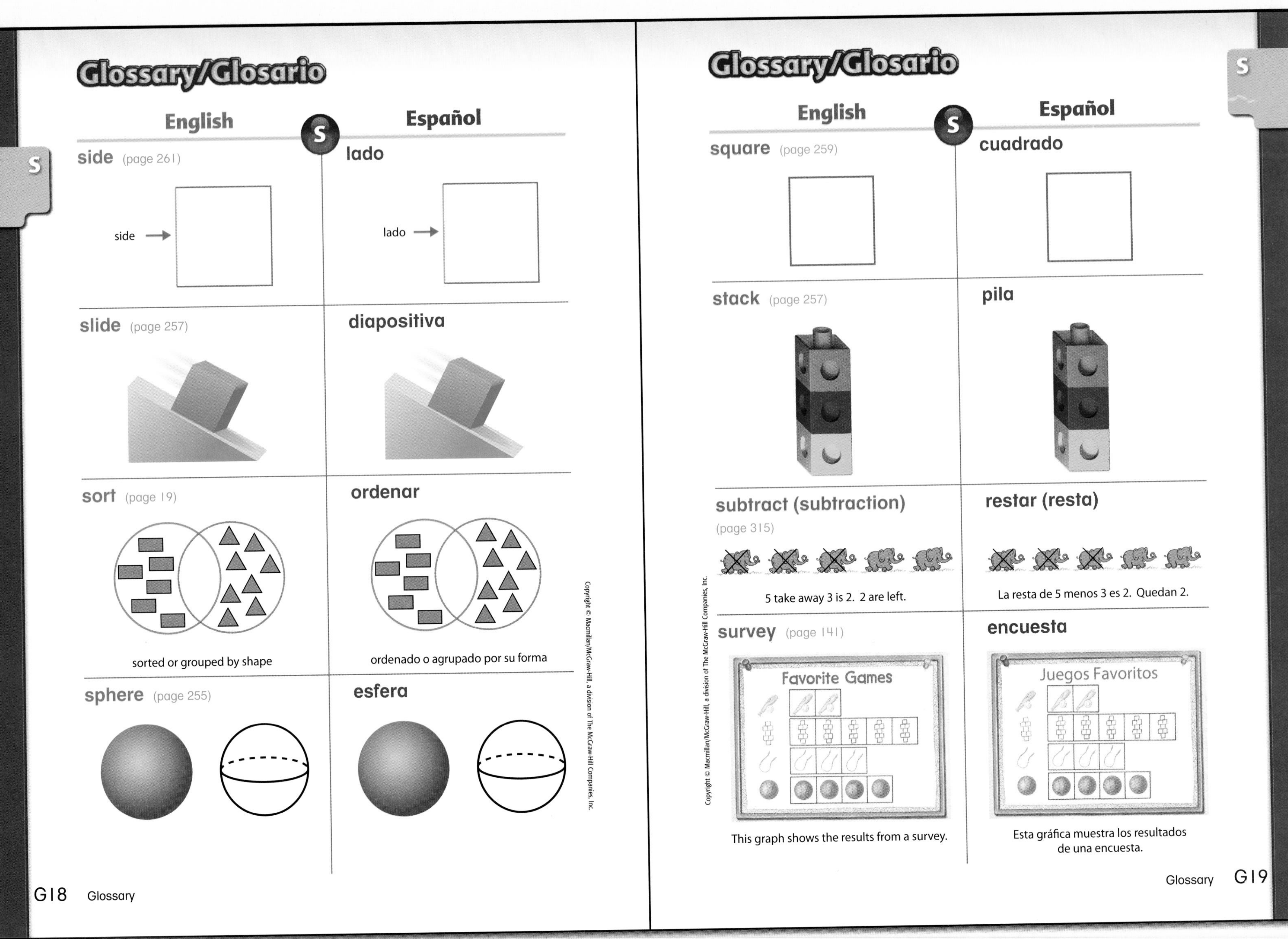

Glossary/Glosario

S

English	Español
side (page 261) side →	**lado** lado →
slide (page 257)	**diapositiva**
sort (page 19) sorted or grouped by shape	**ordenar** ordenado o agrupado por su forma
sphere (page 255)	**esfera**

Glossary/Glosario

S

English	Español
square (page 259)	**cuadrado**
stack (page 257)	**pila**
subtract (subtraction) (page 315) 5 take away 3 is 2. 2 are left.	**restar (resta)** La resta de 5 menos 3 es 2. Quedan 2.
survey (page 141) Favorite Games This graph shows the results from a survey.	**encuesta** Juegos Favoritos Esta gráfica muestra los resultados de una encuesta.

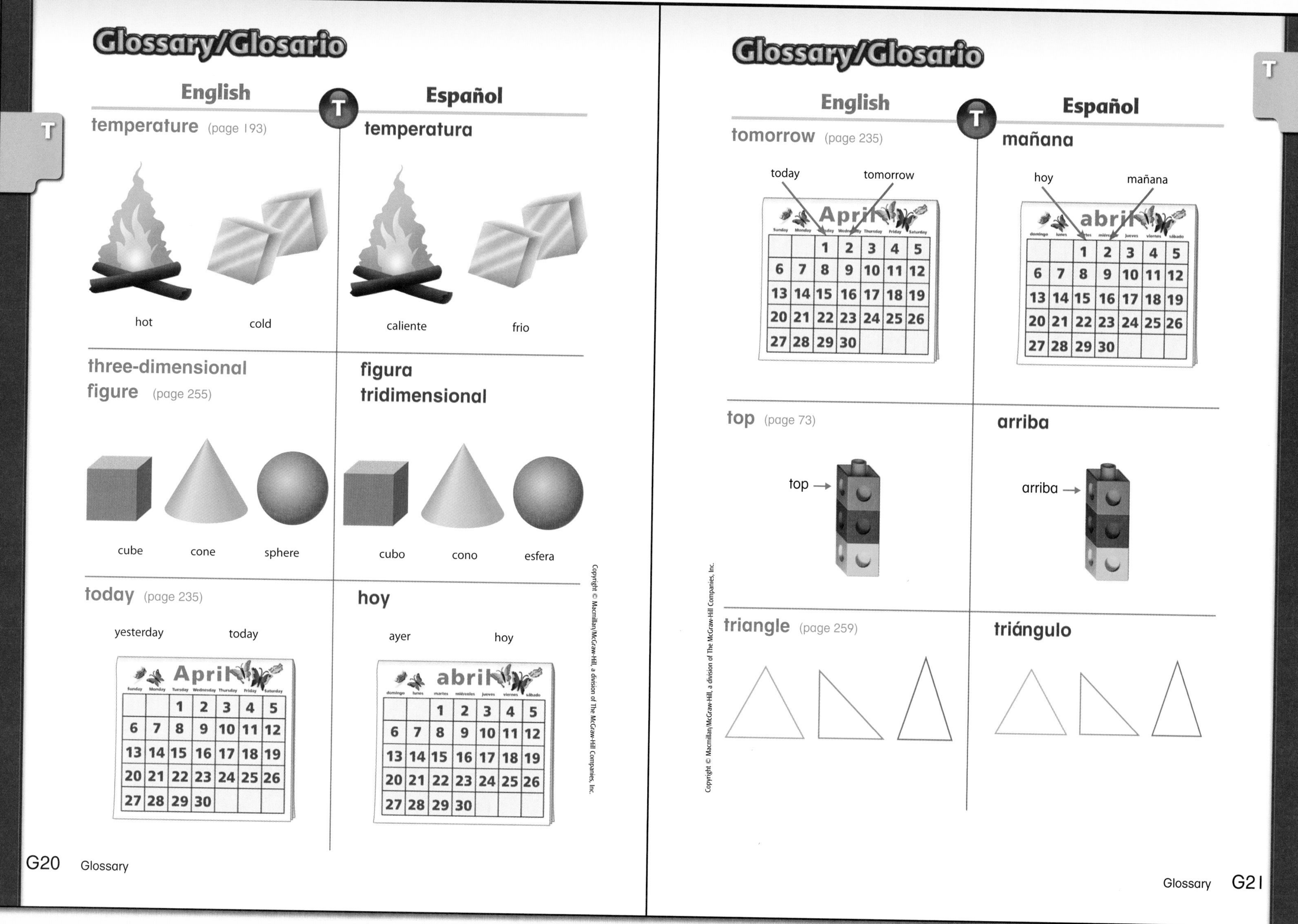

Glossary/Glosario

English	Español
temperature (page 193)	**temperatura**
hot, cold	caliente, frio
three-dimensional figure (page 255)	**figura tridimensional**
cube, cone, sphere	cubo, cono, esfera
today (page 235)	**hoy**
yesterday, today	ayer, hoy

Glossary/Glosario

English	Español
tomorrow (page 235)	**mañana**
today, tomorrow	hoy, mañana
top (page 73)	**arriba**
top →	arriba →
triangle (page 259)	**triángulo**

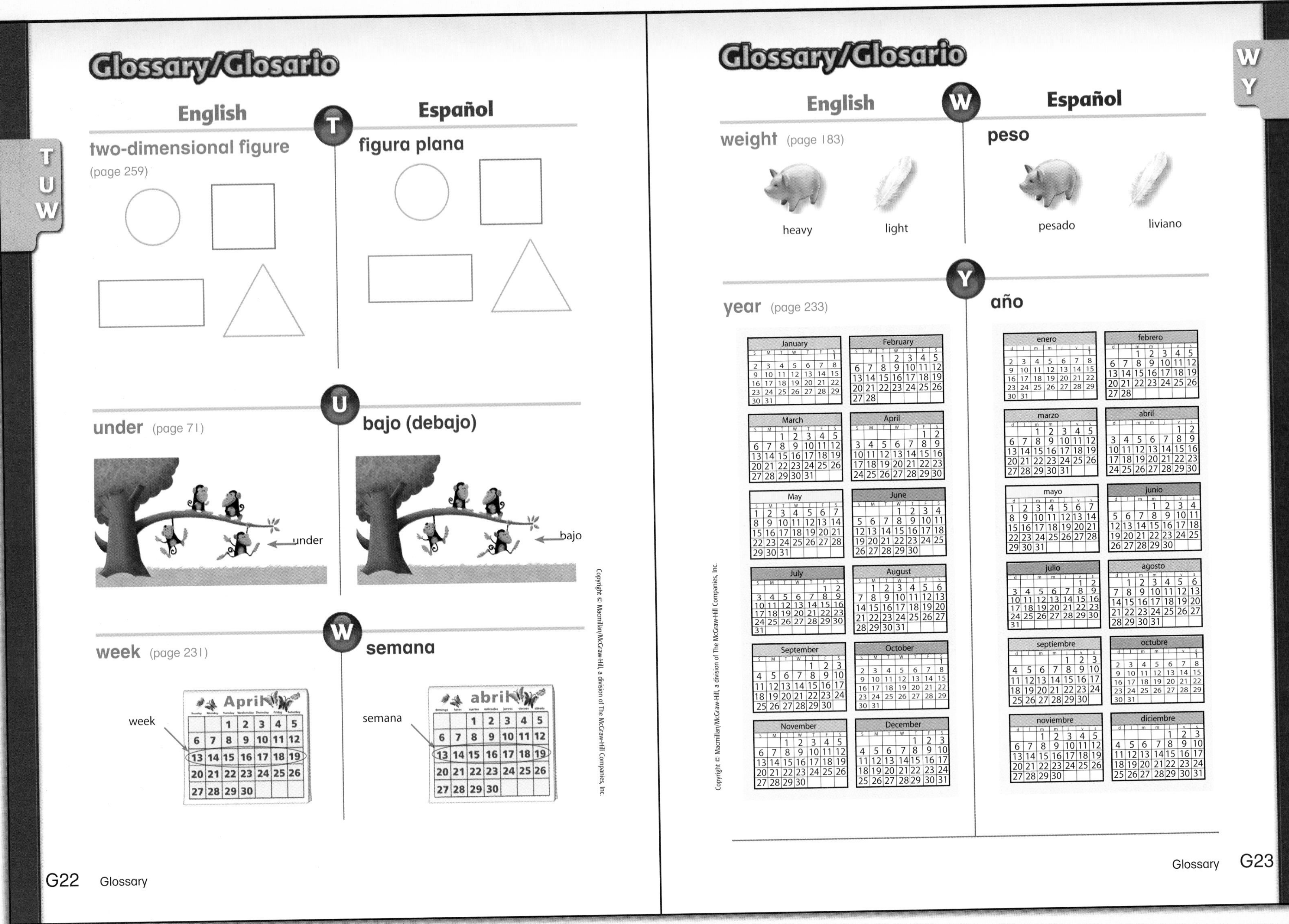

Glossary/Glosario

English		Español
two-dimensional figure (page 259)	T	**figura plana**
under (page 71)	U	**bajo (debajo)**
week (page 231)	W	**semana**

Glossary/Glosario

English		Español
weight (page 183)	W	**peso**
year (page 233)	Y	**año**

Glossary/Glosario

English	Español
Y	
yesterday (page 235)	**ayer**

yesterday today

April

Sunday	Monday	Tuesday	Wednesday	Thursday	Friday	Saturday
		1	2	3	4	5
6	7	8	9	10	11	12
13	14	15	16	17	18	19
20	21	22	23	24	25	26
27	28	29	30			

ayer hoy

abril

domingo	lunes	martes	miércoles	jueves	viernes	sábado
		1	2	3	4	5
6	7	8	9	10	11	12
13	14	15	16	17	18	19
20	21	22	23	24	25	26
27	28	29	30			

Photo Credits

Unless otherwise credited, all currency courtesy of the US Mint.

vi-viii Doug Martin; **1** Ariel Skelley/CORBIS; **2** David M. Dennis/Animals Animals - Earth Scenes; **3** (tl cl)Stockbyte/Getty Images, (bl bcl)Burke/Triolo Productions/Brand X Pictures/Getty Images, (c)Pat O'Hara/CORBIS, (tc)Goran Kapor/Alamy; **4** (tl)Siede Preis/Getty Images, (cl)Burke/Triolo Productions/Brand X Pictures/Getty Images, (cr)Getty Images, (tr)joSon/Getty Images, (br)Pat O'Hara/CORBIS; **5** FAN travelstock/Alamy; **6** Image Source/CORBIS; **7** John Henley/CORBIS; **9** Cory Morse/Getty Images; **11** CORBIS Super RF/Alamy; **13** Randy Lincks; **15** (others)Eclipse Studios, (tl)Brand X Pictures/PunchStock; **16** (bl)Eclipse Studios, (tl)Brand X Pictures/PunchStock; **17** (party hat rabbit cap)IndexOpen, (helmet)Ryan McVay, (fish)G.K. Vikki Hart/Getty Images, (orange)Stockdisc/PunchStock, (pineapple bear)Getty Images, (starfish)Ian Cartwright/Getty Images, (teddy)Getty Images; **18** (plane chair brush)Photos.com, (helicopter)CORBIS, (stool)Getty Images; **25** (tcr)Ryan McVay/Getty Images, (cr)Getty Images, (cl)CORBIS; **27** (drum)Getty Images, (sticks picks)IndexOpen, (bow)Masterfile, (xylophone)C Squared Studios/Getty Images, (Glockenspiel)Chris Stock/Lebrecht/The Image Works; **32** (top to bottom)Stockdisc, CORBIS, Fielding Piepereit, Dave King/Getty Images, photos.com, Masterfile; **33** (tl)Photos To Go, (cl br)Getty Images, (b)The Stock Asylum, LLC/Alamy, (tr)The McGraw-Hill Companies; **34** (c)Getty Images, (t)Richard Hutchings/Digital Light Source; **35** (cl bl)Getty Images, (bcl)PhotoLink/Getty Images; **39** F. Lukasseck/Masterfile; **41** (cr br)Eclipse Studios, (bl)Richard Hutchings/Digital Light Source, (tl)The McGraw-Hill Companies; **42** Richard Hutchings/Digital Light Source; **50** (tl)artpartner-images.com/Alamy, (tc)BL Productions/SuperStock, (c bl)photos.com, (bc)super stock; **57** (bird)James Urbach/SuperStock, (saw)photos.com, (wood)Ted Morrison/SuperStock RF, (hammer)IndexOpen, (nail)Masterfile, (paint)SuperStock RF, (brush)Tony Hutchings/Getty Images, (screw driver)photolibrary.com.pty.ltd/Index Stock, (screw)Leonard Lessin/Peter Arnold, Inc., (birdhouse)Peter Ardito/Index Stock; **58** (hat)Masterfile, (dog)Alison Barnes Martin/Masterfile, (fire hat)IndexOpen, (cowboy hat)Getty Images, (trout)Ron Steiner/Alamy, (pony)G.K. Vikki Hart/Getty Images, (rabbit)PunchStock; **61** (b)Tony Perrottet/Alamy Images, (t)CORBIS; **62** (b)Jochen Sand/Getty Images, (t)Steve Niedorf Photography/Getty Images; **64** (t bl)McGraw-Hill Companies, (cl c)G.K. Vikki Hart/Getty Images, (tcl bl)Getty Images; **67** S Purdy Matthews/Getty Images; **69 70** Eclipse Studios; **81** (others)The McGraw-Hill Companies, (tl)Richard Hutchings/Digital Light Source; **85** (children)Richard Hutchings/Digital Light Source, (maracas)George Doyle/Getty Images, (bell drum guitar)C Squared Studios/Getty Images, (tambourine triangle)Getty Images; **86** (cl)Lebrecht Music and Arts Photo Library/Alamy, (bl bcr)Richard Hutchings/Digital Light Source, (tcl t)C Squared Studios/Getty Images, (tl)Getty Images; **89** (checkers)Jupiterimages, (boots)Digital Vision/Getty Images, (sunglasses)Ingram Publishing/Alamy Images, (flops)Punchstock, (playground)Andrea Rugg/Beateworks/CORBIS, (umbrella)Getty Images; **90** (soccer)Ryan McVay/Getty Images, (kite)C Squared Studios/Getty Images, (paints)Jupiterimages, (bike)CORBIS, (jacks)Getty Images; **91** (bc)CORBIS, (t)Jupiterimages; **92** (b)The McGraw-Hill Companies, (r)Richard Hutchings/Digital Light Source; **97** Image Source/SuperStock; **98** Getty Images; **99 100** Eclipse Studios; **105** (bag)CSquared Studios/Getty Images, (others)Mazer; **115** (fish)Ingram Publishing/Alamy, (birds guinea pigs)G.K. & Vikki Hart/Getty Images, (scratching post)Photospin/Imagestate, (seed bell)Mazer Corporation, (fish food)The McGraw-Hill Companies/Jacques Cornell; **116** (wheel)Jason Reed/Getty Images, (bottle collar)Mazer Corporation, (leash)Photospin/Alamy, (mouse)Sergio Piumatti/Destinations, (birdcage)Kathleen Finlay/Masterfile, (rawhide)Getty Images; **123** (bl)Getty Images, (tl t)C Squared Studios/Getty Images, (cl)Brand X Pictures/Getty Images; **127** The McGraw-Hill Companies; **129** (bcr b br)Eclipse Studios, (c)The McGraw-Hill Companies; **130** Eclipse Studios; **132** Photodisc Green/Getty Images; **143** (t)Artifacts Images, (bc)Ariel Skelley/CORBIS; **144** (b)Richard Hutchings/Digital Light Source, (t)Bruce Hershey/Jupiterimages; **146** (c)D. Hurst/Alamy, (tl)Creatas/PunchStock, (bl)C Squared Studios/Getty Images, (b)Getty Images; **149** Raul Touzon/Getty Images; **151 152** Eclipse Studios; **155** (tc)Jupiterimages, (others)photos.com; **156** Masterfile; **157** Ryan McVay/Getty Images; **158 159** Getty Images; **161** (l)Brand X Pictures/PunchStock, (cl)Siede Preis/Getty Images, (cr r)The McGraw-Hill Companies; **162** (l)D. Hurst/Alamy, (cr)Don Farrall/Getty Images, (cl r)C Squared Studios/Getty Images; **163 164** Stockdisc/PunchStock; **165 166** StudiOhio; **169** (tr)Creatas/Punchstock, (cl)Robert Glusic/Getty Images, (tc)BananaStock/PunchStock, (tcl)PhotoLink/Getty Images, (bcr)CORBIS, (tl)MedioImages/Age Fotostock, (r)Richard Hutchings/Digital Light Source, (br)Brand X Pixtures/PunchStock, (bl)Borland/PhotoLink/Getty Images; **170** Beaconstox/Alamy Images; **172** (boots)Digital Vision/Getty Images, (umbrella)Photos To Go, (sticks)C Squared Studios/Getty Images, (trumpet)Getty Images; **175** CORBIS; **177 178** Eclipse Studios; **183** (t)Richard Hutchings/Digital Light Source, (cl)The McGraw-Hill Companies, (cr br)StudiOhio, (bl)Stockbyte/PictureQuest, (bcl)Getty Images, (tcl)PhotoLink/Getty Images; **184** (workstation)Photodisc/Getty Images, (ladel)Stockbyte/Getty Images, (bowl)Hemera Technologies/Alamy, (juice jug)Dan Brandenburg/iStockphoto, (bike)CORBIS, (helmet)Comstock Images/Alamy; **189** StudiOhio; **195** (b)CORBIS, (tc)The McGraw-Hill Companies/Jacques Cornell; **196** (bc)Dave King/Getty Images, (t)G. I. Bernard/Photo Researchers, (c)Ingram Publishing/Superstock, (bl)Jupiterimages; **197** G.K. & Vikki Hart/Getty Images; **198** Photos To Go; **201** Mark Tomalty/Masterfile; **203** Eclipse Studios; **205** C Squared Studios/Photodisc Green/Getty Images; **206** (cl)Photographers Direct, (bl)Masterfile, (tcl)The McGraw-Hill Companies; **218** The Mcgraw-Hill Companies; **219** (bc)David Buffington/Getty Images, (tc)Comstock/PunchStock; **220** (cr)Michael Houghton/StudiOhio, (bc)Cary Anderson/Eagle Eye Pictures/Photographers Direct; **222** (tl)Karen Whylie/Masterfile, (tcl)Stockdisc/PunchStock, (cr)Getty Images, (tr)Jupiterimages; **224** Getty Images; **225** Jose Luis Pelaez, Inc./CORBIS; **227** (others)Eclipse Studios, (bl b br)Richard Hutchings/Digital Light Source; **228** Eclipse Studios; **229** (cl)Alamy Images, (bl)Getty Images; **230** (tl)Will & Deni McIntyre/CORBIS, (cl)Mike Powell/Getty Images, (bl)USDA; **237** Bill Bachmann/Index Stock Imagery; **241** Richard Hutchings/Digital Light Source; **243** (top to bottom)Digital Vision, Punchstock, PunchStock/Getty Images, CORBIS; **245** (bc)Alamy Images, (tc)Ariel Skelley/Getty Images; **246** Yvona momatiuk/Photo Researchers; **251** Katherine Fawssett/Getty Images; **252** The McGraw-Hill Companies; **253 254** Eclipse Studios; **255** (lemonade funnel)Mazer Corporation, (orange)Davies & Starr/Getty Images, (cube)CORBIS, (party hat)Alamy Images, (blower)Stockbyte/PictureQuest, (globe)Getty Images, (flash light)The McGraw-Hill Companies; **256** (pylon)photos.com, (ball)Punchstock, (egg plum)Getty Images, (megaphone flash light cereal)The McGraw-Hill Companies, (others)Mazer Corporation; **257** (canned goods)Mazer Corporation, (present)CORBIS, (others)The McGraw-Hill Companies/Jacques Cornel; **259** (cl)The McGraw-Hill Companies, (others)Mazer Corporation; **262** (refrigerator)C Squared Studios/Getty Images, (flag tire)Punchstock, (window)Dana Hoff/Beateworks/CORBIS, (cookie sheet)Mazer Corporation, (towel)McGraw-Hill Companies, (switch)Getty Images; **264** (cl t)Getty Images, (tl)McGraw-Hill Companies, (tr)Punchstock, (bl)CORBIS, (bcl b)McGraw-Hill Companies, (tcr)Stockdisc/PunchStock, (tc bl)C Squared Studios/Getty Images; **265** (tcl)Photodisc/Getty Images, (tcr)Alamy Images; **266** The McGraw-Hill Companies; **269** (bc)Davies & Starr/Getty Images, (tr c)Alamy Images, (tc)McGraw-Hill Companies, (bl br)Mazer Corporation; **275** (tc)Mazer Corporation, (tr)The McGraw-Hill Companies; **279** Frans Lanting/Minden Pictures; **280** C Squared Studios/Getty Images; **281 282** Eclipse Studios; **299** (tl)Getty Images, (others)Jupiterimages;

303 (cl) The McGraw-Hill Companies/Ken Cavanagh, (others)The McGraw-Hill Companies; **307** (b)Paul Bricknell/Getty Images, (tr)CORBIS, (tl)Julie Houck/Fotografia/CORBIS; **308** (br)SW Productions/Getty Images, (bl)Purestock/Getty Images, (tc)Bill Losh/Getty Images, (tr)Paul Hardy/CORBIS; **310** (cl)The McGraw-Hill Companies/Ken Cavanagh, (b)Stefano Bianchetti/CORBIS, (bl)Ingram Publishing/Superstock; **312** The McGraw-Hill Companies; **313** Steve Bloom; **315 316** Eclipse Studios; **341** (cl)Suzannah Skelton, (tl)Jupiterimages, (tcl)Getty Images; **342** Mazer Corporation; **343** (tc)AGE Fotostock, (t)Ed-Imaging; **344** (tl)National Resources Conservation Services, (bl c cr)Punchstock, (tc)SHOTFILE/Alamy, (tcr)Getty Images; **346** Mazer Corporation; **CS1** Michael Houghton/StudiOhio; **CS3** (tl)The McGraw-Hill Companies/Ken Cavanagh, (tc)Amanita Pictures; **CS4** (scale)Judith Collins/Alamy, (ruler)The McGraw-Hill Companies/Ken Cavanagh, (watermelon)Jupiterimages, (book)The McGraw-Hill Companies; **CS5** (bl)Stockbyte/Getty Images, (br)Getty Images; **CS6** (cr)Digital Vision/Getty Images, (br)David Toase/Getty Images, (cl)C Squared Studios/Getty Images, (bl)Getty Images; **G01** F. Lukasseck/Masterfile; **G02** Siri Stafford/Getty Images; **G07** (cl)Getty Images, (tl)Stockdisc/PunchStock, (bc)Alamy Images; **G17** Stockdisc/PunchStock; **G23** (bcr)The McGraw-Hill Companies, (br)Getty Images; **LA1** Mark Steinmetz; **LA13** (hamburger)Burke/Triolo Productions/Getty Images, (hot dog pizza)C Squared Studios/Getty Images, (pretzel)Getty Images, (muffins)Alamy Images, (corn)Don Farrall/Getty Images; **LA2** Tim Fuller; **P1** (cl cr)Punchstock, (bl)Jeff Greenberg/PhotoEdit; **P2** (b)Tim Fuller, (bl)Punchstock.

Art Credits:

McGraw-Hill would like to acknowledge the artists and agencies who contributed to illustrating this program: Cover Jim Talbot represented by Mendola Artists; Don Bishop, Gary Ciccarelli, Garth Glazier, Hudoq, Barry Orkin, Tony Randazzo, Studio Liddell represented by AA Reps. Inc.; Garry Colby, Peter Grosshauser represented by Cliff Knecht, Artist Representative.

T3 (b)Stockbyte/Getty Images; **T8** Bloom Works Inc./Alamy; **T12** CORBIS; **T13** Bananastock/PunchStock; **T14-T15** Creasource/Corbis; **13H** (br)Ed-Imaging, (cr)Eclipse Studios; **15** Eclipse Studios; **17B** Jupiterimages; **19** Eclipse Studios; **21** (bc)Richard Hutchings/Digital Light Source, (tl)Eclipse Studios; **23** (tl)Eclipse Studios; **27** (b)Eclipse Studios, (bl)Richard Hutchings/Digital Light Source; **29** Eclipse Studios; **31** (b)Richard Hutchings/Digital Light Source, (t)Eclipse Studios; **39B** The McGraw-Hill Companies; **39G** Getty Images; **41** Eclipse Studios; **43** (b)Richard Hutchings/Digital Light Source, (t)Eclipse Studios; **45** (b)Richard Hutchings/Digital Light Source, (t)Eclipse Studios; **47** Richard Hutchings/Digital Light Source; **49** (b)Richard Hutchings/Digital Light Source, (t)Eclipse Studios; **53** Eclipse Studios; **55** (b)Richard Hutchings/Digital Light Source, (t)Eclipse Studios; **57** (b)Richard Hutchings/Digital Light Source, (t)Eclipse Studios; **59** (b)Richard Hutchings/Digital Light Source, (t)Eclipse Studios; **67H** (br)Richard Hutchings/Digital Light Source, (c)The McGraw-Hill Companies; **69** Eclipse Studios; **71** (t)Eclipse Studios, (t)Richard Hutchings/Digital Light Source; **73** (b)Richard Hutchings/Digital Light Source, (t)Eclipse Studios; **75** (t)Eclipse Studios, (t)Richard Hutchings/Digital Light Source; **77** (bl)Richard Hutchings/Digital Light Source, (tl)Eclipse Studios; **81** (b)Richard Hutchings/Digital Light Source, (t)Eclipse Studios; **81A** (duck green apple)Getty Images, (red apple)Stockdisc/PunchStock; **83** (b)Richard Hutchings/Digital Light Source, (t)Eclipse Studios; **85B** Getty Images; **85** (b)Richard Hutchings/Digital Light Source, (t)Eclipse Studios; **87A** (bell drum) C Squared Studios/Getty Images, (baseball duck)Getty Images, (owl) Digital Vision/PunchStock, (soccer ball) Ryan McVay/Getty Images; **87** (t)Eclipse Studios, (b)Richard Hutchings/Digital Light Source; **89** Richard Hutchings/Digital Light Source; **97H** Richard Hutchings/Digital Light Source; **99-101** Eclipse Studios; **103** (b)Richard Hutchings/Digital Light Source, (tl)Eclipse Studios; **105** Eclipse Studios; **109** (b)Richard Hutchings/Digital Light Source, (t)Eclipse Studios; **111** (t)Richard Hutchings/Digital Light Source, (tl)Eclipse Studios; **113 115** (b)Richard Hutchings/Digital Light Source, (t)Eclipse Studios; **117** (b)Richard Hutchings/Digital Light Source, (tl)Eclipse Studios; **119** (b)Richard Hutchings/Digital Light Source, (t)Eclipse Studios; **127G** Eclipse Studios; **127H** (c)Getty Images, (b)Ed-Imaging; **129–131** Eclipse Studios; **133** Richard Hutchings/Digital Light Source; **135–141** Eclipse Studios; **149H** Ed-Imaging; **151** Eclipse Studios; **153** Richard Hutchings/Digital Light Source; **155–161** Richard Hutchings/Digital Light Source; **163** Eclipse Studios; **165–167** Richard Hutchings/Digital Light Source; **175G** Eclipse Studios; **175H** Ed-Imaging; **177** Eclipse Studios; **179** (b)Richard Hutchings/Digital Light Source, (t)Eclipse Studios; **183** (b)Richard Hutchings/Digital Light Source, (t)Eclipse Studios; **185** Richard Hutchings/Digital Light Source; **189** (bc)Richard Hutchings/Digital Light Source, (tc)Eclipse Studios; **191** Richard Hutchings/Digital Light Source; **193** (bl,)Richard Hutchings/Digital Light Source, (t, tcr)Eclipse Studios; **195** (bc)Richard Hutchings/Digital Light Source, (t)Eclipse Studios; **197** (t)Eclipse Studios, (b)Richard Hutchings/Digital Light Source; **199** Eclipse Studios; **203** Richard Hutchings/Digital Light Source; **205–219** Eclipse Studios; **225B** (tc)Siri Stafford/Getty Images, (tr)Mike Powell/Getty Images; **225G** Eclipse Studios; **225H** Ed-Imaging; **227** Eclipse Studios; **229** Richard Hutchings/Digital Light Source; **231** (bc)Eclipse Studios, (bc)Richard Hutchings/Digital Light Source; **233** (bc)Richard Hutchings/Digital Light Source, (tl)Eclipse Studios; **235** (bc)Richard Hutchings/Digital Light Source, (tcl)Eclipse Studios; **239B** Ed-Imaging; **239** (bc)Richard Hutchings/Digital Light Source, (tl)Eclipse Studios; **241** (bc)Richard Hutchings/Digital Light Source, (tcl)Eclipse Studios; **243** (bc)Richard Hutchings/Digital Light Source, (tcl)Eclipse Studios; **251B** Alamy Images; **251G** The McGraw-Hill Companies; **251H-251** Ed-Imaging; **253–257** Eclipse Studios; **259** (bc)Richard Hutchings/Digital Light Source, (tc)Eclipse Studios; **261–263** Eclipse Studios; **267** Richard Hutchings/Digital Light Source; **267–271** Eclipse Studios; **278** Richard Hutchings/Digital Light Source; **279G–279H** Ed-Imaging; **283B** Ed-Imaging; **283** Eclipse Studios; **287B** Ed-Imaging; **287** Eclipse Studios; **291** (b)Richard Hutchings/Digital Light Source, (t) Eclipse Studios; **293** Eclipse Studios; **297** (b)Richard Hutchings/Digital Light Source, (tl)Eclipse Studios; **299** (b)Richard Hutchings/Digital Light Source, (t)Eclipse Studios; **301** (b)Richard Hutchings/Digital Light Source, (t)Eclipse Studios; **303** (t)Eclipse Studios; **305** Richard Hutchings/Digital Light Source, **305** Eclipse Studios; **313** Ed-Imaging; **315** Eclipse Studios; **317** (bl)Richard Hutchings/Digital Light Source, (tc)Eclipse Studios; **321** (bl)Richard Hutchings/Digital Light Source, (tc)Eclipse Studios; **323** Eclipse Studios; **325** (bl)Richard Hutchings/Digital Light Source, (tl)Eclipse Studios; **331** Eclipse Studios; **333** Richard Hutchings/Digital Light Source; **335** Eclipse Studios; **337** Eclipse Studios; **339–341** Richard Hutchings/Digital Light Source; **341** Eclipse Studios.

Name ______________________

Writing Numbers 0 to 5

0 0

1 1

2 2

3 3

4 4

5 5

Name ______________________

Writing Numbers 6 to 10

6 6

7 7

8 8

9 9

10 10

Name ______________________

Writing Numbers 11 to 15

11 11

12 12

13 13

14 14

15 15

Name

Writing Numbers 16 to 20

16 16

17 17

18 18

19 19

20 20

Name

Writing Numbers 21 to 25

21 21

22 22

23 23

24 24

25 25

Writing Numbers

Name

Writing Numbers 26 to 30

26 26

27 27

28 28

29 29

30 30

WN6 Writing Numbers

WorkMat 1

WorkMat 1: Story Mat

Facts Practice

WorkMat 3: Graphing Mat

WorkMat 3

Copyright © Macmillan/McGraw-Hill, a division of The McGraw-Hill Companies, Inc.

WorkMat 2

WorkMat 2: Two-Part Mat

WorkMats

WorkMat 4

WorkMat 5

WorkMat 4: Sorting Mat/T-Chart

WorkMat 5: Ten-Frame

WorkMat 7: Part-Part-Whole

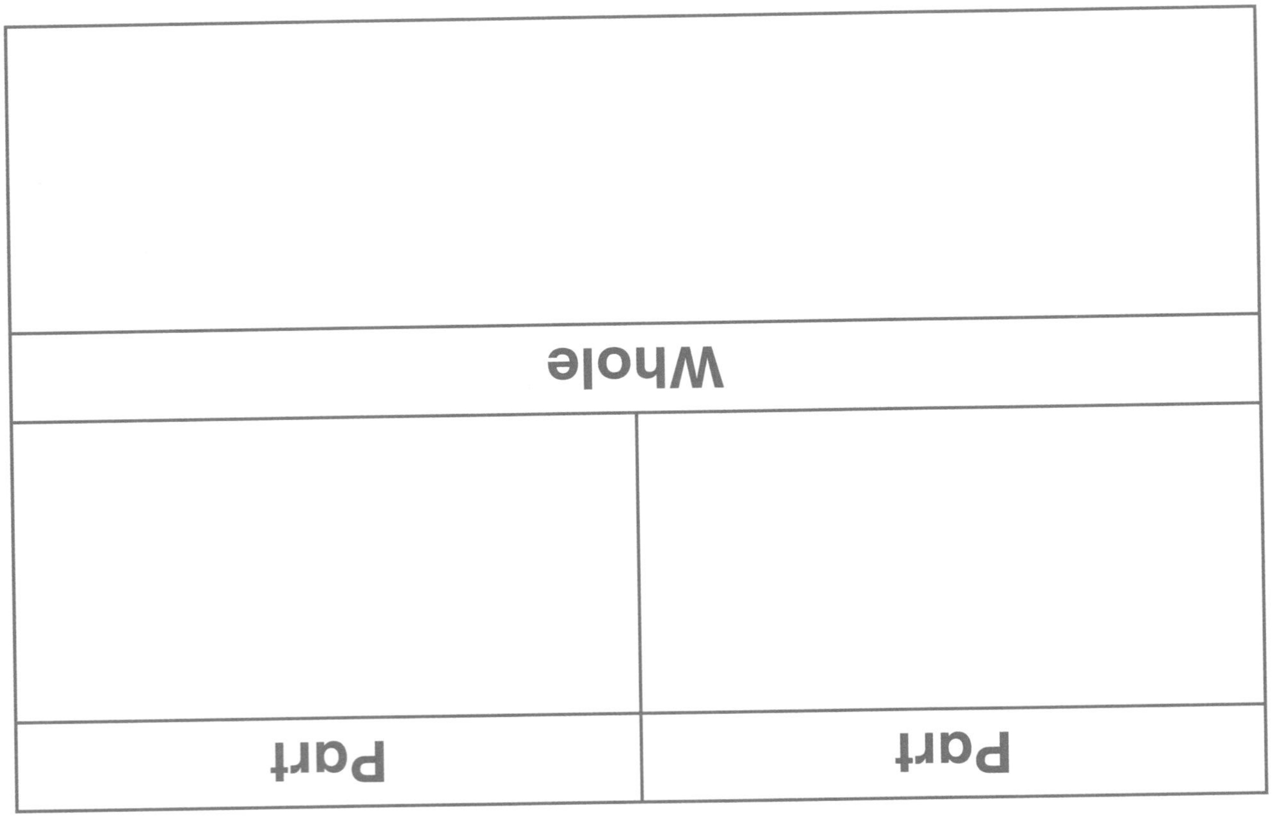

Whole

Part

Part

WorkMat 7

Copyright © Macmillan/McGraw-Hill, a division of The McGraw-Hill Companies, Inc.

WorkMat 6

WorkMat 6: Ten-Frames

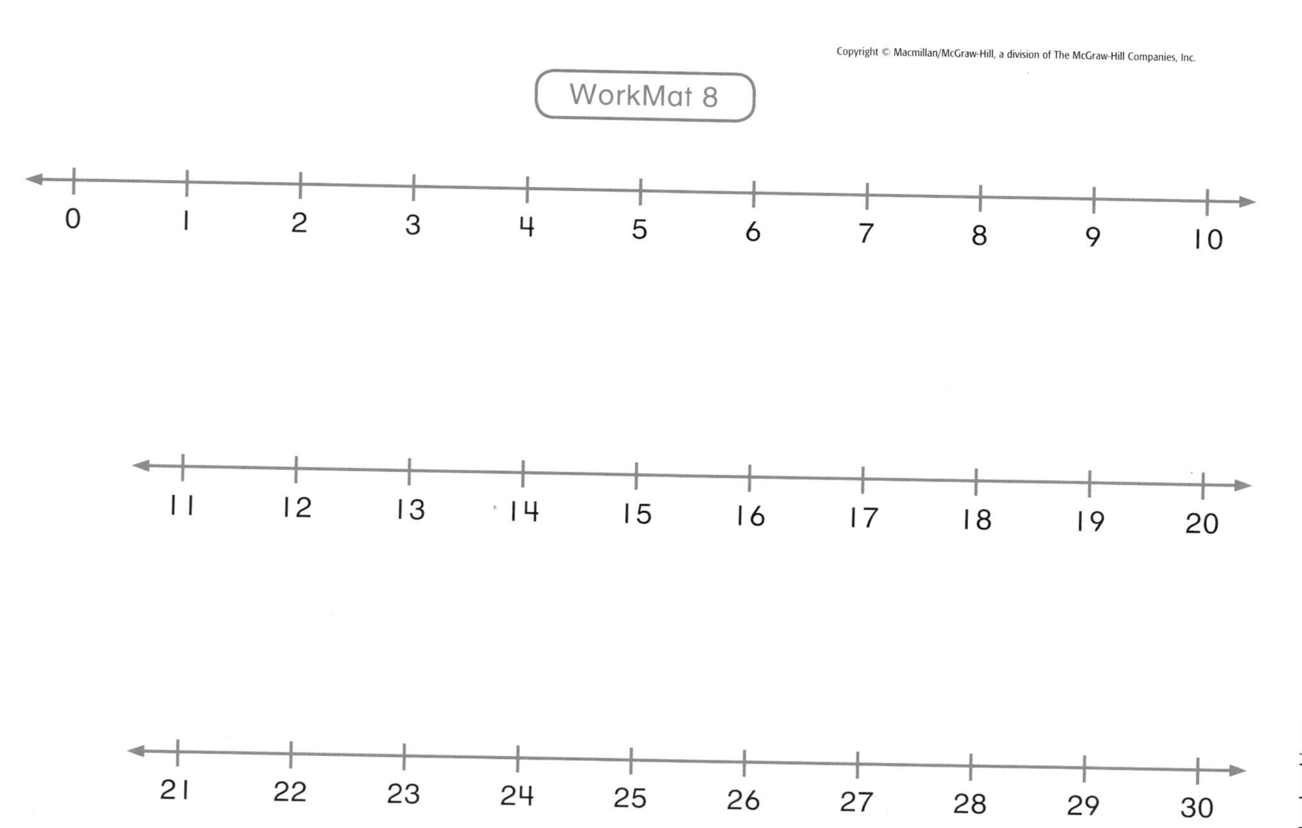
WorkMat 8
0
1
2
3
4
5
6
7
8
9
10
11
12
13
14
15
16
17
18
19
20
21
22
23
24
25
26
27
28
29
30
WorkMat 8: Number Lines

WorkMats

Index

A

B

Index

M

N

Patterns
Patterns are sometimes called the foundation of mathematics and are certainly required for future success in algebra.

Problem Solving
A three-pronged approach helps students apply skills to problem situations. Problem-Solving Strategy lessons teach strategies; Problem-Solving Investigations afford students diverse opportunities to select these strategies; Real-World Problem Solving exercises strengthen students' abilities to apply and solve problems outside the mathematics classroom.

Index